Robinson

537 4120 office

474-6220 home

COLLEGE MATHEMATICS WITH BUSINESS APPLICATIONS

COLLEGE MATHEMATICS WITH BUSINESS APPLICATIONS

JOHN E. FREUND

Professor of Mathematics
Arizona State University

PRENTICE-HALL, INC.
Englewood Cliffs, N.J.

Library of Congress Catalog Card Number 69-10791

Printed in the United States of America

Prentice-Hall International, Inc., *London*
Prentice-Hall of Australia, Pty. Ltd., *Sydney*
Prentice-Hall of Canada, Ltd., *Toronto*
Prentice-Hall of India Private Ltd., *New Delhi*
Prentice-Hall of Japan, Inc., *Tokyo*

Current printing (*last digit*):

10 9 8 7 6 5

PREFACE

In recent years there have been extensive changes in the teaching of mathematics, and this is true, particularly, in courses designed for students of business and economics. Here, the increasing emphasis on quantitative methods has created a demand for textbooks which not only present the reader with a *general understanding and appreciation* of the role played by mathematics in management science, but which also give him an *adequate foundation* to pursue more advanced work in statistics, operations research, inventory theory, electronic data processing, mathematical programming, econometrics, production management, and the like.

As in any area which is in a state of flux, there is quite a diversity of opinion as to what should be included in the kind of course for which this textbook is designed, what should be stressed, what should be omitted, what should be assumed as a prerequisite, and what should be left to more advanced work. So far as prerequisites are concerned, the only prerequisite assumed for this book is some high school algebra, namely, some familiarity (and, hopefully, a lack of fear) of dealing with letters and symbols instead of numbers. To attain a measure of flexibility and accommodate the many suggestions which the author received from the colleagues who reviewed the plan (and various drafts) of this book, a number of topics are included among the exercises *with detailed explanations*. This technique of presenting optional material turned out to be especially suited for this kind of text—it made it possible to introduce special topics, special applications, extra details, and also more advanced material *without cluttering up the main body of the text*. Thus, the reader will find non-linear depreciation, for instance, *explained* among the exercises on exponential function, he will find optional material on analytical geometry (mid-points, perpendicular lines, etc.) *explained* among the exercises on linear and quadratic functions, he will find the Method of Least Squares *explained* among the exercises on partial differentiation, he will find integration by parts, for example, *explained* among the exercises on integration, he will find the elasticity of demand *explained* among the applied exercises on differentiation, and he will find the measurement of subjective probabilities and the measurement of utility *explained* among the exercises on mathematical expectation. To make these special exercises easily recognizable, they are all suitably titled in boldface type (and printed against a gray background).

In accordance with current thought on the teaching of mathematics to students of business and economics, the concept of a *mathematical model* is stressed throughout the book. Mathematical models are introduced in the first paragraph of Section 1.1 with the analogy that

> "a mathematical model is to the phenomenon it describes as a dress form is to a dress,"

and the reader is repeatedly reminded of the continuation of this analogy on page 6, namely, that

> "whereas dress forms make it possible to mass-produce dresses of any given size, abstract mathematical models make it possible to use assembly-line techniques in the application of mathematical ideas."

After he had written about various special kinds of models (namely, special kinds of functions) in Chapters 4 and 5, the author felt that it was only natural to continue with a chapter on *periodic functions.* Thus, Chapter 6 presents a brief introduction to the trigonometric functions, in their capacity as models for such periodic phenomena as the seasonal variation of department store sales, the seasonal variation of farm employment, . . . , and also the long-range business cycles which represent the repeating patterns of rises and declines of business activity. Traditionally, this material has not been included in the basic mathematics taught to students of business and economics, and Chapter 6 may (regretfully) be omitted without loss of continuity.

So far as the overall organization of this book is concerned, let us point out that the material on *calculus,* Chapters 11 through 14, may be taken up before the material on *linear mathematics,* Chapters 7 through 10; in fact, this is how the material was organized in the original draft of the manuscript for this book. Also, the arrangement of the material on linear mathematics makes it possible to study systems of linear equations, linear inequalities, and linear programming in Chapters 7 and 8 without *reference to matrices.* The more rigorous material on matrices in Chapter 9 and the

Simplex Method in Chapter 10 may, thus, be omitted altogether, or it may be taken up immediately following Chapter 8. (Another possibility is to follow Chapter 7 with Chapter 9, and then take up Chapters 8 and 10.)

The last four chapters of the book contain material on probability, decision making, and simulation, and hence an introduction to some of the most interesting and challenging aspects of management science. The approach is thoroughly modern, including some of the more elementary aspects of the Bayesian approach; also, the material in these concluding chapters serves to summarize and review most of the mathematics studied in earlier chapters. (This includes a demonstration of how easily the solution of a game can be reduced to a linear programming problem.)

Most of the traditional material from the mathematics of finance *is* covered in this text, but it is studied within the context of the mathematical ideas which are involved. Thus, linear interest, discount, and depreciation are discussed in the chapter on linear functions; compound interest and discount are discussed in the chapter on exponential functions; annuities certain are treated in the section on geometric progressions; sinking funds, capitalized cost, and perpetuities are treated in the section on infinite series; and endowments, life annuities, and life insurance are mentioned in the chapter on probability.

The author would like to thank his many friends and colleagues, whose suggestions, criticisms, and comments contributed greatly to the final version of this book. Specifically, he is indebted to Professor Jay E. Strum of New York University, Professor Edward L. Wallace of the State University of New York at Buffalo, and Professor Roman L. Weil, Jr. of the University of Chicago, for their helpful reviews of the original plan for this book. Invaluable to the author was the assistance which he received from his niece, Miss Marilyn Ewer, from Professor Al Romano of San Diego State College, and above all from Professor Fred E. Kindig of Ohio State University, who critically reviewed and evaluated in detail several drafts of this book. The author is also indebted to Professor Frank J. Williams of San Francisco State College for his permission to use several exercises and illustrations, and to Mr. Albert J. Martin, Jr., teaching associate at Ohio State University, and other graduate students for their assistance in checking the answers to the exercises and performing other computational chores.

JOHN E. FREUND

Scottsdale, Arizona

CONTENTS

1

MATHEMATICAL MODELS

1.1 INTRODUCTION

It has been said that a mathematical model is to the phenomenon it describes as a dress form is to a dress: *it provides the underlying structure.* This analogy is very important, for in the same way in which many questions concerning a dress can be answered indirectly by examining the form with which it was made, many questions concerning a phenomenon (arising in business, science, or everyday life) can be answered indirectly by examining an appropriate mathematical model. Briefly, a mathematical model can be a set of numbers such as the positive integers 1, 2, 3, 4, 5, . . . , which we use to count; or the fractions 1/2, 3/7, 11/118, . . . , which we might use to divide the income from an estate; or the real numbers which we use in connection with measurements performed with continuous scales. A mathematical model can also be a geometry such as Euclidean geometry (which we use to describe figures in a plane), such as spherical geometry (which provides us with an approximate model for measurements performed on the surface of the earth), or the entirely different and new geometry which had to be invented in connection with the theory of relativity. A mathematical model can also consist of a mathematical formula, a set of equations, or it may consist of entirely new and different kinds of mathematical "objects" which are invented for a special purpose.

To illustrate the general idea of a mathematical model, let us consider a problem faced by the management of a company which frequently rotates its four sales managers among the four regions into which its sales territory has been divided. For this purpose, the management of the company uses the following schemes:

Scheme A: *The sales manager of Region 1 is moved to Region 2, the one of Region 2 is moved to Region 3, the one of Region 3 is moved to Region 4, and the one of Region 4 is moved to Region 1.*

Scheme B: *The sales manager of Region 1 is moved to Region 3, the one of Region 2 is moved to Region 4, the one of Region 3 is moved to Region 1, and the one of Region 4 is moved to Region 2.*

Scheme C: *The sales manager of Region 1 is moved to Region 4, the one of Region 2 is moved to Region 1, the one of Region 3 is moved to Region 2, and the one of Region 4 is moved to Region 3.*

Sometimes they do not rotate the sales managers at all, so let us add

Scheme D: *Each sales manager remains where he is.*

There are many questions that might be asked in connection with these schemes, which are also pictured in Figure 1.1. For instance, the management of the company may want to know what happened to the sales manager who was originally in Region 1 after they apply, in succession, Schemes A, B, C, and then again Scheme A. Also, how many times would they have to apply Scheme A so that each sales manager gets back to the region in which he was at the start; or, if they discover that it was a mistake to use Scheme A, what scheme will they have to use next to get each sales manager back to where he was?

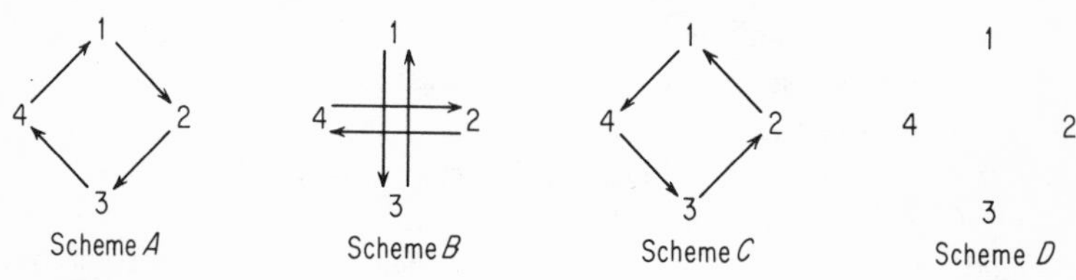

FIG. 1.1

To facilitate answering questions of this kind, let us use the notation $A \cdot B$ to indicate that Schemes A and B are performed in succession (first A and then B); for want of a better name, we shall refer to $A \cdot B$ as the *product* of A and B, and read it as "A times B." To discover the significance of $A \cdot B$ we have only to investigate what happens to each sales manager when these two schemes are used one after the other. Clearly, the sales manager of Region 1 moves first to Region 2 (Scheme A) and then to Region 4 (Scheme B), the sales manager of Region 2 moves first to Region 3 (Scheme A) and then to Region 1 (Scheme B), the sales manager of Region 3 moves first to Region 4 and then to Region 2, and the sales manager of Region 4 moves first to Region 1 and then to Region 3. Thus, *the total effect of $A \cdot B$ is the same as if we had used Scheme C*, and we write $A \cdot B = C$. Similarly, the effect of applying B and C in succession is the same as that of A, the effect of applying C twice in a row is the same as that of B, and the effect of applying A and C in succession is the same as that of D; correspondingly, we write $B \cdot C = A$, $C \cdot C = B$, and $C \cdot A = D$. The results for all possible "products" are shown in the following table, where the first letter is read on the left and the second on top:

	A	B	C	D
A	B	C	D	A
B	C	D	A	B
C	D	A	B	C
D	A	B	C	D

This is the *mathematical model* for the rotation of the sales managers: it consists of the four "numbers" A, B, C, and D, and the very special "multiplication" table given above.

Let us now return to the three questions asked on page 2. To answer the first we have only to evaluate $[(A \cdot B) \cdot C] \cdot A$, where we used parentheses and brackets to indicate the order in which the "multiplications" are to be performed. Referring directly to the table showing all possible "products," we get

$$[(A \cdot B) \cdot C] \cdot A = [C \cdot C] \cdot A = B \cdot A = C$$

and we conclude from the definition of Scheme C that the sales manager who was originally in Region 1 is now in Region 4.

To answer the second question, namely, how often Scheme A has to be applied so that each sales manager returns to the region from which he began, we shall have to see *how often A has to be multiplied by itself to get D*. Observing that

$$A \cdot A = B$$

$$(A \cdot A) \cdot A = B \cdot A = C$$

and

$$[(A \cdot A) \cdot A] \cdot A = C \cdot A = D$$

we conclude that Scheme A has to be used *four times* in order to get each sales manager back to the region from which he began. To answer the third question, we have only to solve the equation

$$A \cdot X = D$$

where X represents the (so far unknown) rotation scheme which returns everyone to where he was before the application of Scheme A. Checking the various possibilities in the "multiplication" table on page 3, we find that $A \cdot A = B$, $A \cdot B = C$, $A \cdot C = D$, and $A \cdot D = A$; hence, the only rotation scheme that does the trick is Scheme C.

Once we have constructed a mathematical model, we can investigate its properties *with the assurance that these properties will also hold for any physical situation to which the model applies.* For instance, it is apparent from the "multiplication" table that our model is *closed,* namely, that the "product" of any two of the rotation schemes must always equal either A, B, C, or D. Observe that this would not have been the case if, instead of Scheme C, the management of the company had used

> **Scheme E:** *The sales manager of Region 1 is moved to Region 3, the one of Region 2 is moved to Region 4, the one of Region 3 is moved to Region 2, and the one of Region 4 is moved to Region 1.*

It will be left to the reader to verify in Exercise 5 on page 6 that the "product" $A \cdot E$ does not equal any of the rotation schemes we have discussed. Other important properties of our model are treated in Exercises 2 and 4 on page 6.

In actual practice, we always check right away whether a model we have constructed for a given problem is already known; that is, we check whether it may already have been constructed (and studied) in connection with an entirely different situation. If this is the case, we can save ourselves a lot of work, for as we have already pointed out, *everything that is known about the properties of a particular mathematical model can be used in connection with any situation to which the model applies.* Thus, powerful tools became available when it was realized that certain models developed in the physical and biological sciences apply also to problems in business and economics. To mention a few examples, models developed in physics have been applied to problems of economic growth, inventory analysis, and the scheduling of production; models developed for games of chance have been applied to advertising, market research, and quality control; and models developed in agriculture have been applied to such things as plant design, product analysis, and other kinds of managerial decisions. Furthermore, models developed for particular problems of management science sometimes find applications in entirely different areas. For instance, models used in connection with the allocation of raw materials have found applications to problems involving advertising and marketing; and models used in connection with franchizing and competition have found applications to problems involving consumer testing, the evaluation of weapons systems, and international trade.

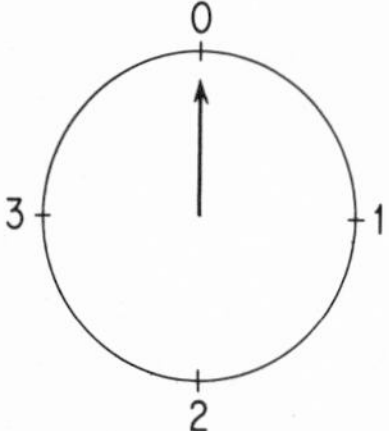

FIG. 1.2

Let us now ask whether the model which we have constructed for the rotations of the four sales managers is really *new*, or whether it has already been studied (by mathematicians) in connection with other situations. To make it brief, the answer is "NO," *the model is not new*, and a relatively simple application may be found in the *algebra of the clock* of Figure 1.2. On the face of this clock are the numbers 0, 1, 2, and 3, and it might be used in a boxing match to measure three-minute rounds with one-minute rest periods in between. The *addition* of these numbers is defined as follows: to add 2 and 3, for example, we start at 0, move the hand 2 spaces, then 3 more spaces, and since the hand will then point at 1 we write $2 + 3 = 1$; similarly, to add 1 and 3 we start at 0, move the hand 1 space, then 3 more spaces, and since the hand will then point at 0 we write $1 + 3 = 0$. Calculating all possible "sums" we obtain

	1	2	3	0
1	2	3	0	1
2	3	0	1	2
3	0	1	2	3
0	1	2	3	0

and it can be seen that this table is *identical* with the one on page 3, with 1, 2, 3, and 0 substituted for A, B, C, and D. Hence, the model which we constructed for the rotations of the four sales managers applies also to the special addition of the numbers of the clock of Figure 1.2. (In Exercise 22 on page 126 the reader will be asked to verify that the model applies also to the multiplication of certain *complex numbers,* and in Exercise 11 on page 261 he will be asked to verify that it applies to the multiplication of certain new mathematical "objects," called *matrices.*)

Thus, the model which we have constructed in this section is already well known to mathematicians; in fact they have a name for it—they call it a *group.* The study of groups is a very interesting one, but we shall not delve into it any further in this book. We have introduced the subject only to illustrate the concept of a mathematical model, and to demonstrate how one and the same model can apply to entirely different situations. In case the reader is disturbed by the fact that our discussion has been fairly abstract, let us point out that *it is precisely its abstractness which makes mathematics so very useful.* After all, what good would it be to know that $3 + 5 = 8$ if this result applied only to horses or cows? Numbers *are* abstract "objects," and this is why their arithmetic finds almost unlimited applications. To return to the analogy with which we began on page 1, we might say that *whereas dress forms make it possible to mass-produce dresses of any given size, abstract mathematical models make it possible to use assembly-line techniques in the application of mathematical ideas.*

EXERCISES

1. Referring to the rotation schemes on page 2 and checking what happens to each of the four sales managers, verify that

   (a) $A \cdot A = B$; (e) $B \cdot C = A$;
   (b) $A \cdot C = D$; (f) $C \cdot A = D$;
   (c) $B \cdot A = C$; (g) $C \cdot B = A$;
   (d) $B \cdot B = D$; (h) $C \cdot C = B$.

2. In ordinary arithmetic, multiplication is said to be *commutative;* that is, $2 \cdot 3 = 3 \cdot 2$, $5 \cdot 7 = 7 \cdot 5$, $4 \cdot 9 = 9 \cdot 4$, and so on. Referring to the table on page 3, verify that the "multiplication" of the rotation schemes is also *commutative.*

3. In ordinary arithmetic, the number 1 plays a very special role—the product of 1 and any number is equal to that number. Referring to the table on page 3, verify that for the rotations of the four sales managers this role is played by Scheme D.

4. In ordinary arithmetic, the product of any number and its *reciprocal* always equals 1, and every number except 0 has a reciprocal. Referring to the table on page 3 and letting Scheme D play the role of 1 (see Exercise 3), find the "reciprocals" of Schemes A, B, and C.

5. Referring to Schemes A and E on pages 2 and 4, show that
   (a) the product $A \cdot E$ leaves the sales manager of Region 2 where he is and rotates those of Regions 1, 3, and 4 as in the first diagram of Figure 1.3;
   (b) the product $E \cdot A$ leaves the sales manager of Region 3 where he is and

rotates those of Regions 1, 2, and 4 as in the second diagram of Figure 1.3. Note that we thus have an example of two mathematical objects whose multiplication is *not commutative;* that is, $A \cdot E$ does not equal $E \cdot A$.

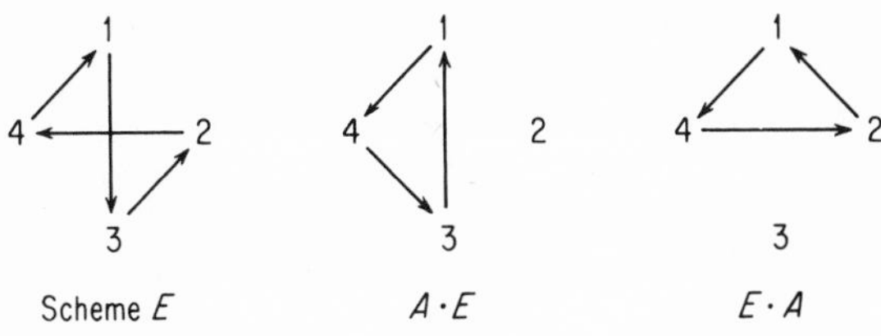

FIG. 1.3

6. The credit manager of a large department store periodically reviews the credit rating of each charge account; he either leaves it alone, *Procedure L*, or he changes it from "good" to "bad" or from "bad" to "good," *Procedure C*. Working with these procedures, $L \cdot C$ means that in two successive reviews an account was first left alone and then changed, $L \cdot L$ means that it was left alone in each case, $C \cdot L$ means that first it was changed and then it was left alone, and $C \cdot C$ means that it was changed twice in a row.
   (a) Construct a "multiplication" table like the one on page 3, namely, a table showing the values of $L \cdot C$, $L \cdot L$, $C \cdot L$, and $C \cdot C$.
   (b) Show that the mathematical model which consists of the "numbers" C and L and the "multiplication" table of part (a) applies also to the ordinary multiplication of -1 and $+1$. Which one has to represent $+1$, C or L?
   (c) Show that the mathematical model which consists of the "numbers" C and L and the "multiplication" table of part (a) applies also to the ordinary addition of *even numbers* (2, 4, 6, 8, . . .) and *odd numbers* (1, 3, 5, 7, . . .), with the even numbers represented by L and the odd numbers by C.

7. In the text as well as in Exercise 6 we began with a physical situation, constructed the appropriate mathematical model, and then looked for other applications of the same model. Now let us reverse this procedure, namely, begin with an abstract mathematical model and see whether it actually has applications. The model which we shall consider in this exercise consists of two "numbers," P and Q, whose "products" are as shown in the following table:

	P	Q
P	P	P
Q	P	Q

   (a) Show that this model applies to the ordinary multiplication of the numbers 0 and 1, with 0 taking the place of P and 1 taking the place of Q.
   (b) Show that this model applies also to the ordinary multiplication of *even numbers* (2, 4, 6, 8, . . .) and *odd numbers* (1, 3, 5, 7, . . .). Will the even numbers have to be represented by P or by Q?
   (c) To find a business application of this model, suppose that P means that

the value of a stock has gone up while Q means that its value has remained unchanged. Now, if $P \cdot Q$ means that the value of the stock first went up and then remained unchanged, the overall effect is that of P, and we write $P \cdot Q = P$. Verify that the other three "products" are as shown in the original table.

(d) A company periodically reviews the salaries it pays to its employees. If P means that a given employee gets a raise and Q means that he does not get a raise, how do we have to interpret the "products" $P \cdot P$, $P \cdot Q$, $Q \cdot P$, and $Q \cdot Q$, so that the model of this exercise will apply?

1.2 SETS

The remainder of this chapter will be devoted to a special mathematical model—the one that applies to *sets*. There are several reasons why this model is important: to begin with, the concept of a set (a collection of objects) is fundamental to mathematics and nowadays it is taught even in the elementary grades; equally important is the fact that the model which we shall develop has many interesting applications (among other things, it is fundamental in the design of digital computers).

In mathematics, the term "set" is used to denote any well-defined collection of objects. In colloquial language it has many synonyms; for instance, we speak of a group of industries, classes of students, teams of athletes, collections of coins or stamps, flocks of sheep, herds of cattle, and so on. The objects (real or abstract) which belong to a set are referred to as its *elements*. For instance, the twelve retail outlets of a candy manufacturer constitute a set and each of these stores is an element of the set; similarly, the six vice presidents of a corporation constitute a set and each of the vice presidents is an element of the set.

Sets are very often specified by actually listing the individual elements, and we refer to this as the "roster method." For instance, if the twelve retail outlets of the candy manufacturer are represented by the first twelve letters of the alphabet, the corresponding set can be denoted

$$\{a, b, c, d, e, f, g, h, i, j, k, l\}$$

and if the six vice presidents of the corporation are named Brown, Jones, Knight, Peters, Smith, and Taylor, we can indicate the corresponding set by writing

{Brown, Jones, Knight, Peters, Smith, Taylor}

Also listing the elements in braces, the possible outcomes of one roll of a die constitute the set

$$\{1, 2, 3, 4, 5, 6\}$$

and the eight possible outcomes for three successive flips of a coin constitute the set

$$\{HHH, HHT, HTH, THH, HTT, THT, TTH, TTT\}$$

where H stands for *heads* and T for *tails*. Note that when the elements of a set are listed in this way, *their order does not matter;* the six vice presidents listed in any order constitute the same set, and $\{1, 2, 3\}$ is the same set as $\{2, 1, 3\}$. Furthermore, *we list (or count) each element of a set only once.* For instance, if Brown and Peters serve on the corporation's finance committee while Jones, Smith, and Peters serve on its committee for research and development, then the set of vice presidents serving on either committee is the set

{Brown, Jones, Peters, Smith}

Even though Peters serves on both committees, he is listed only once. To give another example, the letters needed to spell the word "corporation" constitute the set $\{c, o, r, p, a, t, i, n\}$.

Instead of listing the elements, which is often impractical or even impossible (when there are infinitely many), we can also specify sets by giving rules according to which we can decide whether any given element (object) does or does not belong to a set. Thus, we can speak of the set of all corporations listed on the New York Stock Exchange, which we write as

{corporations listed on the New York Stock Exchange}

or the set of all sales executives attending a certain convention, which we write as

{sales executives attending the given convention}

This is called the "defining method" of specifying sets; for any given corporation we can check whether or not it is listed on the New York Stock Exchange, and for any sales executive we can check whether or not he is attending the given convention.

Sets are usually denoted by capital letters. If we denote the set of the retail outlets of the candy manufacturer with the letter R and the set of the six vice presidents with the letter V, we can write

$$R = \{a, b, c, d, e, f, g, h, i, j, k, l\}$$

V = {Brown, Jones, Knight, Peters, Smith, Taylor}

To indicate that an object belongs to a particular set, for instance, that Jones is one of the vice presidents of the given corporation, we use the Greek letter ϵ (*epsilon*) and write "Jones ϵ V;" this reads "Jones is an element of the set V" or "Jones belongs to the set V." To indicate that an object does *not* belong to a given set we use the symbol $\notin$, with a vertical line through the letter epsilon; for instance, to indicate that a certain store p is *not* one of the retail outlets of the candy manufacturer we write $p \notin R$, which reads "p is *not* an element of the set R." Similarly, to indicate that Mr. Adams is *not* one of the vice presidents of the above-mentioned corporation we write Adams $\notin V$.

In the preceding paragraph we used an equal sign to indicate that the symbols R and $\{a, b, c, d, e, f, g, h, i, j, k, l\}$ represent the *same* set. More generally, when we say that two given sets A and B are equal and write $A = B$, this means that A and B have exactly the same elements; in other words, we write $A = B$ if *every element of A is also an element of B and vice versa.* For instance, if M is the set of all *married* vice presidents of the given corporation and it so happens that all six of them are married, we can write $M = V$; if they are *not* all married, we write $M \neq V$.

It is customary to refer to the set of married vice presidents of the given corporation as a *subset* of the set V. In general, *set A is said to be a subset of set B if and only if every element of A is also an element of B.* In that case we write $A \subset B$, which reads "A is a subset of B" or "A is contained in B." For instance, if six of the retail outlets of the candy manufacturer are located in Los Angeles, four in San Francisco, and one each in Sacramento and San Diego, each city's stores constitute a subset of the set R. Other subsets of R are the one which consists of the manufacturer's five retail outlets in Northern California, and the one which consists of the seven retail outlets in Southern California. Also, the even numbers 2, 4, 6, 8, . . . , constitute a subset of the whole numbers 1, 2, 3, 4, . . . , and the insurance companies that are incorporated in Connecticut constitute a subset of the set which consists of all the insurance companies incorporated in the United States. Corresponding to the symbols $\notin$ and $\neq$ we write $A \not\subset B$ to indicate that A is not a subset of B.

According to the definition which we just gave *every set is a subset of itself*, and to emphasize the fact that a given subset constitutes only part of a set (not the whole set), we refer to it as a *proper subset.* Thus, if the six vice presidents of the corporation (we have been discussing) are *not all married,* then M constitutes a proper subset of V.

In the preceding discussion we continually had to remind the reader that we were referring to the retail outlets of a particular candy manufacturer and to the vice presidents of a particular corporation. To make it clear that our discussion is limited to a particular set, we refer to this set as our *universal set* or as the *universe of discourse.* Generally speaking, a universal set is a set which contains *all the elements with which we are concerned in a given situation.*

Since the answer to a question can well depend on the choice of the universal set, it is always important to state specifically what universal set we have in mind. For instance, the statement that 7/12 of the candy stores are located in Southern California may be correct for the given manufacturer, but it would probably be wrong for the universal set which consists of the retail outlets of another candy manufacturer, or the one which consists of all candy stores in the United States. Similarly, the statement that all of the vice presidents are married may be correct for a given universal set (say, the given corporation), but it may well be wrong for universal sets consisting of the vice presidents of other corporations. In this chapter we shall denote universal sets by the letter I; some authors prefer the letter U (or the Greek letter Ω), and in some special applications (see Chapter 16) we shall use the letter S.

In contrast to the universal set which comprises all the elements of relevance in a given situation, we define the *null set* as the set which has no elements at all. Denoted by the symbol $\varnothing$, the null set is also referred to as the *empty set* or the *void set*. For instance, if P is the set of Presidents of the United States under twenty years of age and Q is the set of all 75-cent pieces coined in the United States, neither set has any elements and we can write $P = \varnothing$ and $Q = \varnothing$.

There are various ways in which we can use sets to form *new sets*. For instance, if four of the six vice presidents of our example are married and constitute the set M, then the two which are not married constitute what we call the *complement* of M and write as M'. Similarly, if L is the set of the six retail outlets of the candy manufacturer which are located in Los Angeles, then L', the complement of L, is the set which consists of the other six retail outlets, namely, those that are *not* located in Los Angeles. In general, *if A is contained in the universal set I, then A', called the complement of A, is the set which is composed of all the elements of I that are not in A*. Thus, if I is the set of all houses listed for sale by a given realtor and C is the set of those listed for under \$20,000, then C' is the set of those houses listed by the realtor which are priced at \$20,000 or more. Also, if I is the set of new cars a dealer has in stock and those with air-conditioning are denoted by the letter A, then those without air-conditioning constitute the complementary set A'.

New sets can also be formed by combining the elements of two or more sets in some fashion. For instance, if $P = \{a, b, d, f, g, h, i, k\}$ is the set of retail outlets of the candy manufacturer which showed a profit during 1968 and $L = \{a, c, d, g, h, l\}$ is the set which consists of all his retail outlets in the Los Angeles area, then $\{a, d, g, h\}$ is the set which consists of all the Los Angeles stores of the candy manufacturer that showed a profit during 1968. We refer to this new set as the *intersection* of P and L and denote it $P \cap L$, which also reads "*P cap L*," or simply as *P and L*." Formally, *the intersection of two sets A and B, denoted $A \cap B$, is the set which consists of all the elements belonging to both A and B*. For instance, if I is the set of all students enrolled at a given college while

F and G represent, respectively, those majoring in business administration and those taking part in intercollegiate athletics, then $F \cap G$ is the set of all students majoring in business (at that college) who take part in intercollegiate athletics. Also, if I is the set of all stocks listed at the New York Stock Exchange while C and D represent, respectively, those which paid a dividend during 1967 and those which currently have a price-earnings ratio of better than 20, then $C \cap D$ is the set of all those stocks (listed at the New York Stock Exchange) which paid a dividend during 1967 and *also* have a current price-earnings ratio of better than 20.

When we form the intersection of two sets we do not literally "combine" their elements; instead we take only those which are contained in both. If we actually want to combine the elements of two sets A and B, that is, take them all together, we form what is called their *union* and denoted $A \cup B$. With reference to our last two examples, the *union* of F and G is the set of all students enrolled at the college who are either majoring in business administration or are taking part in intercollegiate athletics, while the *union* of C and D is the set of all stocks (listed at the New York Stock Exchange) which either paid a dividend in 1967 or have a current price-earnings ratio of better than 20. Formally, *the union of two sets A and B, denoted $A \cup B$, is the set which consists of all elements belonging either to A or to B, including those which belong to both.* We read $A \cup B$ as "the union of A and B," "A cup B," or simply as "A *or* B," (where the "or" is what logicians call the "inclusive or" because $A \cup B$ includes the elements which belong to A as well as B). Referring again to the retail outlets of the candy manufacturer, observe that $P \cup L$ consists of the stores a, b, c, d, f, g, h, i, k, and l; although stores a, d, g, and h are contained in *both* P and L, they are counted only once in $P \cup L$.

Sets and subsets are often depicted by means of *Venn diagrams* like those of Figures 1.4 and 1.5.* In each case the universal set I is repre-

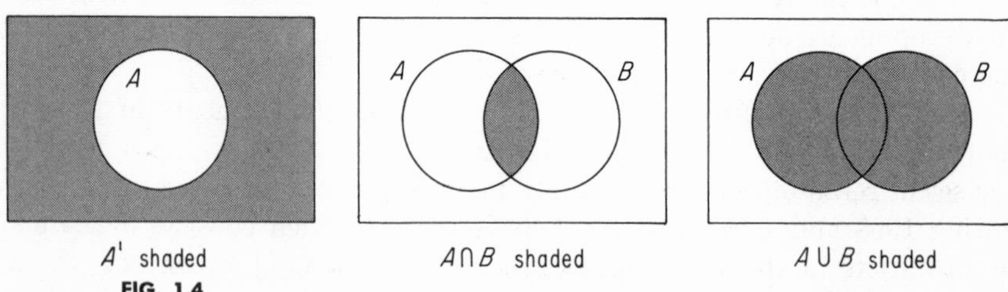

A' shaded $A \cap B$ shaded $A \cup B$ shaded

FIG. 1.4

sented by a rectangle, while sets within I are represented by regions within the rectangle, usually by circles or parts of circles. Thus, the

* These diagrams are named after the British logician who first employed them in 1876.

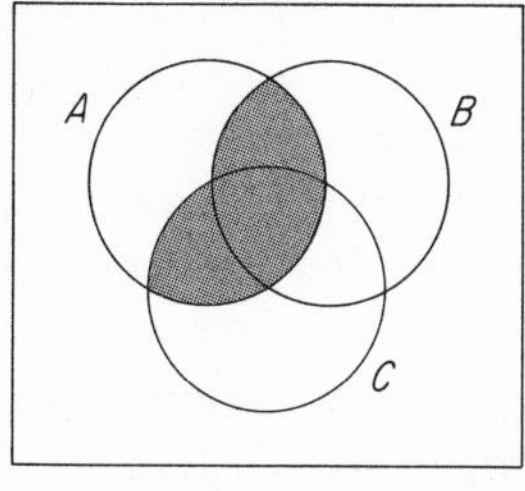

FIG. 1.5

shaded regions of Figure 1.4 represent, respectively, the complement of set A, the intersections of sets A and B, and the union of sets A and B; the sets A and B, themselves, are represented by the respective circles. When we are dealing with three sets, it is customary to draw the corresponding circles as in Figure 1.5. Note that the shaded region of Figure 1.5 represents the set $A \cap (B \cup C)$; it contains everything in A that *also* belongs to either B or C.

Venn diagrams are especially useful in problems in which we are interested in determining how many elements there are in various subsets of a universal set. Suppose, for instance, that a stockbroker has 237 clients, of which 165 are wealthy, 78 are retired, including 59 who are also wealthy. Question: *How many of the broker's clients are neither wealthy nor retired?* Drawing the circles which represent the broker's wealthy clients (set W) and his retired clients (set R) as in the Venn diagrams of Figure 1.6, we begin by writing 59 in the region common to the two circles,

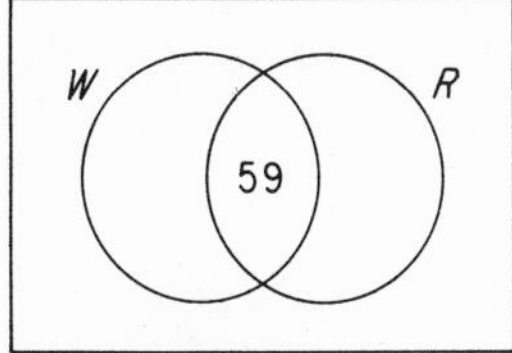

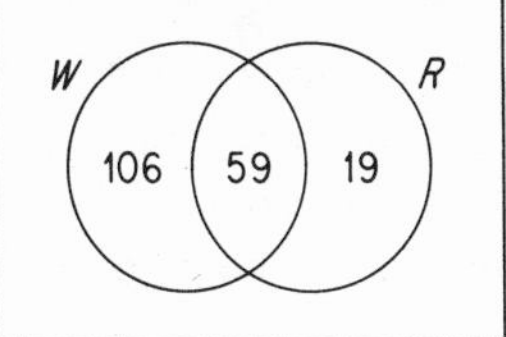

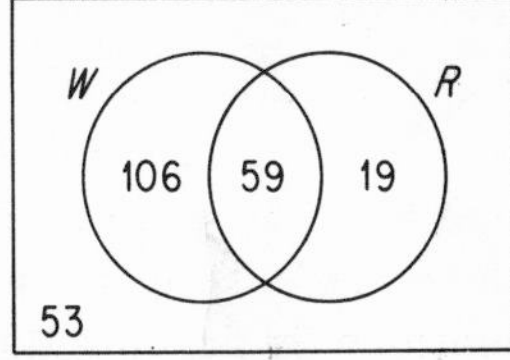

FIG. 1.6

namely, the one which represents the set $W \cap R$. Then we observe that $165 - 59 = 106$ of the broker's clients must be in W but outside R, and that $78 - 59 = 19$ of his clients must be in R but outside W. This accounts for $106 + 59 + 19 = 184$ of his clients, and we conclude that the remaining $237 - 184 = 53$ clients are neither wealthy nor retired.

The following example is very similar, but we shall have to work with percentages rather than numbers, and with three circles instead of two. It concerns a survey in which housewives were interviewed in a supermarket and the following results were obtained: 68 percent shop there regularly, 53 percent are satisfied with the service, 82 percent collect trading stamps, 47 percent shop there regularly and are satisfied with the service, 50 percent are satisfied with the service and collect trading stamps, 64 percent shop there regularly and collect trading stamps, while 46 percent shop there regularly, are satisfied with the service, and collect trading stamps. What we would like to know is

(*a*) *What percentage of these housewives shop there regularly but do not like the service and do not collect trading stamps?*
(*b*) *What percentage of these housewives do not shop there regularly, do not like the service, and do not collect trading stamps?*
(*c*) *What fraction of the housewives who shop there regularly do not collect trading stamps?*

Drawing the circles which represent housewives who shop there regularly (set A), housewives who like the service (set B), and housewives who collect trading stamps (set C) as in the Venn diagrams of Figure 1.7, we begin by writing 46 in the region common to A, B, and C. Then we observe that $47 - 46 = 1$ percent of the housewives shop there

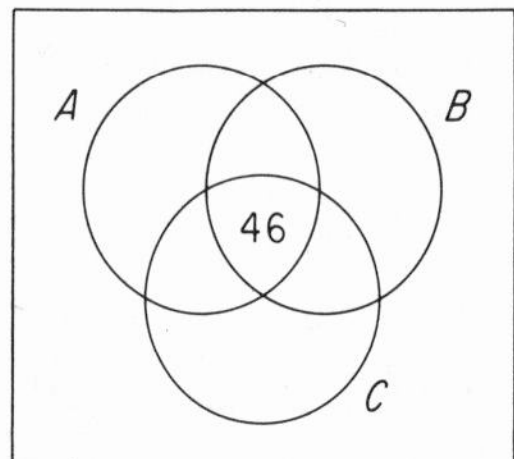

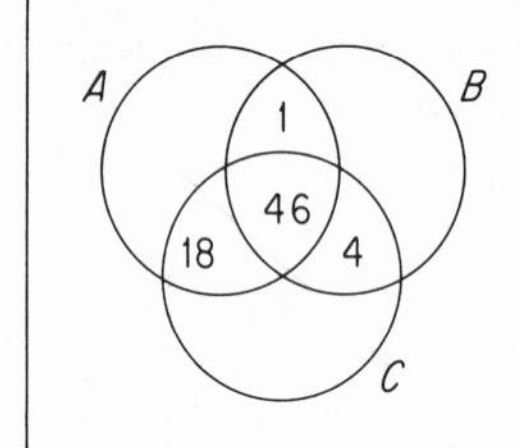

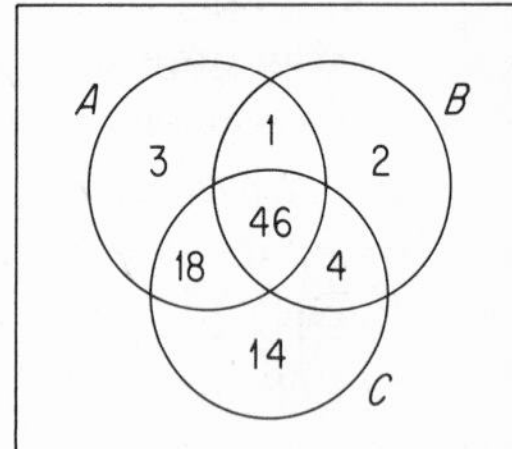

FIG. 1.7

regularly and like the service but do *not* collect trading stamps, that $50 - 46 = 4$ percent of the housewives belong to $B \cap C$ but *not* to A, and that $64 - 46 = 18$ percent of them belong to $A \cap C$ but *not* to B. Filling in these percentages as in the second Venn diagram of Figure 1.7, we then continue by arguing that

$$68 - (18 + 46 + 1) = 3 \text{ percent}$$

of the housewives shop there regularly but do *not* like the service and do *not* collect trading stamps, *which answers Question* (*a*). Similarly, we find that

$$53 - (1 + 46 + 4) = 2 \text{ percent}$$

of the housewives must be in set B but outside A as well as C, while

$$82 - (18 + 46 + 4) = 14 \text{ percent}$$

of the housewives must be in set C but outside A as well as B. Adding all the percentages shown in the third diagram of Figure 1.7, we get

$$3 + 1 + 46 + 18 + 2 + 4 + 14 = 88 \text{ percent}$$

and we conclude that the remaining 12 percent of the housewives do *not* shop there regularly, do *not* like the service, and do *not* collect trading stamps; *this answers Question* (*b*).

To find the answer to Question (*c*), observe that among the 68 percent of the housewives who shop there regularly, $3 + 1 = 4$ percent are outside circle C and, hence, do *not* collect trading stamps. Now then, 4 percent of 68 percent is 4/68 or 1/17, and this is the desired fraction of the housewives who shop there regularly that do *not* collect trading stamps. Further uses of Venn diagrams will be given later in this chapter.

EXERCISES

1. The following sets represent the States in which five different life insurance companies are licensed to sell their policies:

A = {Arizona, California, Nevada, Texas}
B = {California, Washington, Oregon}
C = {Arizona, Nevada, Utah, Washington}
D = {Arizona, California, Washington, Oregon}
E = {Arizona, Texas, Utah}

Check whether each of the following is true or false:

(a) California $\in A$;
(b) Arizona $\in B$;
(c) Texas $\notin D$;
(d) Nevada $\notin C$;
(e) $E \subset C$;
(f) $C \subset E$;
(g) $E \not\subset A$;
(h) $B \not\subset D$;
(i) $A \cap B$ = {California};
(j) $A \cap C$ = {Arizona, Nevada, Texas};
(k) $C \cup E$ = {Arizona, Nevada, Texas, Utah, Washington};
(l) $B \cup D$ = {Arizona, California, Utah, Washington};
(m) $C \cap E = E$;
(n) $C \cup E = E$;
(o) $B \cap D \neq B$;
(p) $A \cap C = D \cap E$.

2. The following sets represent the companies in which four investors bought stock in 1968:

K = {GE, IBM, XRX}
L = {GE, RCA}
M = {AT, GE, IBM, RCA, SY, XRX}
N = {IBM, KO, MGM, RCA, XRX}

Check whether each of the following is true or false:

(a) RCA $\in K$;
(b) XRX $\in M$;
(c) XRX $\notin L$;
(d) KO $\notin N$;
(e) $M \subset K$;
(f) $L \not\subset N$;
(g) $K \subset M$;
(h) $L \subset M$;

(i) $M \cap N = \{\text{IBM, RCA}\}$;
(j) $L \cap N = \{\text{GE, RCA}\}$;
(k) $K \cup L = \{\text{GE, IBM, RCA, XRX, MGM}\}$;
(l) $K \cup N = \{\text{GE, IBM, KO, RCA}\}$;
(m) $L \cap M = L$;
(n) $L \cap N = L$;
(o) $L \cap N = \varnothing$;
(p) $K \cap L = K \cap M$.

3. In a study of magazine circulation and advertising, a research worker considered the universal set

I = {Reader's Digest, TV Guide, Life, Look, McCall's, Time, Newsweek, Ladies' Home Journal}

and the subsets

C = {Reader's Digest, McCall's, Ladies' Home Journal}
D = {TV Guide, Life, Look, Time, Newsweek}
E = {TV Guide, McCall's, Time, Newsweek}

List the magazines which are contained in each of the following sets:

(a) C';
(b) D';
(c) E';
(d) $C \cap E$;
(e) $C \cap D$;
(f) $D \cap E$;
(g) $D \cup E$;
(h) $C \cup D$.

4. A company plans to build a research laboratory somewhere in Connecticut and it asks four different consulting firms to recommend two of the State's eight counties, which are Fairfield, Hartford, Litchfield, Middlesex, New Haven, New London, Tolland, and Windham counties. If their recommendations are given by the sets T = {Hartford, New Haven}, U = {Hartford, Litchfield}, V = {New Haven, New London}, and W = {Fairfield, New Haven}, list the elements of each of the following sets:

(a) T';
(b) W';
(c) $V \cap W$;
(d) $U \cap V$;
(e) $U \cup V$;
(f) $T \cup U$;
(g) $V \cup W$;
(h) $(U \cup V)'$.

5. If I is the set of all television receivers in Phoenix, Arizona, within which A is the set of all color television receivers, B is the set of all receivers that are turned on (at a given moment), C is the set of all receivers that are tuned to Channel 12, and D is the set of all receivers that are out of order, describe (in words) each of the following sets: (a) A'; (b) B'; (c) C'; (d) D'; (e) $A \cap B$; (f) $A' \cap C$; (g) $B \cap C$; (h) $D' \cap C$; (i) $A \cup B$; (j) $A \cup C$; (k) $A \cap D$; (l) $B' \cup D$; (m) $A' \cup C'$; (n) $A' \cap D$.

6. If I is the set of all houses advertised for sale in Chicago (on a given day), within which set A contains all those with two or more baths, set B contains all those with three bedrooms, set C contains all those priced at \$45,000 or more, and set D contains all those that are at least three years old, describe (in words) each of the following sets: (a) A'; (b) B'; (c) C'; (d) D'; (e) $A \cap B$; (f) $A \cap C$; (g) $B' \cap C$; (h) $C \cup D$; (i) $C' \cap D$; (j) $A \cup B$; (k) $A \cup C$; (l) $C \cap D$.

7. In a group of 150 college students 83 are enrolled in a course in accounting, 67 are enrolled in a course in statistics, and 45 are enrolled in both. How many of these students are not enrolled in either course?

8. A market research organization claims that among 200 executives interviewed 124 regularly read the *Wall Street Journal*, 106 regularly read the *U.S. News & World Report*, 35 regularly read both, and 23 read neither on a regular basis. Are these figures compatible, or do they involve a contradiction? Explain your answer.

9. A company has 420 employees, of which 240 got a raise, 115 got a promotion, and 60 got both. How many of the employees got neither a raise nor a promotion?

10. Among 60 visitors to a resort hotel 37 stayed at least for a week, 43 spent at least $30 a day, 32 were completely satisfied with their accommodations, 30 stayed at least for a week and spent at least $30 a day, 26 stayed at least for a week and were completely satisfied with their accommodations, 27 spent at least $30 a day and were completely satisfied with their accommodations, and 24 stayed at least for a week, spent at least $30 a day, and were completely satisfied with their accommodations.

    (a) How many of the visitors stayed at least for a week, spent at least $30 day, but were not completely satisfied with their accommodations?
    (b) How many of the visitors were completely satisfied with their accommodations, but stayed less than a week and spent less than $30 a day?
    (c) How many of the visitors stayed less than a week, spent less than $30 a day, and were not completely satisfied with their accommodations?

11. Among 60 new cars shipped to a dealer there are 8 with air-conditioning, bucket seats, and automatic transmission; 5 with air-conditioning, automatic transmission, but no bucket seats; 3 with air-conditioning, bucket seats, but no automatic transmission; 8 with air-conditioning, but neither bucket seats nor automatic transmission; 24 with automatic transmission, but neither air-conditioning nor bucket seats; 2 with automatic transmission, bucket seats, but no air-conditioning; 3 with bucket seats, but neither air-conditioning nor automatic transmission; and 7 without any of these features.

    (a) How many of these cars have bucket seats?
    (b) How many of these cars have air-conditioning?
    (c) How many of these cars have automatic transmissions as well as bucket seats?
    (d) How many of these cars have neither air-conditioning nor bucket seats?

1.3 THE ALGEBRA OF SETS

Having introduced some of the concepts, some of the language, and some of the notation used in connection with sets, let us now look for the mathematical model according to which sets "behave." If we are given a *particular* universal set I, we could proceed as in Section 1.1 and construct tables showing all possible unions, all possible intersections, and all possible complements. For instance, if I is the universal set of all students attending the University of Arizona (in a given year), and if M and F are, respectively, the sets of all male and all female students enrolled at that university, then the following tables would tell us *all there is to know* about the "arithmetic" of these sets (see Exercise 1 on page 22):

Unions

	I	F	M	$\varnothing$
I	I	I	I	I
F	I	F	I	F
M	I	I	M	M
$\varnothing$	I	F	M	$\varnothing$

Intersections

	I	F	M	$\varnothing$
I	I	F	M	$\varnothing$
F	F	F	$\varnothing$	$\varnothing$
M	M	$\varnothing$	M	$\varnothing$
$\varnothing$	$\varnothing$	$\varnothing$	$\varnothing$	$\varnothing$

Complements: $I' = \varnothing$, $F' = M$, $M' = F$, $\varnothing' = I$

This method of presenting a model for sets has two very definite disadvantages: first, the model which we have constructed applies only to the very special case where a universal set is divided into two parts (like the male and female students of our example); second, for other universal sets and their subsets the size of the required tables can easily become very large. As we shall see in Exercise 17 on page 438, the universal set which consists of the six vice presidents (mentioned on page 8) has $2^6 = 64$ possible subsets; hence, each of the two tables showing all possible unions and all possible intersections would have to have 64 rows and 64 columns. The situation would be even worse for the 12 retail outlets of the candy manufacturer (referred to on page 8); here each of the tables for all possible unions and all possible intersections would have to have $2^{12} = 4{,}096$ rows and 4,096 columns (see Exercise 17 on page 438).

An alternate way of presenting mathematical models duplicates more or less what we do when we explain a game—*instead of spelling out in detail everything that can possibly happen (as we did in the above example), we merely give certain basic rules.* In mathematics, such rules are referred to as *axioms* or *postulates*, and like a constitution in questions of law, they form the basis on which we can decide all questions concerning the manipulation of the mathematical "objects" with which we are concerned.

Using this alternate approach in constructing a mathematical model for the "behavior" of sets, let us begin by stating formally that *for every pair of sets A and B there exists a unique set called their union and a unique set called their intersection; as before, these sets are written* $A \cup B$ *and* $A \cap B$, *respectively.* Now, the formation of unions and intersections are controlled by laws which are very much like some of the basic rules with which the reader must surely be familiar from ordinary arithmetic. Corresponding to the rules which enable us to write $2 + 3 = 3 + 2$, for example, and $2 \cdot 3 = 3 \cdot 2$, we have the two *commutative laws*

Postulate 1: $A \cup B = B \cup A$

Postulate 2: $A \cap B = B \cap A$

There are also the two *associative laws*

Postulate 3: $(A \cup B) \cup C = A \cup (B \cup C)$

Postulate 4: $(A \cap B) \cap C = A \cap (B \cap C)$

which correspond to the rules of (ordinary) arithmetic which enable us to write $(3 + 4) + 5 = 3 + (4 + 5)$, for example, and $(3 \cdot 4) \cdot 5 = 3 \cdot (4 \cdot 5)$. Essentially, the two commutative laws and the two associative laws tell us that when we form unions and intersections of two or more sets *the order in which the sets are combined is immaterial.* Thus, we often write $A \cup B \cup C$, $A \cap B \cap C$, and similar expressions involving more than three sets without parentheses or brackets to indicate which of the sets are to be combined first. Observe that $A \cup B \cup C$ contains all elements that are either in A, in B, or in C, and that $A \cap B \cap C$ contains all the elements which A, B, and C have in common.

In ordinary arithmetic we also have the *distributive law* which combines addition and multiplication; it enables us to "multiply out" $3 \cdot (4 + 5)$, for example, and write it as $3 \cdot 4 + 3 \cdot 5$. Note that this law does *not* hold if we interchange the roles of addition and multiplication; in other words, $3 + (4 \cdot 5)$ is *not* equal to $(3 + 4) \cdot (3 + 5)$. We made this point because, for sets, there are the two *distributive laws*

Postulate 5: $A \cap (B \cup C) = (A \cap B) \cup (A \cap C)$

Postulate 6: $A \cup (B \cap C) = (A \cup B) \cap (A \cup C)$

Either of these rules can be obtained from the other by substituting $\cup$ for $\cap$ and vice versa. Rather than accept these last two postulates blindly, let us verify them with the use of Venn diagrams; actually, we shall verify only Postulate 5, but the reader will be asked to use the same method to verify Postulate 6 in Exercise 5 on page 22. All we really have to show in order to verify Postulate 5 is that the region which represents $A \cap (B \cup C)$ in a Venn diagram is identical with the one which represents $(A \cap B) \cup (A \cap C)$. This is demonstrated in Figures 1.8 and 1.9. In

Figure 1.8, the circle which represents A is shaded one way, the region which represents $B \cup C$ is shaded the other way, and the intersection of these two sets, namely, $A \cap (B \cup C)$, is the region which is shaded *both ways*. In Figure 1.9, the region which represents $A \cap B$ is shaded one way,

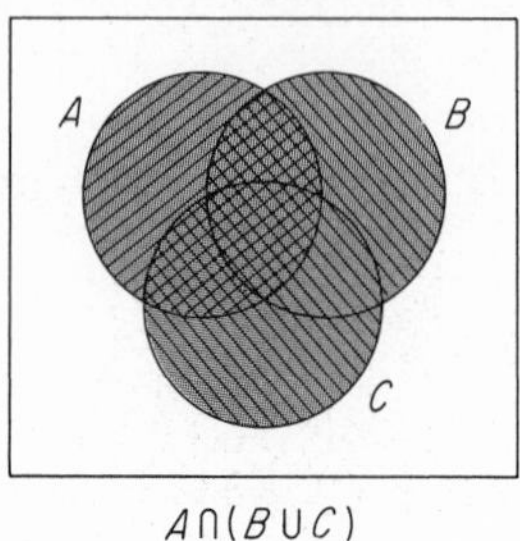

FIG. 1.8

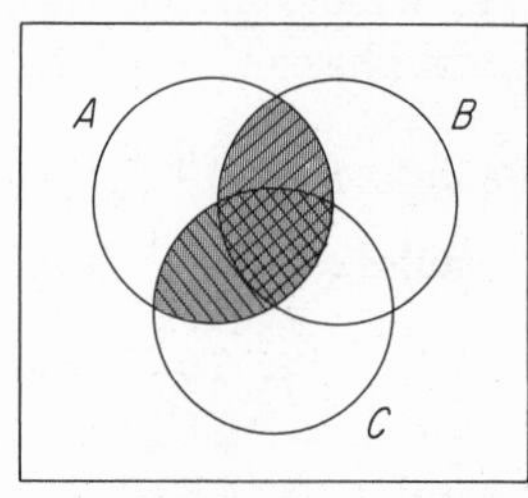

FIG. 1.9

the region which represents $A \cap C$ is shaded the other way, and the union of these two sets, namely, $(A \cap B) \cup (A \cap C)$ is the total region which is shaded one way or the other. It can thus be seen that $A \cap (B \cup C)$ and $(A \cap B) \cup (A \cap C)$ are represented by the same region and we conclude that the two sets are equal.

The remaining three postulates spell out formally what we mean by the universal set I, the null set $\varnothing$, and the complement A' of any set A. To take care of the first two, we assert that I and $\varnothing$ are such that for any set A

Postulate 7: $A \cap I = A$

Postulate 8: $A \cup \varnothing = A$

Observe that $A \cap I = A$ is simply a way of saying that every set A is contained in I, and we could also have expressed this by writing $A \cup I = I$. Similarly, $A \cup \varnothing = A$ is simply a way of saying that $\varnothing$ does not "add" anything (no new elements) to any set A, and we could also have expressed this by writing $A \cap \varnothing = \varnothing$.

So far as complements are concerned, it follows from our definition on page 11 that any set A and its complement A' have no elements in common, and that, together, they contain all the elements of I. Symbolically, we can express this by writing

Postulate 9: $A \cap A' = \varnothing$ and $A \cup A' = I$

This completes the construction of the model which characterizes the "behavior" of sets; it is called the *Algebra of Sets* or *Boolean Algebra*, named after the English mathematician George Boole (1815-1864). Having presented this model, we can now proceed in several ways: we can study *further properties* of sets by combining the above rules, we can study *applications*, or we can look for entirely *different interpretations* of the model (as we did on page 5 in connection with the model which we constructed in Section 1.1). Leaving the second and third alternatives to Sections 1.4 and 1.5, let us use the remainder of this section to demonstrate how the postulates can be used to obtain further rules concerning the "behavior" of sets.

Since this kind of work can be quite tricky, let us merely demonstrate the fact that

$$A \cap A = A$$

for any set A as an illustration of the general procedure that is involved in a formal proof. The most important feature of the proof which follows is that *every step is justified by means of one of the postulates:*

$$\begin{aligned} A &= A \cap I && \text{Postulate 7} \\ &= A \cap (A \cup A') && \text{Postulate 9} \\ &= (A \cap A) \cup (A \cap A') && \text{Postulate 5} \\ &= (A \cap A) \cup \varnothing && \text{Postulate 9} \\ &= A \cap A && \text{Postulate 8} \end{aligned}$$

It is difficult to say *why* we chose this particular sequence of steps; as we said before, this kind of proof can be rather tricky and there is no set rule which always tells us how to proceed. Of course, A and $A \cap A$ are represented by the same region of a Venn diagram and, hence, they are equal, but this argument constitutes a *verification* rather than a formal proof.

The following are some other rules about sets which can be derived from the nine postulates:

$$A \cup A = A, \quad I' = \varnothing, \quad \varnothing' = I, \quad \text{and} \quad (A')' = A$$

The first of these is similar to the rule which we have just proved, while the other three tell us that $\varnothing$ is the complement of I and vice versa, and that *the complement of the complement* of A is A, itself. [In ordinary arithmetic, this last rule corresponds to the fact that $-(-3) = +3$, for example, or $-(-7) = +7$.] Two other important rules, called *de Morgan's laws*, are given by

$$(A \cup B)' = A' \cap B' \quad \text{and} \quad (A \cap B)' = A' \cup B'$$

The first one tells us that "neither A nor B" means the same as "not A *and* not B," while the second tells us that "not both, A and B" means the same as "not A *or* not B." Thus, when we say that "a person is neither healthy nor wealthy," we mean that he is not healthy *and* not wealthy, and when we say that "a person is not (both) healthy and wealthy," we mean that either he is not healthy *or* he is not wealthy.

EXERCISES

1. In the beginning of Section 1.3 we considered the universal set I of all students attending the University of Arizona (in a given year) and the subsets M and F of all male and female students enrolled at this university (in that year). Verify the tables of all possible unions, intersections, and complements on page 18.

2. Using the tables for unions, intersections, and complements on page 18, check whether the following equations hold for the given sets I, M, F, and $\emptyset$:

   (a) $(I \cup F) \cap [(F \cap I) \cup (\emptyset \cap M)] = F$
   (b) $(M \cup \emptyset)' \cup (M \cup F) = I$
   (c) $[(M \cap M') \cap F] \cup (F \cap I)' = \emptyset$

3. The following is a proof of the fact that $A \cup A = A$ for any set A:

$$\begin{aligned} A &= A \cup \emptyset \\ &= A \cup (A \cap A') \\ &= (A \cup A) \cap (A \cup A') \\ &= (A \cup A) \cap I \\ &= A \cup A \end{aligned}$$

   Indicate what postulate justifies each step of this proof.

4. On page 20 we pointed out that Postulate 7 is simply another way of saying that every set A is contained in I, and that we could also have expressed this by writing $A \cup I = I$. Indicate what postulate justifies each step in the following proof, which demonstrates that this is actually true:

$$\begin{aligned} A \cup I &= (A \cup I) \cap I \\ &= (A \cup I) \cap (A \cup A') \\ &= A \cup (I \cap A') \\ &= A \cup (A' \cap I) \\ &= A \cup A' \\ &= I \end{aligned}$$

5. Use Venn diagrams to verify Postulate 6 on page 19.

6. Use Venn diagrams to verify the two de Morgan laws on page 21.

7. Use Venn diagrams to verify that for any two sets A and B

   (a) $A \cup (A \cap B) = A$
   (b) $(A \cap B) \cup (A \cap B') = A$
   (c) $A \cup B = (A \cap B) \cup (A \cap B') \cup (A' \cap B)$.

1.4 APPLICATIONS TO LOGIC*

To illustrate how the Algebra of Sets can be applied to a problem of logic, suppose that the personnel manager of a firm receives the following directive for hiring new salesmen:

---

* This section may be omitted without loss of continuity.

He is to consider only applicants who are college graduates or at least 20 years old, but not college graduates under 20.

This sounds confusing, to say the least, and it may well be that the directive does not say what it is meant to say; in any case, let us show that the directive merely says that *the personnel manager should not hire anyone who is less than 20 years old.* If A is the set of applicants who are college graduates and B is the set of applicants who are less than 20 years old, then $A \cup B'$ is the set of applicants who are college graduates or at least 20 years old, $(A \cap B)'$ is the set of applicants who are *not* college graduates under 20, and according to the directive the personnel manager is supposed to hire only applicants belonging to *both* of these sets, namely, applicants belonging to the set

$$(A \cup B') \cap (A \cap B)'$$

To show that this set equals B', we perform the following steps:

$$\begin{aligned}(A \cup B') \cap (A \cap B)' &= (A \cup B') \cap (A' \cup B') && \text{de Morgan Law}\\ &= (B' \cup A) \cap (B' \cup A') && \text{Postulate 1}\\ &= B' \cup (A \cap A') && \text{Postulate 6}\\ &= B' \cup \varnothing && \text{Postulate 9}\\ &= B' && \text{Postulate 8}\end{aligned}$$

Note that once a rule (such as one of the de Morgan's laws) has been proved or verified, it can be added to the list of rules which we can use to justify the various steps of a proof.

We have thus shown that the directive says that only persons belonging to B' should be considered; in other words, the personnel manager should hire only persons who are at least 20 years old. In case the reader is perplexed by formal proofs of this kind, let us point out that a much simpler way of handling this kind of problem is suggested in Exercise 1 on page 26; it is again based on Venn diagrams. The above proof may have been involved, but it illustrates the important fact that the simplification of an expression involving sets is *purely mechanical*; in fact, it would be an easy job for a computer which has been programmed to operate according to the postulates of Boolean Algebra.

Before we extend our discussion to the analysis of logical arguments, let us first show how relationships among sets can be expressed in terms of equations or inequalities. Consider, for example, the sentence "all stockbrokers are honest." If S is the set of all stockbrokers and H is the set of all honest persons, then the given sentence can be represented by the equation

$$S \cap H' = \varnothing$$

Literally, this says that the set of dishonest stockbrokers is *empty*. Suppose now that we also consider the sentence "some stockbrokers are graduates of business colleges." Letting G be the set of all graduates of business colleges, we can express this second sentence by writing

$$S \cap G \neq \varnothing$$

where $\neq$ indicates as before that the respective sets are not equal. Literally, this inequality says that the set of brokers who are graduates of business colleges is *not empty*.

Finally, let us take the two sentences together and see whether we can arrive at some sort of conclusion about honest persons and graduates of business colleges. Does it follow that "all honest persons are graduates of business colleges," that "some graduates of business colleges are dishonest," or that "some dishonest persons are graduates of business colleges"? No, none of these statements are *valid* conclusions, but if we applied the rules of Boolean Algebra to $S \cap H' = \varnothing$ and $S \cap G \neq \varnothing$, we could show that these two sentences lead to $G \cap H \neq \varnothing$, namely, to the assertion that "some graduates of business colleges are honest."

Rather than go through a detailed proof, however, let us merely verify this result by means of Venn diagrams. To this end, *we blacken any region that corresponds to a set which is known to be empty, and we draw a dotted line along the boundary of any region that corresponds to a set which is not empty.*

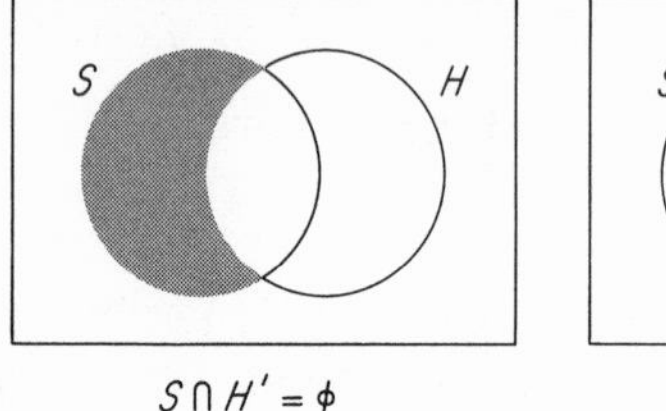

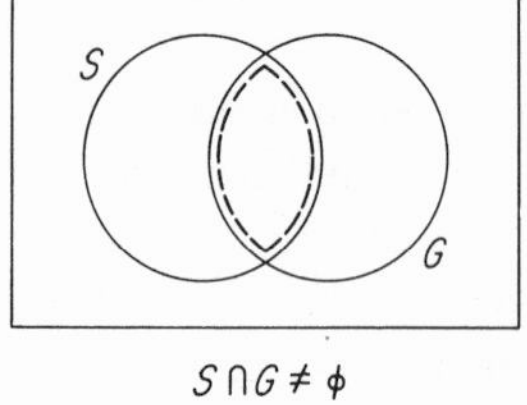

FIG. 1.10

Thus, $S \cap H' = \varnothing$ is represented by the first Venn diagram of Figure 1.10, while $S \cap G \neq \varnothing$ is represented by the second. If we combine these two figures, as in Figure 1.11, we find that so far as G and H are concerned, their intersection is *not empty*. Hence, we conclude that "some graduates of

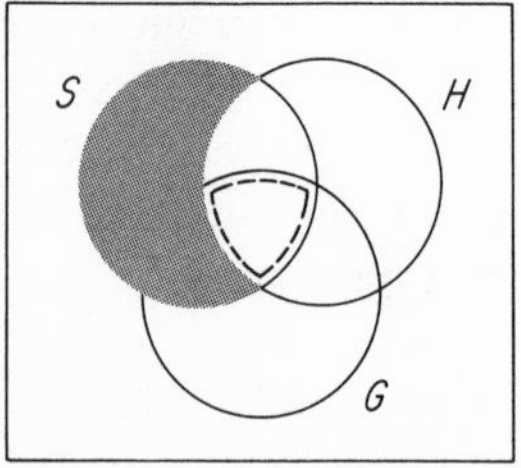

FIG. 1.11

business colleges are honest," or that "some honest persons are graduates of business colleges," which means the same. Symbolically, we write this conclusion as $G \cap H \neq \varnothing$.

To consider another example, suppose that (in the heat of a political campaign) a candidate claims that *since all educated persons are going to vote for him and no educated person is a liar, it follows that all liars are going to vote for his opponent.* To analyze this argument, let us consider the universal set of persons who are going to vote in this election, and the sets E, V, and L, which consist of those who are educated, those who are going to vote for the given candidate, and those who are liars. Now the argument can be expressed as follows:

$$\begin{array}{l} E \cap V' = \varnothing \\ E \cap L \;\, = \varnothing \\ \hline L \cap V \;\, = \varnothing \end{array}$$

where the conclusion (?) is given below the line. The first equation says, in effect, that the set of educated persons who are not going to vote for the given candidate is empty; the second equation says that the set of educated liars is empty; and the conclusion (?) says that the set of liars who are going to vote for the given candidate is empty. Of course, all these arguments are meant to apply only to the given universal set of voters.

Whether or not the given conclusion actually follows from the two premises could be checked by means of Boolean Algebra, and as we have pointed out earlier this kind of work is purely mechanical (though tricky, perhaps) and it could be done by a suitably-programmed computer. Using a Venn diagram instead, we find that the first sentence tells us to blacken the region corresponding to the set $E \cap V'$, namely, that inside circle E and outside circle V in Figure 1.12. The second sentence tells us to blacken

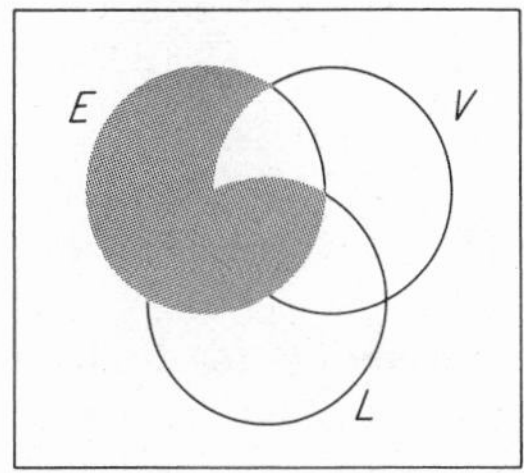

FIG. 1.12

the intersection $E \cap L$, and for the conclusion to be valid, the intersection $L \cap V$ would thus have to be blackened too. Since this is *not* the case, we find that the candidate's conclusion does not follow, namely, that *his argument is not valid.* He overlooked the possibility that *some of the uneducated persons who may vote for him could be liars.*

Observe that we did not say that the candidate's conclusion is *false,* this would have to depend on whether any uneducated liars are actually going to vote for him. Similarly, we did not discuss the truth of the conclusion at which we arrived on page 24, namely, that "some graduates of business colleges are honest." In each case we indicated whether or not the conclusion was *valid,* that is, whether it followed from the information with which we were supplied. So far as the truth of a conclusion is concerned, we can only say that *if the information is true and the argument is valid, then the conclusion must also be true;* on the other hand, *if the information is false, then anything goes, and the conclusion can be either true or false.* Observe that in the example on page 24 the conclusion "some graduates of business colleges are honest" would seem true even though the premise that "all stockbrokers are honest" is highly questionable.

EXERCISES

1. Use a Venn diagram to verify that $(A \cup B') \cap (A \cap B)' = B'$.
2. Use a Venn diagram to simplify the statement "either he is stupid or he is a stupid liar."
3. Use a Venn diagram to simplify the statement "he is either successful and happy, successful and unhappy, or unsuccessful and happy."
4. Use Venn diagrams to verify that "he is either a fraud or eccentric and he is a fraud or a millionaire" means the same as "he is either a fraud or an eccentric millionaire."
5. Letting T stand for television commercials and A for things that are amusing, translate each of the following statements into an equation or an inequality and also indicate it in a Venn diagram by blackening an appropriate region or drawing a dotted line along its boundary:

   (a) All television commercials are amusing;
   (b) Some television commercials are amusing;
   (c) Some television commercials are not amusing;
   (d) No television commercials are amusing.

6. Letting M stand for management consultants and B for brilliant persons, translate each of the following statements into an equation or an inequality and also indicate it in a Venn diagram by blackening an appropriate region or drawing a dotted line along its boundary:

   (a) All management consultants are brilliant;
   (b) All brilliant persons are management consultants;
   (c) No management consultants are brilliant;
   (d) Some management consultants are not brilliant;
   (e) Some brilliant persons are not management consultants;
   (f) Some brilliant persons are management consultants.

7. If C stands for customers and D for persons who are dissatisfied, express in words what is asserted by each of the following equations and inequalities:

(a) $C \cap D = \emptyset$; (c) $C \cap D \neq \emptyset$;
(b) $C \cap D' = \emptyset$; (d) $C \cap D' \neq \emptyset$.

8. If S stands for salesmen and E for extroverts, express in words what is asserted by each of the following equations and inequalities:

(a) $S \cap E = \emptyset$; (d) $S \cap E \neq \emptyset$;
(b) $S \cap E' = \emptyset$; (e) $S' \cap E \neq \emptyset$;
(c) $S' \cap E = \emptyset$; (f) $S' \cap E' \neq \emptyset$.

9. Use a Venn diagram to check the validity of the following argument:

All inexpensive items are bargains.
All bargains are sold out
―――――――――――――――
All inexpensive items are sold out.

10. Use a Venn diagram to check the validity of the following argument:

All executives are self-confident.
No self-confident person is irritable.
―――――――――――――――
No irritable person is an executive.

11. Use a Venn diagram to check the validity of the following argument:

All salesmen are talkative.
No gamblers are talkative.
―――――――――――――――
Some salesmen are gamblers.

12. Use a Venn diagram to obtain a valid conclusion for the following argument:

All shipments are carefully checked.
Nothing that is carefully checked will be unacceptable.
―――――――――――――――
?

13. Use a Venn diagram to obtain a valid conclusion for the following argument:

Some television commercials are ineffective.
All television commercials are carefully planned.
―――――――――――――――
?

1.5 SWITCHING CIRCUITS*

One of the objectives of the first section of this Chapter was to demonstrate how one mathematical model can serve to describe totally different situations. In this section we shall show how Boolean Algebra, the model which we introduced for sets, can also be used in the (seemingly unrelated) analysis of electrical circuits. In particular, we shall consider arrangements

* This section may be omitted without loss of continuity.

of wires and switches between two terminals. Like ordinary light switches, these switches can be open or closed, and how they are set will determine whether current can flow between the two terminals; in general, only a *closed* switch permits current to flow. The letters $A, B, C, \ldots$, which previously denoted sets, will now represent switches like the one shown in Figure 1.13, and before we go any further we shall have to explain what we

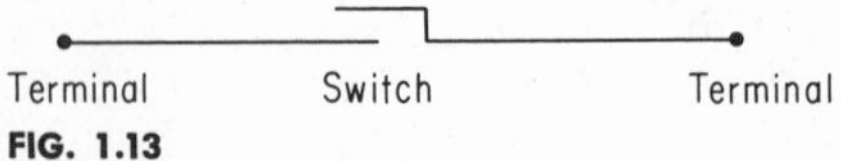

FIG. 1.13

mean by $A \cup B$, $A \cap B$, $A = B$, I, $\varnothing$, and A'. To begin with, $A \cup B$ and $A \cap B$ represent the two arrangements of switches shown in Figure 1.14.

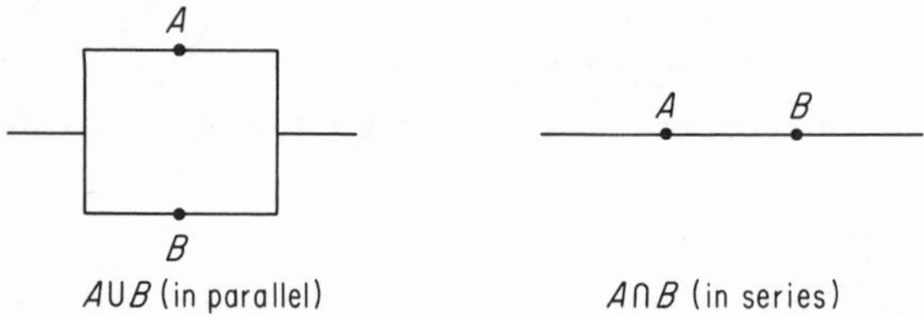

FIG. 1.14

The first one, $A \cup B$, permits current to go through if either switch is closed, and A and B are said to be *in parallel;* the second, $A \cap B$, permits current to go through only if both switches are closed, and A and B are said to be *in series.* When we write $A = B$, this means that the two switches have the same effect, namely, that A is open whenever B is open and A is closed whenever B is closed. Finally, the letter I represents a switch which is *always closed,* $\varnothing$ represents a switch which is *always open,* and A' is a switch which is connected to switch A in such a way that whenever one is open the other is closed.

Before we use Boolean Algebra in the analysis of switching circuits (rather than sets), we should really verify that the postulates apply. For

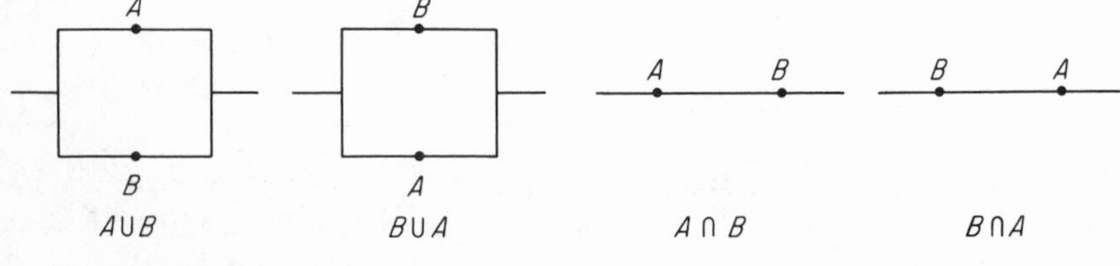

FIG. 1.15

instance, Postulates 1 and 2, the two commutative laws, can be checked by inspecting Figure 1.15, from which it is apparent that the overall effect of $A \cup B$ is the same as that of $B \cup A$, and that the overall effect of $A \cap B$

is the same as that of $B \cap A$. Most of the other postulates can also be checked by inspection; the fact that $A \cap I = A$ and $A \cup \varnothing = A$ is apparent from Figure 1.16—I is always closed, $\varnothing$ is always open, so that

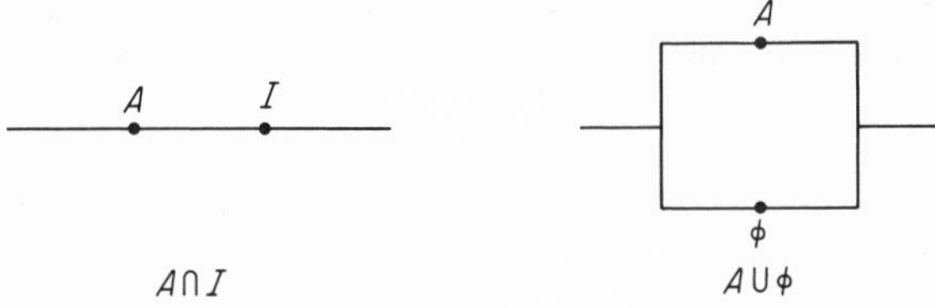

FIG. 1.16

$A \cap I$ and $A \cup \varnothing$ have the same effect as A. This verifies Postulates 7 and 8, and in Exercise 4 on page 32 the reader will be asked to verify Postulate 5, which requires a bit more detail.

The two examples which follow show how Boolean Algebra (and related methods) can be used to great advantage in work with electrical circuits: in the first example we shall simplify a complicated arrangement of

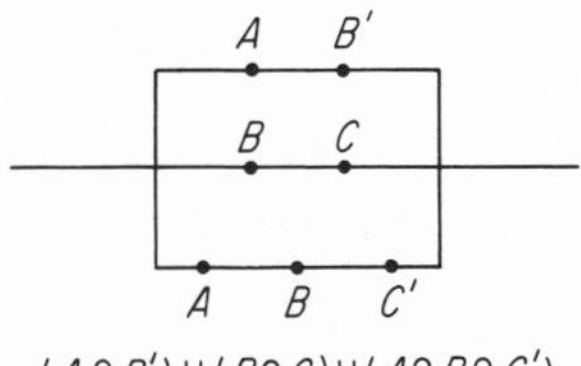

FIG. 1.17

switches, and in the second example we shall design a circuit which serves a specific purpose. Thus, let us first see whether we can simplify the switching network of Figure 1.17, which might be part of the wiring of a very complicated kind of computer. Since the top part is $A \cap B'$, the middle part is $B \cap C$, the bottom part is $A \cap B \cap C'$, and the three parts are *in parallel,* the entire switching arrangement can be written as

$$(A \cap B') \cup (B \cap C) \cup (A \cap B \cap C')$$

To simplify this expression we could proceed as in the proof on page 21, but it will again be much simpler to refer to Venn diagrams. In the first three diagrams of Figure 1.18 we have shaded the regions corresponding to $A \cap B'$, $B \cap C$, and $A \cap B \cap C'$, and in the fourth diagram we have shaded the region which is the union of these three sets. Note that we have thus shaded the region inside circle A and also that common to circles B and C. In other words, we have shaded the region $A \cup (B \cap C)$, and we can conclude that

$$(A \cap B') \cup (B \cap C) \cup (A \cap B \cap C') = A \cup (B \cap C)$$

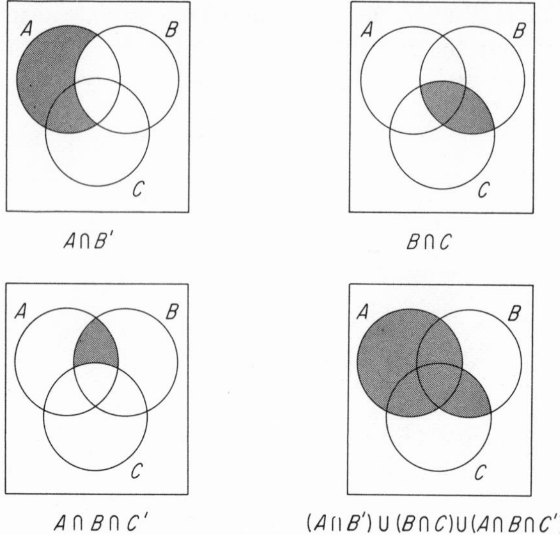

FIG. 1.18

namely, that the switching circuit of Figure 1.17 is equivalent to (can be replaced by) that of Figure 1.19. Thus, a rather complicated arrangement

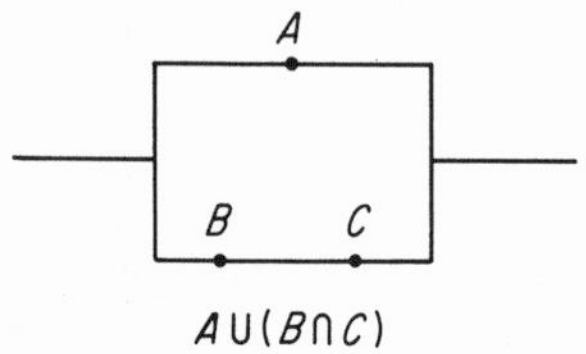

FIG. 1.19

consisting of *seven* switches has been replaced by a much simpler one having only *three.*

To demonstrate how a switching circuit can be designed to fit a particular situation, suppose that two persons play the following version of the game of *matching coins:* each player has a switch which he can open or close; the first player wins if they match (both switches are open or both are closed), and the second player wins if they do not match. The problem is how to wire the switches so that a light will be turned on (current can go through) *if and only if* the first player wins the game. Now, $A \cap B$ represents a circuit which will be closed only when A and B are both closed, and $A' \cap B'$ represents a circuit which will be closed only when A and B are both open. Since we want the circuit to be closed in either case, it follows that $(A \cap B) \cup (A' \cap B')$, namely, the switching arrangement

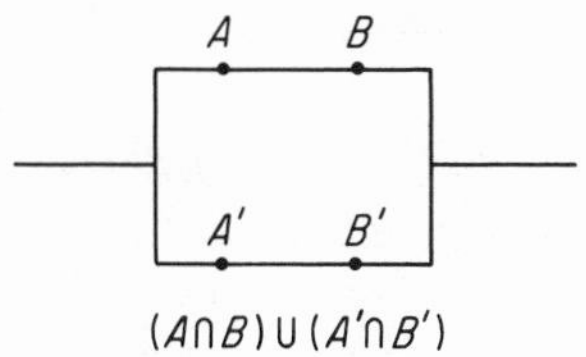

FIG. 1.20

of Figure 1.20, will do the trick. An alternate circuit which will do the same job is given below in Exercise 3.

EXERCISES

1. Write an expression which represents the switching network of Figure 1.21.

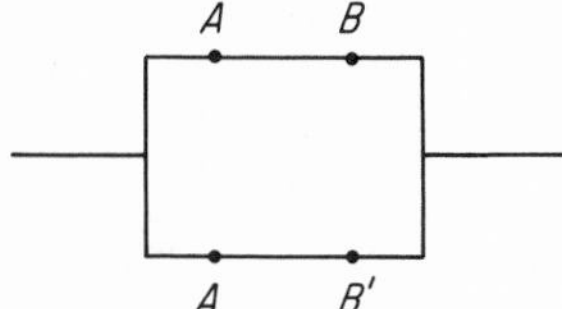

FIG. 1.21

Also show that this expression equals A, so that the entire network can be replaced with the single switch A.

2. Write an expression which represents the switching network of Figure 1.22.

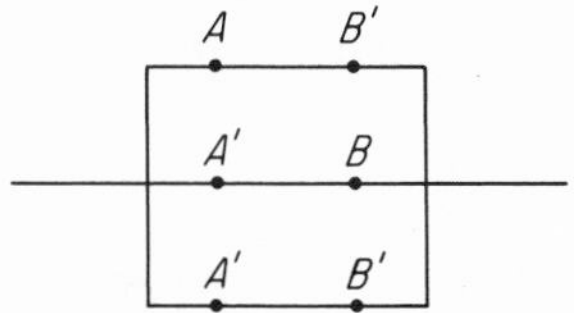

FIG. 1.22

Also show (with the use of a Venn diagram) that this expression equals $A' \cup B'$ and draw the corresponding circuit.

3. Write an expression which represents the switching network of Figure 1.23,

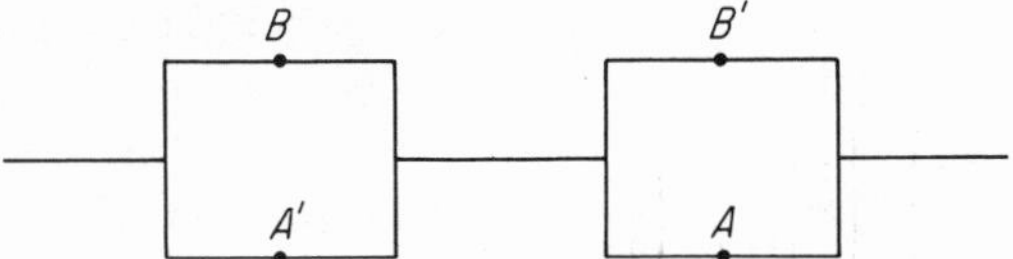

FIG. 1.23

and use Venn diagrams to verify that this circuit could be used for the coin-matching game described in the text. Also verify this directly by checking what happens when each switch (that is, A and B) is open or closed.

4. Verify Postulate 5 by checking whether the circuits given by $A \cap (B \cup C)$ and $(A \cap B) \cup (A \cap C)$ are *both open* or *both closed* no matter how we turn switches A, B, and C. (*Hint:* check each of the *eight cases* A open, B open, C open; A open, B open, C closed, . . . , and A closed, B closed, C closed.)

2

NUMBERS AND NUMERALS

2.1 INTRODUCTION

In the study of numbers there are essentially two kinds of problems: one concerns their arithmetic (namely, the rules according to which they "behave"), and the other concerns the symbols (that is, the numerals) by which they are described.

The first kind of problem concerns the question "What *is* a number?," and we answer it by constructing models—different models for different kinds of numbers. Actually, we shall not have the time to go into this matter in much detail, and we shall limit our discussion to some of the most important features which various kinds of numbers (and other mathematical "objects") have in common. In particular, we shall study those features which will be of relevance in later chapters.

So far as numerals are concerned, the advent of high-speed electronic computers has created special interest in questions of notation. In addition to the decimal notation reviewed in Section 2.3, we shall devote Sections 2.4 and 2.5 to some of the alternate systems of notation that are currently in vogue (in connection with work done on computers).

2.2 NUMBER FIELDS

When we first studied sets, we indicated that their postulates are very similar to some of the laws of "ordinary" arithmetic. Of course, we do not combine numbers by forming unions and intersections, but many of the rules which apply to the unions and intersections of sets apply also to the sums, products, differences, and quotients of numbers. These similarities between numbers and sets are very important, but equally instructive are their *dissimilarities*. For instance, on page 18 we stated that for any pair of sets there exists a unique set called their union and a unique set called their intersection. This means that we can form unions and intersections of sets *with the assurance that the results will also be sets*. Whether or not we can make similar statements for numbers depends on the numbers as well as the operations according to which they are combined. For instance, if we are working with the whole numbers 1, 2, 3, 4, 5, 6, 7, . . . , nowadays called the *natural numbers*, it is true that the sum as well as the product of any two natural numbers will also be natural numbers, but analogous assertions for differences and quotients would be incorrect. Although we can subtract 3 from 5 and get the natural number 2, we cannot subtract 5 from 3 so long as we are working only with natural numbers. The situation would be changed, however, if we considered the *integers*, which include the natural numbers 1, 2, 3, 4, 5, 6, 7, . . . , the corresponding negative numbers -1, -2, -3, -4, -5, -6, -7, . . . , and the number 0. Now we can say that the difference between any two integers is also an integer, and we can write $3 - 5 = -2$, for example, and $8 - 8 = 0$. In more technical terms, we say that the set of integers is *closed* under subtraction, whereas the set of natural numbers is not.

Although there are quite a few things we can do with integers that cannot be done with natural numbers, we still have to be careful when it comes to division. The set of integers is *not closed* under division even if we exclude the number 0; although we can divide 12 by -3, for example, and get -4, or -24 by -4 and get 6, we cannot divide -3 by 12 or -4 by -24 so long as we are working only with integers. To get around this difficulty, we shall have to extend our discussion to the *fractions*, or better the *rational numbers*. [The distinction between these two terms is rather subtle; we say that 3/4, 6/8, and 15/20 are different fractions, but that they represent the same rational number; in other words, the term "fraction" applies to the different numerals (or symbols) which we use to describe rational numbers.] Working with rational numbers, we can now divide -3 by 12 and get $-1/4$, and we can divide -4 by -24 and get 1/6. We still cannot divide by 0, but if we exclude division by 0, we can say that *otherwise* the set of rational numbers is *closed* under division.

Returning again to similarities between sets and numbers, let us observe that the two commutative laws, the two associative laws, and one of the distributive laws on page 19 hold for all of the number systems which we have discussed (namely, the natural numbers, the integers, and the rational numbers). Replacing $\cup$ with a plus sign and $\cap$ with a multiplication sign, we can write $5 + 7 = 7 + 5$, for example $4 \cdot (-3) = (-3) \cdot 4$,

$(3+\frac{1}{2})+\frac{3}{5}=3+(\frac{1}{2}+\frac{3}{5})$, $[(-4)\cdot\frac{1}{3}]\cdot 5=(-4)\cdot(\frac{1}{3}\cdot 5)$, and $(-2)\cdot[\frac{1}{5}+(-7)] = (-2)\cdot\frac{1}{5}+(-2)\cdot(-7)$, but we *cannot* write $3+(4\cdot 5)=(3+4)\cdot(3+5)$. *In ordinary arithmetic there is only one distributive law.*

When we discussed sets in Section 1.2, we singled out two special sets, the empty set $\varnothing$ and the universal set I. So far as the empty set $\varnothing$ is concerned, we stated that $A \cup \varnothing = A$ is simply another way of saying that $\varnothing$ does not "add" anything (no new elements) to any set A, and we suggested that this could also have been expressed by writing $A \cap \varnothing = \varnothing$. Now, if we read "$\cup$" as "plus" and "$\cap$" as "times," it is easy to see that $\varnothing$ shares the following properties with the number 0: zero does not "add" anything to any number A, and the fact that $A + 0 = A$ and $A \cdot 0 = 0$ for any number A is analogous to the fact that $A \cup \varnothing = A$ and $A \cap \varnothing = \varnothing$ for any set A. Incidentally, this argument applies to the integers, the rational numbers, and perhaps others, but *not* to the natural numbers, which do not even include the number zero.

So far as the universal set I is concerned, $A \cap I = A$ becomes $A \cdot I = A$ when we read "$\cap$" as "times," and this suggests that we identify I with the number 1. Surely, it is true for each of the number systems which we have discussed that any number A multiplied by 1 gives that same number A. (The analogy falls apart, however, if we try to read "$\cup$" as "plus"; whereas $A \cup I = I$ holds for any set A, the equation $A + 1 = 1$ holds only for $A = 0$.)

Since multiplication by 1 leaves any number as is, we refer to the number 1 as the *identity element for multiplication* or as the *multiplicative identity*. Similarly, since $A + 0 = A$ for any number A and, hence, the addition of zero leaves any number as is, we refer to the number 0 as the *identity element for addition* or as the *additive identity*. To complete this part of our terminology, let us add that we refer to the sets $\varnothing$ and I, respectively, as the *identity elements* for forming unions and intersections of sets.

If we tried to draw a parallel between the *complement* of a set and a suitable concept of ordinary arithmetic, we would arrive at different results depending on whether we look at the first or the second of the two equations of Postulate 9 on page 20, and also depending on how we read "$\cup$" and "$\cap$." If we proceeded as before, reading "$\cup$" as "plus" and "$\cap$" as "times," we would get $A \cdot A' = 0$ and $A + A' = 1$. The first of these two equations holds only when $A' = 0$ or $A = 0$, the second equation defines A' as $1 - A$, and neither of these analogies is of any value. To look for something more useful, let us see what will happen if we read "$\cup$" as "times" and "$\cap$" as "plus." Now, the first equation of Postulate 9 becomes

$$A + A' = 0$$

which means that A' is the *negative* of the number A, namely, $-A$; clearly,

$3 + (-3) = 0$, $\left(-\frac{1}{2}\right) + \frac{1}{2} = 0$, and so on. The second equation becomes

$$A \cdot A' = 1$$

which means that A' is the *reciprocal* of the number A, namely, $1/A$; clearly, $5 \cdot \frac{1}{5} = 1$, $-2 \cdot \frac{1}{-2} = 1$, and so on.

Actually, A' cannot be *both*, the negative of a rational number as well as its reciprocal (see Exercise 21 on page 126), but our analogy serves to illustrate an important similarity of the roles played by $-A$ in addition and $1/A$ in multiplication. In fact, we refer to them both as *inverses* of the number A; *$-A$ is the inverse of A with respect to addition and $1/A$ is the inverse of A with respect to multiplication.* We also refer to the negative of a number as its *additive inverse* and to the reciprocal of a number as its *multiplicative inverse*. Thus, -7 is the additive inverse of 7 and $1/3$ is the multiplicative inverse of 3. It should be noted that natural numbers include neither additive inverses nor multiplicative inverses (with the exception of the number 1, which is its own multiplicative inverse). On the other hand, integers include additive inverses but not multiplicative inverses (with the same exception as above), while rational numbers include additive inverses as well as multiplicative inverses (with the exception of the number 0, which is its own additive inverse but has no multiplicative inverse).

The two commutative laws, the two associative laws, the distributive law, identity elements, and inverses play very important roles in the models (sets of rules or postulates) which apply to various kinds of numbers and other mathematical objects. Taken all together, they are so important that we make the following definition:

> *Any set of numbers which obey all of the above-mentioned laws, contains the numbers 0 and 1 as well as appropriate inverses for addition and multiplication (except for 0), are said to constitute a field.*

Thus, we can say that the rational numbers constitute a field, while the integers and the natural numbers do not. Although we can let $\varnothing$ and I play the roles of 0 and 1, sets do *not* constitute a field because of the trouble with inverses; as we pointed out in Chapter 1, the model which applies to sets is referred to as a *Boolean Algebra*.

Now that we have defined the mathematical model which is called a field, we can proceed in two different directions. As in Chapter 1, we can use the model to investigate further properties of the numbers to which the model applies (in this case the rational numbers), or we can check whether there might be other kinds of numbers (other kinds of mathematical "objects") to which the model applies. If we chose the first of these two alternatives, we could prove many of the rules concerning the arithmetic of fractions which seem to mystify the beginner. For instance, we could show that

$$-\frac{a}{b} = \frac{-a}{b} = \frac{a}{-b}$$

(where a and b are positive integers), we could show that the product of two negative numbers is positive, or we could show that $-(-p) = p$ for any rational number p. We could also prove the cancellation laws according to which $a = b$ whenever $a + c = b + c$ or $a \cdot c = b \cdot c$ (and c is not equal to zero), and we could demonstrate that if the product of two rational numbers is zero, one or the other must be zero. Owing to our objectives in this book we shall not elaborate, but it is important to realize that all of these rules (and many more) are consequences of the relatively few postulates which define a field (plus appropriate definitions of what we mean by the *negative* of a number, the *difference* between two numbers, the *reciprocal* of a number, and a few more terms).

Turning now to the question whether there are *other* kinds of numbers (besides the rational numbers) which behave according to the rules of a field, the answer is—*YES*! A very simple example of a field is given by the algebra of the clock of Figure 2.1, which is very similar to that of the clock of Figure 1.2 on page 5. Forming sums as on page 5, it is easy to verify the entries in the first of the following two tables:

	0	1	2
0	0	1	2
1	1	2	0
2	2	0	1

Addition

	0	1	2
0	0	0	0
1	0	1	2
2	0	2	1

Multiplication

So far as products are concerned, $2 \cdot 2$ means that we *twice* move the hand *two* spaces starting at 0, and since this leaves the hand pointing at 1, we write $2 \cdot 2 = 1$. All other products are defined in the same way.

Of course, it remains to be seen whether the numbers 0, 1, and 2 of the clock of Figure 2.1 actually constitute a field, namely, whether they satisfy all of the rules listed on page 36. So far as identity elements and inverses are concerned, it is apparent from the above tables that the identity elements for addition and multiplication are 0 and 1 (which should not come as a surprise), that the negative of 1 is 2, the negative of 2 is 1, the reciprocal of 1 is 1, and the reciprocal of 2 is 2. So far as the commutative laws, the associative laws, and the distributive law are concerned, their verification is tedious rather than difficult. For instance, to verify the distributive law

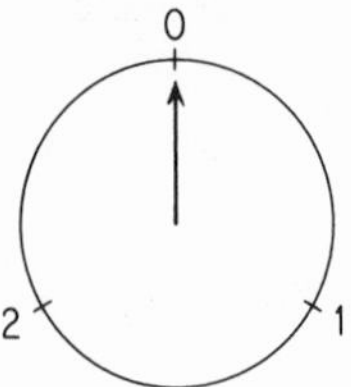

FIG. 2.1

$A \cdot (B + C) = A \cdot B + A \cdot C$, we have to check the *twenty-seven* possibilities which consist of letting A equal 0, 1, or 2, letting B equal 0, 1, or 2, and letting C equal 0, 1, or 2. For instance, for $A = 2$, $B = 1$, and $C = 2$, we get

$$\begin{aligned} 2 \cdot (1 + 2) &= 2 \cdot 1 + 2 \cdot 2 \\ 2 \cdot 0 &= 2 + 1 \\ 0 &= 0 \end{aligned}$$

which turns out to be correct. Leaving it to the reader to check some of the other possibilities in Exercise 5 on page 41 (and some of the other laws in Exercise 6 on page 42), let us merely state the result that the numbers 0, 1, and 2 of the clock of Figure 2.1, indeed, constitute a field. In contrast to the rational numbers (of which there are infinitely many), we say that the numbers 0, 1, and 2 of the clock in Figure 2.1 constitute a *finite field.*

An important distinction between the field of rational numbers and the finite field we have just discussed is that the first is *ordered* whereas the other is not. So far as the ordering of the rational numbers is concerned, one (and only one) of the following must be true for any two rational numbers a and b: *a is equal to b, a is greater than b, or a is less than b.* Thus, 4 is greater than (but not equal to or less than) -2, $2/3$ is less than (but not equal to or greater than) 5, and $\frac{17}{25}$ is equal to (and not less than or greater than) $\frac{34}{50}$. To picture this ordering of the rational numbers, we have only to look at Figure 2.2, where they are identified with points in the usual way,

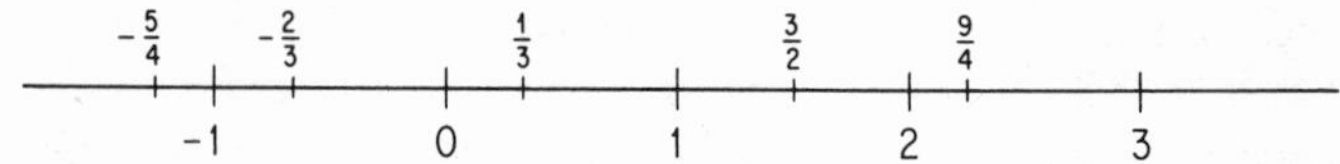

FIG. 2.2

that is, along a straight line with the greater number always to the right and the smaller one to the left. Observe that no such ordering is possible for the three numbers of the clock of Figure 2.1. Starting with 0 and repeatedly adding 1, we get

$$0, 1, 2, 0, 1, 2, 0, 1, 2, 0, 1, 2, \ldots \ldots$$

and it can be seen that 1 is to the left of 2 and also to its right; thus, in one sense we can say that 1 is smaller than (comes before) 2, but we can also say that 2 is smaller than (comes before) 1. Of course, this kind of thing cannot happen when we deal with rational numbers; they constitute an *ordered field*.

The idea of associating numbers with distances and, hence, with points on a line (as in Figure 2.2), dates back to ancient times. Until the fifth century B.C. it was believed that all distances could be measured by means of rational numbers, but this was proved to be wrong when Pythagoras discovered that there is no rational number whose square equals 2, namely, that there is no rational number which corresponds to the length of the diagonal of the unit square of Figure 2.3. (Each side of this square is of

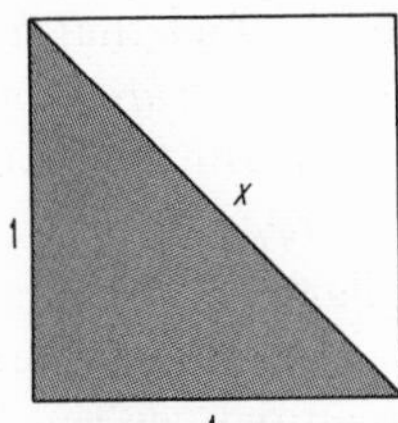

FIG. 2.3

length 1, the diagonal is of length x, and according to the Pythagorean theorem $x^2 = 1^2 + 1^2 = 2$.) In Exercise 8 on page 42, the reader will be asked to duplicate Pythagoras' proof that there is no rational number x such that $x^2 = 2$.

The fact that there were distances that could not be measured by means of rational numbers was quite a blow to Pythagoras and his contemporaries, since a major part of their philosophy was built on the mystical significance they attached to numbers of this kind. Today, we look at this from an entirely different point of view. If there is no rational number whose square equals 2 and if we want to have a number whose square is 2, we simply go ahead and define one. In other words, we construct a *new model* which includes the rational numbers, but which includes also numbers such as the one whose square equals 2. Incidentally, we refer to this particular number as the *square root of 2* and write it as $\sqrt{2}$; since it is not a rational number, we refer to it as *irrational* (meaning non-rational).

For a long time after Pythagoras, the square root of 2 was the only irrational number known. About a century later it was shown that the numbers whose squares are 3, 5, 6, 7, 8, 10, 11, 12, 13, 14, 15, and 17 are also irrational, and today it can be shown that there are infinitely more irrational numbers than rational numbers. They include such numbers as π, which arises in connection with the circumference and the area of a circle, and the number e used in connection with logarithms (see Section 5.3).

The number system which enables us to measure any distance, that is, assign a number to any point on a line, is what we call the *real numbers.* It consists of the rational numbers as well as the irrational numbers which, so to speak, fill the gaps. Like the rational numbers, the real numbers constitute an *ordered field,* but they have an additional property which makes them *completely ordered.* A formal definition of this term will be given in Chapter 11, but essentially "completely ordered" means that there are no gaps, namely, that there is a real number corresponding to each point on a line.

The distinction between rational numbers and irrational numbers is important to the mathematician, but it is of very little significance so far as practical applications are concerned. This is due to the fact that *any irrational number can be approximated to any desired degree of accuracy by means of a rational number.* For instance, if we have to perform calculations involving $\sqrt{2}$, we can use instead the rational number $1\frac{41}{100}$, or if more accuracy is required, the rational number 1.414214. Similarly, the circumference of a circle with the radius 1/2 is equal to π, which can be approximated with the rational number 3.1416. If more accuracy is required, we can look up π in a table in which it is given to more decimals. It is of interest to note that the decimal expansion of π has always intrigued mathematicians. In 1873 the English mathematician William Shanks published an approximation of π which was given to 707 decimals, a feat to which he devoted 15 years of his life in the hope of discovering specific patterns among the digits. This

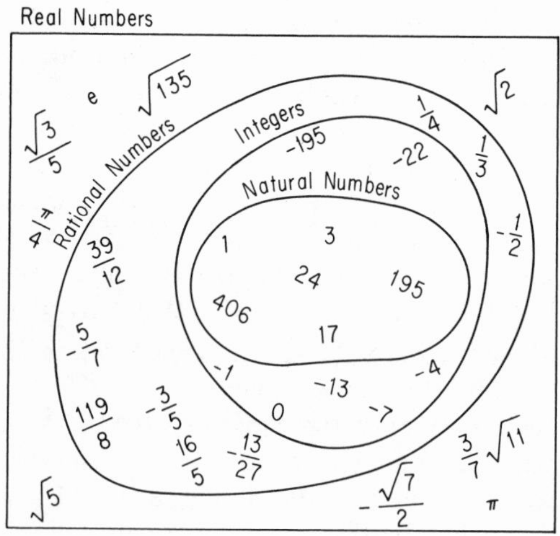

FIG. 2.4

may seem rather pathetic today, in view of the fact that in recent years electronic computers have calculated the value of π to thousands of decimals in a matter of minutes. Incidentally, the decimal representation of real numbers brings out an important distinction between rational and irrational numbers; this will be discussed later in this chapter on page 46.

To summarize the number systems we have mentioned in this section, let us consider the diagram of Figure 2.4. It shows that the real numbers consist of rational numbers and irrational numbers; the rational numbers include the integers, which in turn include the natural numbers.

EXERCISES

1. Decide whether each of the following sets is closed under ordinary addition and also whether it is closed under ordinary multiplication (if not, give an example):

(a) The even integers 2, 4, 6, 8, 10, 12, . . . ;
(b) The odd integers 1, 3, 5, 7, 9, 11, . . . ;
(c) The negative integers;
(d) The irrational numbers.

2. If the subtraction of integers were commutative and associative, we would be able to write $a - b = b - a$ and $(a - b) - c = a - (b - c)$ for any integers a, b, and c. Choose suitable numbers to demonstrate that the subtraction of integers is neither commutative nor associative.

3. If the division of non-zero rational numbers were commutative and associative, we would be able to write $a \div b = b \div a$ and $(a \div b) \div c = a \div (b \div c)$ for any non-zero rational numbers a, b, and c. Choose suitable numbers to show that the division of non-zero rational numbers is neither commutative nor associative.

4. It can be shown that the set of all numbers of the form $a + b\sqrt{2}$, where a and b are real numbers, constitute a field.

(a) What is the additive inverse of $2 - 3\sqrt{2}$?

(b) Verify that $\frac{5}{7} - \frac{3}{7}\sqrt{2}$ is the multiplicative inverse of $5 + 3\sqrt{2}$.

(c) Write the multiplicative inverse of $\sqrt{2}$ in the form $a + b\sqrt{2}$, where a and b are real numbers.

5. On page 38 we started to show that the distributive law $A \cdot (B + C) = A \cdot B + A \cdot C$ holds for the Algebra of the clock of Figure 2.1 by checking one of the twenty-seven possibilities. Show that the law holds also for

(a) $A = 2$, $B = 2$, and $C = 2$;
(b) $A = 2$, $B = 2$, and $C = 1$;
(c) $A = 1$, $B = 2$, and $C = 1$;
(d) $A = 2$, $B = 1$, and $C = 1$.

6. To verify the two associative laws $(A + B) + C = A + (B + C)$ and $(A \cdot B) \cdot C = A \cdot (B \cdot C)$ for the Algebra of the clock of Figure 2.1, we have to check the twenty-seven possibilities which consist of letting A equal 0, 1, or 2, letting B equal 0, 1, or 2, and letting C equal 0, 1, or 2. Check whether each of these two laws holds for

(a) $A = 0$, $B = 1$, and $C = 2$;
(b) $A = 1$, $B = 1$, and $C = 2$;
(c) $A = 2$, $B = 2$, and $C = 2$;
(d) $A = 1$, $B = 2$, and $C = 2$.

7. Referring to the arithmetic of the clock of Figure 1.2 on page 5, let us define multiplication in the following way: to obtain $2 \cdot 3$, for example, we start at 0, *twice* move the hand *three* places, and since it will then point at 2 we write $2 \cdot 3 = 2$. Similarly, to obtain $3 \cdot 3$ we begin at 0, *thrice* move the hand *three* places, and since it will then point at 1 we write $3 \cdot 3 = 1$. Show that one of the non-zero numbers of this clock does *not* have a multiplicative inverse and, hence, that the algebra of this clock is *not* a field.

8. **PROOF THAT $\sqrt{2}$ IS NOT A RATIONAL NUMBER.** The Pythagorean proof that $\sqrt{2}$ is irrational is of the type called *reductio ad absurdum*, which means that we shall assume that there exists a rational number whose square equals 2 and then show that this leads to a contradiction (and, hence, to the conclusion that the assumption must have been incorrect.)

(a) By definition, the *even integers* 2, 4, 6, 8, . . . , are all of the form $2 \cdot k$ where k is a positive integer, and the *odd integers* 1, 3, 5, 7, . . . , are all of the form $2 \cdot k - 1$, where k is a positive integer. Show that *the square of an even integer is even,* that *the square of an odd integer is odd,* and hence that *if the square of an integer is even, the integer itself must be even.*

(b) Assume that there exists a rational number a/b whose square equals 2, where a and b are positive integers which have no common factors. (This last part does not really constitute an additional assumption since common factors could always be cancelled.) Use the result obtained in (a) to show that the integer a must be *even.*

(c) Using the result obtained in (b) and substituting $2c$ for a, where c is a positive integer, show that the integer b must be *even.*

(d) Prove that there can be no rational number which equals $\sqrt{2}$ by demonstrating that the results of (b) and (c) contradict part of the assumption made in (b).

9. **OTHER IRRATIONAL NUMBERS.** The numbers 3, 6, 9, 12, 15, . . . , are referred to as the *multiples of 3;* they are all of the form $3 \cdot k$, where k is a positive integer. Making use of the fact that if the square of a positive integer is a multiple of 3 then the integer itself must be a multiple of 3, prove that $\sqrt{3}$ is an irrational number. [*Hint:* pattern your proof after parts (b), (c), and (d) of Exercise 8.]

2.3 NUMERALS: THE DECIMAL NOTATION

Ever since human beings began to count, they have used different words and different symbols (originally, perhaps, different sounds) to represent the simplest kinds of numbers, that is, the first few natural numbers. Then they specified larger units, like the tens, hundreds, thousands, etc., we use today, and they grouped numbers accordingly. Although, historically, the number ten has always played a special role, it does not follow by any means that numbers (or objects) must necessarily be grouped by tens—this is due only to the fact that human beings have ten fingers, constituting the most primitive, yet the most widely used calculating "machine" known to man.

The number ten played a special role even in the hieroglyphics of ancient Egypt. The symbols which they used to denote one, ten, hundred, and thousand are shown in Figure 2.5 together with groupings of these

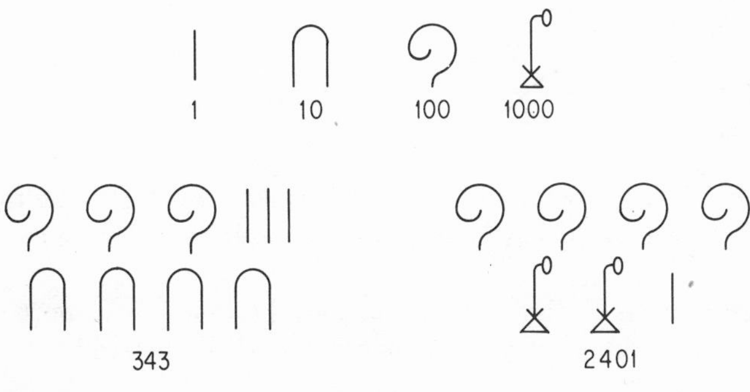

FIG. 2.5

symbols representing the numbers 343 and 2,401. It should be apparent that with these symbols it is quite a task to perform even the simplest operations of arithmetic; indeed, in the days of ancient Egypt, mathematicians (or, at least, specialists) had to be consulted to perform even the simplest additions and multiplications.

The *Hindu-Arabic* (*decimal*) *notation* we take for granted today did not become known in Europe until the Middle Ages, although it is known to have been used as early as 600 A.D. It appealed to the practically-minded merchants of the fourteenth and fifteenth centuries even before the advantages of this notation were generally acknowledged by mathematicians. We may well say that with the introduction of the Hindu-Arabic numerals mathematics became "public property."

The main feature of the Hindu-Arabic (decimal) notation is that it combines the use of symbols for *zero, one, two*, . . . , and *nine* with the convention that the position of each digit tells us whether it represents ones, tens, hundreds, thousands, and so on. It is a *positional notation*, a fact which is stressed nowadays even in the elementary grades. Thus, in 234 the 2 represents hundreds, the 3 represents tens, and the 4 represents ones; in other words,

$$234 = 2 \cdot 10^2 + 3 \cdot 10^1 + 4 \cdot 10^0$$

where *by definition* $10^0 = 1$ (see also discussion on page 135). Similarly, in 1,579 the 1 represents thousands, the 5 represents hundreds, the 7 represents tens, and the 9 represents ones, namely,

$$1{,}579 = 1 \cdot 10^3 + 5 \cdot 10^2 + 7 \cdot 10^1 + 9 \cdot 10^0$$

Once the significance of the positional notation is understood, it is easy to follow the logic behind the various tricks that are taught to us in elementary arithmetic. For instance, to multiply 87 by 35, we write (more or less automatically)

$$\begin{array}{r} 87 \\ \underline{35} \\ 435 \\ \underline{261} \\ 3045 \end{array}$$

First we multiply 87 by 5 and then we multiply it by 3, moving the second product one place to the left because we are really multiplying by 30 rather than 3.

The advantages of the decimal notation becomes even more apparent once we start working with fractions. If we asked the reader to subtract $\frac{2689}{4943}$ from $\frac{3581}{3733}$, for example, it would probably take him a very long time, and if we asked him to perform similar calculations in the hieroglyphic notation of ancient Egypt he may well have to give up in despair.

In order to adapt the Hindu-Arabic decimal notation to work with fractions, observe that when a digit is moved *one place to the right,* the number it represents is *divided by ten;* similarly, when a digit is moved *two places to the right,* the number it represents is *divided by one hundred,* and so on. With this argument we can divide 7 by 10 by moving the 7 one place to the right, and to indicate that this has been done we write the result as 0.7. The *decimal point* (which was introduced early in the seventeenth century) is the key of this notation as it indicates the "place value" of each digit. It enables us to write 0.1 for 1/10, 0.07 for 7/100, 0.003 for 3/1000, and so on. (The purpose of the 0 to the left of the decimal point is mainly to make sure that the decimal point does not get lost; it is also correct to write the above fractions as .1, .07, and .003.)

The great advantage of the decimal notation for work with fractions is that we can add, subtract, multiply, and divide fractions using the same rules and the same methods as for whole numbers. The problem of adding

3.42 and 1.89 is essentially the same as that of adding 342 and 189, and the problem of multiplying 3.56 by 2.14 is essentially the same as that of multiplying 356 by 214. The only difference is that in each case the decimal point will be in a different place in the final answer.

Since the decimal notation simplifies most calculations involving fractions, let us indicate briefly how fractions written in the form a/b (namely, as the ratio of two integers) are converted into this notation. Actually, all we have to do is perform a long division. Taking the fraction 3/4, for example, we divide 3 by 4, getting

```
    0.75
4 | 3.00
    2 8
    ---
     20
     20
     --
      0
```

Thus, the decimal equivalent of 3/4 is 0.75. [To justify the "carrying down" of zeros, observe that we could just as well have multiplied 3 by 100, divided by 4, and then divided the result by 100 (to compensate for the 100 by which we originally multiplied); this would have given us first $(3 \cdot 100) \div 4 = 75$, and then $75 \div 100 = 0.75$.] This illustrates how we obtain the decimal representation of a *positive* fraction, but the procedure for *negative* fractions is just about the same. To obtain the decimal representation of $-\frac{3}{4}$, we simply put a minus sign in front of the decimal representation of $\frac{3}{4}$, getting -0.75.

When we convert a fraction into the decimal notation it can happen, as it did in our example, that we will sooner or later get a remainder of 0. If that is the case, we have completed the division, and we refer to the fraction as a *terminating decimal fraction*, or simply as a *terminating decimal.* Thus, $3/4 = 0.75$ is a terminating decimal fraction, and so are $1/2 = 0.5$ and $123/64 = 1.921875$.

When we perform a long division it can also happen that there is never a remainder of 0. This happens, for example, when we divide 14 by 33, for which we get

```
     0.4242...
33 | 14.0000
     13 2
     ----
        80
        66
        ---
        140
        132
        ---
          80
          66
          --
          14
        .....
```

Here the remainder is alternately 14 and 8, and (carrying the long division as far as we want) we can write

$$\frac{14}{33} = 0.424242424242424242...$$

where the "..." indicates that the division does not end. In contrast to terminating decimals, we refer to the decimal representation of 14/33 as a *repeating decimal fraction,* or simply as a *repeating decimal;* other examples of repeating decimals are

$$\frac{1}{3} = 0.3333333333333333...$$

$$\frac{2}{7} = 0.285714285714285714...$$

To simplify this notation, we sometimes indicate by means of *bars* which number or which sequence of numbers repeats; thus, we could write 14/33 as $0.\overline{42}$, 1/3 as $0.\overline{3}$, and 2/7 as $0.\overline{285714}$.

It is easy to show that *the decimal representation of every rational number terminates or repeats.* After all, if we divide the positive integer a by the positive integer b in order to get the decimal representation of a/b, the only possible remainders in each step of the long division are 0, 1, 2, ..., and $b - 1$. Consequently, the remainder must repeat sooner or later [no later than the $(b + 1)$st step], and we get a decimal which either terminates or repeats. An interesting fact which we shall demonstrate in Exercise 4 on page 327 is that the converse is also true, namely, that *every terminating or repeating decimal represents a rational number.* It follows from this that if decimals which neither terminate nor repeat are to represent real numbers, these will have to be *irrational.* This is an interesting way of looking at the irrational numbers (as well as the real numbers in general), and we shall pursue it further in Section 11.4.

A minor (though annoying) disadvantage of the decimal notation is that the decimal point often manages to get lost or misplaced during the course of calculations. Somehow 34.687 becomes 34,687, 0.000981 becomes 0.0000981, and so forth. In order to avoid mistakes of this kind, it has become common practice (at least, in scientific work) to use what is called the *scientific notation.* In this notation each number is written as a *product* of a number between 1 and 10 and an appropriate power of 10. Thus, 346.87 is written $3.4687 \cdot 10^2$ and 0.000981 is written as $9.81 \cdot 10^{-4}$. In case the reader is not familiar with negative exponents, let us point out that $10^{-1} = 1/10$, $10^{-2} = 1/100$, $10^{-3} = 1/1000$, and in general $10^{-k} = 1/10^k$ for any positive integer k; also $10^0 = 1$, as we already pointed out on page 44. Further work with negative exponents may be found in Section 5.2.

It requires some practice to convert numbers from the ordinary decimal notation to the scientific notation and vice versa, but it is not really difficult. All we have to do is count how many places the decimal point has to be moved to the left or to the right so that we get a number between 1 and 10. If the decimal point has to be moved n places to the left, where n is a positive integer or zero, the exponent of 10 is n; if the decimal point has to be moved n places to the right, the exponent of 10 is $-n$. Thus, for 346.87 the decimal point has to be moved two places to the left (to yield a number between 1 and 10) and we write it as $3.4687 \cdot 10^2$; for 0.000981 the decimal point has to be moved four places to the right (to yield a number between 1 and 10) and we write it as $9.81 \cdot 10^{-4}$.

There are several modifications of the scientific notation which make it easier to keep track of decimal points in work with high-speed electronic computers; they involve what we call *floating point decimals*. To convert a number into a floating point decimal, we write it first as the *product* of a number between 0.1 and 1 and an appropriate power of 10; in other words, we move the decimal point to the left of the first non-zero digit, and account for this by multiplying by an appropriate power of 10. In contrast to the scientific notation, we then *code* the exponent in some fashion and "incorporate" it into the number. For example, while 346.87 is written as $3.4687 \cdot 10^2$ in the scientific notation, it is written as $34687E3$ in the *E-notation* of floating point arithmetic. Actually, this means $0.34687 \cdot 10^3$, and it should be observed that the letter E separates the magnitude or "mantissa" of the number from the exponent of 10. Using this notation, we would write the number 0.000981 as $981E{-3}$, meaning $0.981 \cdot 10^{-3}$. For negative numbers we simply leave the minus sign in front, so that -0.035, for example, becomes $-35E{-1}$.

In order to avoid the appearance of minus signs as in $981E{-3}$, the exponents are sometimes *coded* by adding 50, so that the exponents from -50 to 49 are represented by the numbers from 0 to 99 (or better, by the numbers from 00 to 99, adding a zero to the left of the one-digit numbers). This will avoid negative exponents so long as we do not have to work with quantities which are numerically less than 10^{-50}, and such small numbers are extremely rare in business applications. It is easy to check that in this notation we write 346.87 as $34687E53$ and 0.000981 as $981E47$.

An alternate modification is to write numbers in the so-called *normalized floating-point* form. In this form the exponent plus 50 is given by the first two digits, and it is followed by the sequence of digits which constitute the number and zeros (if necessary) to give the resulting "computer word" a prescribed number of digits, usually 10. We would thus write the number

346.87 as 5334687000 and we would write 0.000981 as 4798100000. Also, it is easy to check that 5523046600 in the normalized floating-point notation represents the number 23,046.6.

EXERCISES

1. Convert each of the following fractions into the decimal notation and indicate whether the decimal terminates or repeats:

(a) 7/125; (b) 4/11; (c) 6/13; (d) 9/14; (e) 13/40; (f) 3/64; (g) 37/60; (h) 137/625; (i) 137/7.

2. Convert each of the following decimals into the scientific notation:

(a) 13.45; (b) 0.00271; (c) 1,785.4; (d) 0.00000034; (e) 2,348,500; (f) 0.035846.

3. Convert each of the following numbers from the scientific notation to the ordinary decimal notation:

(a) $2.1466 \cdot 10^4$; (b) $1.81 \cdot 10^{-2}$; (c) $1.4763 \cdot 10^5$; (d) $3.5552 \cdot 10^{-6}$; (e) $7.269 \cdot 10^6$; (f) $9.9934 \cdot 10^{-5}$.

4. Convert each of the numbers of Exercise 2 into the E-notation of floating-point arithmetic.

5. Convert the following numbers from the E-notation of floating-point arithmetic to ordinary decimals:

(a) $258E-2$; (b) $26463E5$; (c) $-75589E-5$; (d) $53536E7$; (e) $-5316E1$; (f) $646E-4$.

6. Convert each of the following numbers into the E-notation of floating-point arithmetic with 50 added to the exponent:

(a) 0.00000081; (b) 12.31; (c) 1,359,400; (d) $1.584 \cdot 10^{15}$; (e) $6.75 \cdot 10^{-12}$; (f) 0.0000000000064.

7. Convert each of the following numbers from the E-notation of floating-point arithmetic with 50 added to the exponent into ordinary decimals:

(a) $34875E57$; (b) $235E50$; (c) $-55E44$; (d) $34105E46$; (e) $-1335E51$: (f) $9856E54$.

8. Convert each of the numbers of Exercise 2 into the normalized floating-point notation.

9. Convert each of the following numbers from the normalized floating-point notation to ordinary decimals:

(a) 5123800000; (d) 4310507300;
(b) 4650000500; (e) 5013500000;
(c) 5823504670; (f) 4964537000.

2.4 NUMERALS: THE BINARY NOTATION

The decimal system is a positional notation using the *base* (or *radix*) 10. This means that when a digit is moved one place to the left the number it represents is multiplied by 10, and when a digit is moved one place to the right the number it represents is divided by 10. There is no denying the advantages of positional notations, but as we pointed out on page 43, the base 10 (that is, the decimal notation) is used mainly because human beings happen to be endowed with ten fingers. Counting with their fingers as well as their toes, or only with the fingers on one hand, different cultures are known to have used the base 20 (the *vigesimal system*) and the base 5 (the *quinary system*). The Babylonians used the base 60 (the *sexigesimal system*), and we still use this system today in the measurement of time—there are 60 seconds to a minute and 60 minutes to an hour.

In the vigesimal system (base 20) the symbol 23 would stand for *forty-three*, namely, $2 \cdot 20 + 3$; in the quinary system (base 5) the same symbol would stand for *thirteen*, namely, $2 \cdot 5 + 3$; and in the sexigesimal system (base 60) it would stand for *one hundred and twenty three*, namely, $2 \cdot 60 + 3$.

Whereas the decimal system requires the ten digits 0, 1, 2, 3, 4, 5, 6, 7, 8, and 9, the quinary system requires only the five digits 0, 1, 2, 3, and 4, since *five* is written as 10, *six* as 11, and so on. Similarly, the vigesimal system requires twenty different digits for the numbers from zero through nineteen, and the sexidecimal system requires sixty different digits for the numbers from zero through fifty-nine. In another system, the *hexadecimal system* which we shall discuss in Section 2.5, the base is sixteen and we use the digits 0, 1, 2, 3, 4, 5, 6, 7, 8, 9, A, B, C, D, E, and F; the six letters take care of the numbers *ten*, *eleven*, *twelve*, *thirteen*, *fourteen*, and *fifteen*, while *sixteen* is written as 10.

It has been said that arithmetic would be much easier if human beings had twelve fingers, since this would have led to the use of the *duodecimal system* discussed in Exercise 11 on page 62, which has certain advantages over the decimal notation. However, when it comes to electronic computers, it would be even better if we counted only with our two ears (or eyes) and used the *binary system*, namely, *base* 2.

To explain this remark, let us point out that in the decimal system there are *ten* possible digits for each position. For instance, in the desk calculator of Figure 2.6 there are *ten buttons* (or *nine buttons* not counting zero) in each column, and it would take $7 \cdot 9 = 63$ buttons to record any integer from 0 to 9,999,999. (To record a zero in any given column, we

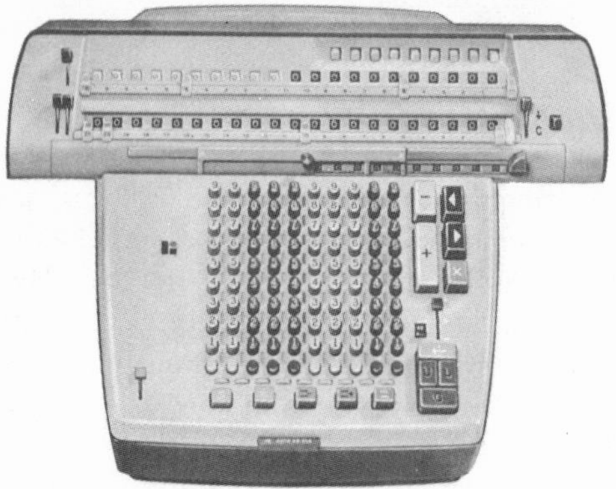

FIG. 2.6

simply do not press down any button at all.) As the reader will be asked to verify in Exercise 6 on page 56, 24 buttons can do the same job in the binary scale. Of course, in an electronic computer we do not use buttons, but tubes which can be turned on or off, switches which can be open or closed, parts of magnetic tape which may or may not be charged, or positions on punchcards which may or may not be punched. In any case, it stands to reason that if 24 components can do the job of 63, this will entail considerable savings (of expensive electronic equipment).

In the binary scale there are no digits other than 0 and 1. When a 1 is moved one place to the left, the number it represents is *multiplied by two;* when it is moved one place to the right, the number it represents is *divided by two*. Thus, 10 stands for *two*, 100 stands for *four*, 1000 stands for *eight*, 10000 stands for *sixteen*, and so on. Also, 0.1 stands for *one half*, 0.01 stands for *one fourth*, 0.001 stands for *one eighth*, and so forth. More generally, 111 represents the number *seven* since

$$1 \cdot 2^2 + 1 \cdot 2^1 + 1 \cdot 2^0 = 1 \cdot 4 + 1 \cdot 2 + 1 \cdot 1 = 7$$

also, 11010 stands for the number *twenty-six* since

$$\begin{aligned} &1 \cdot 2^4 + 1 \cdot 2^3 + 0 \cdot 2^2 + 1 \cdot 2^1 + 0 \cdot 2^0 \\ &\qquad = 1 \cdot 16 + 1 \cdot 8 + 0 \cdot 4 + 1 \cdot 2 + 0 \cdot 1 = 26 \end{aligned}$$

and 10.1 stands for *two and a half* since

$$1 \cdot 2^1 + 0 \cdot 2^0 + 1 \cdot 2^{-1} = 1 \cdot 2 + 0 \cdot 1 + 1 \cdot \frac{1}{2} = 2\frac{1}{2}$$

The mechanics of converting integers from the decimal notation to the binary notation is quite easy; in fact, it can often be done mentally, requiring only *repeated division by two.* We write down the divisions, the quotients, and the remainders (as indicated below) until there is a quotient of 0, and the remainders *read from bottom to top* will give the original number in the binary notation. For instance, to convert 35 into the binary scale we write

Division	*Quotient*	*Remainder*	
$35 \div 2$	17	1	↑
$17 \div 2$	8	1	
$8 \div 2$	4	0	*read up*
$4 \div 2$	2	0	
$2 \div 2$	1	0	
$1 \div 2$	0	1	

and the answer is 100011. To demonstrate *how* and *why* this method works, suppose that some number N has the binary representation $abcd$, where a, b, c, and d are binary digits, namely, 0 or 1. This means that

$$N = a \cdot 2^3 + b \cdot 2^2 + c \cdot 2^1 + d \cdot 2^0 = 8a + 4b + 2c + d$$

Now, if we repeatedly divide by 2 as in the above table, we get

Division	*Quotient*	*Remainder*	
$N \div 2$	$4a + 2b + c$	d	↑
$(4a + 2b + c) \div 2$	$2a + b$	c	*read up*
$(2a + b) \div 2$	a	b	
$a \div 2$	0	a	

and the number N becomes $abcd$ in the binary scale.

To give another illustration, let us convert 769 into the binary notation by performing the following divisions:

Division	*Quotient*	*Remainder*	
$769 \div 2$	384	1	↑
$384 \div 2$	192	0	
$192 \div 2$	96	0	
$96 \div 2$	48	0	
$48 \div 2$	24	0	*read up*
$24 \div 2$	12	0	
$12 \div 2$	6	0	
$6 \div 2$	3	0	
$3 \div 2$	1	1	
$1 \div 2$	0	1	

Reading the remainders from bottom to top, we find that the binary representation of 769 is 1100000001. It should be noted that this method works only for converting *integers* from the decimal system to the binary notation. When it comes to *fractions*, we repeatedly *multiply by two* (rather than *divide by two*) as is illustrated in Exercise 4 on page 55.

Although conversion to the binary scale can be tedious, though not really difficult, this is compensated for by the fact that binary arithmetic is exceedingly simple.* All we have to remember is given in the following addition and multiplication tables:

	0	1
0	0	1
1	1	10

Addition

	0	1
0	0	0
1	0	1

Multiplication

It may take some time to get accustomed to working in the binary scale where we "carry" and "borrow" *two* instead of *ten*, but once the habit of working in the decimal notation has been overcome, the advantages of the binary system will be quite apparent.

To illustrate an addition performed with numbers written in the binary scale, let us find the sum of the following numbers

```
 1101
  110
10100
  101
 1001
─────
```

First adding the digits in the righthand column, we get $1 + 0 + 0 + 1 + 1 = 11$ (*three*), and we write a 1 at the bottom of this column and carry 1 to the second column from the right. Continuing in this way we find that, including the 1 we carried from the first column, the numbers in the second column total 10 (*two*), which means that we write a 0 at the bottom of this column and carry the 1 to the third. Now, the numbers in the third column total 101 (*five*), which means that we write a 1 at the bottom of this column and carry a 1 to the *fifth* column from the right. The final answer is 110101, as the reader will be asked to verify in Exercise 8 on page 56 by converting the original numbers as well as their sum into the decimal scale.

* The simplicity of binary arithmetic also facilitates the design of electronic computers, that is, it simplifies the circuitry required to perform the various arithmetical operations.

The advantages of the binary system become even more apparent in multiplication, where we have to consider only multiplication by 0 and 1. For instance, to multiply 11011 by 1101, we write

$$
\begin{array}{r}
11011 \\
\underline{1101} \\
11011 \\
11011 \\
\underline{11011} \\
101011111
\end{array}
$$

using the customary tricks of multiplication with a positional notation. Actually, the numbers we multiplied were 27 and 13, whose product is 351, and to check our answer we find that 101011111 in the binary scale stands for

$$
\begin{aligned}
2^8 + 2^6 + 2^4 + 2^3 + 2^2 + 2^1 + 2^0 & \\
&= 256 + 64 + 16 + 8 + 4 + 2 + 1 \\
&= 351
\end{aligned}
$$

So far as subtraction is concerned, the only thing we have to watch is that in the binary scale we "borrow" *two* instead of *ten*. For instance, to subtract 1101 from 10010, we write

$$
\begin{array}{r}
10010 \\
\underline{-\ 1101} \\
101
\end{array}
$$

and this answer may be checked by converting the two numbers as well as their difference into the decimal notation (see Exercise 10 on page 56).

The mechanics of division in the binary notation is as in the decimal notation, though actually it is simpler because we have no numbers to worry about except 0 and 1. For instance, to divide 100101100101 by 100111 (2405 by 39) we write

$$
\begin{array}{r|l}
\multicolumn{1}{r}{} & \underline{111101} \\
100111 & 100101100101 \\
 & \underline{100111} \\
 & 1001000 \\
 & \underline{100111} \\
 & 1000010 \\
 & \underline{100111} \\
 & 110111 \\
 & \underline{100111} \\
 & 1000001 \\
 & \underline{100111} \\
 & 11010
\end{array}
$$

Thus, the quotient is 111101 and the remainder is 11010 (or 61 and 26 in the decimal notation).

To give another illustration, let us convert the fraction 5/32 into a binary fraction. Actually dividing 101 (*five*) by 100000 (*thirty-two*), we get

```
              0.00101
100000 | 101
         100 000
         -------
           1 00000
           1 00000
           -------
                 0
```

and to check this result we have only to observe that the first 1 stands for $2^{-3} = 1/8$, the second 1 stands for $2^{-5} = 1/32$, so that 0.00101 actually stands for $1/8 + 1/32 = 5/32$.

The result which we obtained in the last example is the *terminating binary fraction* 0.00101. Had we used the same method (long division) to convert the decimal fraction 1/3, we would have obtained the *repeating binary fraction* 0.0101010101010101..., namely, $0.0\overline{10}$ in accordance with the notation introduced on page 46.

Once the habit of working with decimals is overcome, the reader will find that there are many advantages to working in the binary scale. Even though numbers will be longer (that is, require more places) and we will have to manipulate more columns, this inconvenience is negligible compared to the advantage that there are no digits other than 0 and 1. Of course, for work with electronic computers there is the added advantage pointed out on page 50, namely, the advantage that binary numbers are more easily and more economically simulated with tubes that are on or off, switches that are open or closed, circuits that do or do not carry a current, parts of magnetic tapes that are charged or not charged, and so on.

EXERCISES

1. Using the method indicated on page 51 (namely, repeated division by 2), convert each of the following numbers from the decimal to the binary notation:

   (a) 27; (c) 261; (e) 1,058;
   (b) 139; (d) 583; (f) 2,375.

2. Integers are usually converted from the binary scale to the decimal scale by simply adding the corresponding powers of 2. For instance, for 1101011 we get $1 \cdot 2^6 + 1 \cdot 2^5 + 0 \cdot 2^4 + 1 \cdot 2^3 + 0 \cdot 2^2 + 1 \cdot 2^1 + 1 \cdot 2^0 = 64 + 32 + 8 + 2 + 1 = 107$. Use this method to convert the following binary integers into the decimal notation:

(a) 10111; (d) 11000001;
(b) 101010; (e) 100000011;
(c) 11101011; (f) 110011010101.

There exists a short-cut technique for converting integers from the binary to the decimal notation, which is called the *double-dabble method* (where *dabble* means "double and add"). It consists of doubling the first digit (on the left) and adding 0 or 1 depending on whether the next digit is 0 or 1. Then we double this sum and add 0 or 1 depending on whether the next (third) digit is 0 or 1, and we repeat this process until the sum contains the last digit (on the right). For example, for 1101011 we get

	dabble	*double*	*dabble*	*double*	*dabble*	*dabble*	
1	1	0	1	0	1	1	
	3	6	13	26	53	107	
						↑ *answer*	

Use this method to verify the results obtained for parts (a), (b), (c), and (e).

3. The method illustrated in Exercise 2 (namely, expansion in terms of powers of 2) applies also to the conversion of binary fractions into the decimal notation. For instance, to convert the binary number 1011.101 into the decimal notation we write it as

$$1\cdot 2^3 + 0\cdot 2^2 + 1\cdot 2^1 + 1\cdot 2^0 + 1\cdot 2^{-1} + 0\cdot 2^{-2} + 1\cdot 2^{-3}$$

which equals $8 + 2 + 1 + 1/2 + 1/8 = 11.625$. Use this method to convert the following binary numbers into the decimal notation:

(a) 0.11; (d) 110011.01;
(b) 1.01; (e) 101110.001;
(c) 1001.1; (f) 11011.111.

4. To convert a decimal fraction less than 1 into the binary notation, we repeatedly *multiply* the fractional part by 2 as in the following table, where the method is applied to the number 0.6875:

Multiplication		*Integral Part*	*Fractional Part*
			.6875
$.6875 \times 2$	|	1	.3750
$.3750 \times 2$	*read*	0	.7500
$.7500 \times 2$	*down*	1	.5000
$.5000 \times 2$	↓	1	.0000

Reading the integral parts from top to bottom, we find that the answer is 0.1011. Generally speaking, the process terminates as soon as the fractional part is zero, in which case the result is a *terminating binary fraction;* otherwise, the fractional part will have to repeat sooner or later, and the result will be a *repeating binary fraction.* [For instance, the decimal fraction 0.7 becomes the repeating binary fraction 0.10110011001100110 ... , which can also be written as $0.1\overline{0110}$ (see page 46).] Use this method to convert each of the following decimal fractions into the binary notation and indicate whether it terminates in this notation or whether it repeats:

(a) 0.25; (c) 0.3; (e) 0.2.
(b) 0.625; (d) 0.3125;

Also illustrate *how* and *why* this method works by applying it to the fraction F which has the binary representation $0.rstu$ (where r, s, t, and u are binary digits, namely, 0 or 1). $\left(\textit{Hint:}\text{ write } F \text{ as } r\cdot\frac{1}{2} + s\cdot\frac{1}{4} + t\cdot\frac{1}{8} + u\cdot\frac{1}{16}\cdot\right)$

5. To convert a decimal fraction *greater than one* (that is, a "mixed" number) into the binary notation, we convert the integral part by the method illustrated in the text on page 51, and the fractional part by the method shown in Exercise 4. Thus, convert the following decimals into the binary notation:

(a) 27.75; (c) 1,349.5;
(b) 113.875; (d) 7.8.

6. Verify that 9,999,999 is a twenty-four digit number in the binary notation.

7. Evaluate each of the following sums, where the numbers are all given in the binary notation:

(a) 10 + 111; (c) 10101 + 10011 + 11110;
(b) 11 + 101 + 100; (d) 1100 + 101 + 1101 + 1111 + 1001.

Also check the results by converting the numbers as well as their sums into the decimal notation.

8. Verify the addition on page 52 by converting each of the five numbers as well as their sum into the decimal notation.

9. Evaluate each of the following products, where the numbers are all given in the binary notation:

(a) $111\cdot 101$; (c) $110011\cdot 1101$;
(b) $1101\cdot 1011$; (d) $101010\cdot 1011$.

Also check the results by converting the numbers as well as their products into the decimal notation.

10. Check the subtraction on page 53 by converting the two numbers as well as their difference into the decimal notation.

11. Subtract 110 from 1001 and check the result by converting these two binary numbers as well as their difference into the decimal notation.

12. Subtract 110011 from 10011011 and check the result by converting these two binary numbers as well as their difference into the decimal notation.

13. Divide 110111 by 1011 and check the result by converting these two binary numbers as well as their quotient into the decimal notation.

14. Convert 1/3 into a binary fraction by actually performing the long division $1 \div 11$ in the binary notation.

15. Convert 3/7 into a binary fraction by actually performing the long division 11 ÷ 111 in the binary notation.

16. BINARY CODED DECIMALS. The advantages of two number systems can sometimes be combined by working in one system but *coding* the digits with reference to another. Thus, when we use *binary coded decimals* we work with decimals (that is, to the base *ten*), but instead of the digits 0, 1, 2, 3, 4, 5, 6, 7, 8, and 9 we use the four-digit binary groupings 0000, 0001, 0010, 0011, 0100, 0101, 0110, 0111, 1000, and 1001. In this notation we would write the number 365 as 0011 0110 0101, and we would write the number 1,047 as 0001 0000 0100 0111. Convert each of the following numbers into binary coded decimals:

(a) 42; (c) 1,508;
(b) 203; (d) 27,619.

What numbers (written as ordinary decimals) are represented by the following binary coded decimals:

(e) 0110 0100; (g) 0101 0101 0100;
(f) 0001 0011 1001; (h) 1000 0100 0111 0010.

2.5 NUMERALS: THE HEXADECIMAL NOTATION

Although the binary notation has many advantages in arithmetic and in the design and circuitry of electronic computers, it is not economical so far as the storage or the recording of data is concerned. For instance, to record the number *eight* on a punchcard requires *four* columns in the binary scale, to record the number *three thousand* requires *twelve* columns, and (as we pointed out on page 50) to record a seven-digit number in the decimal notation may require as many as twenty-four digits in the binary notation. Furthermore, the binary notation utilizes only one position in each column of a punchcard (with a hole indicating the binary digit 1 and the absence of a hole indicating the binary digit 0) and this obviously wastes a lot of space.

What we have said here suggests that it might be better to use the decimal notation so far as the input and output of computers are concerned, and leave it to the computers to convert internally to and from the binary system. This can be done, and has been done, but current practice is to go even further, that is, use a number whose base (radix) is *greater than ten*. The one that is most widely used at this time is the *hexadecimal system* (also called the *sexadecimal system*) which uses the base *sixteen*. Of course, we could use the *duodecimal system* with the base 12, the *vigesimal* system with the base 20, and many others, but since $16 = 2^4$ conversion from the hexadecimal system to the binary system (and vice versa) is especially simple, and this is important so far as work with computers is concerned.

We already mentioned the hexadecimal system briefly on page 49, where we indicated that it uses the digits 0, 1, 2, 3, 4, 5, 6, 7, 8, 9, A, B, C, D, E, and F for the integers from zero through fifteen. Then, the number *sixteen* is written as 10 (namely $1 \cdot 16^1 + 0 \cdot 16^0$, where $16^0 = 1$), the number *seventeen* is written as 11, . . . , the number *thirty* is written as $1E$ (namely, $1 \cdot 16^1 + 14 \cdot 16^0$), and we have to get accustomed to the fact that $6 + 8 = E$ rather than 14, since 14 now denotes the number *twenty* (namely, $1 \cdot 16^1 + 4 \cdot 16^0$). Also, $2CB7$ represents the number

$$\begin{aligned} 2 \cdot 16^3 + 12 \cdot 16^2 + 11 \cdot 16^1 + 7 \cdot 16^0 & \\ &= 2 \cdot 4096 + 12 \cdot 256 + 11 \cdot 16 + 7 \cdot 1 \\ &= 11{,}447 \end{aligned}$$

in the decimal notation, and $0.A3$ represents the fraction

$$\begin{aligned} 10 \cdot 16^{-1} + 3 \cdot 16^{-2} &= 10(1/16) + 3(1/256) \\ &= \frac{163}{256} \end{aligned}$$

Conversion to and from the hexadecimal system is greatly facilitated by means of the following table, which also gives the binary representation of the integers from 0 through fifteen with zeros added (when necessary) so that *each hexadecimal digit is equivalent to a grouping of four binary digits:*

Decimal Notation	*Hexadecimal Notation*	*Binary Notation*
0	0	0000
1	1	0001
2	2	0010
3	3	0011
4	4	0100
5	5	0101
6	6	0110
7	7	0111
8	8	1000
9	9	1001
10	A	1010
11	B	1011
12	C	1100
13	D	1101
14	E	1110
15	F	1111

To convert numbers from the hexadecimal notation to the binary notation, we simply substitute for each hexadecimal digit the corresponding group of four binary digits (as shown in the above table). For instance, $1E$ (the number *thirty*) becomes 00011110, or 11110 after we drop the unnecessary zeros at the left-hand side. Similarly, $C29$ becomes 110000101001, $0.A3$ becomes the binary fraction 0.10100011, and $3.F4$ becomes the mixed binary number 11.111101 after we drop the unnecessary zeros at the left and at the right.

The problem of converting numbers from the binary notation to the hexadecimal notation is solved just as easily. First we divide the binary number into groups of four digits starting at the right (or at the "decimal" point), if necessary adding zeros at the left or at the right. Then we simply replace each group of four binary digits by the corresponding hexadecimal digit shown in the above table. For instance, to convert the binary number 1001101 into the hexadecimal scale we first write it as 0100 | 1101, and then as $4D$ (replacing 0100 by 4 and 1101 by D). Similarly, the binary number 1100101001 is first written as 0011 | 0010 | 1001, and then as 329 (replacing 0011 by 3, 0010 by 2, and 1001 by 9). When we work with fractions or mixed numbers we may have to add zeros at the right or at both sides. For example, the binary fraction 0.111 is first written as 0.1110, and then as $0.E$ (replacing 1110 by E), and 10.11 (standing for 2.75 in the decimal notation) is first written as 0010.1100, and then as $2.C$ (replacing 0010 by 2 and 1100 by C).

Calculations with hexadecimal numbers follow the same rules as calculations with decimals, except that we "carry" and "borrow" *sixteen* rather than *ten*. Aside from the fact that we have to overcome habits formed in connection with decimals (where $7 + 7 = 14$ and not E), hexadecimal arithmetic presents the difficulty that the basic addition and multiplication tables are larger than those for decimals. In the hexadecimal system, a table showing all possible sums of the numbers from 0 through F has 256 entries, while in the decimal system a table showing all possible sums of the numbers from 0 through 9 has only 100 entries. The same is true also for products. Of course, this is where the binary system excelled; in that system the basic addition and multiplication tables have only the four entries shown in the tables on page 52.

Since the hexadecimal system is used mainly for *storing* data or for *recording* them (in connection with the input or print out of electronic computers), we shall not devote any time to its arithmetic. If calculations are to be performed in the binary system and the input as well as the output are to be given in the hexadecimal system, all we really have to know is how to convert from one system to the other. This still leaves the problem of converting numbers from the decimal system to the hexadecimal system and vice versa, which is discussed in Exercises 3 through 6 below.

Although the binary system and the hexadecimal system are currently favored for work with electronic computers, other number systems have been used and are still being used. Some of these are given in the exercises which follow, together with systems which are of more general (that is, historical) interest.

EXERCISES

1. Convert each of the following binary numbers into the hexadecimal notation:

(a) 1101; (e) 0.11101;
(b) 100001110010; (f) 1.1;
(c) 1001100110; (g) 1100.00000011;
(d) 0.10101011; (h) 1000110.1001101.

2. Convert each of the following hexadecimal numbers into the binary notation:

(a) 45; (e) 0.4D;
(b) AF; (f) D.02;
(c) 30D; (g) 13.25;
(d) 0.AA; (h) 24D.109.

3. To convert a decimal number to the hexadecimal notation, we can proceed as in the method illustrated on page 51, except that we repeatedly divide by *sixteen* instead of *two* and write the remainders in the hexadecimal notation. For instance, to convert the number 23,268 into the hexadecimal notation we get

Division	*Quotient*	*Remainder*	
23,268 ÷ 16	1,454	4	↑
1,454 ÷ 16	90	14 (or E)	|
90 ÷ 16	5	10 (or A)	*read up*
5 ÷ 16	0	5	|

and the answer is 5AE4. Use this method to convert the following numbers from the decimal to the hexadecimal notation:

(a) 2,005; (c) 76,881;
(b) 32,951; (d) 305,933.

4. Convert the numbers of parts (a) and (b) of Exercise 3 first into the binary scale according to the method explained in the text on page 51, and then into the hexadecimal scale by the method explained in the text on page 59.

5. Convert the mixed decimal 253.4375 first into the binary scale by the method explained in Exercise 5 on page 56, and then into the hexadecimal scale by the method explained in the text on page 59.

6. There are many ways in which a number can be converted from the hexadecimal system to the decimal system. We can use repeated division by *ten* (instead of *two*) and the method illustrated on page 51, we can multiply each digit by the corresponding power of *sixteen*, or we can use the following method (which is similar to the *double-dabble* method of Exercise 2 on page 55): We begin with the first digit on the left, multiply it by *sixteen* and add the next digit; then we multiply the result by *sixteen* and add the next digit; and we repeat this process until we have added the last digit on the right. Thus, to convert $5AB$ into the decimal notation, we write $5 \cdot 16 = 80$, $80 + 10 = 90$, $90 \cdot 16 = 1440$, and $1440 + 11 = 1451$ (since B stands for *eleven* and A for *ten*). Similarly, to convert $2{,}3C7$ into the decimal notation, we write $2 \cdot 16 = 32$, $32 + 3 = 35$, $35 \cdot 16 = 560$, $560 + 12 = 572$, $572 \cdot 16 = 9{,}152$, and $9{,}152 + 7 = 9{,}159$ (since C stands for *twelve*). Use this method to convert the following hexadecimal numbers into the decimal notation:

(a) $3C2D$; (c) 12345;
(b) $2AA9$; (d) $2E35F$.

7. THE QUINARY SYSTEM. In the quinary scale the base is *five*, so that the first few nonnegative integers are written as 0, 1, 2, 3, 4, 10, 11, 12, 13, 14, 20, 21, 22, 23, 24, 30, . . . ; also 100 stands for *twenty-five*, 1000 stands for *hundred and twenty-five*, 10000 stands for *six hundred and twenty-five*, and so on. Convert the following decimals to the quinary scale using repeated division by *five* (instead of *two*) in the method illustrated on page 51:

(a) 13; (c) 127; (e) 3,024;
(b) 49; (d) 784; (f) 5,615.

8. BIQUINARY CODED DECIMALS. If we work with decimals (that is, to the base *ten*), but use the two-digit quinary groupings 00, 01, 02, 03, 04, 10, 11, 12, 13, and 14 instead of the digits 0, 1, 2, 3, 4, 5, 6, 7, 8, and 9, we would be working with *quinary coded decimals* (see also Exercise 16 on page 57). If we now substitute for the right-hand digits 0, 1, 2, 3, and 4 the three-digit binary groupings 000, 001, 010, 011, and 100, we would obtain

Decimal Digit	*Biquinary Coding*
0	0 000
1	0 001
2	0 010
3	0 011
4	0 100
5	1 000
6	1 001
7	1 010
8	1 011
9	1 100

and the numbers 365 and 1,047 would be written as 0 011 1 001 1 000 and 0 001 0 000 0 100 1 010. Convert each of the following numbers (decimals) into biquinary coded decimals:

(a) 63; (c) 2,409;
(b) 411; (d) 35,648.

What numbers (written as ordinary decimals) are represented by the following biquinary coded decimals:

(e) 1 000 0 010; (g) 1 011 1 001 1 001;
(f) 0 001 1 000; (h) 0 010 0 100 1 001 1 010.

9. THE OCTAL SYSTEM. In the octal scale the base is *eight*, so that the first few nonnegative integers are written 0, 1, 2, 3, 4, 5, 6, 7, 10, 11, 12, 13, 14, 15, 16, 17, 20, . . . ; also 100 stands for *sixty-four*, 1000 stands for *five hundred and twelve*, and so forth. Convert the following numbers from the decimal notation to the octal scale by repeatedly dividing by *eight* (instead of *two*) in the method illustrated on page 51:

(a) 39; (d) 824;
(b) 71; (e) 1,035;
(c) 309; (f) 3,672.

10. THE OCTAL SYSTEM, CONTINUED. Making use of the fact that $8 = 2^3$, we can convert from the octal scale to the binary notation by substituting for the digits 0, 1, 2, 3, 4, 5, 6, and 7 the following groups of three binary digits: 000, 001, 010, 011, 100, 101, 110, and 111. Thus, the octal number 147 becomes 001100111, or better 1100111 (without the extra zeros), in the binary notation. Use this method to convert the following numbers from the octal system to the binary notation:

(a) 12; (c) 1,043;
(b) 56; (d) 6,344.

Replacing each grouping of three binary digits by the corresponding digit in the octal scale (and adding zeros when necessary), convert each of the following numbers from the binary system to the octal scale:

(e) 110010; (g) 1101111101;
(f) 1001; (h) 1001101110000.

11. THE DUODECIMAL SYSTEM. In this system the base is *twelve*, and the integers from zero through eleven are represented by the symbols 0, 1, 2, 3, 4, 5, 6, 7, 8, 9, X, and E. Convert the following numbers from the decimal scale to the duodecimal scale by repeatedly dividing by *twelve* (instead of *two*) in the method illustrated on page 51:

(a) 23; (c) 293;
(b) 64; (d) 2,536.

12. THE DUODECIMAL SYSTEM, CONTINUED. What repeating decimal fractions are represented by the duodecimal fractions 0.2, 0.4, and 0.8?

3

FUNCTIONS

3.1 INTRODUCTION

One of the most important concepts of mathematics concerns the relationship, or correspondence, between the elements of two sets. To illustrate what we mean by a relationship between the elements of two sets, let us consider Figures 3.1 and 3.2, where secretaries are assigned to

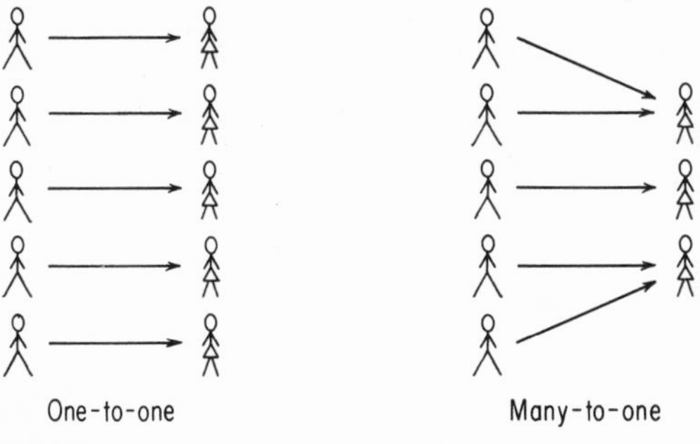

FIG. 3.1

the executives of a firm in four different ways. In each case there are *two sets* (the executives and the secretaries), and in each case we indicate by means of arrows a relationship, or correspondence, between the elements of the respective sets. In the first diagram of Figure 3.1 the correspondence is said to be *one-to-one;* one secretary is assigned to each executive, and vice versa. Further examples of one-to-one correspondences are the one between all new cars a dealer has in stock and their factory invoices, and the one between husbands and wives in a monogamous society. The second diagram of Figure 3.1 illustrates what is called a *many-to-one* correspondence; in several instances the executives share the services of a secretary, yet each executive has one and only one secretary that he can use. Another example of a many-to-one correspondence is the one shown in the following table, which tells us how a sales manager assigns his three salesmen (Smith, Brown, and Jones) to the eight Mountain States:

State	*Salesman*
Montana	Smith
Idaho	Smith
Wyoming	Smith
Colorado	Brown
New Mexico	Jones
Arizona	Jones
Utah	Jones
Nevada	Jones

There is one salesman for each state, yet more than one state for Smith and Jones.

In the first diagram of Figure 3.2 the correspondence is said to be *one-to-many;* each secretary works for only one of the executives, yet several

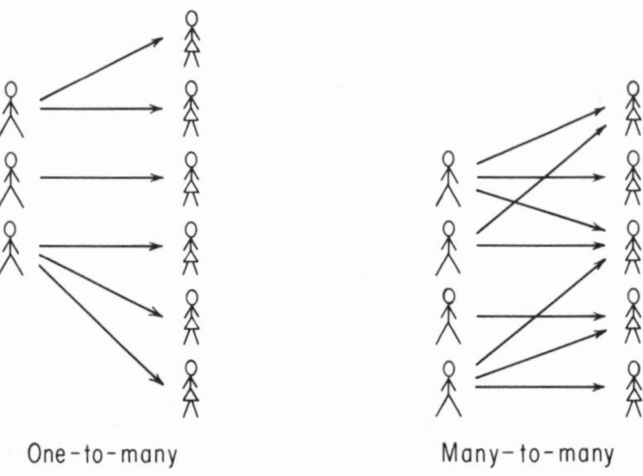

FIG. 3.2

of the secretaries can be assigned to the same one. Another example of a one-to-many relationship is that between the television stations in San Francisco and the receivers which are tuned to their respective programs at any given time—many different receivers can be tuned to the same program, but each receiver can be tuned only to one. Finally, the second diagram of Figure 3.2 illustrates what is called a *many-to-many* correspondence; the secretaries are pooled so that some of the executives have the services of several secretaries and some of the secretaries work for more than one executive. Another example of a many-to-many correspondence is that between the corporations listed on the New York Stock Exchange and their stockholders of record at any given time—most companies' stock is owned by thousands of persons, and many of these own stock in several of the companies listed on the New York Stock Exchange.

It may have occurred to the reader that the nature of a correspondence (whether it is one-to-one, many-to-one, one-to-many, or many-to-many) may depend on the role we assign to each of the two sets. Actually, this does not apply to relationships which are one-to-one or many-to-many (in which case it does not matter whether we assign secretaries to executives or executives to secretaries), but it does apply to the other two kinds of relationships. For instance, if we assign states to salesmen rather than salesmen to states in the example on page 64, we obtain

Salesman	*Sales Territory*
Smith	Montana, Idaho, Wyoming
Brown	Colorado
Jones	New Mexico, Arizona, Utah, Nevada

and it can be seen that this relationship is now one-to-many rather than many-to-one.

In mathematics we refer to the relationship which assigns territories to salesmen as the *inverse* of the relationship which assigns salesmen to territories. Similarly, the relationship which assigns debtors to creditors is the *inverse* of the relationship which assigns creditors to debtors, and the relationship which assigns students to teachers is the *inverse* of the relationship which assigns teachers to students. Note that if a relationship is one-to-one or many-to-many, the *inverse* relationship is of the same kind. If a relationship is one-to-many, however, its *inverse* is many-to-one, and if a relationship is many-to-one its *inverse* is one-to-many.

In this book we shall be concerned mainly with relationships between *two sets of numbers*—sets of numbers representing supply and demand, sets of numbers representing the age and the value of different pieces of property, sets of numbers representing the unit cost of a product and the number of items produced, and so on. Furthermore, we shall limit our discussion to relationships that are either one-to-one or many-to-one, namely, relationships like those shown in Figure 3.1, where each element of the first set corresponds to one and only one element of the second set.*

* This really does not exclude one-to-many relationships since we can always interchange the roles played by the two sets, but it does exclude relationships which are many-to-many. These are excluded because they often lead to mathematical difficulties which we would just as soon avoid, and also because they do not play an important role in the mathematical models we shall study in this text.

Relationships like these are referred to as *functions,* and to distinguish between the two sets (whose elements they relate) we refer to the first as the *domain* of the function, and to the second as its *range.* More formally:

> *A function is a correspondence which assigns to each element of a set, called its domain, exactly one element of a set, called its range.*

Among the following tables, where the elements of the domain are always listed on the left, (a) and (b) represent functions, while (c) does not:

(a)

Year	*Sales*
1960	$365,043
1961	$285,957
1962	$567,481
1963	$950,325
1964	$1,668,694

(b)

Time	*Temperature*
8 a.m.	66°
9 a.m.	73°
10 a.m.	76°
11 a.m.	78°
12 noon	78°
1 p.m.	73°

(c)

Age (years)	*Height (inches)*
27	70
31	72
28	66
31	69
30	68
30	71

In (c), the relationship between the ages and the heights of a group of six persons is *not* a function; corresponding to several of the ages there is more than one height, and this makes the relationship many-to-one (see also Figure 3.3). Of course, this argument does not apply to just any ages and heights, and in Exercise 7 on page 68 the reader will find examples where the relationship between ages and heights is *not* many-to-one.

So far we have displayed functions by means of tables like the one on page 64 and the first two of the ones shown above, or by means of diagrams like those of Figure 3.1. In either case, we indicate how the elements of the range are matched to those of the domain, and this shows that a function is actually a *set of pairs—a set of ordered pairs,* to be exact. They are ordered in the sense that we must always specify which number belongs to the domain and which one belongs to the range. This process of listing all possible pairs is easy when the number of pairs is small, but it can be quite cumbersome when the number of pairs is large, and im-

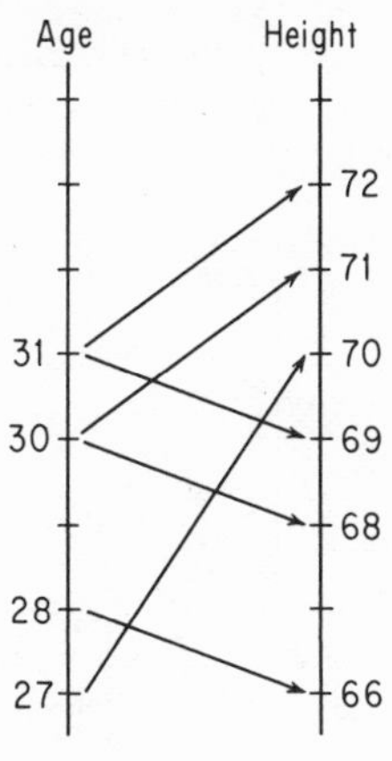

FIG. 3.3

possible when there are infinitely many. This is why we often turn to alternate methods of expressing functional relationships; in Section 3.2 we shall express them by means of mathematical equations, and in Section 3.3 we shall express them geometrically by means of graphs.

EXERCISES

1. State whether the following correspondences are one-to-one, many-to-one, one-to-many, or many-to-many, and explain your answers:
   (a) The correspondence between the six New England States and their governors.
   (b) The correspondence between the six New England States and their representatives in the United States Congress.
   (c) The correspondence between professional football players and the teams for which they play (on a given day).
   (d) The correspondence between all students enrolled at U.C.L.A. in a given semester and the courses which they take.
   (e) The correspondence between the persons attending a large cocktail party and the number of Martinis which they drink.
   (f) The correspondence between all housewives in Buffalo, New York, and the department stores in which they shop.
   (g) The correspondence between civil service employees and their social security numbers.
   (h) The correspondence between church members and the congregations to which they belong.
2. Which of the correspondences of Exercise 1 are functions and which of them have inverses that are functions?
3. Figure 3.4 presents relationships among the elements of the sets $A =$

$\{-2, -1, 1, 2\}$, $B = \{1, 4\}$, and $C = \{6, 8, 12, 14\}$. State for each one whether the correspondence is one-to-one, many-to-one, one-to-many, or many-to-many.

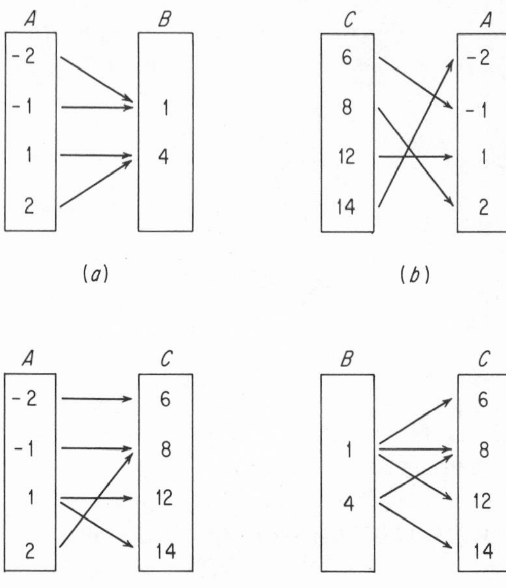

FIG. 3.4

4. Under what conditions would the relationship between all freshmen at Prescott College and their home towns be one-to-one? Under what conditions would it be many-to-one? Could it be one-to-many or many-to-many?

5. Under what conditions would there be a one-to-one relationship between the major airlines and the prices at which their stock is traded on a given day? Explain also under what conditions this relationship would be one-to-many, under what conditions it would be many-to-one, and under what conditions it would be many-to-many. In which cases would it be a function?

6. Under what conditions would there be a one-to-one relationship between the six restaurants located near a college campus and the price which they charge for a hamburger sandwich? Explain also under what conditions this relationship would be one-to-many, under what conditions it would be many-to-one, and under what conditions it would be many-to-many. In which cases would it be a function?

7. Among the four vice presidents of a company one is 47 years old and 71 inches tall, a second is 53 years old and 68 inches tall, a third is 52 years old and 69 inches tall, while the fourth is 45 years old and 72 inches tall.

   (a) What sets of numbers constitute the domain and the range of the function which establishes a correspondence between the ages and the heights of these vice presidents?

(b) What kind of correspondence would we get if the first vice president were replaced by someone who is 45 years old and 71 inches tall?
(c) What kind of correspondence would we get if the third vice president were replaced by someone 53 years old and 72 inches tall?

8. Under what conditions would the relationship between all banks in the San Diego area and the interest they charge on new-car loans be one-to-one? Under what conditions would it be many-to-one, under what conditions would it be one-to-many, and under what conditions would it be many-to-many? In which cases would it be a function?

3.2 FUNCTIONS AND EQUATIONS

If set X is the domain of a function, set Y is its range, and x and y denote their respective elements, then one value of y must be associated with each x. In the examples of the preceding section we actually showed which y corresponded to each x, but in most situations it is easier (and preferable) to express relationships by means of equations. Suppose, for example, that a plant has the capacity to produce anywhere from 1 to 6 electric power generators per day; the daily overhead is \$900, and the direct cost (materials and labor) of producing one of the generators is \$185. On the basis of all this information, the production manager wants to know *how the unit cost (namely, the cost per generator) is related to the number of generators produced on any given day.* To express this relationship by means of an equation, we have only to argue that if x generators are produced, the total cost is $900 + 185x$, namely, the overhead *plus* the direct cost of producing x generators. Since this is the cost of x generators, we then divide the total cost by x, and find that the cost per generator, namely, the *unit cost,* is given by

$$y = \frac{900 + 185x}{x}$$

This equation and the fact that the domain is the set $X = \{1, 2, 3, 4, 5, 6\}$ specifies the function which relates the unit cost of these generators to the number produced on any given day. Note that this particular relationship *is* a function—there is a unique value of y for each value of x. To find the y which corresponds to any particular x, we have only to substitute into the above equation; for $x = 3$, for example, we get

$$y = \frac{900 + 185 \cdot 3}{3} = \$485$$

and it will be left to the reader to verify that the values corresponding to $x = 1, 2, 4, 5$, and 6 are, respectively, $y = 1{,}085, 635, 410, 365$, and 335 (see also page 71). Since these values of y are *all different,* we find that the relationship between the number of generators produced and the unit cost is not only a function, but a *one-to-one correspondence.*

To give an example of a function that is *not* a *one-to-one correspondence,* consider a new-car dealer who sells a certain model car with anywhere from 0 to 8 extras (such as power steering, radio, air-conditioning, special bumpers, and so on). If x is the number of extras he puts on these cars, he knows from past experience that he can expect to sell

$$y = 40 + 8x - x^2$$

cars during the model year. This equation expresses the functional relationship between x, the number of extras, and y, the number of cars he can expect to sell during the model year. The domain of the function is the set

$$X = \{0, 1, 2, 3, 4, 5, 6, 7, 8\}$$

and if we calculate y for different values of x it will soon become apparent that the function is *not* a one-to-one correspondence. In fact, for $x = 2$ and $x = 6$ we get the *same* value of y, namely,

$$y = 40 + 8(2) - 2^2 = 52$$

and

$$y = 40 + 8(6) - 6^2 = 52$$

Observe that the number of cars the dealer can expect to sell during the model year increases from $y = 40$ (corresponding to 0 extras) to $y = 56$ (corresponding to 4 extras) and then it decreases again to $y = 40$ (corresponding to 8 extras). Perhaps, this *many-to-one* relationship can be explained by the fact that although most persons like the extras, too many extras will put the price of the cars beyond their budget.

It is important to note that if a function is a one-to-one correspondence, then the *inverse relationship* is also a one-to-one correspondence, and, hence, also a function. Thus, in our first example we can "solve for x," and express the number of generators produced in terms of the unit cost by means of the equation

$$x = \frac{900}{y - 185}$$

[This result was obtained by multiplying both sides of the original equation by x, subtracting $185x$ from both sides, writing $yx - 185x$ as $x(y - 185)$, and finally dividing both sides by $y - 185$.] Observe that the domain of this *inverse function* is the set {1,085, 635, 485, 410, 365, 335}, which was the range of the original function.

If we tried to do the same thing in the second example, we could get an equation which expresses x in terms of y (see Exercise 10 on page 125), but this equation would *not* represent a function—for some values of y (for instance, $y = 52$) there would be more than one value of x.

When we work with functions, we generally refer to x (the symbol which denotes the elements of the domain) as the *independent variable*, and to y (the symbol which denotes the elements of the range) as the *dependent variable*. To justify this terminology, we have only to point out that in our first example the unit cost, y, *depends* on the number of generators produced, x, and in our second example the number of cars the dealer can expect to sell, y, *depends* on the number of extras, x. Since this kind of dependence can easily be misunderstood, let us point out that it is not meant to imply a *cause-effect* relationship. This is demonstrated by the fact that in the first example we could solve for x, the number of generators produced, and make this variable the one which "depends" on the unit cost. Originally, it was the unit cost which "depended" on the number of generators produced.

To emphasize this kind of dependence of y on x, we often use for y the symbol $f(x)$, which reads "f of x" or more explicitly "the value of the function at x." The advantage of this notation, called the *functional notation*, is that it leads to considerable simplifications; its only disadvantage is that $f(x)$ might be mistaken for the product of two separate quantities f and x. To illustrate the advantages of this notation, let us return to our first example, where we can now write the equation relating the unit cost of the generators to the number produced as

$$f(x) = \frac{900 + 185x}{x}$$

If someone wanted to know what value of y corresponds to $x = 3$, he would simply ask for $f(3)$, and if he wanted to know what values of y correspond to $x = 1$ and $x = 5$, he would simply ask for $f(1)$ and $f(5)$. The answers are

$$f(3) = \frac{900 + 185 \cdot 3}{3} = 485$$

$$f(1) = \frac{900 + 185 \cdot 1}{1} = 1{,}085$$

and

$$f(5) = \frac{900 + 185 \cdot 5}{5} = 365$$

and this agrees with the results on page 69. Of course, nothing has been changed except the notation.

Referring to our second example (the one concerning the extras the dealer puts on his cars), we might substitute for y the symbol $g(x)$ rather than $f(x)$ to make it clear that we are dealing with a different function. We would thus write the equations as

$$g(x) = 40 + 8x - x^2$$

and $g(2)$, for example, would stand for the number of cars *with two extras* the dealer can expect to sell during the model year. Similarly, $g(0)$ would stand for the number of cars *without any extras* he can expect to sell during the model year, and referring to the results on page 70 we can write $g(2) = 52$ and $g(0) = 40$.

Generally speaking, it does not matter whether we write the value of a function as $f(x)$, $g(x)$, $F(x)$, $h(x)$, $\varphi(x)$, . . . , so long as we do not use the *same* symbol for two *different* functions in one and the same problem. Also, there is no reason why the independent variable has to be referred to as x. For instance, if it represents the number of items produced, sold, or consumed we often use the letter n, and if it represents a price we often use the letter p. Thus, the production cost of n radios might be denoted $C(n)$, and the demand for milk might be denoted $D(p)$, where p is the price per quart.

If we want to refer to a function, itself, instead of its values, we use the corresponding letter in bold-face type. In other words, the relationship between the number of extras and the number of cars given by the equation $g(x) = 40 + 8x - x^2$ is referred to as the function **g**. Also, in our first example the relationship between the number of generators produced and the unit cost is the function **f**, and in the last sentence of the preceding paragraph we referred to a function **C** with the values $C(n)$ and to a function **D** with the values $D(p)$.

3.3 THE GRAPH OF A FUNCTION

In the first example of the preceding section we had no difficulty in finding the equation which related the unit cost to the number of generators produced; it was simply the total cost divided by the number produced. In the second example we claimed that the equation (which related the dealer's expected sales to the number of extras he puts on the cars) was based on *past experience*. We did not say *how* it was based on past experience, but the usual procedure is to plot whatever data are available on a piece of graph paper and look for patterns which justify the use of a particular equation. Since the problem of determining an equation by inspecting a graph is difficult, to say the least, let us first investigate the inverse problem, namely, that of plotting a graph which represents a given function.

To represent a function graphically, we use two perpendicular lines called the *coordinate axes;* along one of these lines (usually the horizontal line) we measure x and along the other line we measure y, starting in each case from the point at which the two lines intersect. This point is referred to as the *origin*, and the two coordinate axes are appropriately called the *x-axis* and the *y-axis*. To complete the picture, we indicate units of length on the two axes (not necessarily the same for each one) as shown in Figure 3.5. Observe that if x is *positive* we go to the *right* and if it is *negative* we go

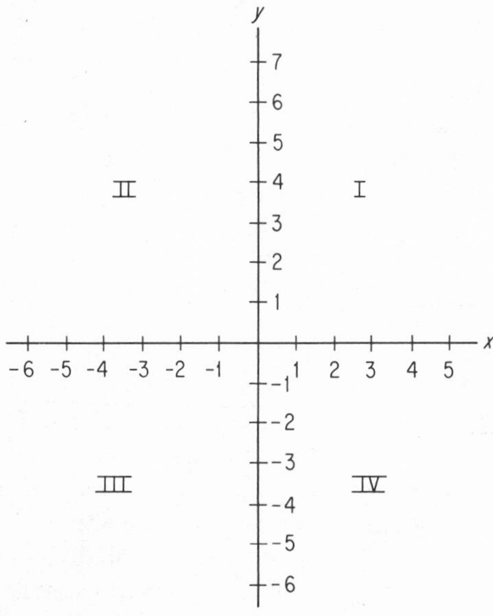

FIG. 3.5

to the *left;* so far as y is concerned, if it is *positive* we go *up* and if it is *negative* we go *down*.

We are now ready to establish a one-to-one correspondence between pairs of numbers and the points of the plane. The two numbers we shall assign to a point tell us how far we have to go first in the direction of the x-axis and then in the direction of the y-axis until the point is reached. For instance, for $x = 3$ and $y = 4$ we get the point P of Figure 3.6, and for $x = -1$ and $y = -2$ we get the point Q. It is customary to refer to the two numbers which are thus assigned to a point as its *coordinates*. Specifically, we refer to them as its *x-coordinate* and its *y-coordinate* (or its *abscissa* and its *ordinate*). To simplify our notation, we let (x, y) represent the point whose coordinates are the numbers x and y, and it should be observed that the x-coordinate always comes first. Thus, points P and Q of Figure 3.6 are denoted $(3, 4)$ and $(-1, -2)$, and, similarly, $(5, -4)$ stands for the point whose x-coordinate is 5 and whose y-coordinate is -4,

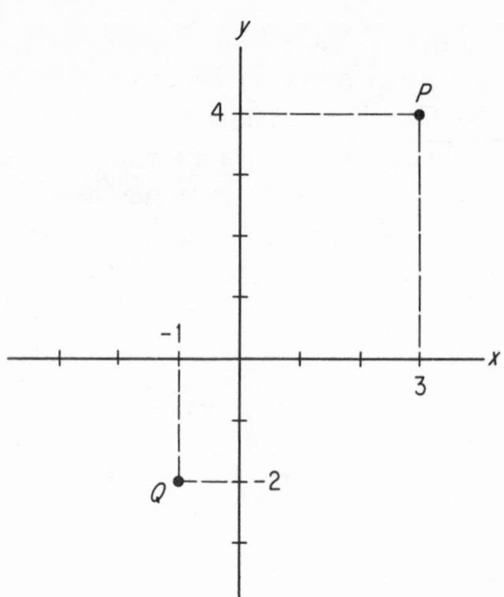

FIG. 3.6

$(-1, 3)$ stands for the point whose x-coordinate is -1 and whose y-coordinate is 3, and $(0, 0)$ stands for the origin.*

Let us also point out that the coordinate axes divide the plane into four parts called *quadrants*, which are numbered as in Figure 3.5. In the first quadrant x and y are both positive, in the second quadrant x is negative and y is positive, in the third quadrant x and y are both negative, and in the fourth quadrant x is positive and y is negative. Since most business problems deal with positive quantities, we shall be concerned mainly with points in the first quadrant, but if we regard losses as negative profits, deductions as negative additions, deficits as negative income, etc., we shall also have the occasion to work with points in the other three quadrants.

According to our definition, a function assigns one value of y to each value of x within its domain, and (as we pointed out on page 66) it establishes a set of ordered pairs which we can now write as (x, y). Each of these pairs corresponds to a point, and if we plot all of the points we obtain what is called the *graph* of the given function. To illustrate this idea, let us return to the first example of Section 3.2, where y was calculated by means of the equation

$$y = \frac{900 + 185x}{x}$$

* The idea of employing coordinates to label points is widely used even in everyday life. For instance, we may visit a friend who lives on 325 Fourteenth Avenue, or we may be watching a hockey game from Seat 12 in Row 5. Although these numbers may not refer to *all* the points of a plane, the desired location can in each case be found on the basis of *two* numbers.

for $x = 1, 2, 3, 4, 5$, and 6. Making the necessary substitutions or using the results on page 69, we get the six pairs (1, 1085), (2, 635), (3, 485), (4, 410), (5, 365), and (6, 335), where x is always listed first. Then, plotting the corresponding points as in Figure 3.7, we obtain the graph of the given function.

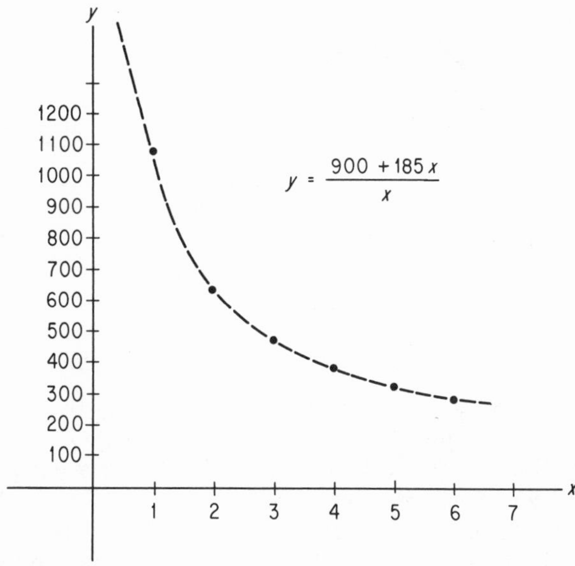

FIG. 3.7

It may be tempting to draw a curve through these six points (like the dashed curve of Figure 3.7), but this would be meaningless unless we change the domain. So long as the domain of the function is the set $\{1, 2, 3, 4, 5, 6\}$, namely, the number of electric power generators that can actually be produced, it is meaningless to plot points corresponding to, say, $x = \frac{1}{2}$, $x = 2\frac{3}{4}$, or $x = 5\frac{7}{10}$. However, if we changed the domain of the function, say, to the set of all real numbers on the interval from $\frac{1}{2}$ to $6\frac{1}{2}$ (and forgot about the physical meaning which we attached to x and y), the dashed curve would, indeed, be the corresponding graph.

If the domain of a function consists of very many points, perhaps infinitely many, it may be impractical or even impossible to plot each individual point. In that case we can only hope that a general picture of the overall pattern can be obtained by plotting some of the points. For instance, if we tried to plot the graph of the function given by the equation

$$y = 2 + x$$

over the domain X of the real numbers, we would soon discover that all

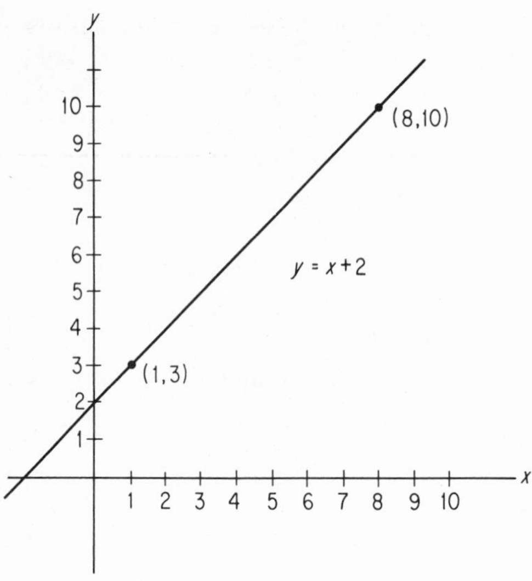

FIG. 3.8

of the points fall on a straight line. If we knew for sure that this is the case, it would suffice to find the coordinates of, and plot, two points. Calculating the values of y which correspond to, say, $x = 1$ and $x = 8$, we would obtain $y = 2 + 1 = 3$ and $y = 2 + 8 = 10$, the points (1, 3) and (8, 10), and, hence, the straight-line graph shown in Figure 3.8.

Now suppose that we want to plot the graph of the function which is given by the equation

$$y = x^3 - 9x^2 + 24x$$

for all real values of x. Starting with the points corresponding to $x = 1$,

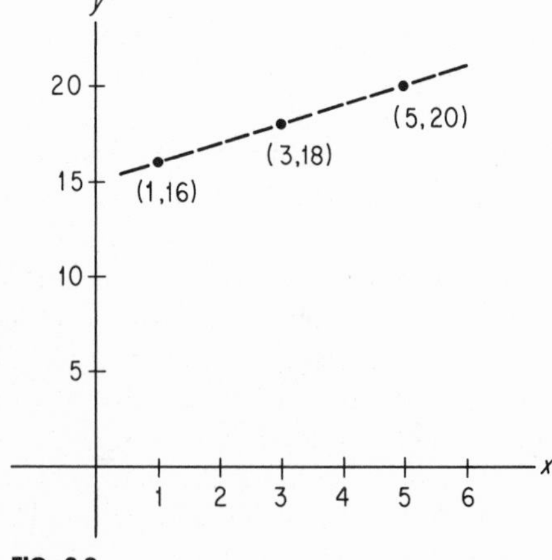

FIG. 3.9

$x = 3$, and $x = 5$, we find (by substitution) that the corresponding values of the function are $y = 16$, $y = 18$, and $y = 20$. Plotting the points (1, 16), (3, 18), and (5, 20) as in Figure 3.9, we discover that they fall on a straight line, and we may be tempted to conclude that the whole graph of the function is, in fact, given by this line. However, the error of this conclusion becomes apparent as soon as we try to plot more points. For $x = 2$ and $x = 4$, for example, we obtain

$$y = 2^3 - 9 \cdot 2^2 + 24 \cdot 2 = 20$$

$$y = 4^3 - 9 \cdot 4^2 + 24 \cdot 4 = 16$$

and, hence, the points (2, 20) and (4, 16), which are shown in Figure 3.10 together with the three points of Figure 3.9. Whether or not the smooth curve which we have drawn through the five points of Figure 3.10 actually represents the function given by $y = x^3 - 9x^2 + 24x$ is difficult to decide.

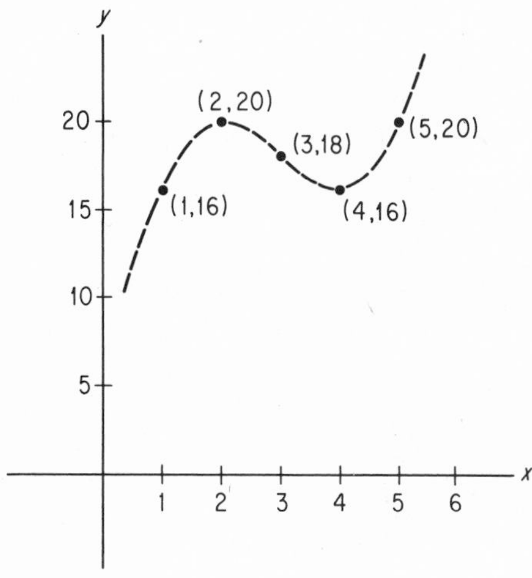

FIG. 3.10

It is conceivable that the actual graph of the function oscillates wildly between the points or beyond the range of the five points for which we have determined the value of y. For the time being, we shall avoid this kind of question by limiting our work to functions whose graphs are smooth curves which can be drawn on the basis of relatively few points—the reader will have to take our word for that. Later on, in Chapter 13, we shall discuss a method which enables us to answer the question we raised about the curve of Figure 3.10.

So far we have studied problems in which functions were expressed either by showing which element of the range is assigned to each element of the domain (as in the examples of Section 3.1) or by expressing the functional relationship by means of an equation (as in the examples of Section 3.2). Now let us study situations where functional relationships are expressed directly in graphical form. This happens, for example, when a barograph records changes in the barometric pressure directly on a rotating drum, when an electrocardiograph records variations of the heart beat directly on strips of paper, or when the vibrations of an airplane wing are recorded directly on magnetic tape. In situations like these we are given the graph of a function, and we are faced by the extremely difficult task of finding the corresponding equation.

To illustrate a similar, yet easier, problem, let us refer again to the example on page 70, where we said that the equation which relates expected new-car sales to the number of extras was *based on past experience.* It is quite possible that this equation was obtained by the following process, which is widely used in science, or for that matter in any kind of research: being given data which show what values of y are associated with certain values of x, we plot the corresponding points (x, y) on a piece of graph paper and carefully examine the resulting configuration for any clues which might reveal information about the nature of the relationship. Once it is decided what *kind* of curve seems to provide the "best fit," the final step consists of determining its equation. This problem is similar, yet different, from the one discussed in the preceding paragraph. We are no longer looking for the equation of a function whose graph *coincides* with observed data; all we want is the equation of a function whose graph more or less fits the overall pattern of the data.

The procedure we have just outlined goes under the heading of "curve fitting," and to explain what it all means, it will be best to consider a concrete example. Thus, let us investigate the following data obtained in a study of the relationship between family income and the corresponding expenditures for clothing. In the following table, each pair of values of x and y correspond to one family (interviewed as part of this study):

Income (dollars)	x	3,200	4,400	5,800	3,700	5,000	6,900	8,500	10,000
Clothing (dollars)	y	240	410	380	400	460	540	700	840

Plotting the points (3200, 240), (4400, 410), . . . , and (10000, 840), we obtain the results shown in Figure 3.11, and before we go any further, let us repeat that *we are not looking for a curve which actually passes through all of these points.* As it would hardly seem reasonable to expect *all* families with the same income to spend identical amounts on clothing, we are really looking for a curve which describes the overall pattern of the relationship. If families having the same income spend different amounts on clothing, we generally attribute the differences to *chance,* and whatever relationship we may discover tells us only what *average* clothing expenditures correspond to a given income.

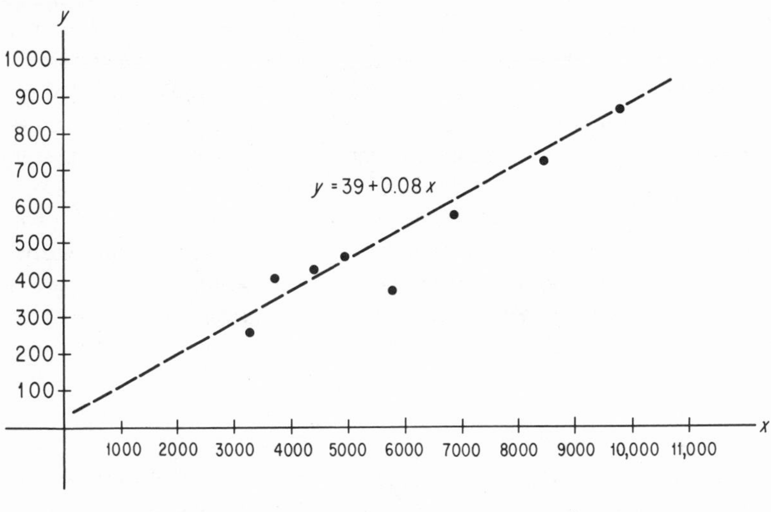

FIG. 3.11

Taking a close look at Figure 3.11, we conclude that the overall pattern may well be described by means of a straight line, and, hence, the next step is to select the line which somehow provides the best possible fit. In statistics, this is generally done by a technique called the *method of least squares,* which requires some knowledge of calculus and will be discussed later in Chapter 13. So far as the work of this chapter is concerned, let us merely state that the equation of the function whose graph (line) provides the best fit is

$$y = 39 + 0.08x$$

For details, see Exercise 11 on page 203.

Having obtained this equation, we can now use it to estimate or predict the average annual clothing expenditures of a family having a given income. For an annual income of \$4,000, for example, we predict average clothing expenditures of

$$y = 39 + 0.08(4{,}000) = \$359$$

Similarly, for a family with an annual income of \$7,500 we predict average clothing expenditures of

$$y = 39 + 0.08(7{,}500) = \$639$$

Although we gave this last example mainly to illustrate an important use of graphs and equations, it also helps to explain the difference between *statistical* and *deterministic* relationships. The relationship between family income and clothing expenditures is *statistical*—the value of y which we calculate for a given x is only an average, and families having the same income may well spend different amounts of money on clothing. In contrast, the relationship in our first example of Section 3.2 is *deterministic*—corresponding to a given value of x (that is, for a given number of generators) there is one and only one well-determined unit cost. [There is no question here of differences in unit cost that might be attributed to chance; of course, chance factors might enter the determination of the overhead and the costs of labor and materials, but that is something else.] So far as the second example of Section 3.2 is concerned (the one which deals with the number of extras the dealer puts on his cars), we shall leave it to the reader to decide whether the relationship is statistical or deterministic.

EXERCISES

1. Find the range of the function (on page 70) which relates the dealer's expected new car sales to the number of extras he puts on the cars.

2. The demand for a certain kind of candy bar is such that the *product* of the demand (in thousands of cartons) and the price per carton (in cents) is always equal to 150,000, so long as the price is not less than \$1.00 or more than \$2.50. Express this relationship between the price and the demand by means of an equation, and use it to calculate the demand when the price is (a) \$1.00, (b) \$1.25, (c) \$1.50, (d) \$2.00, (e) \$2.40, and (f) \$2.50. Also find the domain of this function.

3. An office machine is supposed to be checked once a month. If this is not done (but the machine is checked at least once a year), the expected cost of repairs is \$15 *plus* ten times the *square* of the number of months the machine has gone without being checked. Express this relationship between the number of months the machine has gone without being checked and the expected cost of repairs by means of an equation, and use it to calculate the expected cost of repairs when the machine has not been checked for (a) 2 months, (b) 4 months, (c) 6 months, (d) 8 months, and (e) 12 months.

4. If $f(x) = 2x + 7$ for any real number x, find (a) $f(0)$, (b) $f(2)$, (c) $f(5)$, (d) $f(-1)$, (e) $f(-3)$, and (f) $f(-10)$.

5. If the demand d for a product is given by $d(p) = p^2 - 20p + 105$ for $p = 2$, 3, 4, 5, 6, 7, 8, 9, and 10 cents, calculate (a) $d(2)$, (b) $d(5)$, (c) $d(7)$, and (d) $d(10)$.

6. Find the range of the function whose values are given by $G(x) = 1 + 2^x$ for $x = 1, 2, 3$, and 4. Also evaluate

$$\frac{G(4) - G(2)}{G(3) - G(1)}$$

7. If $F(x) = \dfrac{x+2}{x-2}$ for any real value of x greater than 2, find (a) $F(3)$, (b) $F(4)$, (c) $F(6)$, (d) $F(7)$, (e) $F(10)$, and (f) $F(27)$.

8. Given $g(x) = x + 3$ and $h(x) = x^2 - 1$ for all integers x, find

(a) $g(0) + h(0)$; (c) $h(7) - g(5)$;

(b) $g(1) \cdot h(2)$; (d) $\dfrac{h(10)}{g(6)}$.

9. The *absolute value function* is such that its value equals x when x is a positive real number or zero, and its value equals $-x$ when x is a negative real number. If the value of this function at x is written as $|x|$, find (a) $|1|$, (b) $|-1|$, (c) $|0|$, (d) $|-2|$, (e) $|3|$, (f) $|-5|$, (g) $|15|$, and (h) $|-20|$. What is the range of this function?

10. Construct a coordinate system like the one of Figure 3.5 and plot the following points:

(a) $(2, 4)$; (d) $(-5, -2)$; (g) $(-3, 1)$;
(b) $(3, -2)$; (e) $(-1, 6)$; (h) $(-3, -3)$;
(c) $(0, -4)$; (f) $(3, 0)$; (i) $(0, 0)$.

11. Referring to Figure 3.12, find the coordinates of (a) Point P, (b) Point Q, (c) Point R, (d) Point S, (e) Point T, and (f) Point U.

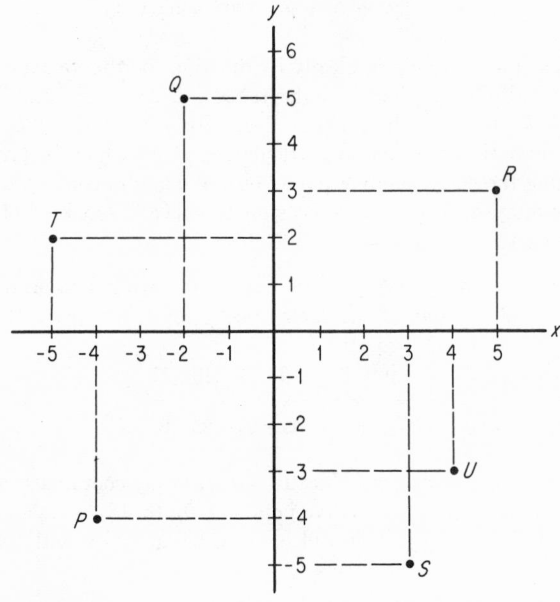

FIG. 3.12

12. Use the results of Exercise 4 to plot the graph of the function whose values are given by the equation $y = 2x + 7$ for all real values of x. What kind of curve do we seem to get?

13. Using the results of Exercise 5, plot the graph of the function which is given by the equation $d(p) = p^2 - 20p + 105$ for $p = 2, 3, 4, 5, 6, 7, 8, 9$, and 10. (*Hint:* label the coordinate axes p and $d(p)$ instead of x and y.)Draw a smooth curve through these points, but be careful not to extend it beyond $p = 10$. Why?

14. Using the result of Exercise 7, plot the graph of the function which is given by $y = \frac{x+2}{x-2}$ for all real values of x greater than 2. What happens to y when we substitute greater and greater values of x?

15. Use the results of Exercise 2 to plot the graph of the function which relates the demand for the given kind of candy to its price. Draw a smooth curve through the six points.

16. Use the results of Exercise 3 to plot the graph of the function which relates the expected cost of repairs to the number of months the office machine has gone without being checked. Draw a smooth curve through the five points.

17. A furniture manufacturer has the following data on the total cost, y, of filling an order for x custom-made chairs:

Number of chairs x	1	2	5	8	10	15
Total cost (dollars) y	100	250	400	700	850	1300

(a) Display this information graphically by drawing coordinate axes with suitable scales and plotting the six points (1, 100), (2, 250), . . . , and (15, 1300).
(b) Check *visually* whether the function given by $y = 50 + 80x$ can be used to approximate the above data by calculating y for each of the given values of x, plotting the corresponding points on the diagram constructed in part (a), and joining them by means of a smooth curve. What kind of curve do we seem to get?

18. The manager of a chain of grocery stores has the following data on the supply, $f(p)$, of certain fresh vegetables and their price, p, in dollars per crate:

Price (dollars) p	4	6	8	10	17
Supply (thousand crates) $f(p)$	0	12	21	25	27

(a) Display this information graphically by drawing coordinate axes with suitable scales and plotting the five points (4, 0), (6, 12), . . . , and (17, 27). Of course, the coordinate axes will have to be labeled p and $f(p)$ instead of x and y.
(b) Check *visually* whether the function given by

$$f(p) = 30 - \frac{60}{p-2}$$

can be used to approximate the above data by calculating $f(p)$ for each of the given values of p, plotting the corresponding points on the diagram constructed in part (a), and joining them by means of a smooth curve.

(c) Use the equation of part (b) to calculate $f(62)$ and $f(122)$ and discuss the *practical* significance of the results.

19. COMPOSITE FUNCTIONS. If $f(x)$ and $g(x)$ are the values of two functions, we refer to the function with the values $f[g(x)]$ as a *composite function.* For instance, if $f(x) = \frac{x+2}{x}$ and $g(x) = 2x + 3$, then, by substitution,

$$f[g(x)] = \frac{g(x)+2}{g(x)} = \frac{(2x+3)+2}{2x+3} = \frac{2x+5}{2x+3}$$

To find a value of a composite function, we either substitute the given value of x into the expression obtained for $f[g(x)]$, or we first evaluate $g(x)$ and then substitute the result into the formula for the function **f**.

(a) With reference to the two functions given above, find $f[g(1)]$ by substituting $x = 1$ directly into the expression obtained for $f[g(x)]$, and verify the result by first evaluating $g(1)$ and then substituting its value into the formula for **f**.

(b) With reference to these two functions **f** and **g** find an expression for $g[f(x)]$, and find the values of this *composite function* for $x = 3$ and $x = 9$. As in part (a), verify the results by calculating the values of this composite function in two different ways.

20. COMPOSITE FUNCTIONS, CONTINUED. If $f(x) = x^2 + 1$ and $g(x) = x + 2$ are the equations of two functions defined for all real numbers x, find

(a) an expression for $f[g(x)]$;

(b) the values of $f[g(x)]$ for $x = 0$, 1, 2, and 3 by substituting directly into the formula obtained in (a);

Also verify the results of part (b) by first calculating $g(0)$, $g(1)$, $g(2)$, and $g(3)$, and then substituting the results into the formula for **f**.

3.4 FUNCTIONS RELATING MORE THAN TWO VARIABLES

Although many situations can be described with the use of functions involving one independent variable and one dependent variable, there are also problems in which we must consider *more than one independent variable.* For instance, the cost of a product may depend on the price of raw materials as well as the cost of labor; the supply of a product may depend on the size of its potential market, its retail price, and also the prices of competing products; and the profits of a resort hotel may well depend on the state of the economy in general, prices charged by competing hotels, the weather, and numerous other factors. To be more specific, let us consider the equation

$$z = 130 + 12x + 27y$$

which relates z, the cost of a certain product in dollars, to x, the cost of raw materials in dollars per pound, and y, the cost of labor in dollars per hour. Observe that corresponding to any pair of values of x and y there is one and only one value of z. In fact, if we specify the domains of x and y, we refer to the relationship as a *function of two independent variables*—in our example, the two independent variables are x and y, while the dependent variable is z.

Generalizing the functional notation introduced on page 71, we can replace z with the symbol $f(x, y)$, which reads "f of x and y," and for $x = \$1.20$ and $y = \$4.60$, for example, we get

$$f(1.20, 4.60) = 130 + 12(1.20) + 27(4.60) = \$268.60$$

This means that the product will cost \$268.60 when raw materials cost \$1.20 per pound and labor costs \$4.60 an hour. The example we have given here involves two independent variables, but it is easy to see how our argument (the definition of a function and the notation) can be generalized to situations where the number of independent variables is greater than two.

To draw the graph of a function involving the variables x, y, and z, we have to use a three-dimensional coordinate system like the one shown in Figure 3.13. It consists of three mutually perpendicular axes, the *x-axis*

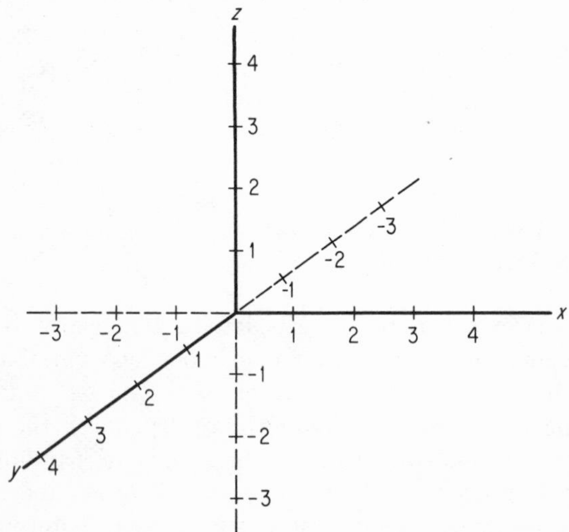

FIG. 3.13

going from *left to right,* the *y-axis* going from *front to back,* and the *z-axis* going *up and down.* The point at which the three axes meet (and from which we begin to measure along each of the axes) is again called the *origin.* With reference to this kind of axes, any point in space can be located by means of three numbers called its *x-, y-,* and *z-coordinates.* The x-coordinate tells us how far we must go in the direction of the x-axis (starting at the origin), the y-coordinate tells us how far we must then go in the direction of the y-axis, and the z-coordinate tells us how far we must finally go up or down. Generalizing the notation introduced on

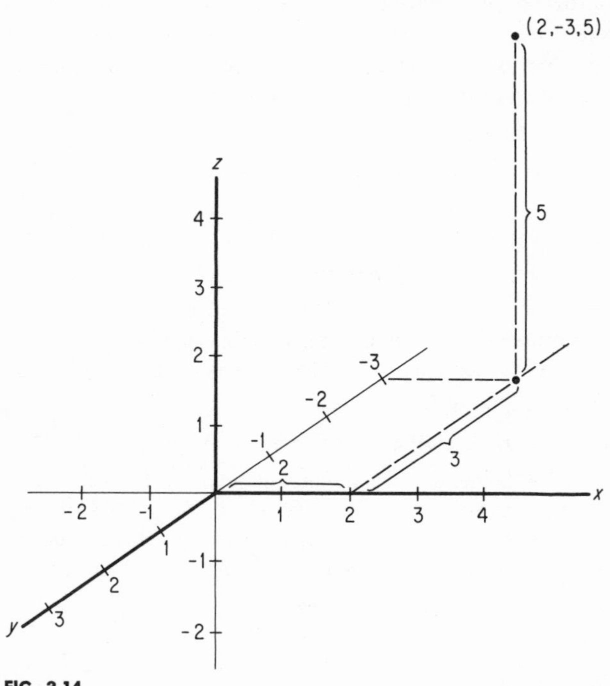

FIG. 3.14

page 73, we shall let (x, y, z) denote the point whose respective coordinates are the numbers x, y, and z. Thus, the point $(2, -3, 5)$ is reached by first going 2 units to the right (starting at the origin), then 3 units "towards the back," and then 5 units up, as shown in Figure 3.14. In case the reader finds it difficult to picture three-dimensional coordinate systems like those of Figures 3.13 and 3.14, it may help to think of the positive parts of the x- and y-axes as the lines in which two walls meet the floor of a room, and to think of the positive part of the z-axis as the line in which these two walls meet. The point $(2, -3, 5)$ will then lie *above* the floor, *behind* the wall whose bottom edge is the x-axis, and *to the right* of the wall whose bottom edge is the y-axis.

Referring again to our numerical example, we already showed that $z = 268.60$ corresponds to $x = 1.20$ and $y = 4.60$, namely, that the point (1.20, 4.60, 268.60) is part of the graph of the function which is given by the equation $z = 130 + 12x + 27y$. As the reader will be asked to show in Exercise 1 below, (1, 6, 304), (2, 5, 289), (3, 4, 274), (5, 3, 271), and (4, 2, 232) are also points on the graph of this function; if they are all plotted together, we will find that they lie on a plane, and this is true for the graph of any function which is given by an equation of the form $z = a + bx + cy$ (where a, b, and c are numerical constants). This will be discussed further in Chapter 7. In conclusion, let us point out that when there are *more than two independent variables* we can study the equation of a function, but we cannot picture its graph since this would require a space of more than three dimensions.

EXERCISES

1. Verify that the points (1, 6, 304), (2, 5, 289), (3, 4, 274), (5, 3, 271), and (4, 2, 232) must lie on the graph of the function given by the equation

$$z = 130 + 12x + 27y.$$

2. If the prices of two given commodities are x and y (cents per dozen) then the demand for the first commodity (in 1000 dozens) is given by

$$z = 100 - 3x + 5y$$

where x and y are both positive integers less than 30.

(a) What will be the demand for the first commodity when it sells for 20 cents a dozen while the second commodity sells for 18 cents a dozen?

(b) What will be the demand for the first commodity when it sells for 15 cents a dozen while the second commodity sells for 22 cents a dozen?

3. If a company spends x dollars on research and development and y dollars on advertising, its profit (in dollars) is given by

$$f(x, y) = 40{,}000 + 50x + 30y + \frac{xy}{100}$$

for all positive integers x and y less than 25,000.

(a) What will be the company's profit if it spends \$2,000 on research and development and \$5,000 on advertising?

(b) What will be the company's profit if it spends \$10,000 on research and development and \$8,000 on advertising?

(c) If the company is planning to spend \$4,000 on research and development and hopes to make a profit of \$590,000, how much should they spend on advertising?

4. If $g(x, y) = x^2 + y^2 + 3$ for all real values of x and y, find

(a) $g(1, -3)$; (c) $g(0, 6)$; (e) $g(1, 1)$;
(b) $g(-2, 5)$; (d) $g(-2, -2)$; (f) $g(-4, 0)$.

5. If $f(x, y, z) = x + 2y - 3z$ for all real values of x, y, and z, find

   (a) $f(1, 0, -4)$; (c) $f(-2, 5, -1)$;
   (b) $f(2, -1, 3)$; (d) $f(3, 6, 2)$.

6. Draw a three-dimensional system of coordinates like that of Figure 3.13 and plot the points $(3, 2, 4)$, $(-2, 4, 6)$, $(0, 3, -1)$, $(5, 0, 0)$, $(0, 4, 0)$, $(-1, -2, -1)$, $(0, 0, -1)$, and $(-4, -3, 5)$.

7. It is customary to refer to the plane which contains the x- and y-axes as the *xy-plane;* this is the plane for which we suggested on page 85 that the reader try to visualize part of it as the floor of a room. If we define the *xz*- and *yz-planes* analogously, state for each point of Exercise 6 whether it lies above, below, or on the xy-plane; whether it lies in front of, in back, or on the xz-plane; and whether it lies to the left of, to the right, or on the yz-plane.

8. Using a three-dimensional system of coordinate axes like that of Figure 3.13, plot the points $(3, 0, 0)$, $(0, 4, 0)$, and $(0, 0, 5)$, and connect them with straight lines to indicate the plane on which they all lie. Judging from this diagram, does this plane also contain the point $(0, 0, 1)$? Does it seem to contain the point $(1\frac{1}{2}, 0, 2\frac{1}{2})$?

9. (*Continuation of Exercise 8*) By substituting the coordinates of the original three points, verify that the plane of Exercise 8 has the equation

$$z = 5 - \frac{5}{3}x - \frac{5}{4}y$$

and then check whether it also contains the points $(0, 0, 1)$, $(1\frac{1}{2}, 0, 2\frac{1}{2})$, and $(3, 4, -5)$.

4

LINEAR AND QUADRATIC FUNCTIONS

4.1 INTRODUCTION

In this chapter and in Chapters 5 and 6 we shall study special kinds of functions which provide important models for many situations that arise in business and economics. The two kinds of functions to which we shall devote most of this chapter are the *linear functions* and the *quadratic functions;* actually, these functions are included in a more general type treated briefly in Section 4.9, but they are of sufficient importance to be taken up separately. Several other special functions are presented among the exercises on page 116 and on page 125.

4.2 LINEAR FUNCTIONS

In Chapter 3 we claimed that the graph of the function given by $y = 2 + x$ is a straight line. Actually, we only plotted a few points (two to be exact), but if we had plotted more we would have found that they all lie on the straight line of Figure 3.8 on page 76. It is for this reason that we refer to the given function (and to any other function whose graph is a straight line) as *linear*. As we shall demonstrate later on page 93, any equation of the form

$$y = a + bx$$

is the equation of a line (or, more rigorously, it is the equation of a function whose graph is a straight line). Here a and b are numerical constants referred to, respectively, as the *constant term* and the *coefficient of* x. Thus, $y = 3 - 5x$, $y = 6 + 7x$, and $y = 12.4 + 0.8x$ are all equations of straight lines, and so are $u = 1 - 3v$, $z = 5 + 12t$, and $F = 30 - 4G$, where we simply used different letters instead of x and y.

There are two main reasons why we begin our study of special kinds of functions with those whose graphs are straight lines: *they are easiest to handle, mathematically, and they have many important applications.* Aside from the fact that linear functions provide the exact models for many relationships arising in business (and elsewhere, for that matter), they are also used to *approximate* more complicated kinds of relationships, and they play a major role in describing the overall patterns of statistical relationships (as we saw in the example on page 78).

Before we consider any of these applications, let us demonstrate first that the graph of any function given by an equation of the form $y = a + bx$ is, in fact, a straight line. Since this is by no means obvious, or self-evident, let us begin by explaining what we mean by the *slope* of a line segment connecting two points. Then we shall use this concept to give a formal definition of what we mean by a line, and finally we shall complete the proof by showing that the graph of any function given by an equation of the form $y = a + bx$ *is* a line.

The idea of a *slope* is of great importance in business and economics because it measures the *rate* at which changes are taking place—how rapidly a company's sales are growing, how fast the value of the dollar is dwindling, how quickly or how slowly the Consumer Price Index is going up or down, and so forth. To give a concrete example, let us consider the following data on the sales of three medium-sized companies in two different years:

	1962	1967
Sales of Company X	500,000	600,000
Sales of Company Y	500,000	1,200,000
Sales of Company Z	500,000	300,000

As can be seen from this table, all three companies originally had sales of \$500,000 in 1962, but whereas the sales of the first company showed a modest increase in 1967, those of the second company showed a very substantial increase, while those of the third company decreased. More specifically, the sales of Company X increased by \$100,000 over a period of 5 years or *on the average* by $\frac{100{,}000}{5} = \$20{,}000$ per year; those of Company Y increased by \$700,000 or *on the average* by $\frac{700{,}000}{5} = \$140{,}000$ per year; while those of Company Z decreased by \$200,000 or *on the average* by $\frac{200{,}000}{5} = \$40{,}000$ per year.

Graphically, this information about the three companies' sales can be displayed as in Figure 4.1, where we "coded" the years so that 1960 corresponds to $x = 0$, 1961 corresponds to $x = 1$, 1962 corresponds to $x = 2, \ldots,$ where we gave the sales in units of \$100,000, and where we

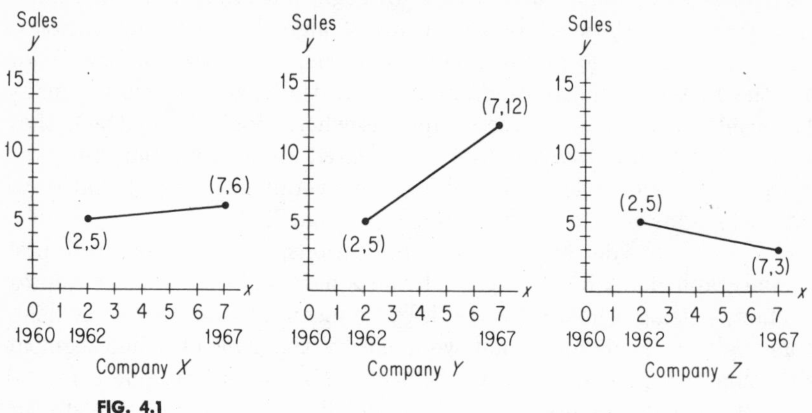

FIG. 4.1

connected the respective points by means of straight lines. For Company X the line segment has a slight *upward slope* (going from left to right), for Company Y *the slope is much steeper*, and for Company Z the line segment actually *slopes downward.* The way in which we have used the word "slope" in these examples is exactly how it is used, for instance, by railroads to measure the inclination of its tracks: if a train has to climb 4 feet while traveling through a horizontal distance of 1,000 feet, the track is said to have an upward slope of "four in a thousand," or simply a slope of 0.004. Referring to a horizontal x-axis and a vertical y-axis, we might thus say that

$$\text{slope} = \frac{\text{change in } y}{\text{change in } x}$$

More specifically, if we consider the line segment which joins the points P and Q of Figure 4.2, namely, the points (x_1, y_1) and (x_2, y_2), we find that the change in y is given by the difference $y_2 - y_1$, that the change in x is given by the difference $x_2 - x_1$, and, hence, that *the slope of the line segment* PQ *is given by*

$$\frac{y_2 - y_1}{x_2 - x_1}$$

[The use of *subscripts* as in x_1 (x*-sub-one*), y_1 (y*-sub-one*), x_2 (x*-sub-two*), and y_2 (y*-sub-two*) is a widely-used and very convenient way of distinguishing between the coordinates of different points.]

To illustrate the use of this last formula, let us refer again to the three

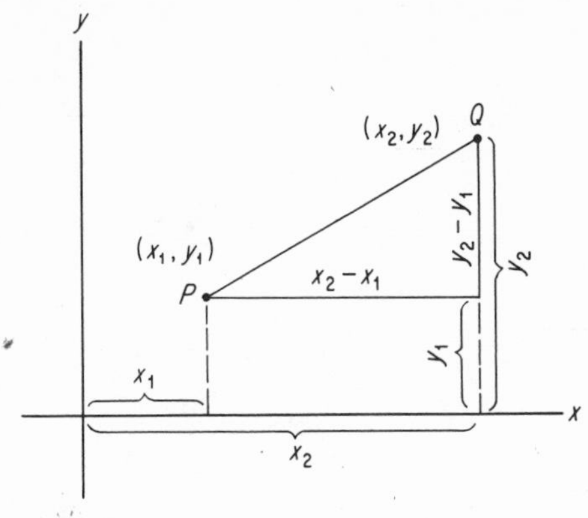

FIG. 4.2

diagrams of Figure 4.1. For Company X we find that the slope of the line segment connecting the points (2, 5) and (7, 6) is

$$\frac{6-5}{7-2} = \frac{1}{5}$$

which represents an *average annual increase* in sales of 1/5 of \$100,000, or \$20,000. Similarly, for Company Y the slope of the line segment connecting the points (2, 5) and (7, 12) is

$$\frac{12-5}{7-2} = \frac{7}{5}$$

which represents an *average annual increase* in sales of 7/5 of \$100,000, or \$140,000; and for Company Z the slope of the line segment connecting the points (2, 5) and (7, 3) is

$$\frac{3-5}{7-2} = -\frac{2}{5}$$

which represents an *average annual decrease* in sales of 2/5 of \$100,000, or \$40,000.

These examples show that if there is an *increase* (going from left to right) the slope is *positive*, and the greater the increase the greater is the slope. They also indicate that if there is a *decrease* (going from left to right) the slope is *negative*, and Figure 4.3 shows that a slope of -12, for example, is indicative of a much sharper decline than a slope of -3. Note that -12 and -3 are given by the ratios $\frac{3-15}{3-2} = \frac{-12}{1}$ and $\frac{7-10}{3-2} = \frac{-3}{1}$, which means that in the first case we go down 12 units while moving one unit to the right, whereas in the second case we only go down 3. Also, if there is *no change*, as in the first diagram of Figure 4.4, the y-coordinates of the two points are the same, the line segment is *horizontal*, and *the slope is zero.*

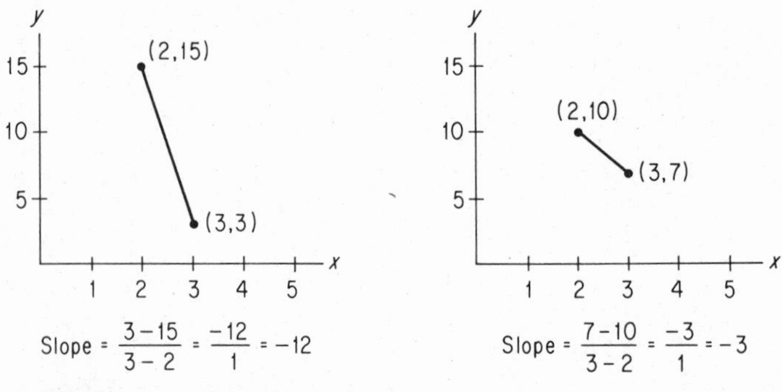

FIG. 4.3

If the x-coordinates of two points are the same, as in the second diagram of Figure 4.4, the line segment is *vertical*, and *the slope* (involving division by zero) *is undefined.* As must be apparent from our discussion, the slope of a line segment is closely related to its *direction;* later, in Chapter 6, we

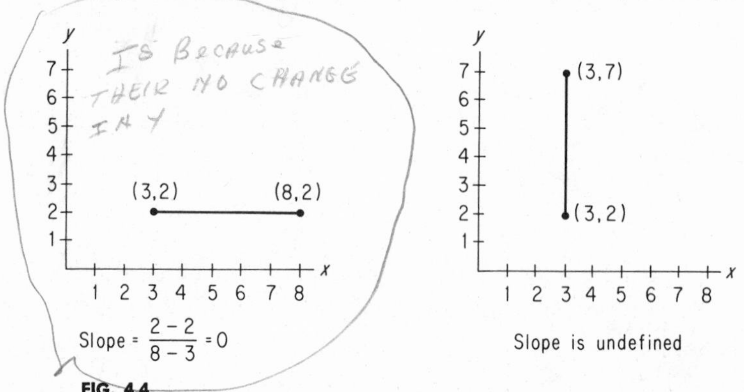

FIG. 4.4

shall see how it can actually be expressed in terms of the *angle* which a line segment makes with the x-axis or a line parallel to it.

We are now ready to show that $y = a + bx$ is the equation of a straight line, provided we define a line as *a set of points having the following property: the line segments which connect any two of the points must all have the same slope.** With this definition it is easy to check whether three given points lie on a straight line. For instance, if we are given the points (1, 1), (5, 3), and (9, 5), we find that the slope of the line segment connecting the first two is $\frac{3 - 1}{5 - 1} = \frac{1}{2}$, that the slope of the line segment connecting the first and

* This definition does not include *vertical* lines, but we can take care of this by replacing the last six words with the phrase "must all have the same slope or must all be undefined."

the third is $\frac{5-1}{9-1} = \frac{1}{2}$, that the slope of the line segment connecting the second and the third is $\frac{5-3}{9-5} = \frac{1}{2}$, and, hence, that the three points lie on a straight line. In Exercise 3 on page 94 the reader will be asked to use the same kind of argument to show that the points (1, 2), (4, 5), and (6, 8) do *not* lie on a straight line. Incidentally, the common slope of the line segments connecting any two points on a line is referred to as the *slope of the line*. Thus, we say that the line which passes through the points (1, 1), (5, 3), and (9, 5) has the slope 1/2.

Suppose now that a function has the equation $y = a + bx$, and that x_1 and x_2 are the x-coordinates of two arbitrary points which lie on its graph. This means that the y-coordinates of these points must be $y_1 = a + bx_1$ and $y_2 = a + bx_2$, and we find that the slope of the line segment which connects them is

$$\frac{y_2 - y_1}{x_2 - x_1} = \frac{(a + bx_2) - (a + bx_1)}{x_2 - x_1}$$

$$= \frac{bx_2 - bx_1}{x_2 - x_1}$$

$$= \frac{b(x_2 - x_1)}{x_2 - x_1}$$

$$= b$$

Thus, any line segment connecting two points on the graph of $y = a + bx$ has the constant slope b, and we conclude that *the graph must be a straight line*. Not only that, but we can also conclude that the x-coefficient, b, is the slope of the line. For instance, if we are given the equations $y = 3 + 7x$ and $y = 12 - 4x$, we can say without any further ado that they represent lines having slopes of 7 and -4.

So far as the constant a is concerned, it is simply the value of y which corresponds to $x = 0$; geometrically speaking, $(0, a)$ is the point at which the line $y = a + bx$ cuts the y-axis and we call it the *y-intercept*. Combining all this terminology, we refer to $y = a + bx$ as the *slope-intercept form* of the equation of a straight line.

We also say that $y = a + bx$ is the equation of a line given in *explicit form*, solved for y. This distinction is important because there are situations in which we may want to change the equation so that x is expressed in terms of y. To take care of this, we have only to subtract a from both sides of the equation $y = a + bx$, and divide by b. This gives

$$x = -\frac{a}{b} + \frac{y}{b}$$

and we say that the equation of the line is now in *explicit form*, solved for x.

If the equation of the line is changed to $y - bx = a$ or $a + bx - y = 0$, we say that it is in *implicit form*, which means that it is solved for neither x nor y. To complete our terminology, let us add that if c, d, and e are numerical constants,

$$cx + dy = e$$

is said to be the *standard form* of the equation of a straight line; it has the advantage that it can easily be generalized to situations in which there are more than two variables (see page 192).

To convert the equation of a line from one form to another requires but very simple algebra. For instance, to change $2x - 3y = 7$ into the slope-intercept form we have only to solve for y, getting $3y = 2x - 7$ and, hence,

$$y = -\frac{7}{3} + \frac{2}{3}x$$

Thus, the slope of the line is 2/3 and it cuts the y-axis at the point $(0, -\frac{7}{3})$.

EXERCISES

1. Find the slopes of the line segments connecting the following pairs of points:

   (a) (2, 2) and (4, 6); (d) (3, −1) and (5, 7);
   (b) (−2, −1) and (1, 5); (e) (−1, −1) and (4, −9);
   (c) (−1, 4) and (7, 0); (f) (−5, 0) and (1, 12).

2. Verify that the points (−1, −11), (2, 1), and (4, 9) lie on a straight line.

3. Verify that the points (1, 2), (4, 5), and (6, 8) do *not* lie on a straight line.

4. Two line segments are said to be *parallel* if they have the same slope. Which of the line segments of Exercise 1 are parallel?

5. If Mr. Jones' salary increased from \$7,000 in 1963 to \$11,400 in 1967, Mr. Brown's salary increased from \$9,000 in 1964 to \$12,600 in 1967, and Mr. Smith's salary increased from \$7,000 in 1965 to \$9,500 in 1967, which man's salary increased at the highest rate? How much should each one have made in 1968 if their salaries had kept increasing at the same rates?

6. Find the slopes of the following lines:

   (a) $y = -12 + 8x$; (c) $3x - 4y = 12$;
   (b) $x = 4 + \frac{1}{2}y$; (d) $3x + 8y + 24 = 0$.

7. Find the equation of the line which has the slope $b = 5$ and which cuts the y-axis at the point (0, 2). Does this line contain the point (2, 12)? Does it contain the point (−1, −4)?

8. Change the line $4x - 2y = 5$ into the slope-intercept form, and read off its slope as well as its y-intercept.

9. If the demand for a certain kind of ice cream (in thousands of pints) is given by

$$d = 20 - \frac{1}{8}p$$

where p is the price (in cents per pint), what is the significance of the slope of the corresponding line? Be careful about the units.

10. If a businessman estimates the annual cost of operating his car (in dollars) as

$$C = 1{,}200 + 0.09m$$

where m is his total mileage, what is the significance of the slope of the corresponding line? Should his figures be questioned by the Internal Revenue Service, if the businessman reports that he drove 15,000 miles and claims a deduction of \$2,950?

4.3 LINEAR FUNCTIONS: APPLICATIONS

Among the best-known applications of linear functions are those relating to *simple interest, simple discount,* and *linear depreciation.* For instance, if we borrow P dollars (called the *principal*) at the simple interest rate i (namely, at $100 \cdot i$ percent a year), the annual interest is $P \cdot i$ and the *amount* A we owe at the end of n years is given by

$$A = P + (P \cdot i)n$$

This simple interest formula is usually written as

$$A = P(1 + i \cdot n)$$

which is obtained by "factoring out" P; we wrote the formula the other way mainly to emphasize the point that there is a linear relationship between n and A. This will also become apparent the moment we substitute numbers. For instance, if we borrow \$10,000 at the simple interest rate $i = 0.06$ (namely, at 6 percent), the amount we owe after n years is

$$\begin{aligned} A &= 10{,}000(1 + 0.06n) \\ &= 10{,}000 + 600n \end{aligned}$$

Here the independent variable is n, the dependent variable is A, and the relationship is obviously linear. Note that the slope of the corresponding line is the *constant* interest of \$600 (6 percent of \$10,000) which is added each year. Actually, the formula can also be used when money is borrowed for days or months, so long as we remember that the n-units are years. Thus, the amount we owe after 1 month is obtained by substituting $n = 1/12$ and the amount we owe after a year and a half is obtained by substituting $n = 3/2$.

In *simple discount* problems we subtract (rather than add) a constant amount for each year (month, or day), and a formula for the *present value* of a sum of money due at a later date is given in Exercise 5 on page 102. In actual practice, simple interest and simple discount are used only for short-term transactions; otherwise, we use *compound interest* and *compound discount,* which we shall study in Chapter 5.

Linear depreciation is one of several methods approved by the Internal Revenue Service for depreciating business property. If the original cost of the property is C dollars and it is depreciated linearly over N years, its *value* (undepreciated balance) V at the end of n years is given by

$$V = C - \left(\frac{C}{N}\right)n$$

which can also be written as

$$V = C\left(1 - \frac{n}{N}\right)$$

by "factoring out" C. Here the independent variable is n, its domain is the set of integers 0, 1, 2, 3, . . . , and n, and the dependent variable is V. For instance, if office furniture worth \$3,000 is depreciated over 10 years, the undepreciated balance after n years is given by

$$\begin{aligned} V &= 3{,}000\left(1 - \frac{n}{10}\right) \\ &= 3{,}000 - 300n \end{aligned}$$

Note that after 10 years (that is, for $n = 10$) we get

$$V = 3{,}000 - 300(10) = 0$$

which means that the property is completely depreciated. The above formula relating V and n is obviously linear; another (non-linear) method of depreciation will be taken up in Chapter 5 (see Exercise 13 on page 143).

The characterizing feature of all linear functions is that *the values of the function increase (or decrease) at a constant rate.* This constant rate is the slope of the corresponding line, and as we indicated on page 93, it equals the slope of any line segment connecting two of its points. In the two numerical examples of this section, the constant rates of change were 600 and -300, and to consider another example suppose that a druggist knows that he can expect to sell 18 rolls of movie film at the regular price of \$2.45, and that for each 5 cent decrease in the price of this film he will sell an extra 3 rolls. If x is the price (in cents) and y is the number of rolls of film (he can expect to sell), then the constant rate of change is

$$\frac{\text{change in } y}{\text{change in } x} = \frac{3}{-5} = -\frac{3}{5}$$

for we said that he will sell 3 extra rolls of film when he *decreases* the price per roll by 5 cents. To find the linear equation which relates y to x, let us refer to Figure 4.5 and make use of the fact that the slope of the line is $b = -\frac{3}{5}$ and that (according to the original information) it must pass through the point (245, 18). Now, if we take an arbitrary point Q on this

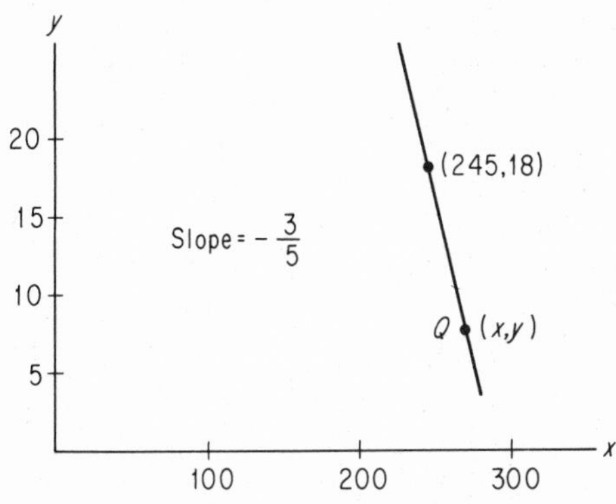

FIG. 4.5

line with the coordinates (x, y), then the slope of the line segment which joins Q and (245, 18) is $\frac{y - 18}{x - 245}$, and since this quantity must equal $-\frac{3}{5}$ we can write

$$\frac{y - 18}{x - 245} = -\frac{3}{5}$$

Multiplying both sides of this equation by $x - 245$ and also by 5, we get $5(y - 18) = -3(x - 245)$, and upon further simplification this becomes

$$y = 165 - \frac{3}{5}x$$

Having obtained this equation, we can now use it to calculate the druggist's expected sales for any given price x. For example, if he charges \$2.25 per roll he can expect to sell

$$y = 165 - \frac{3}{5}(225) = 30 \text{ rolls of film}$$

and if he charges \$1.75 he can expect to sell

$$y = 165 - \frac{3}{5}(175) = 60 \text{ rolls of film}$$

In this last example we found the equation of a line which had a *given slope* and passed through a *given point.* To treat this kind of problem systematically, suppose we want to find the equation of the line which has the slope b and which passes through the point (x_1, y_1), namely, Point P of

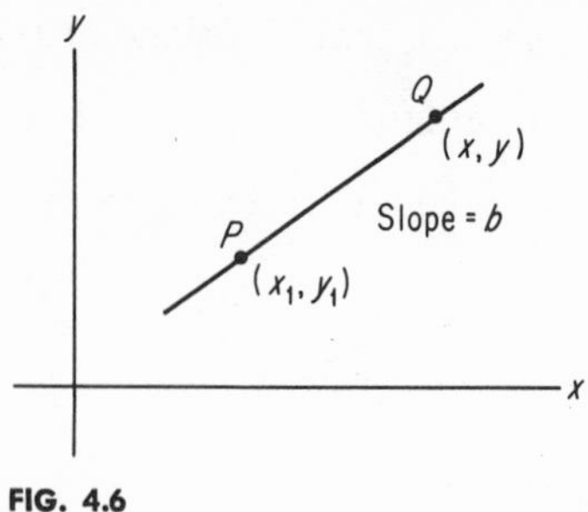

FIG. 4.6

Figure 4.6. Now, if we take any arbitrary point Q on the line with the unknown coordinates (x, y), we can write the slope of line segment PQ as $\frac{y - y_1}{x - x_1}$, and since this quantity must equal b we get

$$\frac{y - y_1}{x - x_1} = b$$

This is the *point-slope formula* for the equation of a straight line, and it can also be written as

$$y - y_1 = b(x - x_1) \qquad \textit{or as} \qquad y = y_1 + b(x - x_1)$$

For most practical applications the third form is the *most convenient.*

To illustrate the use of these formulas, suppose that an insurance company had 23,400 policy holders in 1965 and that the *trend* (the overall pattern of growth) is linear, with an average annual increase of 2,750 policy holders. This last quantity is called the *annual trend increment* and it is, in effect, the slope of the line which describes the company's growth. Thus, $b = 2{,}750$, and if we *code* the years so that 1960 corresponds to $x = 0$ and successive years are labeled 1, 2, 3, . . . , we find that the trend line must pass through the point (5, 23,400). Consequently, its equation is given by

$$\begin{aligned} y &= 23{,}400 + 2{,}750(x - 5) \\ &= 23{,}400 + 2{,}750x - 13{,}750 \\ &= 9{,}650 + 2{,}750x \end{aligned}$$

and it should be observed that the y-intercept, 9,650, is the number of policy holders the company should have had in the year 1960 (which corresponds to $x = 0$). To predict how many policy holders the insurance company should have in the year 1975, for example, we have only to substitute $x = 15$, getting

$$\begin{aligned} y &= 9{,}650 + 2{,}750(15) \\ &= 50{,}900 \end{aligned}$$

This assumes, of course, that the growth will *continue to be linear* and that it will *continue at the same rate* (of 2,750 new policy holders per year). Whether or not such assumptions are reasonable is difficult to say; in most cases this is a matter of economics (rather than mathematics), foresight, and quite a bit of luck.

Another important formula for the equation of a straight line is the *two-point formula* which enables us to write down the equation of a line in terms of the coordinates of two of its points. Referring to Figure 4.7,

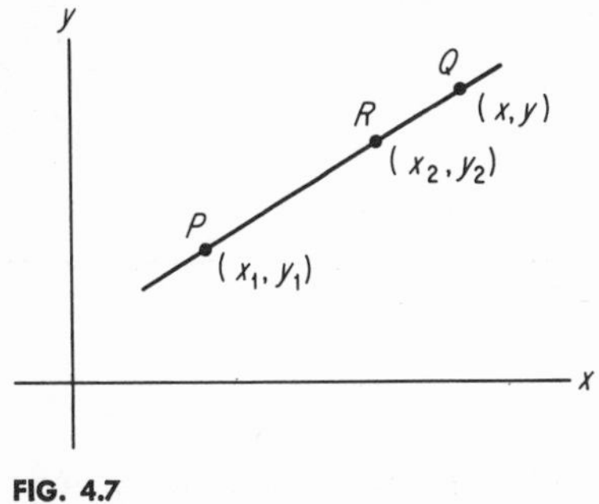

FIG. 4.7

suppose that we want to find the equation of the line which passes through points P and R, whose coordinates are (x_1, y_1) and (x_2, y_2). Now, if we take any other point on this line, say, the point Q of Figure 4.7 with the unknown coordinates (x, y), we know from the definition of a line (on page 92) that the slope of line segment PQ must equal that of line segment PR, namely, that

$$\frac{y - y_1}{x - x_1} = \frac{y_2 - y_1}{x_2 - x_1}$$

This is the *two-point formula* for the equation of a straight line, and if we multiply both sides by $x_2 - x_1$ we find that it can also be written as

$$y - y_1 = \frac{y_2 - y_1}{x_2 - x_1}(x - x_1)$$

To illustrate the use of this formula, let us suppose that the total amount of money spent annually on radio advertising (in the United States) grows at a constant rate. Given the information that the actual 1955 and 1965 expenditures for radio advertising were, respectively, 545 and 889 million dollars, let us find the equation of the trend line which passes through these two points, and use it to predict the amount which will be spent on radio advertising in the year 1972. Coding the years so that 1955 corresponds to $x = 0$ and subsequent years correspond to $x = 1, 2, 3, \ldots$, we shall thus have to find the equation of the line which passes through the points (0, 545) and (10, 889) of Figure 4.8. Substituting $x_1 = 0$, $y_1 =$

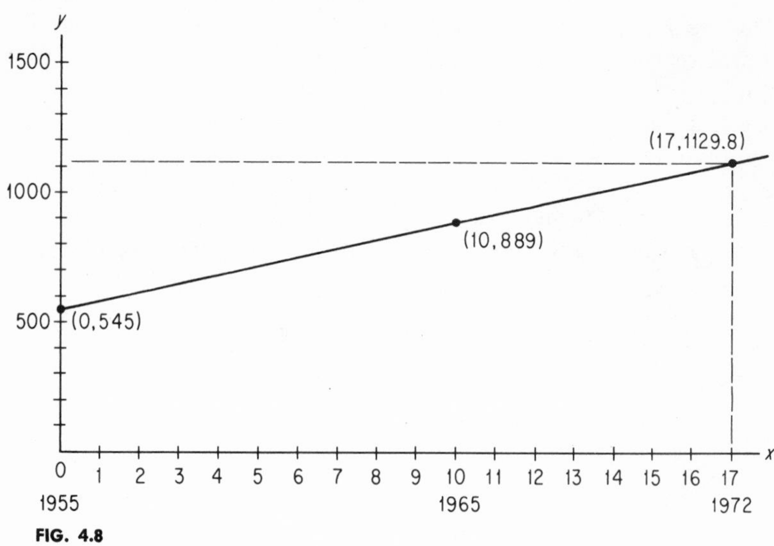

FIG. 4.8

545, $x_2 = 10$, and $y_2 = 889$ into the two-point formula for the equation of a straight line, we get

$$y - 545 = \frac{889 - 545}{10 - 0}(x - 0)$$

$$= 34.4x$$

and, hence,

$$y = 545 + 34.4x$$

This is the equation of the trend line of Figure 4.8, where the years are coded as indicated and the y-units are in millions of dollars. Now, if we substitute $x = 17$ (corresponding to the year 1972), we can predict that the total expenditures for radio advertising will be

$$y = 545 + 34.4(17)$$

$$= 1{,}129.8 \text{ (namely, \$1,129,800)}$$

Of course, this prediction is again based on the assumption that the growth pattern will continue unchanged, namely, that the line can be extended.

When we use the two-point formula or the formula for the slope of a line segment on page 90, it does not matter which point is referred to as (x_1, y_1) and which point is referred to as (x_2, y_2). It is important, however, to be careful to take the differences of the y-coordinates and the differences of the x-coordinates *the same way*. It is also important to observe that the two-point formula cannot be used when the x-coordinates of the two points are equal, namely, when we are dealing with a *vertical* line. The equation of the vertical line which passes through the point (x_1, y_1) is

$$x = x_1$$

which simply expresses the fact that each point on this line has the same x-coordinate x_1. For horizontal lines we can use any one of the formulas which we have discussed; since the slope of a horizontal line is *zero* (see page 91), the slope-intercept formula leads to $y = a$, and the two-point formula leads to $y = y_1$, where y_1 is the common y-coordinate of any point on the line. To summarize, equations such as $x = 3$, $x = -7$, and $x = 12$ represent vertical lines (the ones shown in Figure 4.9), while

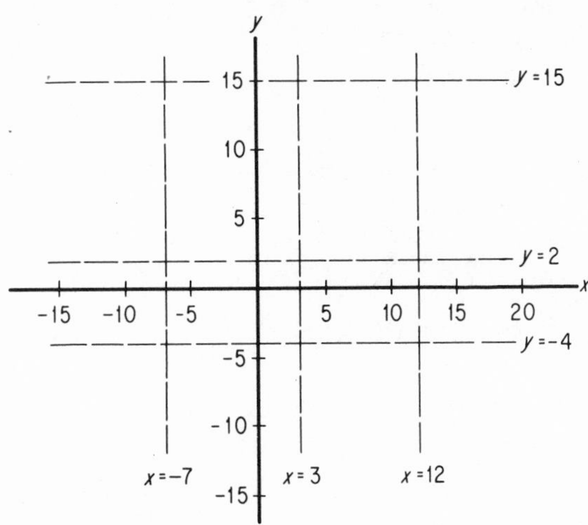

FIG. 4.9

equations such as $y = 2$, $y = -4$, and $y = 15$ represent horizontal lines. In particular, the equation of the x-axis is $y = 0$ and the equation of the y-axis is $x = 0$.

EXERCISES

1. Mr. Jones wants to borrow $3,000 to buy a new car and pay off the loan with monthly payments stretched over a period of three years. If the dealer charges him 6 percent simple interest and computes the monthly payments by dividing the total amount due in three years by 36, how much will Mr. Jones have to pay each month? (See also Exercise 14 on page 316).
2. Mr. Brown wants to borrow $2,750 and pay it back in a lump sum after 5 years. How much will he have to pay after 5 years if he is being charged 8 percent simple interest?
3. Mr. Smith borrows a sum of money for which he is charged 5 percent simple interest. How much did he borrow originally, if he owes $3,972.10 after three years?

4. To compute the interest on short-term transactions, bankers frequently use a 360-day year. If this method is being used, how much do we owe on November 12, 1968, for $1,000 borrowed at 8 percent simple interest on August 14, 1968?

5. **SIMPLE DISCOUNT.** In simple interest problems the interest rate applies to the *principal* P, to which the interest is added at the end of each year. If the rate is applied to the *amount* A due at the end of n years, we refer to it as a *discount rate*, and in simple discount problems the same discount is subtracted annually to obtain the *present value* P. Thus, if the discount rate is d (or $d \cdot 100$ percent), the present value is determined by the formula $P = A - (A \cdot d)n$, which can also be written as

$$P = A(1 - d \cdot n)$$

after we factor out A.

(a) If the discount rate is 9 percent, find the present value of $4,500 due at the end of 4 years.
(b) If someone is willing to pay us $4,320 now for a promissory note for $6,000 due 4 years hence, at what rate is he discounting the note?
(c) Using a 360-day year and a simple discount rate of 9 percent, calculate the present value of a note for $3,000 due in 60 days.

6. An apartment building worth $250,000 was built in 1949. What is its value (for tax purposes) in 1967, if it is being depreciated linearly over 40 years?

7. A school system bought $180,000 worth of new school buses in 1964. What is the value of these buses in 1969, if they are being depreciated linearly over a period of 9 years?

8. Find the equation of the line which

(a) passes through the point (1, 2) and has the slope $b = 3$;
(b) passes through the point (2, −7) and has the slope $b = -2$;
(c) passes through the points (3, 2) and (5, 3);
(d) passes through the points (−1, 2) and (3, 8).

9. In 1963 a company earned $3.17 per share and it expects this figure to increase by 24 cents a year. Coding the years so that 1960 corresponds to $x = 0$ and successive years correspond to $x = 1, 2, 3, \ldots$, use the point-slope formula to find the equation which will enable us to predict the company's earnings per share for future years. What should be the company's earnings per share in 1971? What is the significance of the value which we would get if we substituted into the formula $x = -1$?

10. The sales manager of a local television station claims that a company's sales will increase by $25 for every additional dollar spent on television commercials. If a furniture store has averaged monthly sales of $148,000 while spending $100 a month on television commercials, find the equation which relates the company's expected average monthly sales to the amount spent on television com-

mercials. What can we say about the store's average monthly sales, if its management decides to spend $500 a month on television commercials?

11. A manufacturer of floor tiles can expect to sell 26 thousand vinyl asbestos tiles if he charges 15 cents per tile, but only 8 thousand if he charges 19 cents per tile. Assuming that the relationship is linear, use the two-point formula to find the equation of the line which relates the number of vinyl asbestos tiles the manufacturer can expect to sell to their price. How many of these tiles can he expect to sell if he charges 18 cents per tile?

12. A machine purchased new for $10,000 has a scrap value of $1,200 after 10 years. If its value is depreciated linearly (from $10,000 to $1,200), find the equation of the line which enables us to determine its value after it has been in use any given number of years. What is its value after 3 years? Also, generalize the method used in this problem so that it applies to a machine which is purchased at the original cost C, has the scrap value S, and is depreciated linearly (from C to S) over a period of N years; that is, find a formula giving the value of the machine after x years.

13. Two distinct lines are said to be *parallel* if they have the same slope (or if they are both vertical).

    (a) Is the line $2x - 3y = 5$ parallel to the line $6x - 9y = 8$?
    (b) Is the line $7x - 3y = 4$ parallel to the line $14x - 6y = 8$?
    (c) Is the line $3x + 5y = 2$ parallel to the line $3x - 5y = 12$?
    (d) What conditions must be satisfied by the coefficients a, b, d, and e so that the lines $ax + by = c$ and $dx + ey = f$ will be parallel? What further condition will have to be imposed so that the two lines will not coincide?

14. The total number of chicken dinners which a well-known restaurant in Southern California served on Mother's Day 1955 through 1963 was 13,600, 14,000, 14,200, 14,600, 14,800, 15,000, 15,200, 15,900, and 16,200.

    (a) Plot these data on a piece of graph paper, with the years *coded* so that 1955 corresponds to $x = -4$ and successive years correspond to $x = -3, -2, -1, 0, 1, \ldots$
    (b) To check a statistician's claim that the line $y = 14{,}800 + 300x$ pretty well describes the overall trend, plot it on the diagram constructed in part (a) and judge by eye how well it fits the given data. (*Hint:* it takes the coordinates of two points to plot the line. Why would it be better to choose those corresponding to $x = -4$ and $x = 4$ rather than those corresponding to $x = 0$ and $x = 1$?)

4.4 DISTANCES AND LINES

It is not difficult to determine the height of a desk, the dimensions of an office, or the length of a piece of land, so long as we can use a yardstick, a tape, or some other direct measuring device. The problem becomes more difficult, however, if we have to determine, say, the distance between two warehouses on opposite sides of a lake, or the distance between two towns with mountains and rivers in between. To consider a specific example, let us investigate a problem faced by the management of a company with an assembly plant in Town A, which has to decide whether to locate a new parts-manufacturing plant in Town B or in Town C. To simplify the problem, let us assume that the parts are shipped by air, so that the only thing that matters is the distances between Town A and Towns B and C. Of course, we could compare these distances by measuring them on a map, but since our purpose is to show how it can be done also by assigning numbers to points and then using an appropriate formula, let us proceed in this round-about way.

To begin with, let us construct a system of coördinate axes and superimpose it on the map, so that we can assign coordinates to the Towns A, B, and C as indicated in Figure 4.10. All we need now is a formula for the

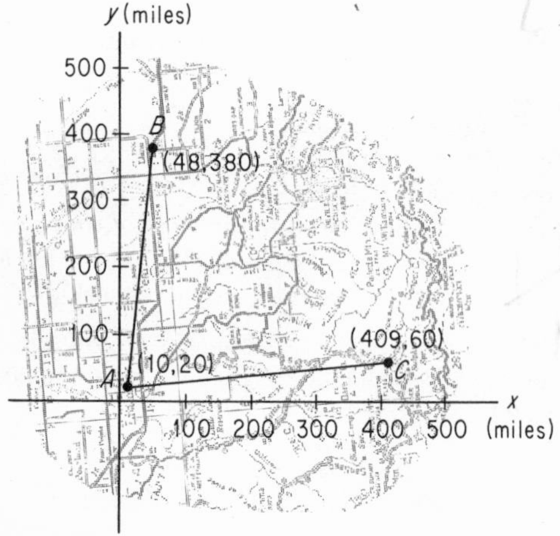

FIG. 4.10

distance between two points with known coordinates, that is, a formula which expresses the distance between two given points (x_1, y_1) and (x_2, y_2) in terms of the coordinates x_1, y_1, x_2, and y_2. To derive such a *distance formula*, let us consider Figure 4.11, where we plotted two points P and Q with the coordinates (x_1, y_1) and (x_2, y_2), and drew a horizontal line through P and a vertical line through Q. Let us now take a look at triangle PQR—its sides are of length $x_2 - x_1$, $y_2 - y_1$, and d (denoting the length of PQ), and in accordance with the *Pythagorean Theorem* we can write

$$d^2 = (x_2 - x_1)^2 + (y_2 - y_1)^2$$

(As the reader should be able to recall from elementary geometry, this theorem states that *the square of the hypotenuse of a right triangle equals*

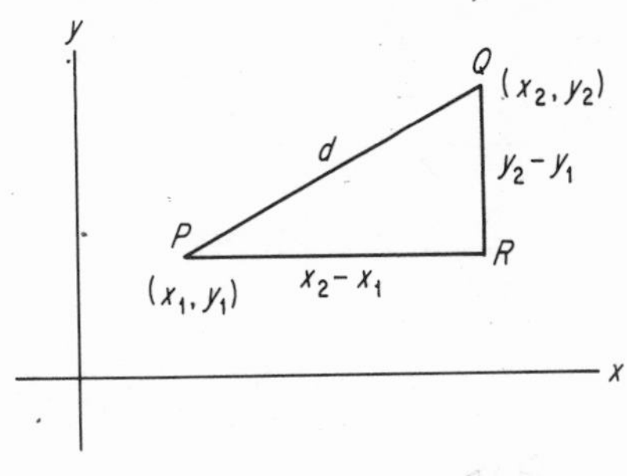

FIG. 4.11

the sum of the squares of the other two sides.) Finally, taking square roots, we get

$$d = \sqrt{(x_2 - x_1)^2 + (y_2 - y_1)^2}$$

and this is the desired formula which expresses the distance between two given points in terms of their coordinates.

Returning now to our numerical example and the points of Figure 4.10, we find that the distance between Towns A and B is

$$\sqrt{(48 - 10)^2 + (380 - 20)^2} = \sqrt{131{,}044} = 362 \text{ miles}$$

and that the distance between Towns A and C is

$$\sqrt{(409 - 10)^2 + (60 - 20)^2} = \sqrt{160{,}801} = 401 \text{ miles}$$

This shows that Town B is closer to the assembly plant than Town C, and if this outweighs all other considerations (such as tax advantages, wages, and the availability of labor), we conclude that the new plant should be built in Town B.

Let us now consider another problem in which the distance formula plays an important role. Suppose that a department store has two retail outlets, a Downtown Store and an Uptown Store, and that its management wants to build a storage warehouse which is just as far from one store as it is from the other. Suppose, furthermore, that when a coordinate system is superimposed on a map, the two stores are at the points (1, 9) and (13, 5), namely, at the points U and D of Figure 4.12. An obvious choice would be to build the warehouse halfway between the two stores, but this may be impossible; this point may be in the middle of a freeway, in a piece of property that is not for sale, or perhaps in a park or in a lake. Thus, let us look for other points which are *equidistant* from the two stores, and let us suppose that the point P of Figure 4.12 fits the description. Its coordinates are x and y, and by using the distance formula we find that the distances from point P to points U and D are, respectively,

$$\sqrt{(x - 1)^2 + (y - 9)^2} \qquad \text{and} \qquad \sqrt{(x - 13)^2 + (y - 5)^2}$$

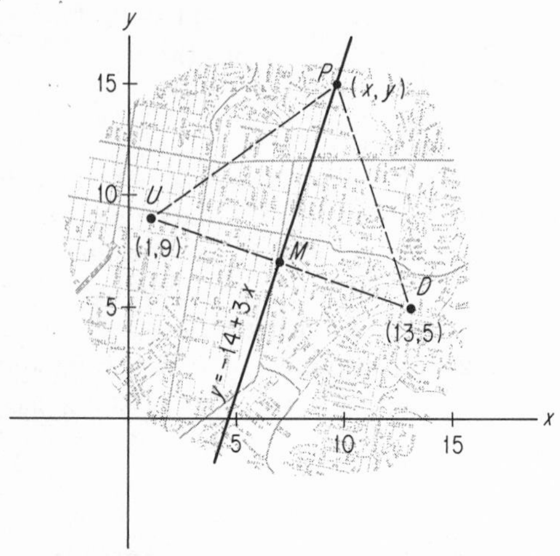

FIG. 4.12

Since these two quantities are supposed to be equal, we can write

$$\sqrt{(x-1)^2+(y-9)^2} = \sqrt{(x-13)^2+(y-5)^2}$$

and, squaring both sides and making use of the fact that $(a+b)^2 = a^2 + 2ab + b^2$, we get

$$(x^2-2x+1)+(y^2-18y+81) = (x^2-26x+169)+(y^2-10y+25)$$

Further simplification yields $24x - 8y = 112$, and, finally,

$$y = -14 + 3x$$

Thus, we have shown that all points which are equidistant from the points (1, 9) and (13, 5) must lie on the line $y = -14 + 3x$. Substituting $x = 0$ and $x = 5$, for example, we find that the points $(0, -14)$ and (5, 1) are included among the potential sites for the warehouse of the department store.

In elementary geometry we refer to the line $y = -14 + 3x$ as the *perpendicular bisector* of the line segment joining points (1, 9) and (13, 5). We do not have to prove that point M of Figure 4.12 is the midpoint of the line segment UD, since every point on the line $y = -14 + 3x$ is as far from U as it is from D. As the reader will be asked to show in Exercise 4 on page 108, the coordinates of point M are (7, 7), and the lengths of UM and MD both equal $\sqrt{40}$. To show that the line $y = -14 + 3x$ is perpendicular to UD, we have only to make use of the fact that triangles UPM and DPM of Figure 4.12 are *congruent;* we can then argue that since angles UMP and DMP are equal, they must both be *right angles.* In any case, it is of interest to note that whereas the line $y = -14 + 3x$ has the slope $b = 3$, the line segment joining points U and D has the slope

$$\frac{5-9}{13-1} = \frac{-4}{12} = -\frac{1}{3}$$

This illustrates a very important result which we shall not prove, namely, that *two lines (or line segments) are perpendicular if and only if the product of their slopes is equal to* -1; clearly, $3(-\frac{1}{3}) = -1$. Not included in this rule are horizontal and vertical lines, in which case one line has a zero slope while that of the other is not defined. By using this rule it can easily be checked that the line $y = 7 + 2x$, for example, *is perpendicular* to the line $y = 3 - \frac{1}{2}x$, that the line $y = 12 + 5x$ *is not perpendicular* to the line $y = -2 + \frac{1}{5}x$, and that the line $3x + 4y = 15$ *is perpendicular* to the line $8x - 6y = 21$.

Mathematically speaking, we have solved the problem about the possible sites at which the warehouse should be located (namely, at some point on the map which lies on the line $y = -14 + 3x$), but there may well be practical considerations for looking for alternate solutions. For one thing, it may be that the two stores are located in Los Angeles, California, while the line passes through Tananarive, the capital of Madagascar, or Charlottetown on Prince Edward Island. Furthermore, a point on the line may be close to the two stores but difficult to reach, and a point near the line (but not on it) may be preferable so far as traffic conditions, tax advantages, or the price of a suitable piece of property is concerned.

EXERCISES

1. Find the distances between the following pairs of points: (a) (1, 1) and (7, 9); (b) (2, 3) and (7, 15); (c) (1, 3) and (7, 4); (d) (10, 10) and (2, −5).

2. A heavy piece of machinery is to be shipped from Town A of Figure 4.13 to Town C, where the x-units and the y-units are both in miles. It can be shipped

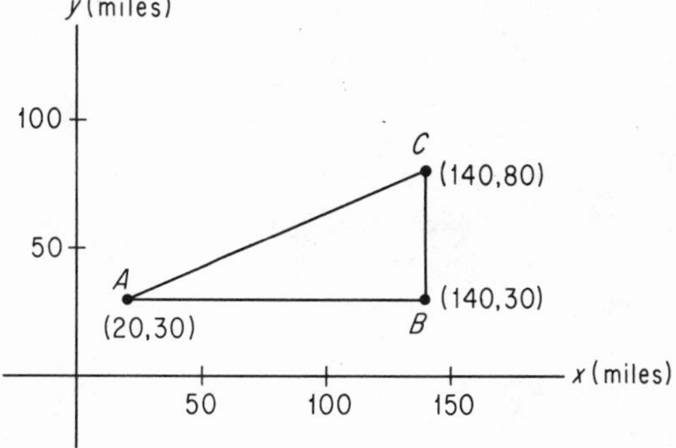

FIG. 4.13

directly by air at a cost of \$5.29 per mile, or by truck via Town B at a cost of \$3.84 per mile. Which is cheaper?

3. A salesman living in Town F of Figure 4.14 regularly visits customers in Towns G and H. If all units are in miles, what is the total length of one round-trip?

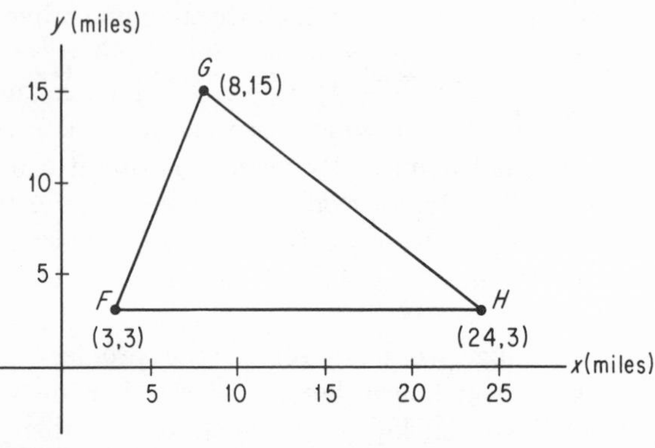

FIG. 4.14

4. MIDPOINTS. The coordinates of the midpoint of a line segment are obtained by *averaging* the respective coordinates of its endpoints. In other words, the coordinates of the midpoint of the line segment connecting (x_1, y_1) and (x_2, y_2) are

$$x = \frac{x_1 + x_2}{2} \qquad \text{and} \qquad y = \frac{y_1 + y_2}{2}$$

To prove these two formulas, we have only to refer to Figure 4.15 (where we have drawn horizontal and vertical lines through two arbitrary points P and Q and their midpoint M) and make use of the fact that point R is the midpoint of PS and point T is the midpoint of QS.

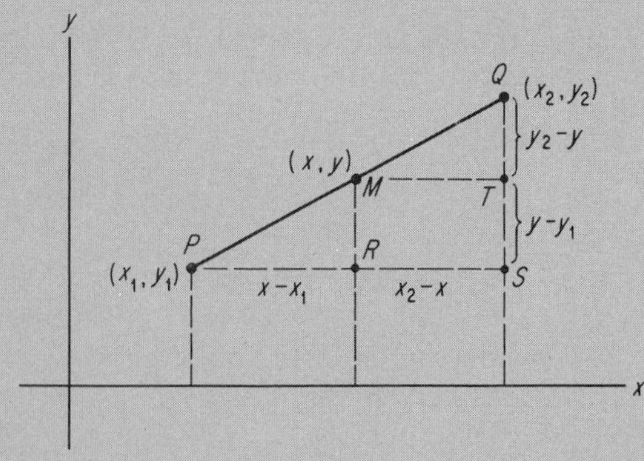

FIG. 4.15

(a) Derive the above formulas for x and y by following the indicated suggestions.

(b) With reference to the example on page 105, verify that the midpoint between (1, 9) and (13, 5) is the point (7, 7), and also verify that it lies on the line $y = -14 + 3x$.
(c) Find the midpoint between (−3, 5) and (17, 7).
(d) With reference to Figure 4.13, where would the plane be located if it had to make an emergency landing halfway between Towns A and C?

5. Check whether any two of the six line segments of Exercise 1 on page 94 are perpendicular.

6. Find the equation of the line which is perpendicular to the line $3x - y = 7$ and passes through the point (2, 1).

7. THE EQUATION OF A CIRCLE. A circle is a plane curve consisting of points which are all at a given distance (called the *radius*) from a fixed point (called

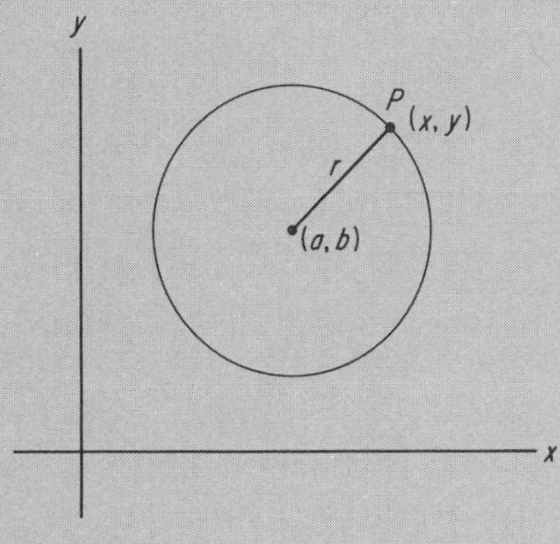

FIG. 4.16

its *center*). As can be seen from Figure 4.16, a direct application of the distance formula leads to the result that if a circle has the radius r and its center at the point (a, b), the coordinates (x, y) of any point on the circle must satisfy the equation

$$(x - a)^2 + (y - b)^2 = r^2$$

(a) Find the equation of the circle which has its center at the origin and the radius $r = 5$. Check by substitution whether or not the following points lie on this circle: (4, 3), (−1, 4), (3, −4), (−5, 0).
(b) Find the equation of the circle which has its center at the point (3, 2) and the radius $r = 10$. How could we check *without plotting the circle* whether the point (8, −10) falls inside of it, on it, or outside of it.
(c) With reference to a suitable system of coordinates superimposed on a map, one salesman is allowed to sell real estate anywhere within the circle $x^2 + y^2 = 100$ while another salesman is allowed to sell real estate

anywhere within the circle $(x - 20)^2 + y^2 = 144$. Do their sales territories overlap?

(d) Is the relationship established by the equation of a circle a function? Explain your answer.

4.5 QUADRATIC FUNCTIONS

Although there are many problems in which graphs consist of points falling on a straight line, or in which straight lines can be used to describe general patterns, we often run into situations like those described in Figures 4.17 and 4.18. Figure 4.17 represents the relationship between the weekly

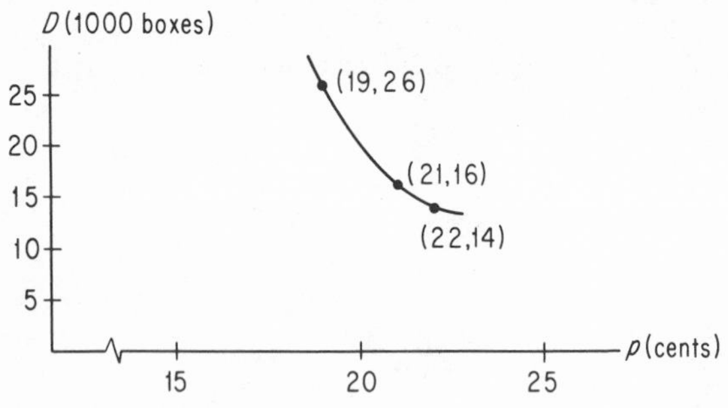

FIG. 4.17

demand for a new product, a detergent, and the price charged per box. Actually, a survey showed that the manufacturer can expect to sell 26,000 boxes a week in a certain market area if he charges 19 cents per box, 16,000 boxes if he charges 21 cents per box, and 14,000 boxes if he charges 22 cents per box. This information is conveyed by the three points of

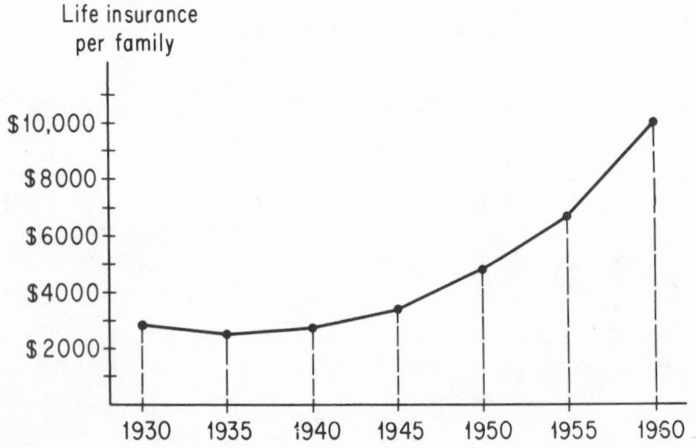

FIG. 4.18 *Source: Life Insurance Fact Book, 1966.*

Figure 4.17, where the D-units are in thousands of boxes and we drew the relatively smooth curve through the given points to emphasize the fact that the relationship between the price and the demand for this product is *not linear*. Figure 4.18 shows how the average life insurance coverage of families has changed throughout the years, and it is apparent that in this example too the overall pattern cannot be described by means of a straight line.

In both of these examples the relationships can be described by means of curves which are *slightly bent*, and this raises the question as to what kinds of equations might provide appropriate mathematical models. Sometimes, the choice of a particular model (equation) is dictated by the nature of the situation, itself, and this is the case, for example, in the illustration on page 69. Most of the time, though, we have no choice but to try various kinds of models (that is, various kinds of equations) and decide more or less subjectively which one provides the *best fit*. (This may sound like "hit or miss," but it can be done in a fairly systematic fashion, particularly, with the use of a high-speed computer.)

For functions like those pictured in Figures 4.17 and 4.18 we often choose the model provided by a *quadratic function*, namely, a function given by an equation of the form

$$y = a + bx + cx^2$$

where a, b, and c are numerical constants and c is *not* equal to zero. Quadratic functions are also referred to as *parabolic functions*, and their graphs as *parabolas*.

The problem of determining the equation of the parabola which actually passes through the three points of Figure 4.17 will be taken up later, in Exercise 10 on page 203. So far as the work of this chapter is concerned, let us merely state the result that this equation is

$$D = 520 - 45p + p^2$$

where p is the price per box (in cents) and D is the weekly demand (in thousands of boxes). To verify this result we have only to substitute $p = 19$, 21, and 22, and check whether the corresponding values of D are 26, 16, and 14; it will be left to the reader to take care of this in Exercise 1 on page 114.

Now suppose that the manufacturer of the detergent wants to use this parabolic model to determine how many boxes of the detergent he might sell if he charged either 15 cents per box or 25 cents per box. Substituting $p = 15$, we find that in the first case

$$D = 520 - 45(15) + 15^2 = 70$$

namely, that there would be a demand for 70,000 boxes. In the second case, substitution of $p = 25$ yields

$$D = 520 - 45(25) + 25^2 = 20$$

which represents a demand for 20,000 boxes of the detergent per week. The first of these results seems rather high and it may well raise some doubts about the appropriateness of the equation with which it was obtained. So far as the second result is concerned, something must definitely be wrong—according to the original data, 14,000 boxes of the detergent were sold when they were priced at 22 cents, and it simply does not make sense that the demand should *go up* when the price is *raised* to 25 cents.

What has happened here is that the manufacturer of the detergent is guilty of carelessly *extrapolating*, namely, of carelessly going beyond the price range to which the quadratic function was meant to apply. It so happens that the overall shape of a parabola given by an equation of the form $y = a + bx + cx^2$ is either like that of Figure 4.19 or like that of Figure 4.20. If the constant c (the coefficient of x^2) is *positive*, we get a graph like that of Figure 4.19; if c is *negative*, we get a graph like that of Figure 4.20. Either the curve goes down, turns, and then goes back up, or it goes

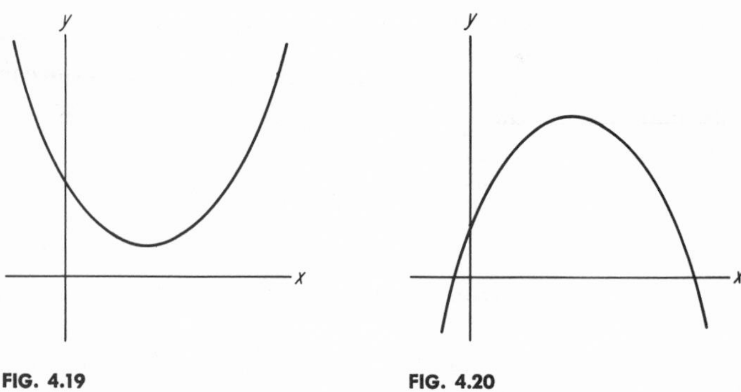

FIG. 4.19 **FIG. 4.20**

up, turns, and then goes back down. How sharply it turns, and at which point it reaches a minimum or a maximum depends on the values of a, b, and c; this is something we shall discuss further in Chapter 13.

The moral of this last example is that *part* of a parabola may well describe a relationship like that displayed in Figure 4.17 or Figure 4.18, but we must be careful to restrict the domain of the function to that part for which we have direct information (or other reasons which justify its fit). If we actually fitted a parabola to the insurance data of Figure 4.18, we would get something like the graph of Figure 4.21, and it is apparent that the domain of the function should not be extended for too many years beyond 1960 (and certainly not to any years prior to 1930).

Let us now consider a problem which actually leads to a quadratic function. Suppose that someone has accepted a job in a new town because he wants to be close to the ocean, and that he is looking for a house which

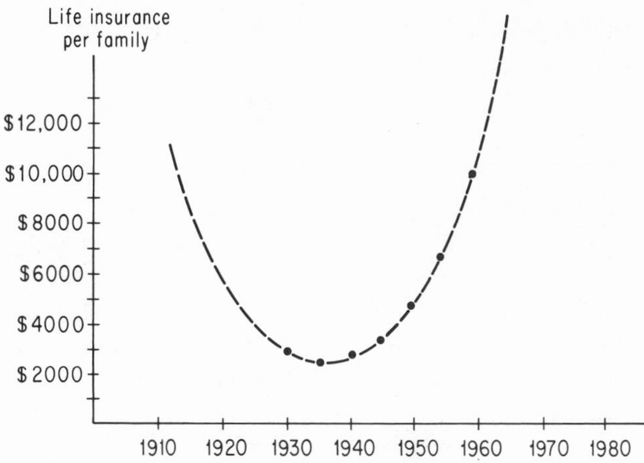

FIG. 4.21 *Source: Life Insurance Fact Book, 1966.*

is *just as far from the office where he will work as it is from the beach.* Getting a map and drawing the coordinate axes so that the x-axis is the shoreline (see Figure 4.22) and the office is at the point (0, 6), let us now see where he should look for a house. If point P is an arbitrary point with the coordinates (x, y), we find that its distance from the office is $\sqrt{(x-0)^2 + (y-6)^2}$, that its distance from the beach is y, and, hence, that

$$\sqrt{(x-0)^2 + (y-6)^2} = y$$

if these two distances are to be equal. Squaring both sides of this equation and making use of the fact that $(y-6)^2 = y^2 - 12y + 36$, we get

$$x^2 + y^2 - 12y + 36 = y^2$$

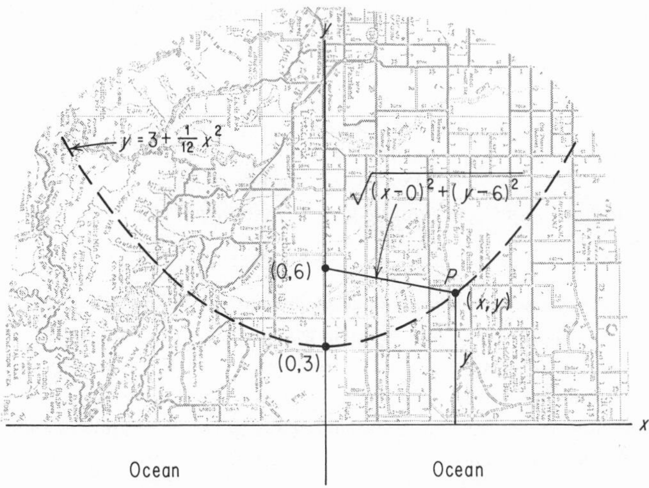

FIG. 4.22

and this equation can be simplified by subtracting y^2 from both sides of the equation, adding $12y$, and then dividing by 12. This gives

$$y = 3 + \frac{1}{12}x^2$$

for the equation of the quadratic function whose graph we have drawn in Figure 4.22. Note that it passes through the point (0, 3), which is halfway between the office and the nearest point of the beach. Any point on this parabola will be just as far from the office as it is from the beach, although it would be desirable, of course, to look for a house which is as close as possible to the point (0, 3). Aside from the fact that this example leads to a parabolic function, we have given it here because a slight variation in the conditions leads to a *hyperbola* or an *ellipse*, two other curves which are of special importance in mathematics (see Exercise 7 and Exercise 8 on pages 115 and 116).

EXERCISES

1. Verify that if $D = 520 - 45p + p^2$, then the values of D which correspond to $p = 19$, 21, and 22 are, respectively, 26, 16, and 14.
2. If $y = 4x - x^2$, find the values of y which correspond to $x = -1, 0, 1, 2, 3, 4$, and 5, and plot the graph of this function. At which point does it seem to have its maximum value? (See also Exercise 2 on page 379.)
3. If $f(x) = 3 - 4x + 2x^2$, find $f(-2)$, $f(-1)$, $f(0)$, $f(1)$, $f(2)$, $f(3)$, and $f(4)$, and plot the graph of this parabolic function. At which point does it seem to assume its minimum value? (See also Exercise 1 on page 379).
4. A travel agency advertises all-expenses-paid trips to the Rose Bowl for special groups. Transportation is by bus, which seats 48 passengers, and the charge per person is $80 *plus* an additional $2 for each empty seat. (Thus, if there are 3 empty seats each person has to pay $86, if there are 5 empty seats each person has to pay $90, and so on.) If there are x empty seats, how many passengers are there on the bus, how much does each passenger have to pay, and what are the travel agency's total receipts? Plot the graph of the function which relates the travel agency's total receipts to the number of empty seats and judge under what conditions its receipts will be greatest (see also Exercise 8 on page 380).
5. A retailer wants to price a toy car which costs him $2.00 so as to maximize his total profit. He knows from experience that if he charges x dollars a piece he will be able to sell $300 - 100x$ of the cars. What is his profit per car when he charges x dollars a piece, and what is his *total profit* for the $300 - 100x$ cars? Calculate his total profit for $x =$ $2.30, $2.40, $2.50, $2.60, and $2.70, and plot the corresponding points on a suitable graph. Judging from this graph, how much should he charge per car so as to maximize his total profit? (See also Exercise 9 on page 380.)
6. According to the *1966 Statistical Abstract of the United States*, the 1950, 1955,

1960, and 1965 production of beer was 89, 90, 95, and 108 million barrels. Coding the years so that $x = 0$ corresponds to 1960, succeeding years correspond to $x = 1, 2, 3, \ldots$, and earlier years correspond to $x = -1, -2, -3, \ldots$, suppose that a statistician finds that the function given by

$$y = 95.6 + 1.84x + 0.12x^2$$

should give a pretty good fit.

(a) Calculate the values of this function corresponding to $x = -10$, $x = -5$, $x = 0$, and $x = 5$, and plot them on a piece of graph paper together with the original data.

(b) Use the quadratic function obtained by the statistician to predict the 1970 production of beer.

7. THE EQUATION OF A HYPERBOLA. Referring to the example on page 113, suppose that the man wants to live closer to the beach than to his job; in fact, he wants the distance to the beach to be only *half* the distance to his office.

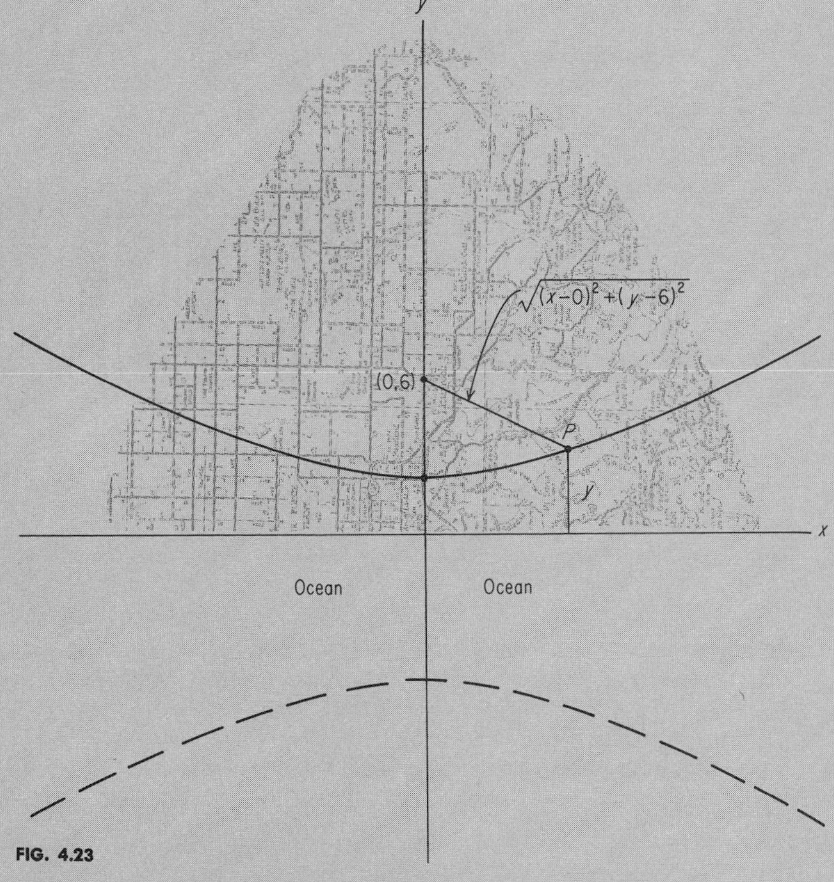

FIG. 4.23

(a) Using the same notation as in Figure 4.22, show that he should look for a house somewhere on the graph of

$$3y^2 + 12y - x^2 = 36$$

(b) This graph, called a *hyperbola*, is shown in Figure 4.23, and it should be observed that it consists of two parts: the solid curve above the x-axis and the dotted curve which lies in the ocean so far as our example is concerned. Verify by direct substitution that the points $(0, 2)$ and $(0, -6)$ lie on this hyperbola, and check whether the original condition is satisfied at these points.

8. THE EQUATION OF AN ELLIPSE. Referring to the example on page 113, suppose that the man does not want to live quite so close to the beach; in fact, he wants the distance to the beach to be *twice* that to his office.

(a) Using the same notation as in Figure 4.22, show that he should look for a house somewhere on the graph of

$$4x^2 + 3y^2 - 48y + 144 = 0$$

(b) This graph, called an *ellipse*, is shown in Figure 4.24, where we can see that its shape is like that of an elongated circle. Verify by direct substitution that the points $(0, 4)$ and $(0, 12)$ lie on this ellipse, and check whether the original condition is satisfied at these points.

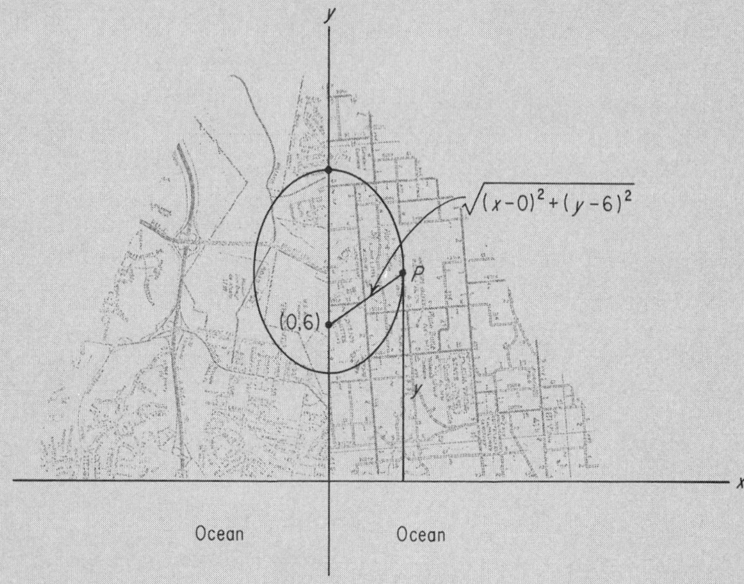

FIG. 4.24

4.6 QUADRATIC EQUATIONS

In Section 3.2 we described the relationship between the number of extras a new car dealer puts on his cars and the number of cars he can expect to sell during the model year by means of the equation

$$y = 40 + 8x - x^2$$

Thus, the relationship is a quadratic function, and since the coefficient of x^2 is *negative*, its graph has the general shape of the parabola of Figure 4.20. Suppose now that the dealer has 52 cars in stock and that he wants to know *how many extras he should put on each of these cars so that he can expect to sell them all without having to turn any customers away*. One way of obtaining an answer to this question is to look at the graph which we have reproduced in Figure 4.25. Judging from this graph, it seems that $x = 2$ and $x = 6$ are

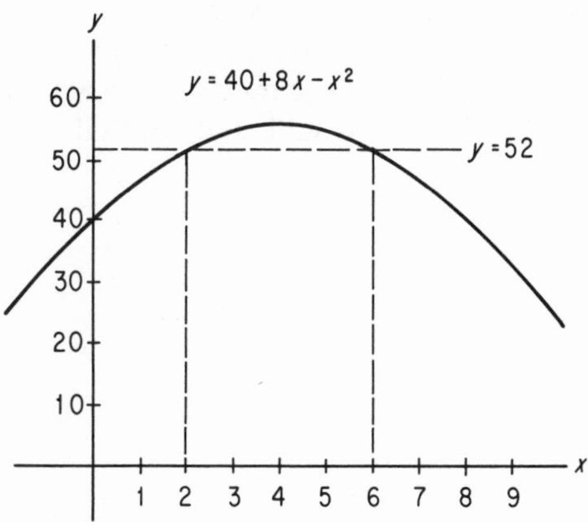

FIG. 4.25

the values of x which correspond to $y = 52$, and we conclude that he should put either 2 or 6 extras on each car. To handle this problem *algebraically*, we must solve the equation

$$52 = 40 + 8x - x^2$$

which can also be written as

$$12 - 8x + x^2 = 0$$

after we add x^2 to both sides of the equation, subtract $8x$, and then subtract 40 (getting the constant term $52 - 40 = 12$).

This equation is referred to as a *quadratic equation* (*in one unknown*), a term which applies to any equation which can be put in the form

$$a + bx + cx^2 = 0$$

where a, b, and c are numerical constants and c is not equal to zero. A *solution* of a quadratic equation is a value of the unknown x which "satisfies" the equation, namely, a value of x which makes $a + bx + cx^2 = 0$ a *true* statement. Thus, $x = 2$ *is* a solution of the given quadratic equation since $12 - 8(2) + 2^2 = 0$, and so is $x = 6$ since $12 - 8(6) + 6^2 = 0$. On the other hand, $x = 3$ is *not* a solution since $12 - 8(3) + 3^2 = -3$ instead of 0.

Quadratic equations can be solved in various ways. One way is to plot the graph of $y = a + bx + cx^2$ and read off the value or values of x which correspond to $y = 0$, namely, the value or values of x at which the curve cuts the x-axis. (This is similar to what we did in Figure 4.25; had we first written the equation as $12 - 8x + x^2 = 0$ and plotted the graph of $y = 12 - 8x + x^2$, the solutions $x = 2$ and $x = 6$ would have been given by the values at which the graph cuts the x-axis.) This graphical method will work nicely if the solutions happen to be whole numbers, if we are good at plotting graphs, or if we are interested only in *approximate solutions*. For instance, to solve the quadratic equation $3 - x^2 = 0$, we might plot the graph of $y = 3 - x^2$ as in Figure 4.26, and read off the answers

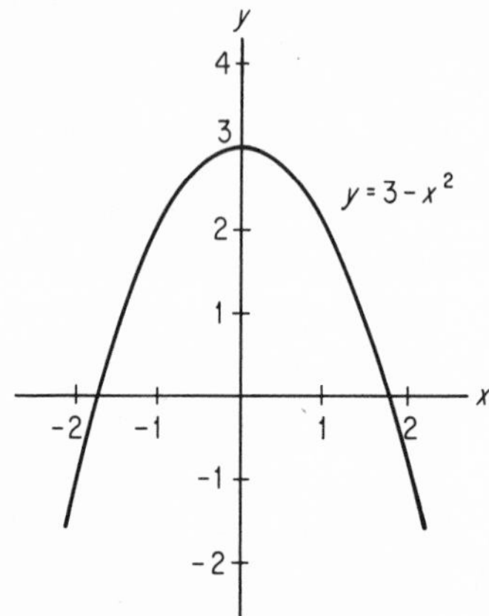

FIG. 4.26

(the x-coordinates of the points where the graph cuts the x-axis) as approximately $x = -1.7$ and $x = 1.7$. If this approximation is too crude, we might observe that the equation can be written as $x^2 = 3$, so that the solutions are given by $x = \sqrt{3}$ and $x = -\sqrt{3}$. Referring to a square-root table (for instance, Table V at the end of this book), we find that the solutions are $x = -1.732$ and $x = 1.732$ correct to three decimals.

The solution of a quadratic equation can sometimes be facilitated by *factoring* and making use of the fact that *if the product of two real numbers is zero, then one or the other must be zero.* Thus, we could have written $12 - 8x + x^2 = 0$ as

$$(x - 2)(x - 6) = 0$$

and we could have concluded that either $x - 2 = 0$ or $x - 6 = 0$, and, hence, that $x = 2$ or $x = 6$. For those readers who have had little or no experience with factoring, some hints are given in Exercises 3 and 4 on page 124. Another special method of solving quadratic equations which involves what is called "completing the square," is discussed in Exercise 5 on page 124.

The methods we have described so far are of no use whatsoever unless $y = a + bx + cx^2$ is easily graphed, unless we are satisfied with approximations, or unless $a + bx + cx^2$ is easily factored. Much more widely used is a general method in which the quadratic equation $a + bx + cx^2 = 0$ is actually *solved symbolically,* so that the solutions of any given quadratic equation can be obtained by substituting the values of a, b, and c into appropriate formulas. Employing the process of "completing the square" referred to above (and explained in Exercise 5 on page 124), it can be shown that the two solutions of $a + bx + cx^2 = 0$ are given by*

$$x = \frac{-b + \sqrt{b^2 - 4ac}}{2c} \quad \text{and} \quad x = \frac{-b - \sqrt{b^2 - 4ac}}{2c}$$

which is usually condensed to

$$x = \frac{-b \pm \sqrt{b^2 - 4ac}}{2c}$$

This formula is called the "quadratic formula," and if we use it in the example where $a = 12$, $b = -8$, and $c = 1$, we get

$$x = \frac{-(-8) \pm \sqrt{(-8)^2 - 4(12)(1)}}{2(1)} = \frac{8 \pm \sqrt{64 - 48}}{2} = \frac{8 \pm 4}{2}$$

Thus, the two solutions of the quadratic equation $12 - 8x + x^2 = 0$ are

$$x = \frac{8 + 4}{2} = 6 \quad \text{and} \quad x = \frac{8 - 4}{2} = 2$$

which agrees, of course, with the results we obtained before.

To consider another example, suppose we want to know how the manufacturer (of the illustration on page 111) should price his detergent so that he can expect a demand for 50,000 boxes. Since the D-units were thousands, we substitute $D = 50$ into the equation $D = 520 - 45p + p^2$, getting $50 = 520 - 45p + p^2$, and, hence, the quadratic equation

---

* To avoid confusion, let us point out that many authors write quadratic equations as $ax^2 + bx + c = 0$, so that the denominator of the solutions is $2a$ instead of $2c$.

$$470 - 45p + p^2 = 0$$

To solve this equation we have only to substitute $a = 470$, $b = -45$, and $c = 1$ into the quadratic formula, and we get

$$p = \frac{-(-45) \pm \sqrt{(-45)^2 - 4(470)(1)}}{2(1)} = \frac{45 \pm \sqrt{145}}{2}$$

Approximating the square root of 145 as 12, we conclude that the two solutions of the given quadratic equation are (approximately)

$$x = \frac{45 + 12}{2} = 28.5 \qquad \text{and} \qquad x = \frac{45 - 12}{2} = 16.5$$

Since $x = 28.5$ lies beyond the price range to which the equation can reasonably be applied (see discussion on page 112), we use the second solution, from which it follows that the manufacturer should come very close to his goal if he prices the detergent at *two* boxes for 33 cents.

When we gave the formula for the solutions of a quadratic equation, we indicated that there are always *two* solutions, no more and no less. This was true in both of our examples, where the solutions were in each case *unequal real numbers*, but it would be a mistake to conclude that the two solutions must necessarily be unequal or, for that matter, that they must necessarily be real numbers. If we take a look at Figure 4.27, for example, which shows

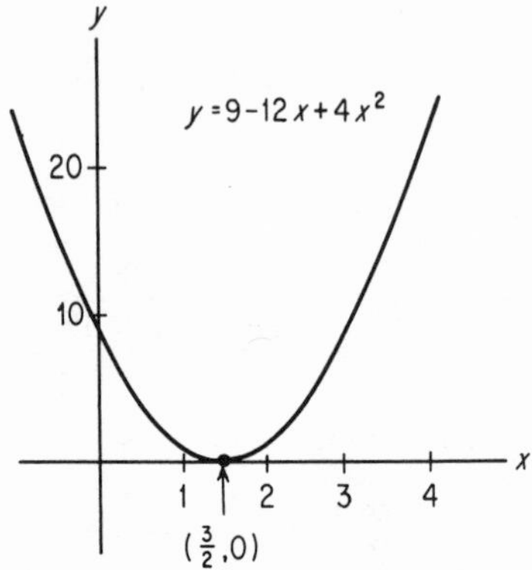

FIG. 4.27

the graph of $y = 9 - 12x + 4x^2$, we find that there is only one point on the curve which corresponds to $y = 0$, namely, the point (3/2, 0). This suggests that the quadratic equation $9 - 12x + 4x^2 = 0$ has only the one solution $x = 3/2$. Now, if we substitute $a = 9$, $b = -12$, and $c = 4$ into the quadratic formula, we get

$$x = \frac{-(-12) \pm \sqrt{(-12)^2 - 4(9)(4)}}{2(4)} = \frac{12 \pm 0}{8} = \frac{3}{2}$$

and it can be seen that the result is the same regardless of the sign. This means that the two solutions of this quadratic equation are equal, and to avoid ambiguities we say that the quadratic equation $9 - 12x + 4x^2 = 0$ has the *double solution* $x = 3/2$. Observe that the quadratic equation $a + bx + cx^2 = 0$ has a double solution whenever $b^2 - 4ac$ (namely, the expression which appears under the radical sign) is equal to zero.

Now let us consider an example where the solutions of a quadratic equation are not even real numbers. Suppose, for instance, that the manufacturer referred to on page 111 finds that his production capacity is limited to 12,000 boxes a week, and that he wants to know for what price per box this capacity will equal the demand. Substituting $D = 12$ into $D = 520 - 45p + p^2$, we obtain $12 = 520 - 45p + p^2$ or $508 - 45p + p^2 = 0$, and it would seem that the manufacturer should be able to find the answer to his question by solving this quadratic equation. Since $a = 508$, $b = -45$, and $c = 1$, the quadratic formula yields

$$p = \frac{-(-45) \pm \sqrt{(-45)^2 - 4(508)(1)}}{2(1)} = \frac{45 \pm \sqrt{-7}}{2}$$

and this is as far as we can go—the square root of -7 is *not* a real number, or in other words, *there is no real number whose square is* -7. (This follows from the fact that the square of a *positive* real number is *positive*, the square of a *negative* real number is *positive*, and the square of *zero* is *zero;* hence, the square of *any* real number must be *positive or zero.*)

Actually, the manufacturer was wrong in trying to find a solution to his problem by substituting $D = 12$ into the equation $D = 520 - 45p + p^2$. As can be seen from Figure 4.28, there is no point on this parabola which

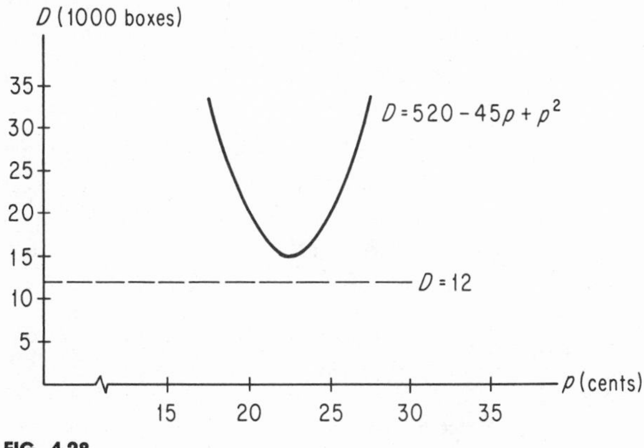

FIG. 4.28

corresponds to $D = 12$, and as we pointed out on page 112, it would be a serious mistake to use the equation $D = 520 - 45p + p^2$ for values of p

(or D) that go far beyond the values for which data were actually obtained. To answer his question, the manufacturer would actually have to get further data, say, study the weekly demand for the detergent when its price is 25, 27, or 30 cents per box. As can well be imagined, the resulting relationship between price and demand will no longer be a parabolic function; it stands to reason that the demand should keep on going down when the price is increased. An alternate kind of curve which might actually fit such data is suggested in Exercise 15 on page 125.

4.7 COMPLEX NUMBERS

If we want to be able to say that *every* quadratic equation has two solutions (which may or may not be equal), we shall have to work with numbers which are more general than the real numbers. Of course, they must include the real numbers, but they must also include the square roots of negative numbers since $3 + x^2 = 0$, for example, has the solutions $x = \sqrt{-3}$ and $x = -\sqrt{-3}$; they must also include quantities such as $1 + \sqrt{-2}$ and $2 - \sqrt{-5}$, which are, respectively, solutions of the quadratic equations $3 - 2x + x^2 = 0$ and $9 - 4x + x^2 = 0$ (see Exercise 23 on page 126).

To take care of this situation, let us introduce the new number $i = \sqrt{-1}$ [which is such that $i^2 = (\sqrt{-1})^2 = -1$], and let us refer to all numbers of the form $a + bi$ (where a and b are real numbers) as *complex numbers*. The symbol i denotes "imaginary," and it was chosen originally because it was difficult to attribute to $\sqrt{-1}$ any "real" (or practical) significance; today, the complex numbers play an indispensible and a very real part in many branches of science and engineering.* Let us remember, therefore, that the number i is as "imaginary" or as "unimaginary" as any other number—as we have stressed throughout the earlier chapters of this book, *all numbers are "unreal" in the sense that they are abstract mathematical objects which behave according to certain rules or postulates.*

It is customary to refer to a as the *real part* of the complex number $a + bi$ and to bi as its *imaginary part*, and so far as the model for complex numbers is concerned we need only the following rules:

(1) *Two complex numbers are equal if and only if their real parts are equal and their imaginary parts are equal.*

(2) *The sum of two complex numbers $a + bi$ and $c + di$ is given by $(a + c) + (b + d)i$.*

---

* For a "real" application of the imaginary numbers i and $-i$ see Exercise 22 on page 126.

(3) *The product of two complex numbers* $a + bi$ *and* $c + di$ *is given by* $(ac - bd) + (ad + bc)i$.

Thus, $2 + 5i$ is *not* equal to $2 + 4i$ even though the real parts of these two complex numbers are equal, and $a - 7i$ is equal to $4 - 7i$ if and only if $a = 4$. Also, the sum of $2 - 3i$ and $4 + 5i$ is

$$(2 + 4) + [(-3) + 5]i = 6 + 2i$$

and the product of these two numbers is

$$[2\cdot 4 - (-3)5] + [2\cdot 5 + (-3)4]i = 23 - 2i$$

Observe that the addition and multiplication of complex numbers is essentially "term by term." Without memorizing the expression for the product of two complex numbers, we could have written

$$\begin{aligned}(2 - 3i)(4 + 5i) &= 2\cdot 4 + 2\cdot 5i + (-3i)\cdot 4 + (-3i)\cdot 5i \\ &= 8 + 10i - 12i - 15i^2 \\ &= 8 - 2i - 15(-1) \\ &= 23 - 2i\end{aligned}$$

where we made use of the fact that $i^2 = -1$ in the next to the last step. The subtraction of complex numbers is also "term by term," and it is discussed in Exercise 17 on page 125; the division of complex numbers is explained in Exercise 20 on page 126.

We shall not devote much time to the study of complex numbers, since we shall not have the occasion to use them much in the remainder of this book. If the reader is interested in these numbers, he will find some of their further properties discussed in Exercise 18 on page 126.

EXERCISES

1. To solve the quadratic equation $1 + 2x - x^2 = 0$ graphically, calculate the values of $y = 1 + 2x - x^2$ for $x = -2, -1, 0, 1, 2, 3,$ and 4, plot the corresponding points, join them with a smooth curve, and read off the x-coordinates of the points where this curve cuts the x-axis. [See also part (d) of Exercise 5 below.]

2. To solve the quadratic equation $11 - 16x + 4x^2 = 0$ graphically, calculate the values of $y = 11 - 16x + 4x^2$ for $x = -1, 0, 1, 2, 3, 4,$ and 5, plot the corresponding points, join them with a smooth curve, and read off the x-coordinates of the points where this curve cuts the x-axis. [See also Exercise 9 below.]

3. **SOLUTION BY FACTORING.** To solve a quadratic equation by *factoring* we make use of the fact that the equation $(x - r)(x - s) = 0$ has the solutions $x = r$ and $x = s$, and that it can also be written in the form $x^2 -$

$(r + s)x + rs = 0$. Thus, we can find the solutions of any quadratic equation of the form $a + bx + x^2 = 0$ by looking for two numbers whose *sum* is $-b$ and whose *product* is a. For instance, to solve the quadratic equation $12 - 7x + x^2 = 0$ we have only to look for two numbers whose sum is 7 and whose product is 12—obviously (?), the answer is 3 and 4; similarly, to solve the quadratic equation $24 + 10x + x^2 = 0$ we have only to look for two numbers whose sum and product are -10 and 24—obviously (?) the answer is -4 and -6. Solve each of the following quadratic equations by factoring:

(a) $6 - 5x + x^2 = 0$; (d) $x^2 - 2x = 24$;
(b) $x^2 = 6 + x$; (e) $-8 + 2x + x^2 = 0$;
(c) $15 + 8x + x^2 = 0$; (f) $x^2 + 2x - 35 = 0$.

4. **SOLUTION BY FACTORING, CONTINUED.** If the x^2-coefficient of a quadratic equation is not 1, we can make it 1 by dividing each term by this coefficient. For instance, to solve $-3 - 5x + 2x^2 = 0$, we could write the equation as $-\frac{3}{2} - \frac{5}{2}x + x^2 = 0$, and then look for two numbers whose sum is 5/2 and whose product is $-3/2$. The answer is 3 and $-1/2$, but in problems like this it is often easier to proceed in a different way. We write

$$-3 - 5x + 2x^2 = (2x + ?)(x + ?)$$

and then replace the question marks with numbers by *trial and error*. Using a little ingenuity and some luck, we get $-3 - 5x + 2x^2 = (2x + 1)(x - 3)$, and the two solutions for x are obtained by putting the two factors *separately* equal to zero. Use either method to solve the following quadratic equations by factoring:

(a) $1 - 4x + 4x^2 = 0$; (c) $1 - 4x + 3x^2 = 0$;
(b) $2 + 5x + 2x^2 = 0$; (d) $1 - 6x + 5x^2 = 0$.

5. **SOLUTION BY COMPLETING THE SQUARE.** In this process we make use of the fact that $(x + a)^2 = x^2 + 2ax + a^2$, and we "complete the square" by adding a^2 to $x^2 + 2ax$. To solve, say, $21 + 10x + x^2 = 0$ by completing the square, we first write this equation as $x^2 + 10x = -21$; then we add the square of half the x-coefficient to each side, getting $x^2 + 10x + 25 = 25 - 21 = 4$, and, hence, $(x + 5)^2 = 4$. Finally, taking the square root of both sides of this last equation, we get $x + 5 = \pm 2$, and we find that the two solutions are $x = -5 + 2 = -3$ and $x = -5 - 2 = -7$. Solve each of the following quadratic equations by completing the square:

(a) $3 + 4x + x^2 = 0$; (c) $x^2 - 2x - 8 = 0$;
(b) $x^2 + 2x - 15 = 0$; (d) $1 + 2x - x^2 = 0$.

6. Use the quadratic formula to solve each of the quadratic equations of Exercise 3.

7. Use the quadratic formula to solve each of the quadratic equations of Exercise 4.

8. Use the quadratic formula to solve each of the quadratic equations of Exercise 5.

9. Use the quadratic formula to solve the quadratic equation

$$11 - 16x + 4x^2 = 0$$

10. On page 70 we said that the equation $y = 40 + 8x - x^2$ can be written in *explicit form, solved for x*. Take care of this by applying the quadratic formula to $(40 - y) + 8x - x^2 = 0$, where the "constant term" is $40 - y$. Also use the resulting equation to find the values of x which correspond to $y = 52$.

11. In connection with Exercise 4 on page 114, how many passengers would have to go on the trip to give the travel agency total receipts of \$2,904?

12. In connection with Exercise 5 on page 114, how much should the retailer charge for each of the toy cars if he wants his total profit to be \$16.00?

13. Referring to the hyperbola of Exercise 7 on page 115, namely, the one given by the equation $3y^2 + 12y - x^2 = 36$, find

(a) the values of x which correspond to $y = 3$;
(b) the values of y which correspond to $x = 9$.

14. Referring to the ellipse of Exercise 8 on page 116, namely, the one given by the equation $4x^2 + 3y^2 - 48y + 144 = 0$, find

(a) the values of x which correspond to $y = 8$;
(b) the values of y which correspond to $x = 3$.

15. In the beginning of Section 4.5 we introduced parabolas as curves which are *slightly bent* (at least, within a certain range) and, hence, suitable to describe relationships like those displayed in Figures 4.17 and 4.18. Another kind of curve which is often used for this purpose is the *hyperbola* (introduced in Exercise 7 on page 115), although the whole curve is usually turned around and shifted about so that its equation can be written as

$$y = \frac{k}{x}, \quad y = \frac{k}{x + a}, \quad \text{or} \quad y + b = \frac{k}{x}$$

where k, a, and b are numerical constants.

(a) Show that the hyperbola

$$D + 30 = \frac{1{,}000}{p}$$

provides a fairly good fit to the price-demand data of the example on page 110 by calculating the demand, D, which corresponds to $p = 19$, 21, and 22, plotting the corresponding points on a diagram like that of Figure 4.17, and joining them by means of a smooth curve.

(b) Use this hyperbola to predict the demand for the detergent when it is priced at 25 cents per box. Is this result more "reasonable" than that which we obtained on page 112 with the use of the parabola?

16. Calculate the following sums and products:

(a) $(2 - 3i) + (4 + 4i)$;
(b) $(-3 + 7i) + (1 + i)$;
(c) $(3 - 5i) + i$;
(d) $6 + (-3 + 2i)$;
(e) $(1 + 3i)(4 - i)$;
(f) $(5 - i)(5 + i)$;
(g) $i(2 - 3i)$;
(h) $(3 + i)(-2 + 4i)$.

17. The subtraction of complex numbers is also "term by term," namely, $(a + bi) - (c + di) = (a - c) + (b - d)i$. Calculate the following differences:

(a) $(5 + 4i) - (3 - 7i)$; (c) $6 - (2 + 3i)$;
(b) $(1 - 7i) - (-1 + 5i)$; (d) $5i - (2 - 4i)$.

18. Like the real numbers, the complex numbers constitute a *field*, and the identity elements for addition and multiplication are again the numbers 0 and 1 (namely, the complex numbers $0 + 0 \cdot i$ and $1 + 0 \cdot i$).

(a) Show that $-a - bi$ is the *additive inverse* (or the *negative*) of $a + bi$, and use this result to write down the negative of $3 - 2i$, $-3 + 5i$, and $2 + 7i$.

(b) Show that $\frac{a}{a^2 + b^2} - \frac{b}{a^2 + b^2}i$ is the *multiplicative inverse* (or the *reciprocal*) of $a + bi$, and use this result to find the reciprocals of $3 + 4i$, $5 - 12i$, and $1 + i$.

19. To evaluate the *quotient* $\frac{c + di}{a + bi}$ we can make use of the result of part (b) of Exercise 18 and *multiply* $c + di$ by the *reciprocal* of $a + bi$. Use this method and the results of part (b) of Exercise 18 to calculate the values of

(a) $\frac{2 - 3i}{3 + 4i}$; (b) $\frac{3 + 5i}{5 - 12i}$; (c) $\frac{-2 + i}{1 + i}$.

20. Quotients of complex numbers can also be obtained by multiplying the numerator as well as the denominator of $\frac{c + di}{a + bi}$ by $a - bi$, called the *complex conjugate* of $a + bi$. Verify this symbolically and use it to evaluate (a) $\frac{3 + 2i}{4 - 3i}$, and (b) $\frac{5 + i}{3 - i}$.

21. If the negative of the number x equals its reciprocal, show that x must be either i or $-i$.

22. Fill in the following multiplication table for the numbers i, -1, $-i$, and 1, and compare it with the multiplication table for the rotation of sales managers which we gave on page 3:

	i	-1	$-i$	1
i				
-1				
$-i$				
1				

What does this mean?

23. Use the quadratic formula to solve each of the following quadratic equations:

(a) $11 - 6x + x^2 = 0$; (d) $x^2 - 10x + 29 = 0$;
(b) $2 - 2x + x^2 = 0$; (e) $3 - 2x + x^2 = 0$;
(c) $13 - 4x + x^2 = 0$; (f) $9 - 4x + x^2 = 0$.

24. Whereas the real numbers are usually associated with the points on a line, the complex numbers can be associated with the points in the plane by letting $a + bi$ correspond to the point (a, b).

(a) Using coordinate axes like those of Figure 3.5 on page 73, plot the points which correspond to $(1 + 5i)$, $(-2 - 3i)$, $(2 - 3i)$, and $(-4 + 2i)$.

(b) What kind of a geometrical figure will we get if we draw line segments connecting the points which correspond to the complex numbers 0 and $a + bi$, those which correspond to 0 and $c + di$, those which correspond to $a + bi$ and $(a + c) + (b + d)i$, and those which correspond to $c + di$ and $(a + c) + (b + d)i$? See what happens, for example, when $a = 3$, $b = 1$, $c = 1$, and $d = 5$. Use the result to *construct* the point which represents the *sum* of $3 + 4i$ and $2 - 3i$, and read off the corresponding complex number.

4.8 SIMULTANEOUS EQUATIONS

Many situations arising in business and economics require that we study several functions of one and the same independent variable. For instance, if a company produces x television sets per week (where x changes from week to week), it may be of interest to express their total cost in terms of x, to express the profit on their sales in terms of x, to express the man-hours of labor required to produce them in terms of x, and so on. In this section we shall limit our study to the case where there are two functions of one independent variable, but later we shall run into situations where there are not only more than two functions, but also several independent variables.

A typical situation in which two quantities depend on the same variable arises in what is often called *break-even analysis*. Suppose, for example, that a company's cost of producing x television sets is given by

$$C = \$12{,}000 + \$80x$$

where the \$12,000 may be looked upon as overhead and \$80 is the direct cost (materials and labor) of producing one set. Now, if the company receives \$120 per set, its total receipts for x sets are given by

$$R = \$120x$$

and we find that cost and receipts are both *linear functions* of x; in fact, their graphs are shown together in Figure 4.29.

As its name implies, the basic problem of break-even analysis is to determine how many units the company will have to produce in order to break even. In other words, the problem is to find the value (or values) of x for which both functions—cost and receipts—have the same value. Geometrically, we can take care of this by finding the point (or points) at which the

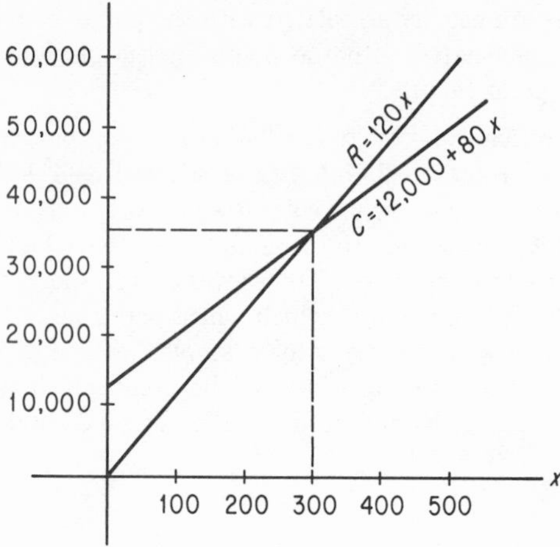

FIG. 4.29

two graphs intersect; algebraically, we simply equate the expressions which represent C and R, and in our example we get

$$12{,}000 + 80x = 120x$$

Solving this equation for x, we get $12{,}000 = 120x - 80x = 40x$, and, hence, $x = 12{,}000/40 = 300$. This means that the company will break even (cost and receipts will both equal $120 \cdot 300 = \$36{,}000$) if it produces and sells 300 sets. As can be seen from Figure 4.29, the cost will exceed their receipts if they produce and sell fewer than 300 sets, and their receipts will exceed the cost if they produce and sell more.

The two functions which we considered in this example were both linear functions, and this made the analysis very easy. Things would have been different, say, if the sets were sold at a discount of 1 percent for 100 sets, at a discount of 2 percent for 200 sets, and in general at a discount of $x/100$ percent for x sets up to a maximum discount of 8 percent. As the reader will be asked to show in Exercise 1 on page 130, the resulting receipts function will then be *quadratic* rather than linear, and to break even they will have to produce and sell 334 sets (the exact answer is $333\frac{1}{3}$ sets). To picture a situation where the cost function is also non-linear, suppose that the sets are shipped two per crate, so that the cost for crates would be the same regardless of whether they ship, say, 153 sets or 154. The situation would also be more complicated if we had to consider such things as discounts applying to bulk purchases of raw materials or the number of sets that can be produced in any one shift.

Let us now consider another important problem in which we must find the conditions under which two functions have the same value. The two functions we shall consider are the supply and the demand for a commodity, while the independent variable is its price p. The supply of a commodity generally increases with its price, the demand decreases, and the market for the commodity is said to be in *equilibrium* when supply equals demand. To illustrate how we determine the price at which the market for a commodity is in equilibrium, suppose that the supply for certain small ceramic insulators is a quadratic function given by the equation

$$S(p) = 2p + 4p^2$$

where p is the price per insulator in cents and the supply is in units of 100 insulators. Suppose, furthermore, that the demand for the insulators is a linear function given by the equation

$$D(p) = 231 - 18p$$

where the units are the same as for $S(p)$. The graphs of these two functions are shown in Figure 4.30, and it is apparent that the two curves intersect

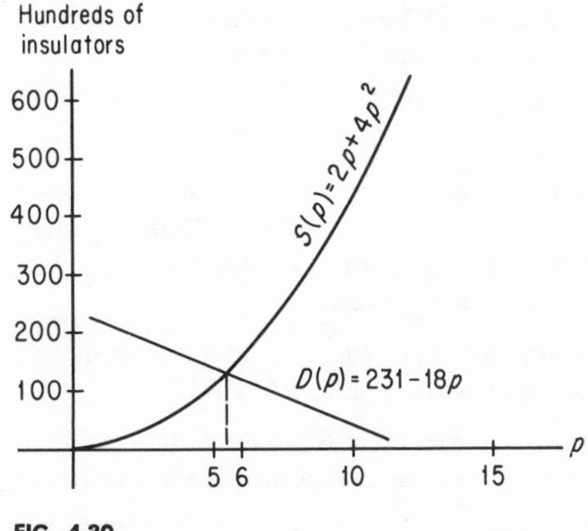

FIG. 4.30

somewhere between $p = 5$ and $p = 6$. To obtain the exact answer, we have only to equate supply to demand, namely, let $S(p) = D(p)$, and solve for p. Thus, we get

$$2p + 4p^2 = 231 - 18p$$

and after collecting terms we obtain the quadratic equation

$$231 - 20p - 4p^2 = 0$$

Solving this equation by means of the quadratic formula, we get $p = 5.5$ and $p = -10.5$, but we can obviously rule out $p = -10.5$ since this value does not lie within the proper domain. (Evidently, the price charged for a product cannot very well be negative.) We have thus shown that supply will equal demand when the price charged for the ceramic insulators is 5.5 cents, or \$5.50 per hundred; the corresponding demand is

$D(5.5) = 231 - 18(5.5) = 132$, which means that at that price there is a demand for 13,200 of the insulators.

So far we have considered problems in which the two functions were either both linear, or one function was linear and the other quadratic. In the exercises which follow, there will also be problems where both functions are quadratic, and where one function is of the hyperbolic kind discussed in Exercise 15 on page 125. In most of these exercises there will be a unique answer, that is, the corresponding graphs will intersect in only one point. When there are several possible answers, they will have to be investigated individually, to see whether one or the other can be ruled out for one reason or another.

EXERCISES

1. Referring to the example on page 127, show that if the discount is as indicated on page 128, the total receipts for x sets are given by

$$R = 120x\left(1 - \frac{x}{10000}\right)$$

for positive values of x up to $x = 800$. Also demonstrate that if this expression for R is equated to the corresponding cost which is $12{,}000 + 80x$, we get a quadratic equation which has the solutions $x = 333\frac{1}{3}$ and $x = 3{,}000$. Explain why $x = 3{,}000$ is *not* a solution to the problem.

2. A manufacturer of office equipment finds that the total cost of making 10 filing cabinets is \$380 while the total cost of making 25 is \$710.

(a) Given that the total cost is linearly related to the number of filing cabinets produced, use the two-point formula to find the equation of the corresponding line.

(b) If the manufacturer can sell the filing cabinets at \$30 apiece, how many will he have to make to break even?

(c) How many would he have to produce to make a profit of \$400? (*Hint:* equate the receipts minus the profit, namely, $30x - 400$, to the cost of producing x filing cabinets, and solve for x.)

3. A manufacturer of Christmas tree ornaments knows that the total cost of making x thousand ornaments of a certain kind is given by

$$C = 600 + 60x$$

where C is in dollars, and that the corresponding sales revenue is given by

$$R = 200x - 4x^2$$

which is also in dollars. (This implies that the price per ornament is reduced when a greater number is put on the market.)

(a) How many thousands of ornaments will the manufacturer have to produce and sell to break even?

(b) Since the manufacturer's profit is given by the difference $R - C$, his profit can be expressed in terms of the number of ornaments produced and sold by means of the equation

$$P = (200x - 4x^2) - (600 + 60x)$$
$$= -600 + 140x - 4x^2$$

where the x-units are thousands and P is in dollars. Calculate P for $x = 10$, 15, 20, and 25, draw a parabola through the corresponding points, and judge *by eye* for what value of x the manufacturer's profit will be a maximum (see also Exercise 10 on page 380).

4. The supply and the demand for a product are given by

$$S = 56p + p^2 \quad \text{and} \quad D = 120 - p^2$$

where p is the price in dollars per carton and the S- and D-units are both one thousand cartons. For what value of p will supply equal demand?

5. The supply and the demand for a product are given by

$$S = 2p + p^2 \quad \text{and} \quad D = 40 - p^2$$

where p is the price of the product in dollars while supply and demand are both in units of one thousand.

(a) Plot the graphs of these two parabolas on one diagram and read off the values of p for which supply equals demand. Which of these values is "impossible"?

(b) Equate supply and demand and solve the resulting quadratic equation for p. What is the corresponding supply?

6. The supply and the demand for a product are given by

$$S = 2p - 20 \quad \text{and} \quad D = \frac{1{,}200}{p}$$

where p is the price charged for the product in cents while the S- and D-units are both one hundred dozens.

(a) Plot the graphs of these two functions on one diagram and read off the value of p for which supply equals demand.

(b) Equating demand and supply, that is, putting $\frac{1{,}200}{p}$ equal to $2p - 20$, solve for the value of p for which the market for the given product will be in equilibrium. What is the corresponding supply?

4.9 POLYNOMIAL FUNCTIONS

Linear and quadratic functions belong to a general type of functions referred to as *polynomial functions*. They are given by equations of the form

$$y = a_0 + a_1x + a_2x^2 + a_3x^3 + \dots + a_kx^k$$

where a_0, a_1, a_2, a_3, ..., and a_k are numerical constants with a_k not equal to zero. Also, k is a positive integer which we call the *degree* of the polynomial function. Note that for $k = 1$ and $k = 2$ we get

$$y = a_0 + a_1x$$

and

$$y = a_0 + a_1x + a_2x^2$$

which means that in these special cases the polynomial functions are linear and quadratic.

In contrast to linear and quadratic functions, polynomial functions of degree higher than 2 have graphs which can turn up and down several times; Figure 4.31, for example, shows the graph of

$$y = 5 + 24x - 50x^2 + 35x^3 - 10x^4 + x^5$$

and it can be seen that the graph turns (changes from going up to going down, or vice versa) 4 times.

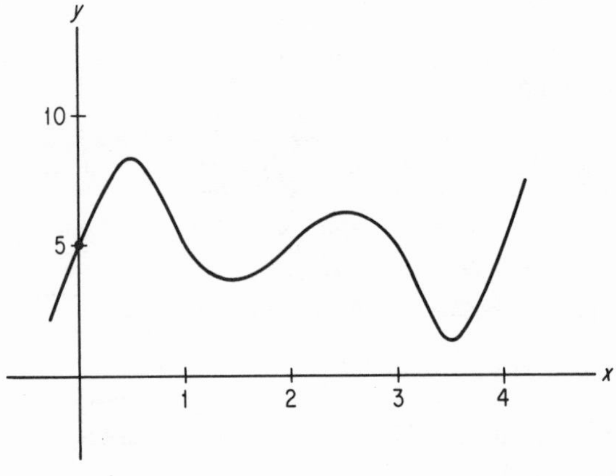

FIG. 4.31

Polynomial functions of degree higher than two or three do not arise in many business applications, and we shall not study them here in any detail. However, in later chapters we shall use them to illustrate some of the basic techniques of differentiation and integration.

5

EXPONENTIAL AND LOGARITHMIC FUNCTIONS

5.1 INTRODUCTION

In this chapter we shall study *exponential functions,* and their inverses, the corresponding *logarithmic functions.* Whereas exponential functions provide important models for the description of economic growth (or for that matter, most any kind of growth), logarithmic functions are usually studied because of the role which they play in numerical computations. Before we investigate these special kinds of functions, we shall devote a section to the so-called *laws of exponents,* with which most readers are probably familiar from elementary algebra. Nevertheless, some of the material of Section 5.2 (particularly, that dealing with non-integral exponents) may be new.

5.2 LAWS OF EXPONENTS

The exponential notation is a mathematical kind of shorthand which dates back to the early 17th century; it saves space and time, and it makes it easy, or at least easier, to write otherwise unwieldy expressions. Formally, *if n is a positive integer, we write*

$$b^n = \underbrace{b \cdot b \cdot b \cdot \ldots \cdot b}_{n \text{ factors}}$$

for any real number b. Here n is called the *exponent of b,* and we read b^n as "the nth power of b" or as "b raised to the power n." (Later on, we shall generalize this definition so that we can speak of b^n even when n is not necessarily a positive integer.) The exponential notation immediately found wide acceptance among mathematicians, who soon discovered that there are certain rules about the manipulation of exponents which provide extraordinary simplifications. For instance, there is the rule which tells us that we can multiply two powers of the same number by simply adding their exponents; symbolically, *if m and n are two positive integers, then*

$$b^m \cdot b^n = b^{m+n}$$

for any real number b. To prove this rule we have only to observe that

$$b^m \cdot b^n = \underbrace{(b \cdot b \cdot \ldots \cdot b)}_{m \text{ factors}} \underbrace{(b \cdot b \cdot \ldots \cdot b)}_{n \text{ factors}} = \underbrace{b \cdot b \cdot b \cdot \ldots \cdot b}_{m+n \text{ factors}} = b^{m+n}$$

Another important rule tells us to *multiply the exponents* when a number raised to a power is, itself, raised to a power; symbolically, *if m and n are positive integers, then*

$$(b^m)^n = b^{m \cdot n}$$

for any real number b. To prove this rule, we have only to write out in full what each of the two expressions mean.

Several other useful rules of exponents will be given in Exercise 1 on page 138, but the only other rule we shall consider here is the one which tells us to *subtract exponents* when we want to divide two powers of the same number; symbolically, *if m and n are positive integers and m is greater than n*, then

$$\frac{b^m}{b^n} = b^{m-n}$$

for any non-zero real number b. To prove this rule we have only to observe that after all common factors are cancelled, we are left with $m - n$ factors (each equal to b) in the numerator, and a 1 in the denominator.

To illustrate some of the simplifications that are brought about by the use of exponents, let us evaluate the quantity $\dfrac{8 \cdot 256}{32 \cdot 4}$, where each of the four numbers can be expressed as a power of 2. Substituting 2^3 for 8, 2^8 for 256, 2^5 for 32, and 2^2 for 4, we get

$$\frac{8 \cdot 256}{32 \cdot 4} = \frac{2^3 2^8}{2^5 2^2} = \frac{2^{11}}{2^7} = 2^{11-7} = 2^4 = 16$$

Things would not have worked out so nicely if we had wanted to evaluate, say, $\dfrac{8 \cdot 253}{31 \cdot 7}$, where there is no obvious way of expressing the four numbers as powers of one and the same number. As we shall see in Section 5.6, however, the exponential notation can be used to great advantage even in problems of this kind.

Now let us suppose that we *erroneously* apply the rule according to which we subtract exponents to simplify $\frac{3^5}{3^5}$ and $\frac{3^4}{3^6}$. In the first case we thus get

$$\frac{3^5}{3^5} = 3^{5-5} = 3^0$$

and in the second case we get

$$\frac{3^4}{3^6} = 3^{4-6} = 3^{-2}$$

but these results are *meaningless* so long as we limit ourselves to the definition on page 133 (in which the exponent has to be a positive integer). Note, however, that these results suggest that *if we want the rule $b^m/b^n = b^{m-n}$ to apply regardless of whether m is greater than, equal to, or less than n*, we have only to define zero and negative exponents so that

$$3^0 = 1 \qquad \text{and} \qquad 3^{-2} = \frac{1}{3^2}$$

which are the results we should actually have obtained for $3^5/3^5$ and $3^4/3^6$. Thus, let us make the following definition:*

If b is a non-zero real number, then $b^0 = 1$, and if furthermore k is a positive integer, then $b^{-k} = 1/b^k$.

With this definition we have extended the concept of an exponent to the set of all integers, and it is easy to verify that the various laws (the three which we gave in the text and the ones of Exercise 1 on page 138) still hold. Using these laws to simplify

$$\frac{(7^2)^3(7^{-5})^2}{7^3(7^4)^{-2}7^0}$$

for instance, and working first separately with the numerator and the denominator, we get

$$\frac{(7^2)^3(7^{-5})^2}{7^3(7^4)^{-2}7^0} = \frac{7^6 7^{-10}}{7^3 7^{-8}\cdot 1} = \frac{7^{-4}}{7^{-5}} = 7^{(-4)\,-\,(-5)} = 7^1 = 7$$

Actually, one of the main objectives of this section is to generalize the concept of an exponent so that it can be any *real number*, not merely a whole number or an integer. Keeping this goal in mind, let us now investigate

---

* We exclude $b = 0$ from the first part of this definition as it might lead to confusion and contradictions in more advanced work if we wrote $0^0 = 1$.

what meaning we might assign to expressions such as $4^{1/2}$, $7^{3/4}$, or $5^{13/11}$, where the exponent is in each case a fraction. Let us see, for example, whether there is any reason for assigning a particular meaning to $4^{1/2}$, keeping in mind, of course, that we do not want to violate any of the laws of exponents which we have already discussed. If the rule which tells us to *multiply exponents* is to apply to exponents of this kind, we must be able to write

$$(4^{\frac{1}{2}})^2 = 4^{\frac{1}{2}\cdot 2} = 4^1 = 4$$

and we find that $4^{1/2}$ is a number whose square equals 4—in other words, $4^{1/2}$ is a *square root* of 4. We said "*a* square root" rather than "*the* square root," because there are two square roots of 4, $+2$ and -2, and either one would do the trick. Having to make a choice, though, we shall say that $4^{1/2}$ denotes $+2$ rather than -2. More generally, this argument (and also that of Exercise 5 on page 138) suggests the following definition:*

> *If b is a positive real number and n is a positive integer, then $b^{1/n}$ is the positive nth root of b, which is ordinarily written $\sqrt[n]{b}$.*

Thus, $64^{1/2} = 8$, $125^{1/3} = 5$, $81^{1/4} = 3$, and $1{,}024^{1/10} = 2$. (Incidentally, in case the reader is not familiar with the terminology which we used in this definition, the "positive nth root of b" is the positive number x which is such that $x^n = b$. In our four examples, 8, 5, 3, and 2 are all positive numbers and $8^2 = 64$, $5^3 = 125$, $3^4 = 81$, and $2^{10} = 1{,}024$.)

We are now ready to consider expressions of the form $b^{p/q}$, where b is a positive real number and p and q are positive integers. If the rule according to which we *multiply exponents* is to apply to exponents of this kind, we must be able to write

$$b^{p/q} = (b^p)^{1/q} \qquad \text{and} \qquad b^{p/q} = (b^{1/q})^p$$

and we thus have *two* interpretations of $b^{p/q}$—it can be looked upon as the qth root of b^p or as the pth power of the qth root of b. Actually, these two interpretations are equivalent, and we can use whichever is the most convenient in any given situation. For instance, to evaluate $81^{3/4}$ we could write

$$81^{3/4} = (81^3)^{1/4} = (531{,}441)^{1/4} = \sqrt[4]{531{,}441} = 27$$

but it is obviously much easier to write

$$81^{3/4} = (81^{1/4})^3 = (\sqrt[4]{81})^3 = 3^3 = 27$$

---

* This definition can be extended to the case where b is negative provided that n is *odd* (see Exercise 7 on page 138), but we shall not have the occasion to use it in this text.

On the other hand, if we wanted to find the value of $2^{5/2}$, we would probably get a *better approximation* by looking up the square root of $2^5 = 32$ in Table V at the end of this book; of course, the other alternative is to look up the square root of 2 and raise it to the 5th power.

To complete our definition of *rational exponents,* we still have to take care of expressions such as $125^{-1/3}$ or $32^{-3/5}$, but if we extend the definition of negative exponents (on page 135) so that it applies also when k is a fraction, we can write

$$125^{-1/3} = \frac{1}{125^{1/3}} = \frac{1}{5} \qquad \text{and} \qquad 32^{-3/5} = \frac{1}{32^{3/5}} = \frac{1}{2^3} = \frac{1}{8}$$

It can easily be checked that with this definition of negative fractional exponents all of the special laws of exponents will still apply.

To complete the job we set out to do in this section, we still have to explain what we mean by *irrational exponents,* namely, what we mean by expressions such as $3^{\sqrt{2}}$ or 5^{π}, where π is the irrational number which arises in connection with the area (or the circumference) of a circle. To take care of this, we have only to write the two exponents in the decimal notation, namely, as

$$\sqrt{2} = 1.414214\ldots \qquad \text{and} \qquad \pi = 3.14159\ldots$$

The two quantities we are trying to evaluate can then be written as

$$3^{\sqrt{2}} = 3^{1.414214\ldots} \qquad \text{and} \qquad 5^{\pi} = 5^{3.14159\ldots}$$

and they can be approximated to any desired degree of accuracy by carrying a sufficient number of decimals. For instance, $3^{\sqrt{2}}$ can be approximated by evaluating

$$\begin{aligned} 3^{1.414} &= 3^{1+\frac{4}{10}+\frac{1}{100}+\frac{4}{1000}} \\ &= 3\left(3^{\frac{4}{10}}\right)\left(3^{\frac{1}{100}}\right)\left(3^{\frac{4}{1000}}\right) \end{aligned}$$

where each factor consists of 3 raised to an integral or fractional power. As we shall see on page 158, where we shall actually evaluate $3^{1.414}$, the answer is approximately 4.73. Similarly, 5^{π} can be approximated by evaluating

$$\begin{aligned} 5^{3.1416} &= 5^{3+\frac{1}{10}+\frac{4}{100}+\frac{1}{1000}+\frac{6}{10000}} \\ &= 5^3\left(5^{\frac{1}{10}}\right)\left(5^{\frac{4}{100}}\right)\left(5^{\frac{1}{1000}}\right)\left(5^{\frac{6}{10000}}\right) \end{aligned}$$

where each factor consists of 5 raised to an integral or fractional power. Of course, the more factors we carry the closer our answer will be to 5^{π}, and as the reader will be asked to verify in Exercise 3 on page 163, the answer is approximately 219.6.

What we have given here is *not* a rigorous definition of irrational exponents, but we have indicated, at least, how expressions involving irrational exponents can be approximated to any desired degree of accuracy by means of products of numbers involving only integral or fractional exponents.

EXERCISES

1. Verify the following laws of exponents by writing each expression in full, that is, without the use of exponents:

(a) If n is a positive integer, then $(ab)^n = a^n b^n$ for any two real numbers a and b.

(b) If n is a positive integer, then $\left(\frac{a}{b}\right)^n = \frac{a^n}{b^n}$ for any real number a and any non-zero real number b.

2. Evaluate each of the following expressions:

(a) $\frac{3^4 3^7}{(3^3)^2}$; (c) $\frac{2^3(2^5)^2}{(2^4)^3}$; (e) $\left(\frac{3}{2}\right)^4\left(\frac{4}{3}\right)^2$;

(b) $\frac{(5^4)^2}{5^5 5^3}$; (d) $\frac{6^5}{2^3 3^4}$; (f) $\frac{(21)^4}{3^3(7^2)^2}$.

3. Simplify each of the following expressions:

(a) $\frac{x^3x^5}{x^2x^4}$; (c) $\frac{(x^3)^5(y^2)^4}{(x^2)^6(y^3)^2}$;

(b) $\frac{x^4x^5}{(2xy)^3}$; (d) $\frac{(x/y)^3y^4}{x^2}$.

4. Write each of the following expressions without negative or zero exponents and simplify:

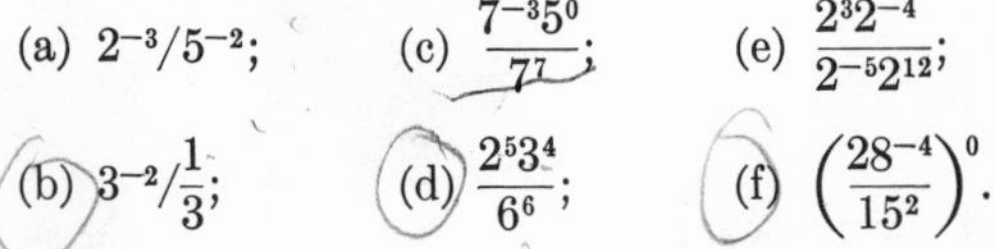

(a) $2^{-3}/5^{-2}$; (c) $\frac{7^{-3}5^0}{7^7}$; (e) $\frac{2^3 2^{-4}}{2^{-5}2^{12}}$;

(b) $3^{-2}/\frac{1}{3}$; (d) $\frac{2^5 3^4}{6^6}$; (f) $\left(\frac{28^{-4}}{15^2}\right)^0$.

5. Simplify $(5^{1/3})^3$ and $(7^{1/5})^5$ and present an argument which demonstrates that $5^{1/3}$ must be a cube root of 5 and that $7^{1/5}$ must be a fifth root of 7.

6. Evaluate each of the following quantities:

(a) $4^{3/2}$; (c) $625^{-3/4}$; (e) $\frac{9^{-2}(1/3)^4}{27^3(9^{-2})^3}$; (g) $\sqrt[4]{\frac{625}{16}}$;

(b) $(1/3)^{-2}$; (d) $16^{5/4}$; (f) $\sqrt[3]{\frac{27}{8}}$; (h) $\sqrt[2]{\frac{49\cdot 3^4}{16\cdot 5^8}}$.

7. If n is a positive *odd* integer and b is a *positive* real number, then $(-b)^{1/n} = -x$, where x is the positive nth root of b. It is customary to refer to $(-b)^{1/n}$ as the *real* nth root of $-b$ and write it as $\sqrt[n]{-b}$. For instance, $\sqrt[3]{-27} = -3$ since $\sqrt[3]{27} = 3$, and it should be noted that $(-3)^3 = -27$. Use this definition to evaluate the following quantities:

(a) $\sqrt[3]{-8}$; (c) $\sqrt[5]{-243x^{10}}$;

(b) $(-64)^{1/3}$; (d) $\left(-\frac{27}{125}\right)^{1/3}$

8. Make use of the fact that $\sqrt{3}$ is approximately 1.73 to approximate $2^{\sqrt{3}}$ with a product of integral and fractional powers of 2.

5.3 AN EXPONENTIAL FUNCTION: COMPOUND INTEREST

Any function which is given by an equation of the form $y = a \cdot b^x$ is referred to as an *exponential function;* it owes its name to the fact that the independent variable appears as the exponent of the constant b, which is called the *base* of the exponential function. In this kind of equation, a and b must be real numbers, b must not equal 1 (because this would give the linear function $y = a$), and in most practical applications a and b are both positive. The domain of an exponential function can be the set of all real numbers, or a subset consisting of, say, the positive real numbers, an interval on the x-axis, or a set of integers as in the example which follows.

A very simple example of an exponential function arises in the study of *compound interest.* As we indicated on page 96, simple interest is used mainly for short-term transactions; for long-term transactions, the interest is added to the principal at regular intervals of time and thereafter the interest, itself, earns interest. This is called *compound interest,* and the interval of time between successive calculations of the interest is called the *conversion period.* If the conversion period is one year, we say that the interest is *compounded annually,* and if we borrow (or invest) P dollars compounded annually at the interest rate i (namely, at $100 \cdot i$ percent), then the amount we owe (or have coming) at the end of n years is given by

$$A = P(1 + i)^n$$

In contrast to the simple interest formula on page 95, where the same interest ($100 \cdot i$ percent of the principal) was added each year, we find that now the interest added at the end of each year is $100 \cdot i$ percent of the principal as well as the interest which has already accumulated. To justify the formula $A = P(1 + i)^n$, we have only to observe that a year's interest on P dollars is $P \cdot i$, so that after one year the P dollars borrowed (or invested) have become

$$P + P \cdot i = P(1 + i)$$

So far as the second year is concerned, we begin with $P(1 + i)$ dollars, the interest is $[P(1 + i)]i$, and at the end of the second year the amount borrowed (or invested) has become $P(1 + i) + [P(1 + i)]i$. Factoring out $P(1 + i)$, we get

$$P(1 + i) + [P(1 + i)]i = P(1 + i)[1 + i] = P(1 + i)^2$$

and this shows that the formula holds for $n = 2$. Note that in each case the amount invested at the beginning of the year is multiplied by $(1 + i)$, and in Exercise 5 on page 142 the reader will be asked to show that this argument holds also for $n = 3$ and $n = 4$. Repeatedly multiplying by $(1 + i)$, we thus find that after n years the amount borrowed (or invested) has become $P(1 + i)^n$.

For instance, if we borrow \$10,000 at 6 percent compounded annually, we substitute $i = 0.06$ (representing 6 hundredths or 6 percent), and the amount we owe after n years is given by

$$A = 10{,}000(1 + 0.06)^n$$

After one year we owe $10{,}000(1 + 0.06) = \$10{,}600$, after two years we owe $10{,}000(1 + 0.06)^2 = \$11{,}236$, after three years we owe $10{,}000(1 + 0.06)^3 = \$11{,}910.16$, and so on.

Even though interest rates are usually quoted on an annual basis, most interest is compounded quarterly, monthly, weekly, or daily. Thus, if we are told that a bank pays 4 percent interest (on savings accounts) compounded quarterly, this does not mean that the bank pays 4 percent every three months or that it actually pays 4 percent a year, but that it pays a fourth of 4 percent, or 1 percent, every three months. Similarly, if a mortgage company charges 6 percent compounded monthly, this means that it charges a twelfth of 6 percent, namely, 1/2 of one percent, each month.

The formula which we use to calculate A when interest is not compounded annually is still $A = P(1 + i)^n$, although n is now the number of conversion periods rather than the number of years, and i is the interest per conversion period. Thus, if we invest \$5,000 at 4 percent compounded quarterly, we substitute $i = \frac{0.04}{4} = 0.01$ into the formula for A, and the amount we have coming, say, after one year (or 4 conversion periods) is

$$A = 5{,}000(1 + 0.01)^4 = 5{,}000(1.040604) = \$5{,}203.02$$

Similarly, the amount we have coming after three years (or 12 conversion periods) is

$$A = 5{,}000(1 + 0.01)^{12} = 5{,}000(1.126825) = \$5{,}634.12$$

and the amount we have coming after five years (or 20 conversion periods) is

$$A = 5{,}000(1 + 0.01)^{20} = 5{,}000(1.220190) = \$6{,}100.95.$$

In case the reader is curious to know where we got the values of $(1.01)^4$, $(1.01)^{12}$, and $(1.01)^{20}$, let us assure him that we did not calculate these quantities directly, but that we looked them up in Table I on page 560. This table is a *compound interest table* which gives the values of $(1 + i)^n$ for selected values of i and n.

As we pointed out above, if money is invested at 4 percent compounded quarterly, this does not mean that it actually yields 4 percent. This rate is only a *nominal rate,* and to find the corresponding actual, or *effective, rate,* we have to investigate what happens to \$1.00 in one year. Using the first result of the preceding paragraph, we find that the answer is $\left(1 + \frac{0.04}{4}\right)^4 = (1.01)^4 = \$1.040604$, and, hence, that the *effective rate* is 0.040604, or approximately 4.06 percent. A general formula which expresses effective rates in terms of nominal rates is given in Exercise 9 on page 142.

So far we have looked upon the compound interest function as an exponential function which is defined for $n = 1, 2, 3, 4, \ldots$. Its equation *is* of the form $y = a \cdot b^x$ [with n, A, P, and $(1 + i)$ substituted for x, y, a, and b], and there is actually no reason why its domain has to be limited to the positive integers $n = 1, 2, 3, 4, \ldots$. To extend its domain to the set of *all integers,* let us observe first of all that for $n = 0$ we get

$$A = P(1 + i)^0 = P \cdot 1 = P$$

This simply means that after 0 years (at the time the money is borrowed or invested) no interest has as yet accumulated and $A = P$. If we go one step further and substitute a *negative* value of n, we are led to the concept of *compound discount;* for instance, for $n = -10$ we get

$$A = P(1 + i)^{-10}$$

and this is the amount we should have invested *10 years ago* in order to have *now* the principal amount P. To consider a numerical example, suppose that we want to know how much money we should have invested 18 years ago at 3 percent compounded semi-annually to have a current balance of \$20,000. Substituting $i = \frac{0.03}{2} = 0.015$ and $n = -18 \cdot 2 = -36$, we find that the answer is given by

$$A = 20{,}000(1 + 0.015)^{-36} = 20{,}000(0.585090) = \$11{,}701.80$$

where the value of $(1 + 0.015)^{-36}$ was obtained from Table II, the *compound discount table* on page 564. Another way of looking at this result is that \$11,701.80 invested *now* at 3 percent compounded semi-annually will provide \$20,000 *eighteen years hence* (perhaps, to pay for a child's college education).

EXERCISES

1. If \$8,000 is invested at 3 percent compounded annually, find the value of this investment after one year, after 5 years, and after 25 years.

2. If someone borrows \$2,000 at 6 percent compounded annually, how much does he owe at the end of the first year, at the end of the second year, and at the end of the third year?

3. If \$2,500 is invested at 4 percent compounded annually, what is the value of this investment after 3 years, after 5 years, and after 20 years?

4. If \$4,000 is invested at i percent compounded annually, what is i if this investment is worth \$6,515.58 after 10 years?

5. On page 139 we showed that the formula $A = P(1 + i)^n$ holds for $n = 1$ and $n = 2$. Continue the argument to show that it holds also for $n = 3$ and $n = 4$.

6. If \$12,000 is invested at 6 percent, what is the value of this investment after 8 years if the interest is compounded (a) annually, (b) semi-annually, and (c) quarterly?

7. If \$600 is borrowed at 5 percent compounded quarterly, how much is owed (a) after 6 months, (b) after a year and a half, and (c) after five years?

8. If \$7,500 is borrowed at 4 percent compounded quarterly and \$4,000 is repaid after 4 years, how much is still owed at that time?

9. **EFFECTIVE RATES AND NOMINAL RATES.** If \$1.00 is invested at the nominal rate of r percent compounded m times a year, its value at the end of one year is $1\cdot\left(1 + \frac{r}{m}\right)^m$. Hence, the "real" interest rate, the *effective rate*, is the amount earned by the dollar during that year, namely,

$$\left(1 + \frac{r}{m}\right)^m - 1$$

What effective rate corresponds to a nominal rate of

(a) 5 percent compounded quarterly;
(b) 4 percent compounded semi-annually;
(c) 6 percent compounded semi-annually;
(d) 6 percent compounded quarterly;
(e) 6 percent compounded monthly.

As the reader can see from parts (c), (d), and (e), the effective rate increases when the interest is compounded more and more often. It does not increase without bound, however, as it can be shown that when m gets larger and larger, the effective rate comes closer and closer to the quantity $e^r - 1$, where e is an irrational number whose value is approximately 2.71828 (see page 325). This is referred to as *continuous conversion,* and in Exercises 9 and 23 on pages 329 and 450 the reader will be asked to show that if money is invested at 6 percent compounded continuously, the effective rate is about 6.18 percent, which is just barely higher than the result which the reader should have obtained in part (e).

10. Find the present value of \$3,500 due in 5 years, if money is worth 4 percent compounded quarterly.

11. Discount \$2,000 for 3 years, if the interest rate is 6 percent, compounded monthly.

12. How much should we deposit in a savings account paying 3 percent compounded semi-annually, if we want these savings to amount to \$4,000 in 15 years?

13. COMPOUND DEPRECIATION. If a property valued at C dollars is to be depreciated by the *double declining balance method* over a period of N years, it is depreciated each year by $\frac{2}{N} \cdot 100$ percent of its value at the beginning of that year. (This makes it different from *linear depreciation*, discussed on page 96, where the property is depreciated each year by the same percentage of the original cost.) Thus, the undepreciated balance is multiplied by $\left(1 - \frac{2}{N}\right)$ each year, and it follows that after n years its value is

$$V = C\left(1 - \frac{2}{N}\right)^n$$

(a) If office furniture worth \$3,000 is to be depreciated by this method over $N = 10$ years, what is the undepreciated balance after the first year, after the second year, and after the third year?

(b) Referring to Exercise 7 on page 102, what would be the answer if the school buses were depreciated by the double declining balance method rather than the straight line method.

[Since the undepreciated balance never becomes zero by this method, the Internal Revenue Service permits tax payers to switch to linear depreciation (of the undepreciated balance) at any time prior to the Nth year.]

14. COMPOUND DEPRECIATION, CONTINUED. If we subtract the undepreciated balance at the end of n years from that at the end of $n - 1$ years, we find that the amount by which the property is depreciated *during the nth year* is given by

$$D = C\left(1 - \frac{2}{N}\right)^{n-1} - C\left(1 - \frac{2}{N}\right)^n = C\left(1 - \frac{2}{N}\right)^{n-1}\left[1 - \left(1 - \frac{2}{N}\right)\right]$$

$$= \frac{2C}{N}\left(1 - \frac{2}{N}\right)^{n-1}$$

where we simplified the expression by factoring out $C\left(1 - \frac{2}{N}\right)^{n-1}$.

(a) If office furniture worth \$3,000 is depreciated by the double declining balance method over $N = 10$ years, by how much is it depreciated during each of the first three years?

(b) If the buses of Exercise 7 on page 102 are depreciated by the double declining balance method over $N = 9$ years, by how much are they depreciated in each of the first four years? If it is desirable to have high income tax deductions for depreciation during these first four years, is the double declining balance method preferable to the straight-line method, according to which the annual depreciation would be $\frac{\$180{,}000}{9} = \$20{,}000$?

5.4 FURTHER EXPONENTIAL FUNCTIONS

If the *base* b of an exponential function is greater than 1 and a is positive, the graph of $y = a \cdot b^x$ has the general shape of the graph of Figure 5.1.

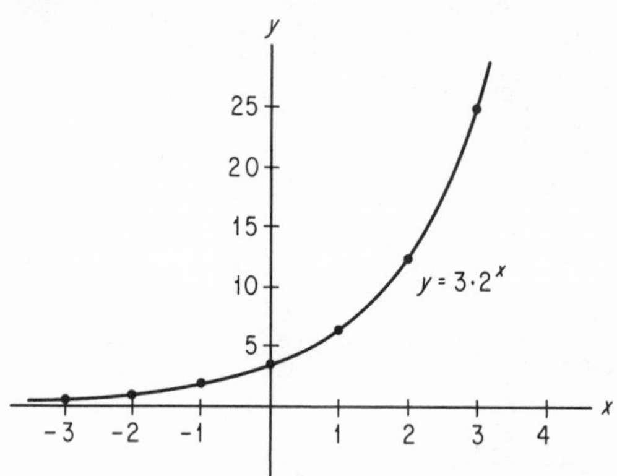

FIG. 5.1

The values of such an exponential function are never negative, and they increase as x increases; in fact, as x increases the values of the function increase more and more rapidly, and this is why exponential functions like that of Figure 5.1 are often used as models for *economic growth* (and for many other phenomena ranging from the spreading of rumors or epidemics to the growth of colonies of mice or schools of fish). It is customary to refer to exponential curves like that of Figure 5.1 as *growth curves*, and another example is the one which we fit to data on the Gross National Product in Figure 5.2.

In most practical situations, the graphs of exponential functions are not easy to plot; at least, not as easy as those of the functions which we studied in Chapter 4. An exception to this rule is the graph of Figure 5.1, since its equation is $y = 3 \cdot 2^x$ and we had to work only with powers of 2. (In fact, we drew the curve through the points for which x equals -3, -2, -1, 0, 1, 2, and 3, and the corresponding values of y are 3/8, 3/4, 3/2, 3, 6, 12, and 24.) The situation is quite a bit more complicated in Figure 5.3, which represents the same data on average family ownership of life insurance in the United

States as Figure 4.18. The equation of the exponential function which we fit to these data is

$$y = 8{,}020(1.08)^x$$

where the years are *coded* so that $x = 0$ corresponds to 1957, while succeeding years are labeled 1, 2, 3, . . . , and earlier years are labeled, -1, -2,

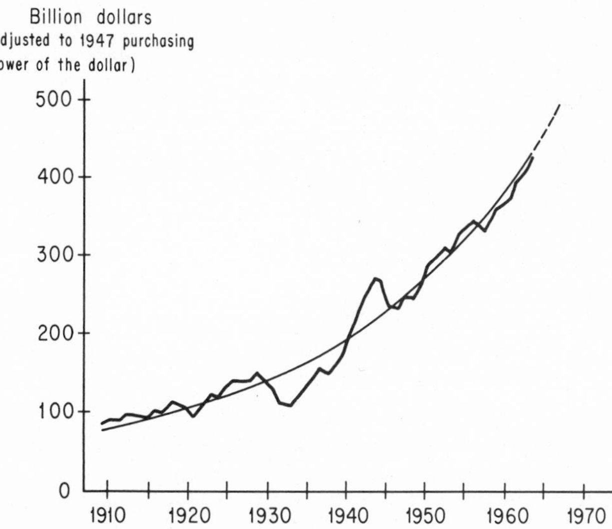

FIG. 5.2. GROSS NATIONAL PRODUCT

-3, . . . Thus, if we wanted to use this equation to predict average family ownership of life insurance in the United States in 1970, we would have to substitute $x = 13$ and calculate the value of

$$y = 8{,}020(1.08)^{13}$$

This could be done directly (namely, by multiplying 8,020 by 1.08 *thirteen times*), but in Section 5.6 we shall illustrate a much easier way of showing that the answer is approximately $21,800. In that section we shall also give a method which enables us to decide whether an exponential function is actually the appropriate model for describing a given situation.

The question of finding the equation of the exponential function which *best fits* given data will not be treated in this text, but it is discussed in most books on statistics (see, for example, the book referred to on page 165). So far as the work of this section is concerned, the reader will have to take our word for it that $y = 8{,}020(1.08)^x$ is the equation of an exponential function which provides a good model for the life insurance data of Figure 5.3.

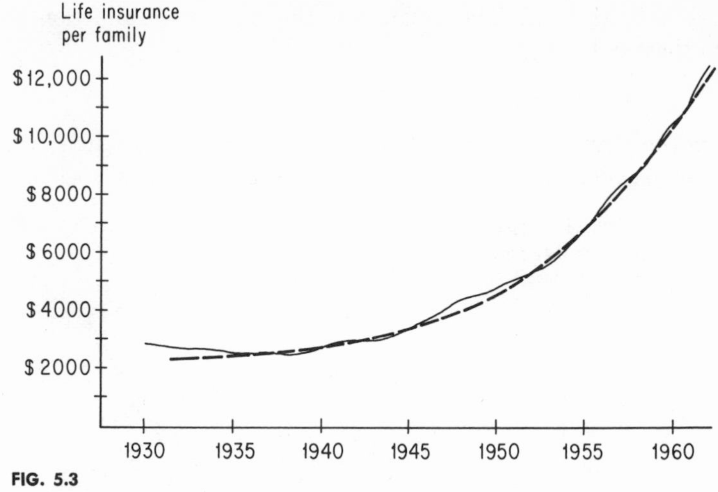

FIG. 5.3

If the *base* b of an exponential function is positive but less than 1 and a is positive, the graph of $y = a \cdot b^x$ has the general shape of the graph of Figure 5.4, representing $y = 3(1/2)^x$. The values of such an exponential function are never negative, and they decrease as x increases, getting closer and closer to zero. At the same time, the rate at which they decrease gets slower and slower, and this is why exponential functions like that of Figure 5.4 are often used as models for *economic decay* (and for many other phenom-

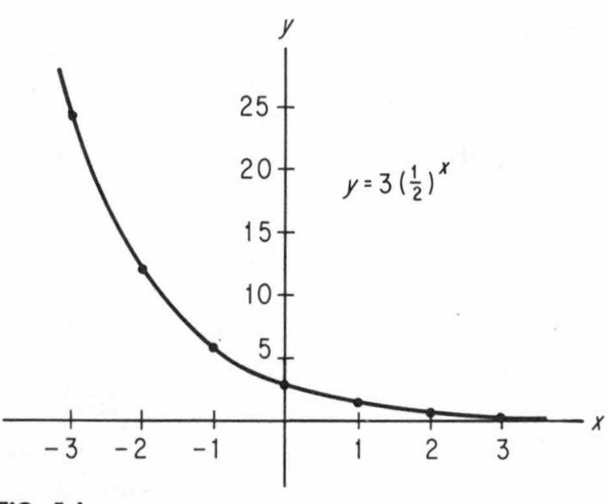

FIG. 5.4

ena ranging from the diminishing of illiteracy or infant mortality to the effect of altitude on atmospheric pressure, radioactive disintegration, and the relationship between price and demand shown in Figure 5.5). The corresponding curves are also referred to as *growth curves*, although they describe growth in an *inverse* sense, namely, in the sense of depreciation, wear and tear, wasting away, or decay.

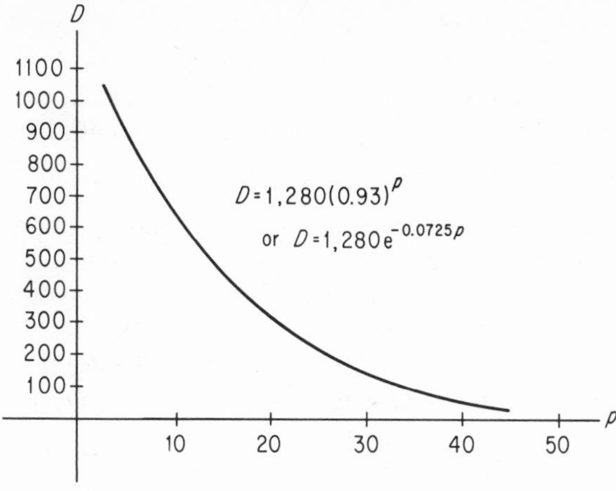

FIG. 5.5

As in the case where b is greater than 1, the graphs of these functions are generally not easy to plot. The demand curve of Figure 5.5 has the equation

$$D = 1{,}280(0.93)^p$$

where D is the demand (say, for a new cake mix) and p is its price in cents. It is apparent from this equation that it would be quite a job to calculate D for any given value of p unless we can use some computational simplification. Such simplifications do exist, and they will be described later in Section 5.6.

When we deal with growth curves describing depreciation or decay (namely, when the *base* b of an exponential function is less than 1), it is common practice to make the exponent *negative* by changing to the base $1/b$. The equation of the function whose graph is shown in Figure 5.4 can thus be changed from

$$y = 3(1/2)^x \qquad \text{to} \qquad y = 3 \cdot 2^{-x}$$

Similarly, the equation of the function whose graph is shown in Figure 5.5 can be changed from

$$D = 1{,}280(0.93)^p \qquad \text{to} \qquad D = 1{,}280\left(\frac{1}{0.93}\right)^{-p}$$

and then to

$$D = 1{,}280(1.075)^{-p}$$

making use of the fact that $\dfrac{1}{0.93}$ is approximately 1.075.

Another modification which is often applied to the equations of exponential functions regardless of whether they describe growth or decay, is to change its base to $e = 2.71828\ldots$, namely, to the irrational number which we mentioned in Exercise 9 on page 142 in connection with the *continuous conversion* of interest. As we shall see in Chapter 8, there are certain theoretical advantages to writing the equation of an exponential function as

$$y = a \cdot e^{cx}$$

instead of $y = a \cdot b^x$, where a and c are real numbers and e is approximately 2.71828. In addition to the theoretical advantages, there is also the practical advantage that *always using the same base* makes it possible to construct widely-applicable tables (such as Table III on page 568, which gives the values of e^x and e^{-x} for various values of x). Following this practice, we could have written the equation of the price-demand function of Figure 5.5 as

$$D = 1{,}280e^{-0.0725p}$$

instead of $D = 1{,}280(0.93)^p$ or $D = 1{,}280(1.075)^{-p}$. This kind of conversion to the base e is not very difficult, and we shall demonstrate on page 162 how it is actually done.

An obvious advantage of this modification is that we can now calculate the demand which corresponds to any price p with the use of Table III. To calculate the demand for the new cake mix when it is priced at 40 cents, for example, we substitute $p = 40$ and get

$$D = 1{,}280e^{-0.0725(40)} = 1{,}280e^{-0.2900}$$

Since the nearest value we can look up in Table III is $e^{-0.3} = 0.741$, we find that the demand for the new cake mix (in the given market area) is approximately

$$D = 1{,}280(0.741) = 948.5 \text{ boxes}$$

when the price is 40 cents per box.

The growth curves mentioned so far in this section apply to situations where the values of a function increase faster and faster (as in Figure 5.1), or where they decrease, slowly approaching zero (as in Figure 5.4). This does not take care of growth problems where the values of a function increase rapidly and then level off, as might happen, for example, when the demand for a new product increases rapidly at first and then levels off. It also does not take care of growth problems where the values of a function decrease rapidly at first and then level off at a value greater than zero, as might happen, for example, when the demand for a novelty item starts out high, but decreases and then levels off. Situations like these can often be described by means of *modified exponential functions* given by equations of the form

$$y = k - a \cdot b^{-x} \qquad \text{or} \qquad y = k - a \cdot e^{-cx}$$

where a, b, c, and k are real numbers, k is positive, and either c is positive or b is greater than 1. If a is also positive, the graph of the function will be like that of the first diagram of Figure 5.6, and if a is negative it will be like that of the second.

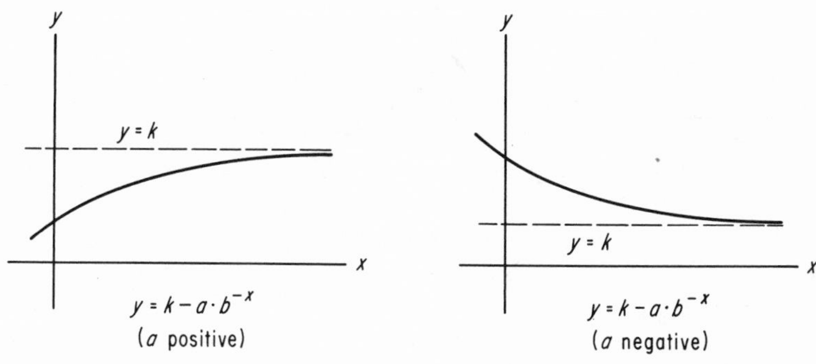

FIG. 5.6

To give a numerical example, consider the curve of Figure 5.7, which shows how the demand for a new meat tenderizer (in thousands of packages) might change with the course of time (in years). First it takes time for

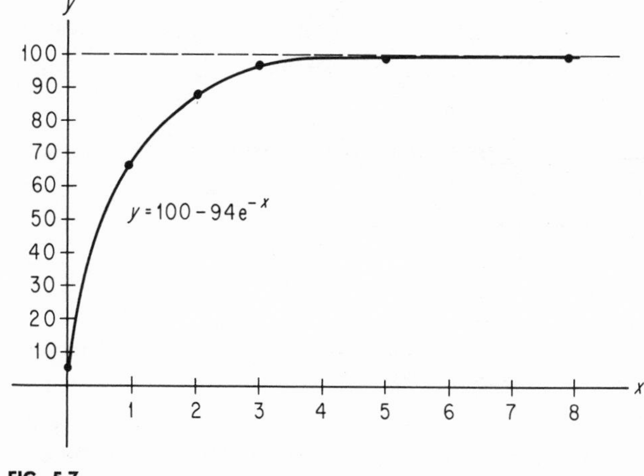

FIG. 5.7

the product to become established, but then its market becomes more or less constant. Supposing that the equation of this modified exponential function is

$$y = 100 - 94e^{-x}$$

we can obtain the values of the function corresponding to $x = 0, 1, 5$, and 8, for example, by substituting the necessary values of e^{-x} obtained from

Table III. Thus, for $x = 0$ we obtain $e^0 = 1$ and $y = 100 - 94 = 6$; for $x = 1$ we obtain $e^{-1} = 0.368$ and $y = 100 - 94(0.368) = 65.4$; for $x = 5$ we obtain $e^{-5} = 0.0067$ and $y = 100 - 94(0.0067) = 99.4$; and for $x = 8$ we obtain $e^{-8} = 0.00034$ and $y = 100 - 94(0.00034) = 99.97$. Plotting these points (and others) as in Figure 5.7, we were able to draw the curve actually shown in that diagram. Observe that the values of this function approach 100 (although they always remain slightly less), and in the language of mathematics we say that the line $y = 100$ is an *asymptote* which is approached by this modified exponential curve.

EXERCISES

1. Calculate the values of $y = 5 \cdot 3^x$ for $x = -2, -1, 0, 1$, and 2, plot the corresponding points, and (through them) draw the graph of the given function.

2. Comparing Figures 5.1 and 5.4, we find that if we viewed the graph of Figure 5.1 through the back of the paper, we would obtain the graph of Figure 5.4. What is the equation of the function whose graph we would see if we viewed the graph obtained in Exercise 1 through the back of the paper?

3. Calculate the values of $\frac{1}{4}(0.2)^x$ for $x = -2, -1, 0, 1$, and 2, plot the corresponding points, and (through them) draw the graph of the given function.

4. The *base* b in $y = a \cdot b^x$ is the quantity by which y is multiplied each time that x is increased by 1.

(a) What is the significance of the value of b in the insurance example on page 145?
(b) What is the significance of the value of b in the demand curve of Figure 5.5?

5. Rewrite the equation of Exercise 3 in the form $y = a \cdot b^{-x}$.

6. Rewrite the equation $y = 12(0.80)^x$ in the form $y = a \cdot b^{-x}$.

7. During its first five years of operation, a company grossed \$80,000, \$140,000, \$200,000, \$375,000, and \$600,000.

(a) Plot these values at $x = 1, 2, 3, 4$, and 5, draw a smooth curve which (more or less) represents the company's gross earnings, and use it to predict the amount which the company should gross during the 7th year (to the nearest \$100,000).
(b) Calculate the values of $y = 50{,}000e^{0.5x}$ for $x = 1, 2, 3, 4$, and 5, and compare these figures with the company's actual gross earnings during the first five years by plotting the corresponding points on the diagram of part (a). (*Hint:* use Table III).
(c) Use the equation of part (b) to predict the amount which the company should gross during the 7th year and compare this prediction with the one of part (a).

8. A study of the automobile tires made by a certain company showed that the proportion of tires still usable after having been driven for x miles is given by

$$y = e^{-0.00012x}$$

   (a) Use Table III to calculate y for $x = 5{,}000$, 10,000, 15,000, 20,000, and 25,000.
   (b) Use the results of part (a) to plot the graph of this exponential function.

9. Suppose that the percentage of television viewers who remember what product is regularly advertised during the daily 6 p.m. news program is given by

$$y = 100 - 98e^{-0.3x}$$

where x is the number of times they have seen the program.

   (a) Use Table III to calculate the percentages which correspond to $x = 1$, 2, 3, 5, 10, and 20.
   (b) Use the results of part (a) to plot the graph of this modified exponential function.

10. A manufacturer's annual profit from the sales of a novelty toy is given by

$$y = 8{,}000 + 30{,}000e^{-0.4x}$$

where y is in dollars and x denotes the number of years the toy has been on the market.

   (a) Use Table III to calculate the manufacturer's annual profit for $x = 1$, 2, 3, 5, 10, and 15.
   (b) Use the results of part (a) to plot the graph of this modified exponential function.

5.5 LOGARITHMIC FUNCTIONS

As is apparent from Figures 5.1 and 5.4 where the constants a and b are both positive and b is not equal to 1, $y = a \cdot b^x$ represents a *one-to-one correspondence* between the set of all real values of x and the set of all *positive* real values of y. The significance of this observation is that the *inverse* (see page 65) of this kind of exponential function is also a function—it assigns a unique value of x to each positive real value of y. In the special case where $a = 1$ and, hence, the equation of the function is $y = b^x$, the inverse of the function is so important that we give it a special name. We call it a *logarithmic function* and write its values (namely, $y = b^x$ solved for x) as

$$x = \log_b y$$

This reads "x is the logarithm of y to the base b," and in case the reader is confused by this notation, let us point out that $x = \log_b y$ is merely another way of writing $y = b^x$. In fact, it is customary to refer to $y = b^x$ as the *exponential form* and to $x = \log_b y$ as the *logarithmic form* of one and the same relationship between x and y. If we had to explain in words what we mean by $\log_b y$, we could say that it is *the power to which we have to raise b to get y*—in other words,

$$b^{\log_b y} = y$$

as can be seen by substituting $\log_b y$ for x in $b^x = y$.

To familiarize ourselves with this notation, let us work out a few examples; for instance, let us find the values of $\log_2 4$ and $\log_3 1/27$. Putting the first quantity equal to x, we find that $x = \log_2 4$ changed into the exponential form becomes $4 = 2^x$, and since $2^2 = 4$, it follows that

$$x = \log_2 4 = 2$$

Similarly, to find $\log_3 1/27$, we change $x = \log_3 1/27$ into the exponential form $1/27 = 3^x$, and since $1/27 = 3^{-3}$, it follows that

$$x = \log_3 1/27 = -3$$

What we have shown here amounts to the fact that 2 has to be raised to the power 2 to get 4, and 3 has to be raised to the power -3 to get 1/27.

It is important to remember that any question concerning a logarithmic function, its values or its graph, can always be answered by referring to the corresponding exponential function, and *vice versa*. In fact, if we wanted to plot the graph of

$$y = \log_b x$$

where b is greater than 1 (and where we have now interchanged the roles played by x and y), we have only to plot the graph of $x = b^y$. For $b = 2$, for example, we thus got the graph of Figure 5.8.

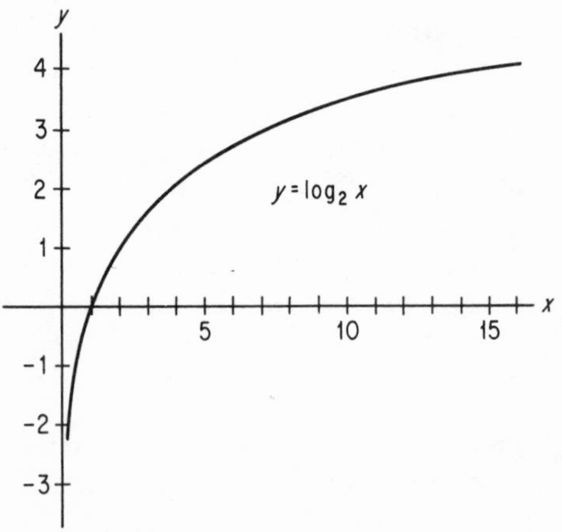

FIG. 5.8

In Section 5.2 we studied certain laws which provide considerable simplifications so far as work with exponents is concerned. In view of the close relationship between exponents and logarithms, it should not be surprising, therefore, that there are corresponding rules which simplify work with logarithms. For instance, corresponding to the first law of exponents of Section 5.2, namely, the one on page 134 according to which $b^m b^n = b^{m+n}$, we now have

$$\log_b M \cdot N = \log_b M + \log_b N$$

for any positive real numbers b, M, and N. In words, *the logarithm of the product of two numbers equals the sum of their logarithms,* and if we knew the values of $\log_b 19{,}381$ and $\log_b 216{,}778$, for example, to some base b, we could multiply these two numbers, or at least find the logarithm of their product, by writing

$$\log_b 19{,}381 \cdot 216{,}778 = \log_b 19{,}381 + \log_b 216{,}778$$

Thus, what would have been a lengthy multiplication can be replaced with a much simpler addition. Let us make it clear, though, that the above rule applies only to the logarithm of a product; some persons always manage to apply it to sums, but, unfortunately, there is no general rule for simplifying $\log_b (M + N)$.

To prove the rule concerning the logarithm of a product, let us substitute m and n for $\log_b M$ and $\log_b N$. Then, changing $\log_b M = m$ and $\log_b N = n$ into the exponential form, we get $M = b^m$ and $N = b^n$, and, hence,

$$M \cdot N = b^m \cdot b^n = b^{m+n}$$

If we then change $M \cdot N = b^{m+n}$ back into the logarithmic form, we get

$$\log_b M \cdot N = m + n = \log_b M + \log_b N$$

and this completes the proof.

Corresponding to the third law of exponents of Section 5.2, namely, the one on page 134 according to which $b^m/b^n = b^{m-n}$, we now have

$$\log_b \frac{M}{N} = \log_b M - \log_b N$$

for any positive real numbers b, M, and N. In words, *the logarithm of a quotient of two numbers equals the difference of their logarithms,* and if we knew the values of $\log_b 34{,}985{,}557$ and $\log_b 5{,}034{,}989$, for example, to some base b, we could divide these numbers, or at least find the logarithm of their quotient, by writing

$$\log_b \frac{34{,}985{,}557}{5{,}034{,}989} = \log_b 34{,}985{,}557 - \log_b 5{,}034{,}989$$

The proof of this rule is very similar to that of the first one, and it will be left to the reader in Exercise 6 on page 155.

Finally, corresponding to the second law of exponents of Section 5.2, namely, the one on page 134 according to which $(b^m)^n = b^{m \cdot n}$, we now have

$$\log_b N^k = k(\log_b N)$$

for any positive real numbers b and N and any real number k. In words, *the logarithm of the kth power of a number equals k times the logarithm of the number,* and if we knew $\log_b 1.005$, for example, to some base b, we could raise 1.005 to the 96th power by making use of the fact that

$$\log_b (1.005)^{96} = 96(\log_b 1.005)$$

Thus, the problem of raising a number to a very high power reduces to a simple multiplication. The proof of this rule, which utilizes the fact that $(b^m)^n = b^{m \cdot n}$, will be left to the reader in Exercise 7 on page 155.

In Exercise 8 on page 155 the reader will be asked to prove two other important rules according to which

$$\log_b b = 1 \quad \text{and} \quad \log_b 1 = 0$$

for any positive number b. Both of these rules are easy to prove by simply changing the equations into the exponential form. It is important to remember that *the logarithm of any number to the same base* (*namely,* $\log_b b$) *is always equal to 1,* and that *the logarithm of 1 is always equal to 0.*

To illustrate how the various rules are actually used, suppose that we are given $\log_{10} 2 = 0.3010$, $\log_{10} 3 = 0.4771$, and $\log_{10} 7 = 0.8451$, and that we are asked to evaluate $\log_{10} \frac{\sqrt{2}}{21}$. Substituting $2^{1/2}$ for $\sqrt{2}$ and $3 \cdot 7$ for 21, we get

$$\begin{aligned}
\log_{10} \frac{\sqrt{2}}{21} &= \log_{10} \frac{2^{1/2}}{3 \cdot 7} \\
&= \log_{10} 2^{1/2} - \log_{10} 3 \cdot 7 \\
&= \tfrac{1}{2}(\log_{10} 2) - (\log_{10} 3 + \log_{10} 7) \\
&= \tfrac{1}{2}(0.3010) - (0.4771 + 0.8451) \\
&= -\ 1.1717
\end{aligned}$$

and it will be left to the reader to judge which rule (or rules) were used in each step. We could go one step further and write the result as

$$\frac{\sqrt{2}}{21} = 10^{-1.1717}$$

but the problem of actually determining the value of $10^{-1.1717}$ will have to be deferred until page 159, after we shall have studied logarithms to the base 10 in some detail.

EXERCISES

1. Change each of the following equations from the exponential form to the logarithmic form:

(a) $7 = 5^x$; (c) $20 = b^4$; (e) $y = 13^{1/3}$;
(b) $y = 7^{2/3}$; (d) $155 = 9^x$; (f) $100 = b^5$.

2. Change each of the following equations from the logarithmic form to the exponential form:

(a) $x = \log_7 23$ (c) $17 = \log_b 4$; (e) $19 = \log_7 y$;
(b) $3 = \log_5 y$; (d) $x = \log_{11} 14$; (f) $25 = \log_b 7$.

3. Evaluate each of the following logarithms by putting it equal to x and changing the equation thus obtained into the exponential form:

(a) $\log_2 32$; (c) $\log_6 36$; (e) $\log_{1/2} 4$;
(b) $\log_5 5$; (d) $\log_3 \frac{1}{81}$; (f) $\log_{23} 1$.

4. Rework part (a) of Exercise 3 by expressing 32 as a power of 2 and then making use of the rule $\log_b N^k = k(\log_b N)$. Using the same idea, rework also parts (b) and (c).

5. Given $\log_{10} 2 = 0.3010$, $\log_{10} 3 = 0.4771$, and $\log_{10} 7 = 0.8451$, evaluate each of the following logarithms:

(a) $\log_{10} 42$; (c) $\log_{10} 7/3$; (e) $\log_{10} 5$;
(b) $\log_{10} \sqrt{6}$; (d) $\log_{10} \sqrt[3]{7}$; (f) $\log_{10} 1{,}764$.

(*Hint:* make use of the fact that $5 = 10/2$.)

6. Prove that $\log_b \frac{M}{N} = \log_b M - \log_b N$ by letting $m = \log_b M$ and $n = \log_b N$, changing these two equations into the exponential form, and then making use of the fact that $b^m/b^n = b^{m-n}$.

7. Prove that $\log_b N^k = k(\log_b N)$ by letting $n = \log_b N$, changing this equation into the exponential form, and then raising both sides of the resulting equation to the power k.

8. Verify that $\log_b b = 1$ and $\log_b 1 = 0$ for any positive number b by changing each of these equations into the exponential form.

9. Calculate the values of $y = \log_3 x$ for $x = 1/9$, $1/3$, 1, 3, 9, and 27, plot the corresponding points, and (through them) draw the graph of this logarithmic function.

10. Calculate the values of $y = \log_4 x$ for $x = 1/64$, $1/16$, $1/4$, 1, 4, and 16, plot the corresponding points, and (through them) draw the graph of this logarithmic function.

5.6 COMMON LOGARITHMS AND NATURAL LOGARITHMS

When we discussed the laws of exponents in Section 5.2, we pointed out that it would be easy to multiply and divide numbers if they could all be expressed as powers of some number b. In the preceding section we demonstrated how easy it would be to multiply and divide numbers if we knew their logarithms to some base b, and it should not come as a surprise that these two things mean *precisely the same.*

This suggests that we pick some special value of b, and construct a corresponding table giving the values of $\log_b N$ for various values of N. Then, we could multiply numbers by adding their logarithms (obtained from the table), we could divide numbers by subtracting their logarithms (obtained from the table), and we could raise a number to the power k by multiplying its logarithm (obtained from the table) by k. In each case, the last step would then consist of finding the number whose logarithm equals the result of the calculations (by referring to the same table).

The values of b which are most widely used for this purpose are 10 and the irrational number $e = 2.71828\ldots$ (which we first met in Exercise 9 on page 142 in connection with the continuous conversion of interest). The choice of 10 hardly needs an explanation—we are accustomed to working with powers of 10, which form the basis of the decimal notation. The alternate choice of the irrational number e is based on theoretical considerations, which we shall touch upon (lightly) in Chapter 12.

Logarithms to the base 10 are called *common logarithms* or *Briggsian logarithms,* named after the English mathematician Henry Briggs, who published the first table of logarithms to the base 10 early in the 17th century. Since logarithms to the base 10 are very widely used in simplifying calculations, it has become common practice to drop the subscript and and write $\log_{10} N$ simply as $\log N$.

Using the third rule of Section 5.5, according to which we can now write $\log_{10} N^k = k(\log_{10} N)$, the common logarithms of integral powers of 10 are easily found. Since $\log_{10} 10 = 1$ (see Exercise 8 on page 155), we get

$$\log_{10} 10^k = k(\log_{10} 10) = k$$

and it might be observed that this also follows *directly* from the definition of a logarithm as the power to which the base has to be raised to get any given number. Since $100 = 10^2$, $1{,}000 = 10^3$, $10{,}000 = 10^4$, and $100{,}000 = 10^5$, we therefore find that $\log 100 = 2$, $\log 1{,}000 = 3$, $\log 10{,}000 = 4$, and $\log 100{,}000 = 5$, and since $0.1 = 10^{-1}$, $0.01 = 10^{-2}$, $0.001 = 10^{-3}$, and $0.0001 = 10^{-4}$, we find that $\log 0.1 = -1$, $\log 0.01 = -2$, $\log 0.001 = -3$, and $\log 0.0001 = -4$. Also, $\log 10^0 = \log 1 = 0$, since $\log_b 1 = 0$ for any base b (see Exercise 8 on page 155), and, of course, $\log 10 = 1$.

When we work with common logarithms, we continually make use of these results in conjunction with the fact *that if one (positive real) number is greater than another, its logarithm is also greater than that of the other.** Thus, since 52.4 is greater than 10 but less than 100, we conclude that log 52.4 is greater than 1 but less than 2. Similarly, since 0.043 lies between 0.01 and 0.1, we conclude that log 0.043 lies between -2 and -1, and since 68,400 lies between 10,000 and 100,000, we conclude that log 68,400 lies between 4 and 5.

The overall size of a table of common logarithms can be held down considerably by making use of the *scientific notation* (see page 46), according to which any positive real number is written as the product of a number between 1 and 10 and an integral power of 10. This enables us to write 52.4, for example, as $5.24 \cdot 10^1$, 0.043 as $4.3 \cdot 10^{-2}$, and 68,400 as $6.84 \cdot 10^4$. Thus, all we need is a table which gives the approximate values of the common logarithms of the numbers between 1 and 10 (say, rounded to two decimals), and we will be able to look up the approximate value of $\log N$ for any positive real number N (suitably rounded, if necessary). For instance, to find log 356 we would write

$$\log 356 = \log 3.56(10^2) = \log 3.56 + \log 10^2 = \log 3.56 + 2$$

and to find log 0.0000471 we would write

$$\begin{aligned} \log 0.0000471 &= \log 4.71(10^{-5}) = \log 4.71 + \log 10^{-5} \\ &= \log 4.71 - 5 \end{aligned}$$

Proceeding this way, we can express the common logarithm of any positive real number as the logarithm of a number between 1 and 10, called the *mantissa*, plus or minus an integer, called the *characteristic*. The mantissa is usually looked up in a table (such as Table IV at the end of this book), and the characteristic is simply the exponent of 10 when the number whose logarithm we are trying to find is converted into the scientific notation.

Referring to Table IV on page 570 (in which all decimal points are omitted and the third digit is given by the headings of the respective columns), we find that $\log 3.56 = 0.5514$ and, hence, that

$$\log 356 = 0.5514 + 2 = 2.5514$$

Similarly, we find that $\log 4.71 = 0.6730$ and, hence, that

$$\log 0.0000471 = 0.6730 - 5$$

This answer could also be written as $0.6730 - 5 = -4.3270$, but *it is generally preferable to leave the fractional part of logarithms positive, so that they represent the corresponding mantissas.*

---

* This can be seen from Figure 5.8 on page 152, although we should add that the rule holds only when b is greater than 1 (which we assumed throughout our discussion).

Having explained how to find the common logarithm of any positive real number (suitably rounded, if necessary), let us now investigate the *inverse problem* of finding the number which corresponds to a given logarithm to the base 10. To illustrate how this is done, let us look for the number whose common logarithm is 3.8722. Since the characteristic is 3, we know that the number must be between $10^3 = 1{,}000$ and $10^4 = 10{,}000$, and since Table IV shows that a mantissa of 0.8722 corresponds to 7.45, we find that the answer is $7.45(10^3) = 7{,}450$. Similarly, to find the number whose common logarithm is $0.8142 - 2$, we have only to refer to Table IV, according to which a mantissa of 0.8142 corresponds to 6.52; hence, the answer is $6.52(10^{-2}) = 0.0652$.

Let us now return to the exercise suggested on page 134, and let us evaluate the quantity $\frac{8 \cdot 253}{31 \cdot 7}\cdot$ Using the rules of Section 5.5 and referring to Table IV, we get

$$\begin{aligned}\log \frac{8 \cdot 253}{31 \cdot 7} &= (\log 8 + \log 253) - (\log 31 + \log 7)\\ &= (0.9031 + 2.4031) - (1.4914 + 0.8451)\\ &= 0.9697\end{aligned}$$

and the only thing that remains to be done is to find the number whose logarithm is 0.9697. Since 9697 is not one of the entries of Table IV we use the nearest one, 9699, and we thus find that the answer is approximately 9.33.

This example did not really illustrate the advantages of using logarithms, since the calculations could easily have been made directly; all we had to do was divide $8 \cdot 253 = 2{,}024$ by $31 \cdot 7 = 217$. Thus, let us consider a different example where we really have no choice but to use logarithms—let us find the approximate value of $3^{\sqrt{2}}$ by evaluating $3^{1.414}$. To this end, we have only to write

$$\begin{aligned}\log 3^{1.414} &= 1.414(\log 3)\\ &= 1.414(0.4771)\\ &= 0.6746\end{aligned}$$

and since the nearest mantissa in Table IV is 6749, we find that the answer is 4.73. *Without using logarithms, we would not even have known how to begin looking for the approximate value of* $3^{\sqrt{2}}$.

To consider one more numerical example, let us now complete the example on page 154, where we had to stop after we showed that

$$\log \frac{\sqrt{2}}{21} = -1.1717$$

All we have to do is find the number whose logarithm is -1.1717, but we have to be careful. It would be a mistake to look for the number which corresponds to a mantissa of 0.1717, for this fractional part is *negative,* and (as we pointed out on page 157) the mantissa must always be *positive.* To take care of this, we simply *add and subtract* a sufficiently large integer, and if we add and subtract 2 in this example, we get

$$\log \frac{\sqrt{2}}{21} = (2 - 1.1717) - 2$$
$$= 0.8283 - 2$$

The nearest entry of Table IV is 8280, corresponding to 6.73, and we thus find that the answer is $6.73(10^{-2}) = 0.0673$.

Let us return now to the example on page 145, and let us verify that the *predicted* 1970 average family ownership of life insurance in the United States is $21,800. The quantity we shall have to evaluate is

$$y = 8{,}020(1.08)^{13}$$

and using the methods of this section we get

$$\log y = \log 8{,}020(1.08)^{13}$$
$$= \log 8{,}020 + 13(\log 1.08)$$
$$= 3.9042 + 13(0.0334)$$
$$= 4.3384$$

The nearest entry of Table IV is 0.3385, corresponding to 2.18, and we thus find that the answer is $2.18(10^4) = \$21{,}800$.

These calculations were quite simple, and they illustrate the fact that *it is often advantageous to change* $y = a \cdot b^x$, *the equation of an exponential function, into the logarithmic form*

$$\log y = \log a + x(\log b)$$

To make this change, we have only to write $\log y = \log (a \cdot b^x) = \log a + \log b^x = \log a + x(\log b)$.

A very important feature of this logarithmic form of the equation of an exponential function is that it expresses a linear relationship between x and $\log y$. (Clearly, if we substitute Y for $\log y$, A for $\log a$, and B for $\log b$, we get the *linear equation* $Y = A + Bx$.) Thus, *an exponential relationship between x and y is equivalent to a linear relationship between x and log y.* This makes it easy to calculate the values of an exponential function (as in the above example), and it also provides a means of deciding whether an exponential function is the *appropriate model* for the relationship between two variables displayed by a set of data. To illustrate, let us return to the insurance example on page 145, which was based in part on the figures shown in the y-column of the following table:

Life Insurance Ownership (*in* $1,000)

	x	y	$\log y$
1952	-5	5.3	0.7243
1953	-4	5.8	0.7634
1954	-3	6.3	0.7993
1955	-2	6.9	0.8388
1956	-1	7.6	0.8808
1957	0	8.3	0.9191
1958	1	8.8	0.9445
1959	2	9.5	0.9777
1960	3	10.2	1.0086
1961	4	10.8	1.0334
1962	5	11.4	1.0569

Source: Life Insurance Fact Book, 1966

Now, if we plot the values of log y (given in the right-hand column of this table) at the corresponding values of x, we get the pattern displayed in Figure 5.9, and it can be seen that the points fall very close to a straight line. This is looked upon as supporting evidence for the contention that the growth of family ownership of life insurance in the United States can be described by means of an exponential function. In other words, it justifies the use of an exponential model.

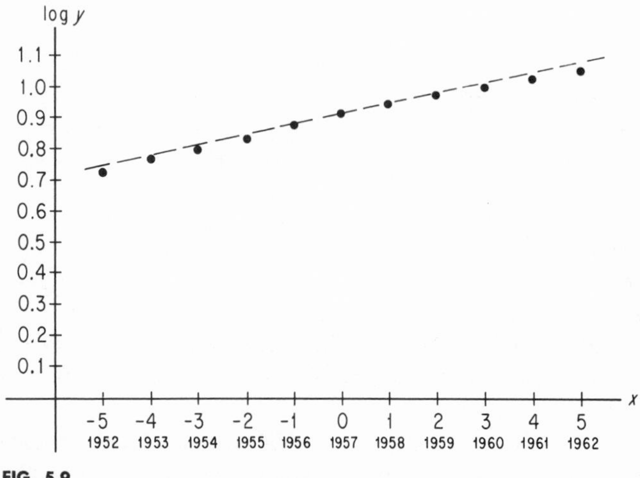

FIG. 5.9

In actual practice, the work we have just described can be simplified greatly by using *semi-logarithmic graph paper*, a special kind of graph paper which has ordinary (equal) subdivisions along one scale, while the subdivisions along the other scale are such that we *automatically* plot the logarithm of a number instead of the number, itself. If we plot our original insurance data on this kind of graph paper, as in Figure 5.10, the pattern we get is identical with that of Figure 5.9. Consequently, there is really no need to calculate the logarithms of the y's; *we can judge directly whether*

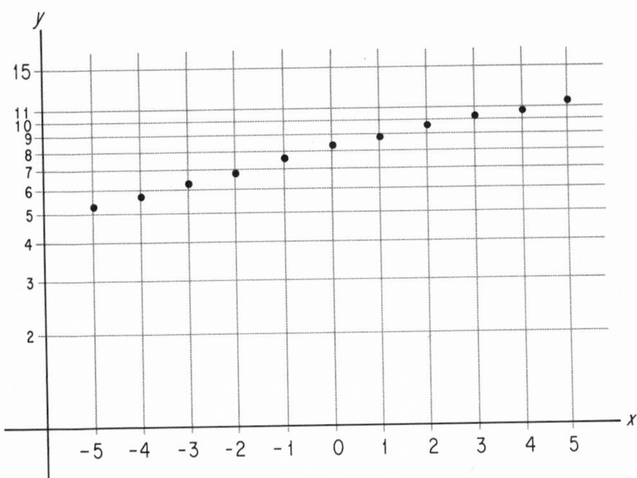

FIG. 5.10

an exponential function provides the appropriate model in a given situation by plotting the data on semi-logarithmic graph paper (which is commercially available) and checking whether the points fall close to a straight line. The same principle is used also in the *slide rule,* a mechanical device which consists of two rulers with logarithmic scales, one sliding in a groove in the other. This makes it possible to multiply two numbers by adding the distances which correspond to their logarithms, or to obtain their quotient by subtracting one of these distances from the other.

So far we have discussed only logarithms to the base 10. They are by far the most widely used in practical computations, but, as we have indicated earlier, there are certain theoretical advantages to working with logarithms to the base $e = 2.71828\ldots$. Such logarithms are referred to as *natural* or *Napierian logarithms* (named after the 16th century Scotch mathematician John Napier), and it is customary to abbreviate $\log_e N$ to $\ln N$, which reads "the natural logarithm of N." Tables of natural logarithms can be found in most handbooks of mathematical tables, but if we have only a table of common logarithms (say, Table IV), we can obtain the natural logarithm of any number by making use of the formula

$$\ln N = \frac{\log N}{\log e} = \frac{\log N}{0.4343} \qquad \text{(approximately)}$$

To prove this relationship between $\ln N$ and $\log N$, let us put $\ln N$ equal to x and change $x = \ln N$ into the exponential form $N = e^x$. If we then take the logarithm of N to the base 10, we get

$$\log N = \log e^x = x(\log e)$$

and $x = \dfrac{\log N}{\log e}$ upon dividing by $\log e$. Since x equals $\ln N$, this completes the derivation of the formula which enables us to change common logarithms into natural logarithms (and *vice versa*). A more general formula for converting logarithms from one base to another is given in Exercise 15 on page 165.

We shall not study natural logarithms in much detail, but since exponential functions are often given with the base e, let us indicate briefly how to change $y = a \cdot b^x$ so that the base of the exponential function becomes e. All we really have to do is change b^x so that it equals e raised to some power, say, e^z. Thus, $b^x = e^z$, and if we make use of the fact that the logarithms of two equal numbers are equal, we can write

$$\ln b^x = \ln e^z \qquad \text{and, hence,} \qquad x(\ln b) = z(\ln e)$$

Finally, since $\ln e = \log_e e = 1$ (see Exercise 8 on page 155), we get $x(\ln b) = z(\ln e) = z$, and we can write

$$y = a \cdot e^{x(\ln b)} \qquad \text{instead of} \qquad y = a \cdot b^x$$

where $\ln b$ can be obtained from a table of natural logarithms or with the use of the formula on page 161.

To illustrate this technique, let us refer back to the example on page 147, where the relationship between the price and the demand for a product was given by the equation

$$D = 1{,}280(0.93)^p$$

Performing the change suggested above, we can now write

$$D = 1{,}280e^{p(\ln 0.93)}$$

and, using the formula on page 161 to find $\ln 0.93$, we get

$$\ln 0.93 = \frac{\log 0.93}{0.4343} = \frac{0.9685 - 1}{0.4343} = \frac{-0.0315}{0.4343} = -0.0725$$

Thus, the equation of this price-demand relationship can be written as

$$D = 1{,}280e^{-0.0725p}$$

EXERCISES

1. Find the common logarithm of each of the following numbers:

(a) 25.8;	(e) 745;	(i) 0.00954;
(b) 0.00258;	(f) 7,450,000;	(j) $10^{2.58}$;
(c) 25,800;	(g) 1.06;	(k) 0.01;
(d) 0.745;	(h) 0.0106;	(l) 0.0000000087.

2. Find the number, the *antilogarithm*, which corresponds to each of the following logarithms to the base 10:

(a) 0.8069; (e) 1.5647; (i) 2.1367;
(b) 3.8069; (f) 0.5647 − 3; (j) 0.6946 − 4;
(c) 0.8069 − 2; (g) 0.5647 − 5; (k) −0.2000;
(d) 8.8069 − 10; (h) 7.5647 − 10; (l) −2.4353.

[*Hint:* in part (d) write the logarithm as 0.8069 − 2 and make a corresponding change in part (h); in parts (k) and (l) use the method described on page 159.]

3. Use common logarithms to evaluate each of the following expressions:

(a) $\frac{(246)(0.125)}{14.6}$; (d) $\frac{13.7}{19.8}$;

(b) $(0.158)(3.69)(12.5)$; (e) $\sqrt[2]{\frac{13.1}{17.9}}$;

(c) $\sqrt[3]{16.5}$; (f) 5^{π}, where π is approximately 3.14.

[*Hint:* in part (d) write the logarithm of 13.7 as 2.1367 − 1 before subtracting the logarithm of 19.8, and in part (e) write the logarithm of 13.1 as 3.1173 − 2 before subtracting the logarithm of 17.9. *Can you see why?*]

4. On page 140, the value of $5{,}000(1.01)^{20}$ was obtained by looking up $(1.01)^{20}$ in Table I. Evaluate this quantity now with the use of logarithms.

5. It is expected that in a certain city the number of families with incomes of x dollars or more in 1972 will be given by

$$y = 50{,}000{,}000x^{-0.4}$$

(a) How many families in this city should have incomes of $5,000 or more in 1972?
(b) How many families in this city should have incomes of $12,000 or more in 1972?
(c) How many families in this city should have incomes of $100,000 or more in 1972?

The equation used in this example, or better its graph, is usually referred to as a *Pareto curve;* it is named after the Italian economist Vilfredo Pareto who first suggested the use of curves of this kind in connection with the distribution of incomes.

6. The demand for a certain product is given by

$$D = 27.4p^{-0.48}$$

where p is its price in cents and D is the demand in units of 1,000.

(a) Find the demand which corresponds to $p = 5$, 10, 15, 20, and 25, and plot the graph of this price-demand function for values of p falling within the range for which points have been obtained.
(b) Supposing that the supply of this product is given by $S = p$, where S is also in units of 1,000, plot the graph of $S = p$ on the diagram obtained in part (a) and find the value of p at which the market for the product is in *equilibrium,* namely, the value of p at which the two curves intersect.

(c) Verify the result of part (b) by actually equating supply to demand, namely, by solving the equation $p = 27.4p^{-0.48}$. [*Hint:* simplify the right-hand side of the equation $\log p = \log (27.4p^{-0.48})$ and solve for $\log p$.]

7. An economist estimates the monthly demand for soap in a certain market area by means of the formula

$$D = 27p^{-0.68}q^{0.42}r^{0.26}$$

where p is the average retail price per bar (in cents), q is the average monthly family income (in dollars), and r is the expected average value of the Consumer Price Index for that month; the demand is in units of 1,000 bars of soap. What estimate will the economist get for $p = 14$ cents, $q = \$1{,}100$, and $r = 127.0$?

8. In an inventory problem which we shall discuss in detail on page 377, the total cost of maintaining inventory on a frozen food item is a *minimum* when the size of each order (in packages) is given by

$$x = \sqrt{\frac{2KR}{I}}$$

where K is the cost of placing an order (in dollars), R is the monthly demand (in packages), and I is the cost (in dollars) of carrying a package in inventory for a month. What is this optimum order size when $K = \$5.00$, $R = 4{,}000$ packages, and $I = \$0.25$?

9. The irrational number e can be defined as the value approached by $\left(1 + \frac{1}{n}\right)^n$ when n increases beyond any bound. Obtain a (relatively crude) approximation of e by calculating the value of this quantity for $n = 100$, namely, $(1.01)^{100}$.

10. Modify the equation $y = 8{,}020(1.08)^x$, whose graph is given in Figure 5.3, so that it will be of the form $y = a \cdot e^{cx}$. Use this result together with Table III to predict the average family ownership of life insurance in the United States in 1977. (*Hint:* the coding of the years is given on page 145.)

11. Rewrite the equation $y = 12(0.80)^x$ of Exercise 6 on page 150 in the form $y = a \cdot e^{cx}$.

12. The registrar of a university predicts each year's enrollment by means of the formula

$$y = 856(1.17)^x$$

where the years are coded so that $x = 0$ corresponds to 1950, $x = 1$ corresponds to 1951, $x = 2$ corresponds to 1952, and so on. What are his predictions for the 1970, 1971, and 1972 enrollment at this university?

13. A company's sales revenue in the years 1960 through 1968 totaled \$41,000, \$48,000, \$59,000, \$70,000, \$84,000, \$100,000, \$120,000, \$150,000, and \$175,000. Plot these data on semi-logarithmic graph paper and judge by eye whether the company's growth (so far as its sales are concerned) can be described by means of an exponential function.

14. The production of effervescent wines in the United States in the years 1950,

1955, 1960, and 1965 totaled 1.06, 1.72, 4.11, and 6.36 million gallons. Plot these data on semi-logarithmic graph paper and judge by eye whether an exponential function adequately describes this growth.

15. On page 161 we derived a formula which enabled us to convert logarithms from the base 10 to the base e, and *vice versa.* Using more or less the same steps, it can be shown that, more generally,

$$\log_a N = \frac{\log_b N}{\log_b a}$$

where a and b are positive numbers greater than 1, and N must be positive. Use this formula to evaluate (a) $\log_2 10$, (b) $\log_3 51$, and (c) $\log_{12} 3.6$.

REFERENCE

Freund, J. E., and Williams, F. J., *Modern Business Statistics.* Englewood Cliffs, N.J.: Prentice-Hall, Inc., 1958.

6

PERIODIC FUNCTIONS*

6.1 INTRODUCTION

The functions which we studied in Chapters 3, 4, and 5 provide models for many situations arising in business and economics, but they are of very little value in describing patterns like those shown in Figures 6.1 and

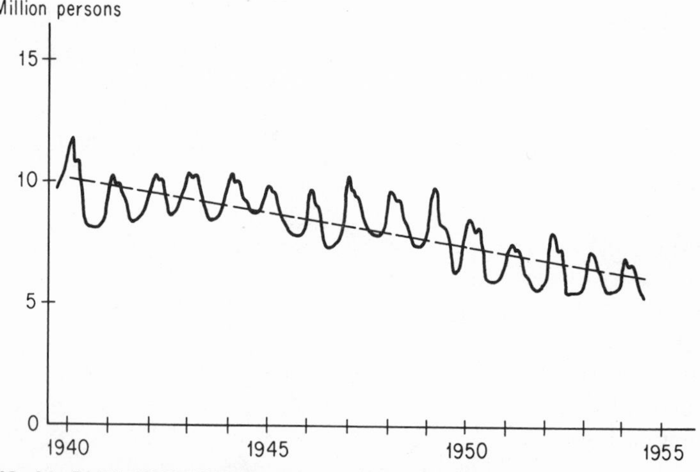

FIG. 6.1. FARM EMPLOYMENT IN THE UNITED STATES

* The material in this chapter is ordinarily not covered in courses in business mathematics, and the whole chapter may be omitted without loss of continuity. The only other references to these functions are on pages 326 and 365.

6.2. The graph of Figure 6.1 represents monthly data on farm employment in the United States, while that of Figure 6.2 represents annual figures of an Index of Wholesale Prices published by the Bureau of the Census. What characterizes these two graphs is that the same pattern (or, at least, very similar patterns) repeat over and over again. In Figure 6.1, the cycles (ups and downs) are referred to as *seasonal variations*, since harvesting is obviously a seasonal occupation, and the same general pattern repeats year after year. In Figure 6.2, each cycle extends over a much longer period

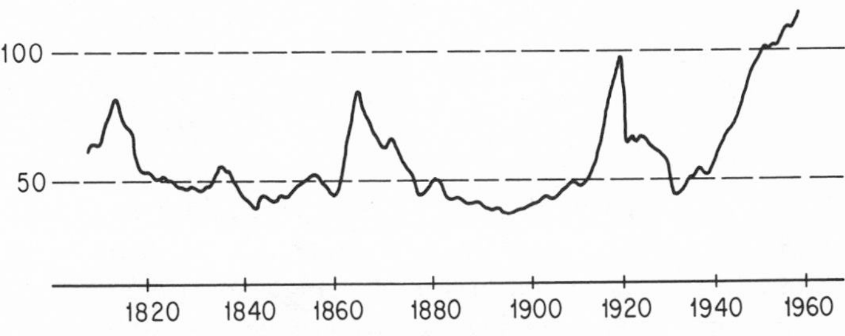

FIG. 6.2. WHOLESALE PRICE INDEX (1947-49 = 100)

of time, something like 50 or 60 years, and we refer to such long-range repeating patterns as *business cycles*. In contrast to the seasonal variations of Figure 6.1, which were easy to explain, the search for possible causes of business cycles has perplexed even the experts; their explanations vary from such profound scientific throries as the *price-dislocation theory* or the *over- and undersavings theories*, to theories which attribute cyclical patterns in economic data to spots on the sun.

In mathematics, we refer to functions which describe such repeating patterns as *periodic*, and foremost among them are the *trigonometric functions* which some readers may have met previously in the study of *trigonometry*. Ordinarily, these functions are introduced with reference to the sides and the angles of right triangles, and this is satisfactory if we are interested primarily in astronomy, surveying, or navigation; say, if we are interested in finding the distance between two stars, measuring the height of a flagpole (without climbing to its top), or determining the width of a river (without swimming across). Although this "right-triangle approach" to the trigonometric functions may be of some value in problems arising in business and economics (say, in plant layout or in assessing an irregularly-shaped piece of property), we shall look upon the trigonometric functions mainly as *models for periodic phenomena* like those displayed in Figures 6.1 and 6.2. It is with this goal in mind that we shall define the trigonometric functions in Section 6.2, and then study their graphs and some of their properties in Sections 6.2 and 6.3.

6.2 TRIGONOMETRIC FUNCTIONS

The way in which we shall introduce the trigonometric functions is more general than the "right-triangle approach," but it still involves the concept of an *angle*, which will have to be explained. Ordinarily, we think of an angle as a geometric figure formed by two intersecting lines (see Figure 6.3), or as something which is formed by two rays or half-lines

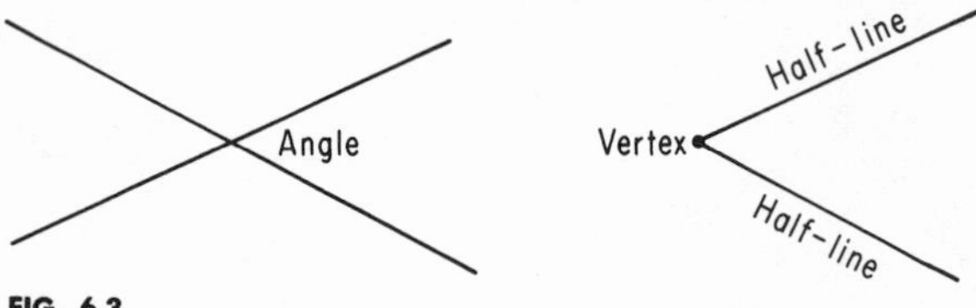

FIG. 6.3

(called its *legs*) emanating from one point (called its *vertex*). This is satisfactory for many applications, but it would not be appropriate, for instance, if we wanted to speak of the sum of two angles or if we wanted to divide an angle in half—this we can do only with numbers. To avoid this difficulty, which is largely linguistic, let us point out that it is common practice to apply the same term to a geometrical object and also to some measure relating to its size. Euclid, himself, used the term "diameter" referring either to a line or to a measure of its length; similarly, we often speak of the side of a triangle as a line segment or as a number representing its length, and we speak of an area as a geometrical figure or as a quantity measuring its size. Thus, when we speak about angles in this chapter, we shall be referring mostly to *angular measurements*, or *amounts of rotation*, namely, the amount of rotation that is required to make one of the half-lines of Figure 6.3 coincide with the other. To make it clear which half-line is to be rotated to coincide with the other (namely, in what *sense* the rotation is to be performed), it is customary to use arrows as in Figure 6.4.

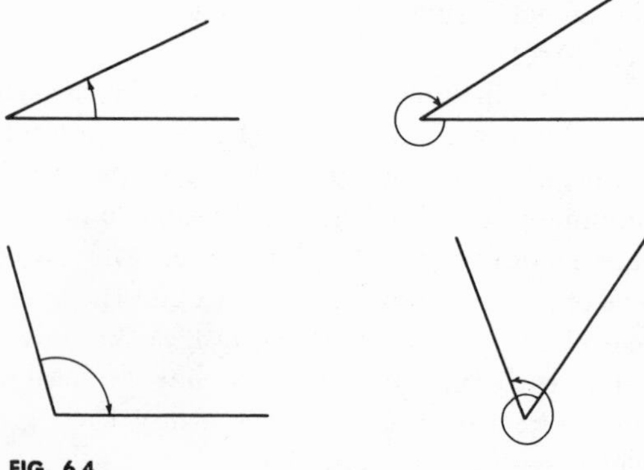

FIG. 6.4

The most common units of angular measurement were introduced by the Babylonians, or perhaps even earlier civilizations. They divided a complete revolution into 360 equal parts which we now call *degrees*. Thus, half a revolution is equivalent to 180 degrees, which we write as 180°,

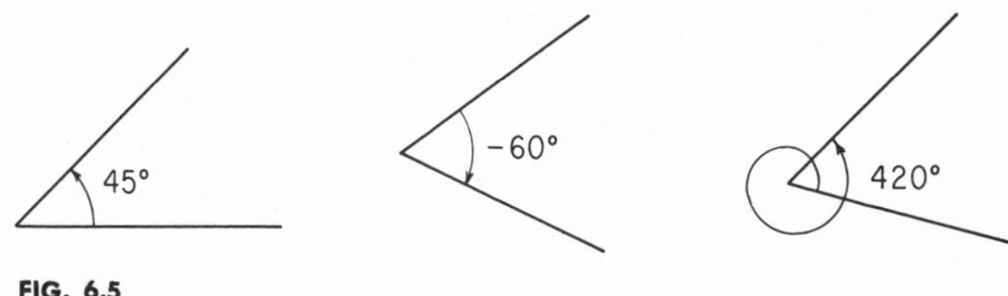

FIG. 6.5

a quarter of a revolution is equivalent to 90 degrees, a tenth of a revolution is 36°, and so on. Furthermore, to distinguish between angles representing *clockwise* and *counterclockwise* rotations, we treat them, respectively, as *negative* and as *positive* amounts of rotation (see Figure 6.5).

An alternate scale for measuring angles is based on the fact that the circumference of a circle with the radius 1 is equal to 2π, where π is an irrational number whose value is approximately 3.1416. A complete revolution is thus identified with an arc length of 2π, and any fractional part of a revolution is identified with the corresponding fraction of 2π. Referring to these new units as *radians*, we can thus say that 360 degrees are equivalent to 2π radians, that a 90 degree angle is equivalent to one of $\pi/2$ radians, that $-30°$ is equivalent to $-\pi/12$ radians, and that 1 degree is equivalent to $\frac{1}{360}\cdot 2\pi = \frac{\pi}{180}$ (or, approximately, 0.01745) radians. There are certain advantages to working with radians which will be explained in Chapter 11 and 12; in this chapter we shall use both kinds of units, though mostly degrees. (Actually, the practice of using different kinds of units for measurnig the same kind of quantity is very common; lengths are measured in centimeters and in inches, temperatures in degrees Fahrenheit and in degrees Centigrade, weights are measured in ounces and in grams, etc.)

Before we introduce the trigonometric functions, which comes next, let us agree to certain conventions. Whenever possible, we shall draw angles as in Figure 6.6, so that one leg (the one from which the arrow emanates) coincides with the horizontal x-axis and the vertex is at the origin. Furthermore, we shall represent angles (that is, angular measures) by means of Greek letters, mostly the letter θ (*theta*). These conventions were followed in Figure 6.7, where we also drew a circle with the radius 1 and its center at the origin. Now, if we let P denote the point at which this circle intersects the "rotating leg" of angle θ, it is apparent from Figure 6.7 that its coordinates x and y will vary with θ. There is a unique value of x and a

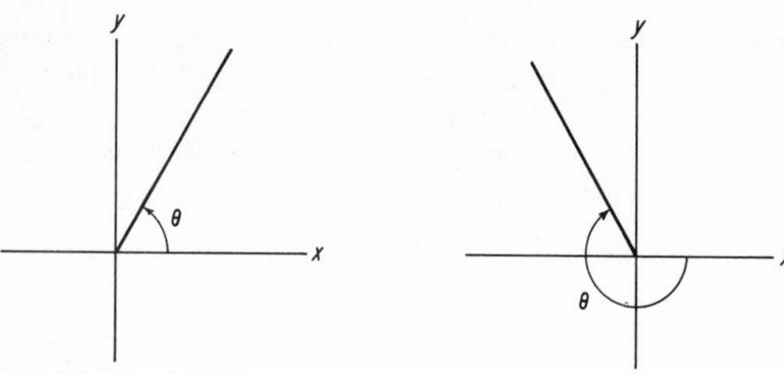

FIG. 6.6

unique value of y for each angle θ, and this means that the correspondence between θ and x and the correspondence between θ and y are both *functions*.

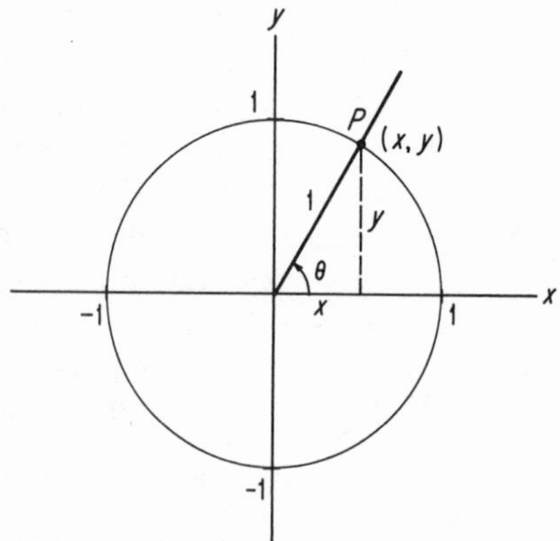

FIG. 6.7

Not only that, but the correspondences are both *many-to-one*, as is apparent from Figure 6.8, where the same point P and, hence, the same values of x and y, correspond to different angles θ.

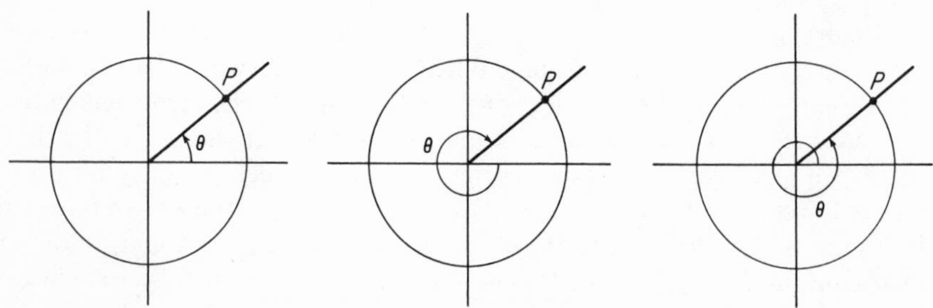

FIG. 6.8

Both of these relationships are referred to as *trigonometric functions.* The one between θ and y is called the *sine function,* and its equation is written as

$$y = \sin \theta$$

where $\sin \theta$ is pronounced "sine θ," with "sine" rhyming with "mine." The relationship between θ and x is referred to as the *cosine function,* and its equation is written as

$$x = \cos \theta$$

where $\cos \theta$ is pronounced "cosine θ." Note that in each case the *domain* of the independent variable θ is the set of all real numbers; the two dependent variables are y and x, and their *range* is the interval from -1 to $+1$. This is apparent from Figure 6.7, where x and y are two sides of a right triangle whose greatest side, the hypothenuse, is equal to 1.

Before we introduce any of the other basic trigonometric functions (altogether, there are *six*), let us indicate first how we can find some of the values of the two functions already defined and, thus, plot their graphs. To begin with, let us point out that the sine function as well as the cosine function are *periodic functions* with a *period* of 360 degrees (or 2π radians). That is, the pattern of the graphs will repeat every 360° (or 2π radians), as is apparent from Figure 6.8, where we get the *same* point P and, hence, the *same* values of x and y when we add to θ any integral multiple of 360° (or 2π radians). For instance, 30° leads to the same point P as 390°, 750°, 1,110°, . . . , or $-330°$, $-690°$, $-1{,}050°$, . . . , and, hence, to the same values of x and y. Thus, if we plot the graph of the sine function or the cosine function from $\theta = 0°$ to $\theta = 360°$, we can complete the picture by repeating the same pattern over and over again.

An obvious way of evaluating $\sin \theta$ and $\cos \theta$ for any given value of θ would be to draw the angle as in Figure 6.7, draw a circle with the radius 1 (*one* inch, *one* centimeter, *one* foot, . . .), and then measure the coordinates of the point P. [It is important, of course, that the radius of the circle be 1, but if the radius of the only circle we can draw (say, by using a silver dollar or the rim of a glass) does not equal one of the common units of measurement, we can nevertheless find $\sin \theta$ and $\cos \theta$ by proceeding as in Exercise 12 on page 179.] In actual practice, the values of trigonometric functions are obtained in this way only if they can be read off by inspection, or if they follow from simple geometrical considerations; otherwise, they are obtained from tables or they are calculated by means of special formulas (see Section 11.4). Some of the values that can be read off by inspection are those corresponding to $\theta = 0$, 90, 180, 270, and 360 degrees. As can be seen from Figure 6.9, the coordinates of point P are $(1, 0)$, $(0, 1)$, $(-1, 0)$, and $(0, -1)$ corresponding to $\theta = 0$, $\theta = 90$, $\theta = 180$, and $\theta = 270$, so that

$$\sin 0 = 0 \text{ and } \cos 0 = 1$$
$$\sin 90 = 1 \text{ and } \cos 90 = 0$$
$$\sin 180 = 0 \text{ and } \cos 180 = -1$$
$$\sin 270 = -1 \text{ and } \cos 270 = 0$$

There is no need to draw a separate picture for $\theta = 360°$, since $\sin 360 = \sin 0 = 0$ and $\cos 360 = \cos 0 = 1$.

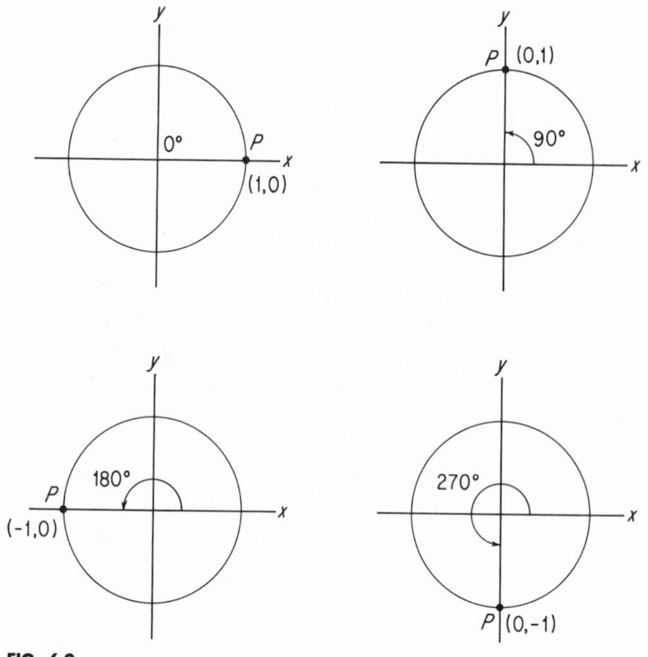

FIG. 6.9

To illustrate how the values of $\sin \theta$ and $\cos \theta$ can sometimes be obtained by means of simple geometrical considerations, let us take $\theta = 45°$. As can be seen from the first diagram of Figure 6.10, the triangle OPQ is an *isosceles right triangle* (namely, a right triangle in which the other two angles are equal), and since sides opposite equal angles are also equal, it follows that $y = x$. Thus, if we apply the Pythagorean theorem to the triangle OPQ, we get $x^2 + x^2 = 1$, $2x^2 = 1$, and, therefore, $x = \sqrt{1/2}$. This square root is approximately 0.7071 (see Table V), so that we have

$$\sin 45 = 0.7071 \quad \text{and} \quad \cos 45 = 0.7071$$

It can also be seen from the two diagrams of Figure 6.10 that the

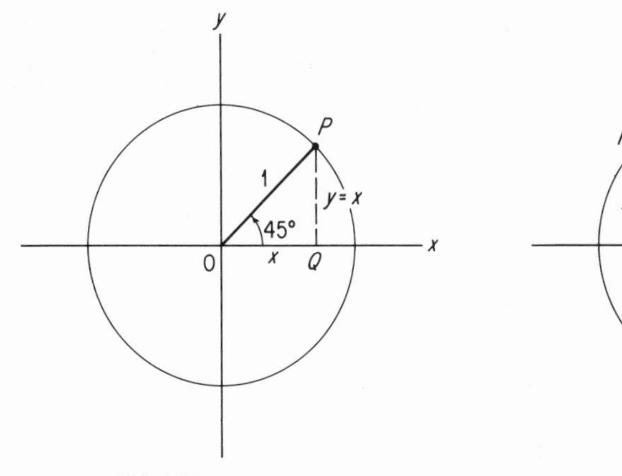

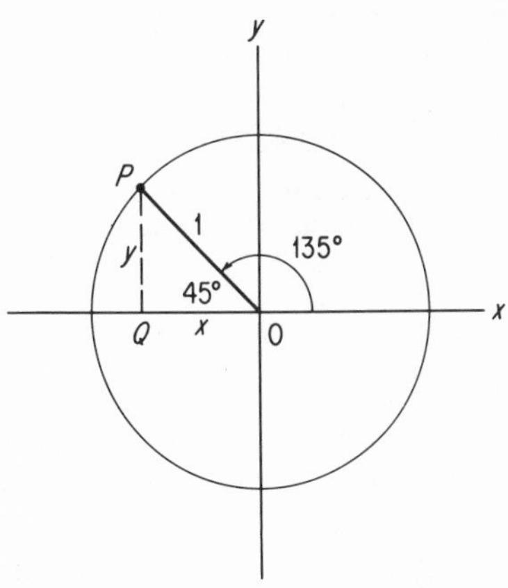

FIG. 6.10

y-coordinates of the points P are the same for 45° and 135°, while the x-coordinates are equal in magnitude but opposite in sign. Thus,

$$\sin 135 = 0.7071 \quad \text{and} \quad \cos 135 = -0.7071$$

and it will be left to the reader to show in Exercise 6 on page 177 that similar arguments lead to $\sin 225 = -0.7071$, $\cos 225 = -0.7071$, $\sin 315 = -0.7071$, and $\cos 315 = 0.7071$.

Using all of the values of $\sin\theta$ and $\cos\theta$ which we have already determined, we can now draw the graphs of these two functions as in Figure 6.11. In each case, the pattern from $\theta = 0$ to $\theta = 360$ is repeated again

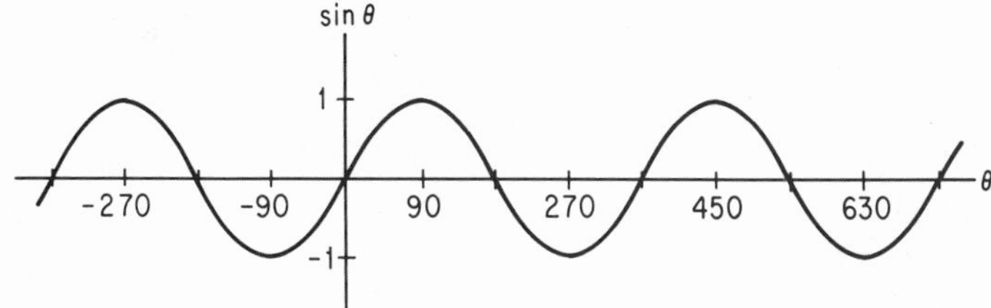

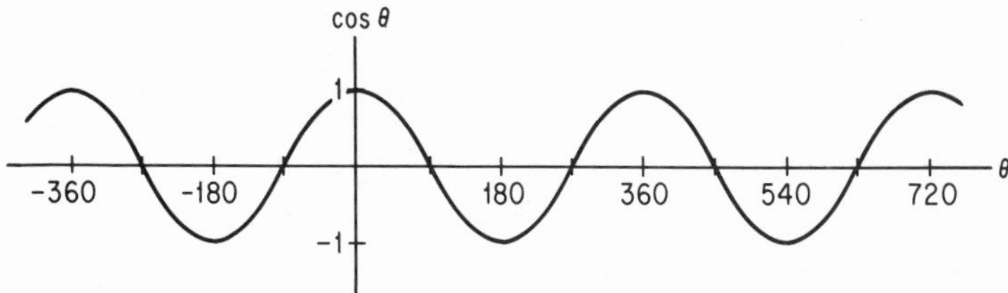

FIG. 6.11

and again, and it is apparent from the two diagrams that the graphs of the sine and cosine functions look very much alike. In fact, we get the impression that the sine curve would coincide with the cosine curve if it were shifted *a quarter of a complete cycle* to the left. This is true, as it can be shown that the equation

$$\cos \theta = \sin (\theta + 90)$$

holds for any value of θ; of course, the units here are in degrees.

It is customary to refer to an equation like this last one as a *trigonometric identity*—"trigonometric" because it relates to trigonometric functions, and "identity" because it holds for all possible values of θ. There are many other important identities pertaining to the values of the sine and cosine functions. For instance, there is the identity

$$\sin^2 \theta + \cos^2 \theta = 1$$

where $\sin^2 \theta$ means $(\sin \theta)^2$ and $\cos^2 \theta$ means $(\cos \theta)^2$. To prove this identity we have only to apply the Pythagorean theorem to the right triangle of Figure 6.7 and substitute $y = \sin \theta$ and $x = \cos \theta$ into $y^2 + x^2 = 1$. Two other important trigonometric identities are

$$\sin (90 - \theta) = \cos \theta$$

$$\cos (90 - \theta) = \sin \theta$$

and they can be proved (at least for positive values of θ less than 90 degrees) by using the definition of Exercise 12 on page 179, and making use of the fact that if one of the acute angles of a right triangle is θ, then the other is $90 - \theta$.

These last two identities are used extensively in connection with Table VI at the end of this book. In this table we can find the values of $\sin \theta$ and $\cos \theta$ (rounded to four decimals) for $\theta = 0, 1, 2, 3, 4, \ldots, 88, 89$, and 90 degrees. Actually, we had to tabulate the values of $\sin \theta$ and $\cos \theta$ only from 0 to 45 degrees, since sin 72 and cos 72, for example, can then be obtained by making use of the fact that

$$\sin 72 = \sin (90 - 18) = \cos 18$$

and

$$\cos 72 = \cos (90 - 18) = \sin 18$$

All this is taken care of automatically in Table VI, where we use the left-hand column and the column headings at the top when we deal with angles from 0 to 45 degrees, and the right-hand column and the column headings at the bottom when we deal with angles from 45 to 90 degrees. Although the entries of the sine and cosine columns of Table VI could be obtained by drawing the angles and performing the required measurements, this is not how it was done. As we shall see in Chapter 11, there exist formulas with which the values of the sine and cosine functions can actually be calculated.

There are also identities which enable us to express $\sin\theta$ and $\cos\theta$ for values of θ less than 0 degrees or greater than 90 degrees in terms of quantities which can be looked up in Table VI. Rather than list them, however, let us indicate how any such problem can easily be handled by drawing a suitable diagram. For instance, if we want to find $\sin 217°$, we have only to draw the angle as in the first diagram of Figure 6.12, and it can be seen by inspection that the y-coordinates of points P and Q are equal in magnitude but opposite in sign. Thus,

$$\sin 217 = -\sin 37 = -0.6018$$

where the value of sin 37 was looked up in Table VI. Similarly, the second diagram of Figure 6.12 leads to $\cos -33 = \cos 33 = 0.8387$ and $\sin -33 = -\sin 33 = -0.5446$, where the values of cos 33 and sin 33 were looked up in Table VI.

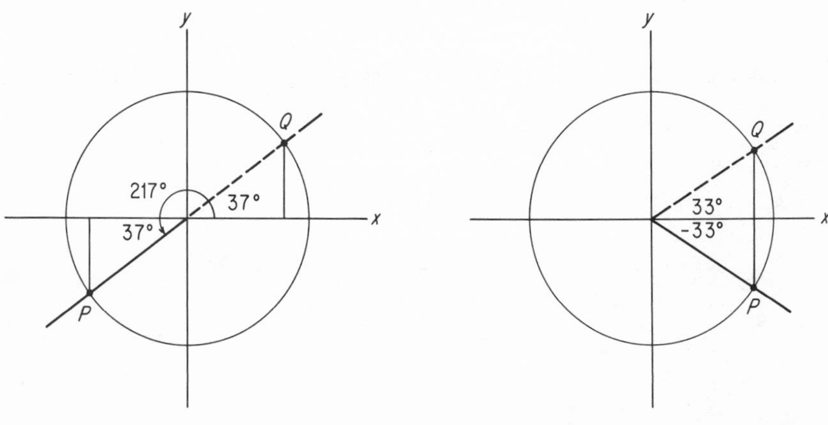

FIG. 6.12

As we indicated on page 171, there are altogether *six* basic trigonometric functions. Another important one is the *tangent function*, whose values are given by

$$\tan\theta = \frac{y}{x}$$

where x and y have the same significance as in Figure 6.7 on page 170. The domain of this function is the set of all the real numbers, except for those values of θ which correspond to $x = 0$. Thus, the tangent function is not defined when $x = \cos\theta = 0$, and it can be seen from Figure 6.11 that the values of θ which must be excluded are $\theta = 90, 270, 450, \ldots, -90, -270, -450, \ldots$. Making use of the fact that $y = \sin\theta$ and $x = \cos\theta$ in the notation of Figure 6.7, we can write the formula for the values of the tangent function as

$$\tan \theta = \frac{\sin \theta}{\cos \theta}$$

and we can, thus, calculate $\tan \theta$ for any value of θ by looking up (or otherwise determining) the corresponding values of $\sin \theta$ and $\cos \theta$. To make things even easier, the actual values of $\tan \theta$ are given in Table VI.

We shall not study the tangent function in any detail, because its graph is not very useful in describing business phenomena or economic data. The tangent function *is* periodic, but as the reader will be asked to show in Exercise 8 on page 177, its graph does not consist of the kind of cycles that are exhibited, for example, in Figures 6.1 and 6.2. Let us point out, though, that the tangent function plays an important role in determining the *direction* of a line. In fact, the slope of the line $y = a + bx$ is given by

$$b = \tan \theta$$

where θ is the angle which the line makes with the x-axis (as in Figure 6.13). Making use of Table VI, we thus find that $y = 3 + 2x$ is the equation of a

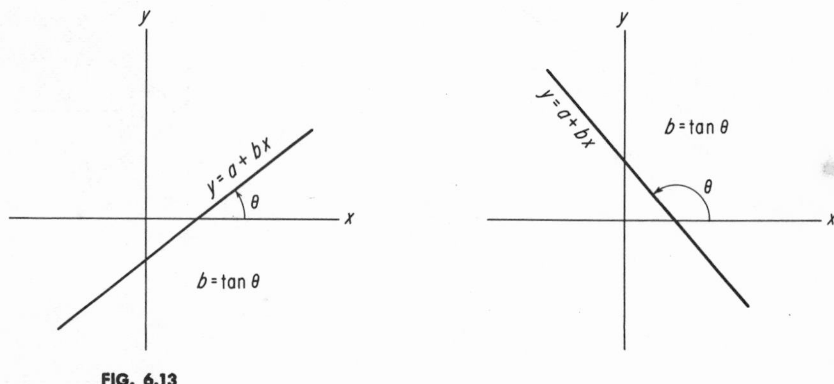

FIG. 6.13

line which makes an angle close to 63° with the x-axis, while $y = 7 - \frac{2}{5}x$ is the equation of a line which makes an angle close to $180 - 22 = 158°$ with the x-axis. To obtain this last result we made use of the identity $\tan (180 - \theta) = -\tan \theta$, but we could also have based our argument on a diagram similar to those of Figure 6.12.

EXERCISES

1. Change each of the following angles from degrees to radians and leave the answer in terms of π: (a) 60°; (b) 120°; (c) 720°; (d) −45°; (e) −270°; (f) 405°; (g) −1,080°; and (h) 390°.

2. Change each of the following angles from radians to degrees: (a) $\pi/6$; (b) 8π; (c) $3\pi/2$; (d) $-5\pi/12$; (e) 3π; (f) $-3\pi/4$; and (g) $6\pi/5$.

3. Show that one radian is approximately 57.3 degrees by substituting 3.14 for π.

4. Referring to Table VI and drawing a diagram like those of Figure 6.12 (when necessary), find (a) sin 35°; (b) sin 78°; (c) cos 17°; (d) cos 69°; (e) sin 212°; (f) cos (−41°); (g) sin 117°; (h) sin (−215°); (i) cos 342°; (j) sin 325°; (k) cos 249°; and (l) cos 140°.

5. Using Table VI, find the positive angle θ less than 90 degrees for which (a) $\sin\theta = 0.5446$; (b) $\sin\theta = 0.9848$; (c) $\cos\theta = 0.6561$; (d) $\cos\theta = 0.8192$; (e) $\sin\theta = 0.2588$; and (f) $\cos\theta = 0.5000$.

6. Draw diagrams similar to those of Figure 6.10 to verify the values of sin 225, cos 225, sin 315, and cos 315 given on page 173.

7. Following the suggestion on page 174, show that for any *acute* angle θ (namely, for positive values of θ less than 90 degrees),

$$\sin(90 - \theta) = \cos\theta \qquad \text{and} \qquad \cos(90 - \theta) = \sin\theta$$

8. Use the following steps to construct the graph of the tangent function:

   (a) Referring to Table VI, find the values of $\tan\theta$ for $\theta = 0, 5, 10, 15, \ldots,$ 75, 80, and 85 degrees.
   (b) Making use of the identity $\tan(180 - \theta) = -\tan\theta$ and the results of part (a), find the values of $\tan\theta$ for $\theta = 95, 100, 105, \ldots, 170, 175$, and 180 degrees.
   (c) Measuring θ along the horizontal scale and the values of $\tan\theta$ along the vertical scale, plot the points obtained in parts (a) and (b) and join the two sets separately by means of smooth curves.
   (d) Extend the graph obtained in part (c) over the interval from −270° to 450° by making use of the fact that the tangent function has a period of 180°, namely, that the pattern repeats every 180 degrees.
   (e) What happens to the values of $\tan\theta$ when θ approaches 90° *from the left* (that is, when θ comes closer and closer to 90° yet always remains less)? What happens to the values of $\tan\theta$ when θ approaches 90° *from the right?*

9. Find the angles (rounded to the nearest degree) at which the following lines cut the x-axis:

   (a) $y = -2 + x$; (c) $y = 1 + 4x$; (e) $x - 10y + 20 = 0$;
   (b) $y = 3 - x$; (d) $y = 5 - 4x$; (f) $3x - 2y = 4$.

10. **THE SECANT, COSECANT, AND COTANGENT FUNCTIONS.** The three basic trigonometric functions which we did not discuss in the text, the *secant*, *cosecant*, and *cotangent* functions, are such that their values are the *reciprocals* of the corresponding values of the cosine, sine, and tangent functions. Symbolically,

$$\sec\theta = \frac{1}{\cos\theta}, \quad \csc\theta = \frac{1}{\sin\theta}, \quad \text{and} \quad \cot\theta = \frac{1}{\tan\theta}$$

where sec θ reads as "secant θ," csc θ reads as "cosecant θ," and cot θ reads as "cotangent θ." The domains of these functions consists of all the values of θ for which the corresponding reciprocals are defined; in addition to this, cot θ is assigned the value *zero* when tan θ is undefined. Referring to Table VI and taking the reciprocal (when necessary), evaluate each of the following:

(a) csc 30°; (d) cot 39°; (g) sec 64°;
(b) sec 0°; (e) csc 90°; (h) cot 118°;
(c) csc 71°; (f) sec 5°; (i) sec 236°.

[*Hint:* for parts (h) and (i) draw diagrams similar to those of Figure 6.12.] Also use the identity $\sin^2 \theta + \cos^2 \theta = 1$ and the definition of tan θ on page 175 to verify that

(j) $\cot \theta = \dfrac{\cos \theta}{\sin \theta}$;

(k) $1 + \tan^2 \theta = \sec^2 \theta$;

(l) $1 + \cot^2 \theta = \csc^2 \theta$

for all values of θ for which these functions are defined.

11. **THE SECANT, COSECANT, AND COTANGENT FUNCTIONS, CONTINUED.** Referring to Figure 6.11 on page 173, read off the values of sin θ for various values of θ between 0 and 360 degrees, calculate their reciprocals, and use the resulting points to plot the graph of the cosecant function. What happens to the values of csc θ when θ approaches 180° from the left and when it approaches 180° from the right? Note that the graph which we get for the cosecant function is not suitable for describing patterns like those of Figures 6.1

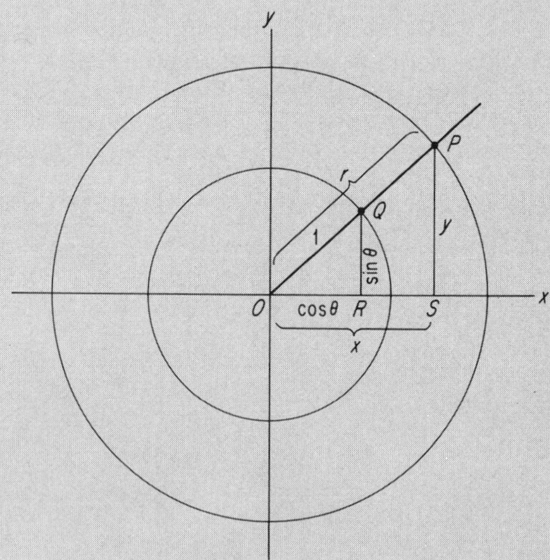

FIG. 6.14

and 6.2, and this is true also for the graphs of the secant and cotangent functions.

12. RIGHT-TRIANGLE DEFINITIONS OF THE TRIGONOMETRIC FUNCTIONS. Had we drawn a circle with the radius r instead of a circle with the radius 1 in Figure 6.7 on page 170, the values of $\cos\theta$ and $\sin\theta$ would *not* have been given by the coordinates of the point P. As can be seen from Figure 6.14, however, where we have drawn *two* circles, one with the radius 1 and one with the radius r, triangles OQR and OPS are *similar*, so that their respective sides are proportional. Hence, $\frac{OQ}{OP} = \frac{QR}{PS}$ or $\frac{1}{r} = \frac{\sin\theta}{y}$, $\frac{OQ}{OP} = \frac{OR}{OS}$ or $\frac{1}{r} = \frac{\cos\theta}{x}$, and it follows that

$$\sin\theta = \frac{y}{r} \quad \text{and} \quad \cos\theta = \frac{x}{r}$$

Of course, this reduces to $\sin\theta = y$ and $\cos\theta = x$ when $r = 1$, but there are certain advantages to this more general approach. This is true, particularly, when we deal with problems in which we have to work only with *acute*

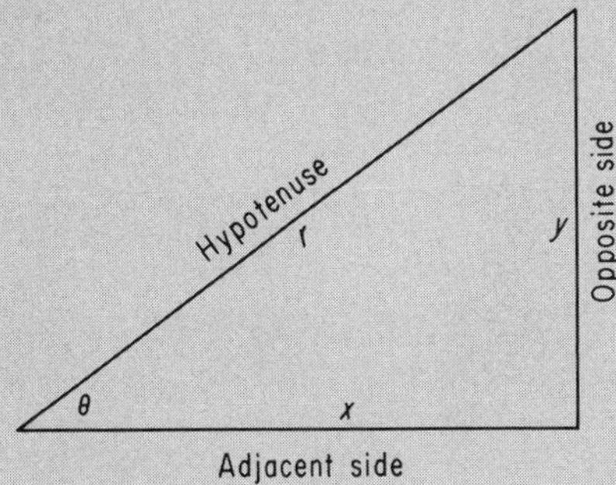

FIG. 6.15

angles (namely, with positive values of θ less than 90 degrees). In that case we can label x, y, and r as in Figure 6.15, and give the following "right-triangle" definition of the trigonometric functions:

$$\sin\theta = \frac{\text{Opposite side}}{\text{Hypothenuse}}$$

$$\cos\theta = \frac{\text{Adjacent side}}{\text{Hypothenuse}}$$

and by the same token

$$\tan\theta = \frac{\text{Opposite side}}{\text{Adjacent side}}$$

in accordance with the definition on page 175. Use these formulas to solve the following problems:

(a) If we are driving along a road which has an upward inclination of 7°, how many feet do we actually climb while traveling through a distance of 2,000 feet?

(b) Find the height of a television tower whose shadow is 80 feet long when the angle of elevation of the sun (see Figure 6.16) is 41°.

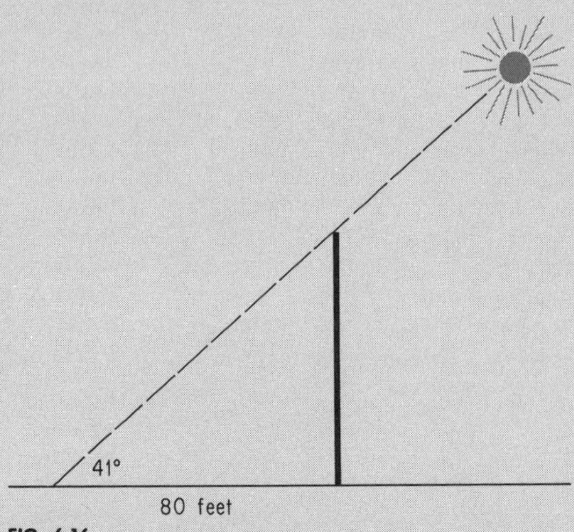

FIG. 6.16

(c) Figure 6.17 is part of a map of a golf course, with its first tee at point A and its first hole at point B. Even though A and B are assumed to be in the same horizontal plane, the distance from A to B (that is, the "length" of the first hole) cannot be measured directly because of the

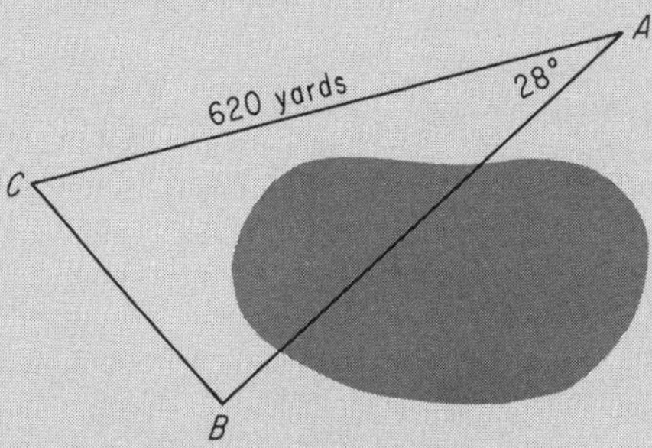

FIG. 6.17

lake in between. To solve this problem, a surveyor locates a point C which is such that BC is perpendicular to AB and AC can be measured without crossing the lake. What is the "length" of the first hole, if the surveyor finds (with the use of a tape and a transit) that AC is 620 yards and that angle CAB measures 28°?

(d) Figure 6.18 shows an irregularly-shaped piece of land. Find its total area (in square feet), making use of the fact that the area of a rectangle is given by the product of its length and its width, while the area of a

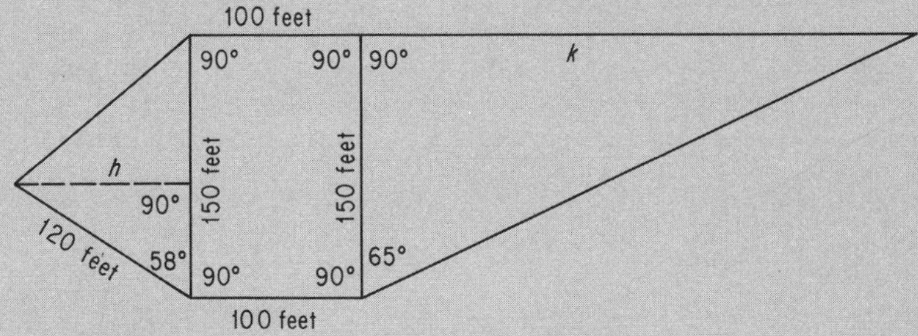

FIG. 6.18

triangle is given by *half* the product of its base and its altitude. (*Hint:* first find the altitude h of the triangle on the left and the altitude k of the triangle on the right.)

(e) Making use of the fact that in a 30°-60°-90° triangle the length of the hypothenuse is twice that of the side adjacent to the 60° angle (see Figure 6.19), show that the length of the side opposite the 60° angle is

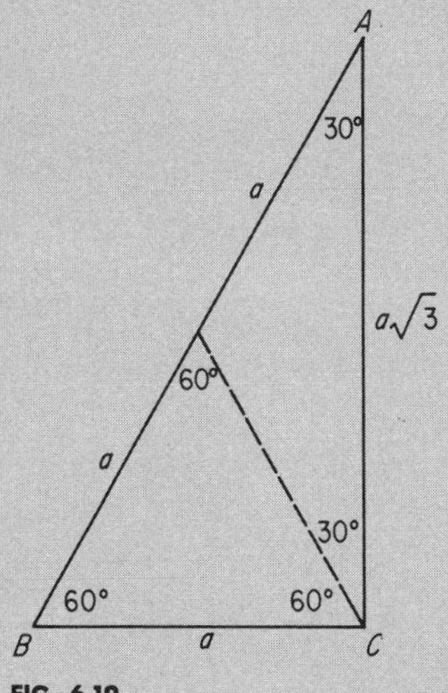

FIG. 6.19

$\sqrt{3}$ times that of the side adjacent to it. Use this result to evaluate sin 60°, cos 60°, tan 60°, sin 30°, cos 30°, tan 30°, sin 120°, cos 120°, sin 240°, cos 240°, sin 150°, cos 150°, sin 210°, and cos 210°.

13. POLAR COORDINATES. It is apparent from Figure 6.14 that the point P would be determined (that is, it could be located) if we knew θ and r. If we wanted to, we could use θ and r to calculate its "ordinary" coordinates by means of the formulas $x = r(\cos\theta)$ and $y = r(\sin\theta)$, but it is generally easier to plot P by measuring off the angle θ and then moving through the distance r along its "rotating leg." The values of θ and r which thus lead to a given point are referred to as its *polar coordinates*, and there are quite a few problems in which they are easier to work with than the corresponding *rectangular coordinates* x and y. [For instance, in rectangular coordinates the equation of the circle which has its center at the origin and the radius a is $x^2 + y^2 = a^2$ (see Exercise 7 on page 109)—in polar coordinates it is simply $r = a$.] Draw a pair of perpendicular axes with the same units for x and y and plot the points which have the following polar coordinates (with r always listed first):

(a) $(4, 60°)$; (c) $(1, 3\pi/2$ radians$)$;
(b) $(2, 135°)$; (d) $(5, -\pi/6$ radians$)$.

If a negative value of r is meant to imply that we must go in the opposite direction along the "rotating leg" of the angle θ, plot the points which have the following polar coordinates:

(e) $(-1, 45°)$; (g) $(-3, \pi$ radians$)$;
(f) $(-4, 210°)$; (h) $(-5, -3\pi/4$ radians$)$.

14. POLAR COORDINATES, CONTINUED. If we know the x- and y-coordinates of a point and want to find its polar coordinates, we simply substitute into the formulas

$$r = \pm\sqrt{x^2 + y^2}$$

$$\tan\theta = \frac{y}{x}$$

which are obtained by applying the Pythagorean theorem to the triangle OPS of Figure 6.14 and referring to the definition of $\tan\theta$ on page 175.* An important aspect of these formulas is that *the answer we get is not unique.* For $x = 1$ and $y = 1$, for instance, we get

$$r = \pm\sqrt{2} \qquad \text{and} \qquad \tan\theta = 1$$

and it can be seen that there are already two possibilities for r. So far as θ is concerned, one possibility is $\theta = 45°$ (see Figure 6.10), but since the tangent function is periodic (its graph repeats every 180 degrees), we can add or subtract $180°$ any number of times. Thus, θ can also equal $225°$, $405°$, $585°, \ldots$, or $-135°$, $-315°$, $-495°, \ldots$. We have to be careful, though, to combine the right value of r with each of these values of θ. For instance, to get the point whose x- and y-coordinates are $(1, 1)$, we would have to combine $\theta = 45°$ with $r = +\sqrt{2}$, $\theta = 225°$ with $r = -\sqrt{2}$, $\theta = 405°$

* In more advanced work we refer to the inverse of the tangent function as the *arc tangent function*, and we write

$$\theta = \text{arc tan}\,\frac{y}{x}$$

for the angle between $-90°$ and $90°$ for which the value of the tangent function is y/x.

with $r = \sqrt{2}$, $\theta = -135°$ with $r = -\sqrt{2}$, and so on. To get unique answers to the questions which follow, we shall agree (so far as this exercise is concerned) to choose θ so that it is always positive or zero and less than 180 degrees. Thus, find a set of polar coordinates for each of the points whose x- and y- coordinates are

(a) $(0, 1)$; (d) $(3, 4)$; (g) $(-4, 3)$;
(b) $(1, -1)$; (e) $(5, 12)$; (h) $(1, \sqrt{3})$;
(c) $(-3, 3)$; (f) $(-12, 5)$; (i) $(\sqrt{3}, -1)$.

(*Hint:* Use Table VI, if necessary, and in the last two parts make use of the fact that $\tan 60° = \sqrt{3}$ and $\tan 30° = 1/\sqrt{3}$.)

15. THE TRIGONOMETRIC FORM OF A COMPLEX NUMBER. In Exercise 24 on page 127 we established a one-to-one correspondence between the complex numbers and the points in the plane by identifying the complex number $x + iy$, where x and y are real numbers, with the point (x, y). Now, if we change to polar coordinates (see Exercise 13) and substitute $r(\cos\theta)$ for x and $r(\sin\theta)$ for y, we get

$$x + iy = r(\cos\theta) + i\cdot r(\sin\theta)$$
$$= r(\cos\theta + i\cdot\sin\theta)$$

and we refer to $r(\cos\theta + i\cdot\sin\theta)$ as the *trigonometric form* of the complex number $x + iy$. Following the procedure of Exercise 14, change each of the following complex numbers into the trigonometric form:

(a) i; (c) $1 + i$; (e) $-5 + 5i$;
(b) $1 - i$; (d) $1 + i\sqrt{3}$; (f) $4\sqrt{3} - 4i$.

[*Hint:* in parts (d) and (f) and in parts (g) and (h) below make use of the fact that $\cos 60° = \sin 30° = 1/2$ and that $\sin 60° = \cos 30° = \sqrt{3}/2$ (see last part of Exercise 12).] Also, change each of the following complex numbers from the trigonometric form to the so-called *standard form* $x + iy$, where x and y are real numbers:

(g) $3(\cos 60° + i\cdot\sin 60°)$; (i) $\frac{1}{2}(\cos 270° + i\cdot\sin 270°)$;
(h) $5(\cos 150° + i\cdot\sin 150°)$; (j) $2(\cos 45° + i\cdot\sin 45°)$.

16. THE TRIGONOMETRIC FORM OF A COMPLEX NUMBER, DE MOIVRE'S THEOREM. The work of the preceding exercise can be used to great advantage when a complex number has to be raised to a power, say, when we have to evaluate $(2 + 2i)^6$ or $i^{1/3}$. When the power is a positive integer, we use the special form of *De Moivre's Theorem* according to which

$$[r(\cos\theta + i\cdot\sin\theta)]^n = r^n(\cos n\theta + i\cdot\sin n\theta)$$

For instance, to evaluate $(2 + 2i)^6$ we first write $2 + 2i$ in the trigonometric form as $\sqrt{8}(\cos 45° + i\cdot\sin 45°)$, and then we get

$$\begin{aligned}[\sqrt{8}(\cos 45^\circ + i\cdot\sin 45^\circ)]^6 &= (\sqrt{8})^6(\cos 6\cdot 45^\circ + i\cdot\sin 6\cdot 45^\circ)\\ &= 512(\cos 270^\circ + i\cdot\sin 270^\circ)\\ &= 512(0 - i)\\ &= -512i\end{aligned}$$

To find the *mth root* of a complex number, where m is a positive integer, we use another form of *De Moivre's Theorem* according to which

$$[r(\cos\theta + i\cdot\sin\theta)]^{\frac{1}{m}} = r^{\frac{1}{m}}\left(\cos\frac{\theta + 360k}{m} + i\cdot\sin\frac{\theta + 360k}{m}\right)$$

for $k = 0, 1, 2, \ldots,$ and $m - 1$.* *Note that by substituting these m values of k we thus get m different mth roots.* For instance, to find the *three* cube roots of i we first write i as $1(\cos 90^\circ + i\cdot\sin 90^\circ)$, and then we get

$$\begin{aligned}[1(\cos 90^\circ + i\cdot\sin 90^\circ)]^{\frac{1}{3}} &= 1^{\frac{1}{3}}\left(\cos\frac{90 + 360k}{3} + i\cdot\sin\frac{90 + 360k}{3}\right)\\ &= \cos(30 + 120k) + i\cdot\sin(30 + 120k)\end{aligned}$$

Then, letting $k = 0, 1$, and 2, we find that the three cube roots of i are

$$\cos 30^\circ + i\cdot\sin 30^\circ$$

$$\cos 150^\circ + i\cdot\sin 150^\circ$$

$$\cos 270^\circ + i\cdot\sin 270^\circ$$

where the third one is readily identified as $0 + i(-1) = -i$. Making use of the fact that $\cos 30^\circ = \sqrt{3}/2$ and $\sin 30^\circ = 1/2$ (see Figure 6.19), we find that the other two cube roots of i can be written as

$$\frac{\sqrt{3}}{2} + \frac{1}{2}i \quad \text{and} \quad -\frac{\sqrt{3}}{2} + \frac{1}{2}i$$

Use this theory to evaluate each of the following expressions:

(a) $(1 - i)^4$; (e) $(1 + i)^3$;
(b) $(1 - i)^7$; (f) $(1 + i\sqrt{3})^5$;
(c) $(1 - i\sqrt{3})^4$; (g) $\sqrt{2\sqrt{2} + i\cdot 2\sqrt{2}}$;
(d) $(-2 - 2i)^3$; (h) $\sqrt[4]{-1}$.

6.3 FURTHER GRAPHS OF TRIGONOMETRIC FUNCTIONS

In Section 6.1 we used the seasonal pattern of farm employment and the long-range cyclical pattern in wholesale prices as examples of phe-

* It is assumed here that the angles are measured in degrees; if they are measured in radians, $2\pi k$ must be substituted for $360k$.

nomena which are of a periodic nature. Then, in Section 6.2, we introduced the sine and cosine functions to provide models for phenomena of this kind, namely, phenomena which consist of patterns, or cycles, which repeat over and over again. It is true, of course, that these two trigonometric functions *are* periodic, but when it comes to the construction of mathematical models for patterns like those of Figures 6.1 and 6.2, we still have a long way to go. The problem of finding a periodic function which truly describes a given periodic phenomenon (say, the annually repeating pattern of department store sales, the hourly variations in the traffic on the Santa Ana Freeway, or the long-range cycles in the prices of railroad stocks) is *extremely difficult*, and we shall not be able to go that far in this book. To come close, though, we shall indicate in this section how the sine and cosine functions can be *modified* (shifted, rotated, contracted, expanded, and otherwise distorted) to meet particular needs.

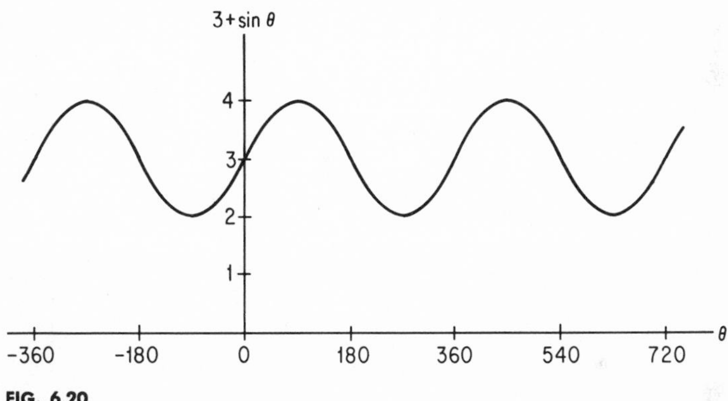

FIG. 6.20

For instance, we can move the entire sine curve up or down by simply adding or subtracting a suitable constant; thus, Figure 6.20 gives the graph of

$$f(\theta) = 3 + \sin\theta$$

where the dependent variable is denoted $f(\theta)$. If we want to change the *amplitude* of the cycles, namely, make each "wave" go higher or less high, we simply multiply by a suitable constant; Figure 6.21, for example, gives the graph of $f(\theta) = \sin\theta$ as well as those of

$$f(\theta) = 3(\sin\theta) \qquad \text{and} \qquad f(\theta) = \frac{1}{2}(\sin\theta)$$

Another possibility is to change the length of each cycle, or *period*, and this is done by multiplying θ by a suitable constant; thus, Figure 6.22 gives the graph of $f(\theta) = \sin\theta$ together with those of

$$f(\theta) = \sin\frac{1}{2}\theta \qquad \text{and} \qquad f(\theta) = \sin 3\theta$$

For $f(\theta) = \sin\frac{1}{2}\theta$ the *period* is 720° (or 4π radians), since the interval from 0°

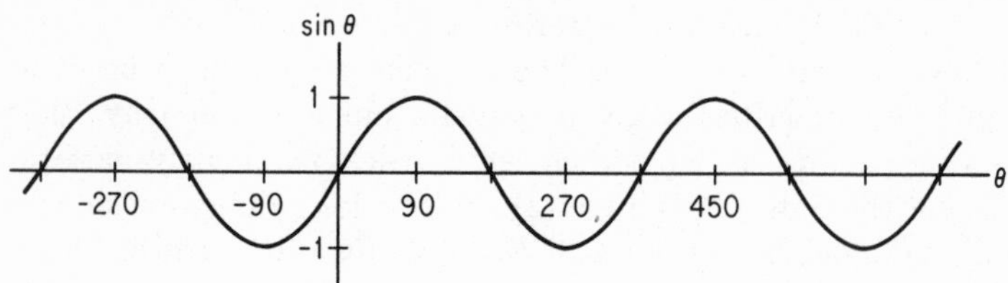

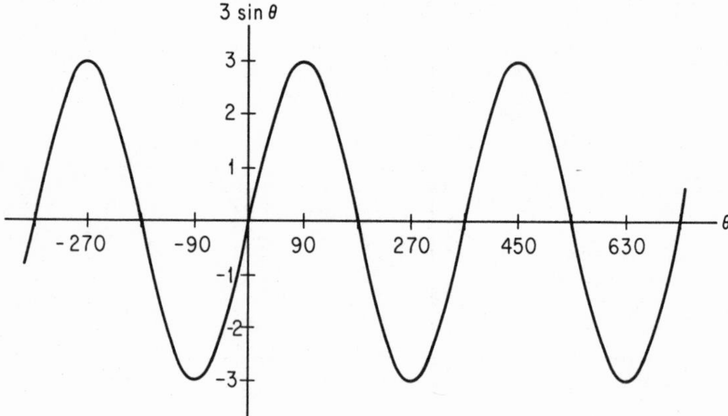

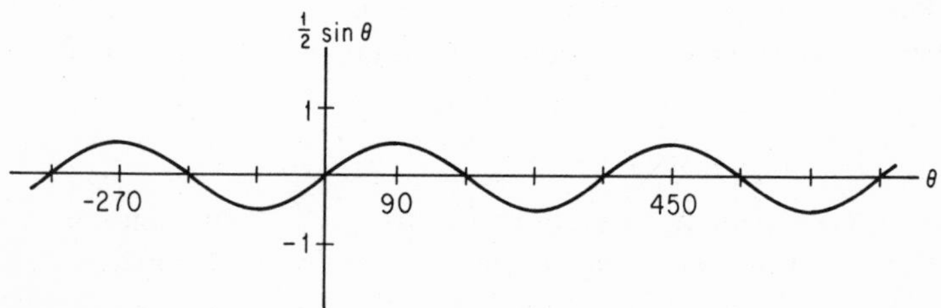

FIG. 6.21

to 360° corresponds to one complete cycle of the sine function, and, hence, the interval from $\frac{1}{2}\theta = 0°$ to $\frac{1}{2}\theta = 360°$ corresponds to one complete cycle of $f(\theta) = \sin\frac{1}{2}\theta$. For $f(\theta) = \sin 3\theta$ the *period* is 120° (or $2\pi/3$ radians), since the interval from $3\theta = 0°$ to $3\theta = 360°$ (namely, the interval from $\theta = 0°$ to $\theta = 120°$) corresponds to one complete sine wave. Note that the first

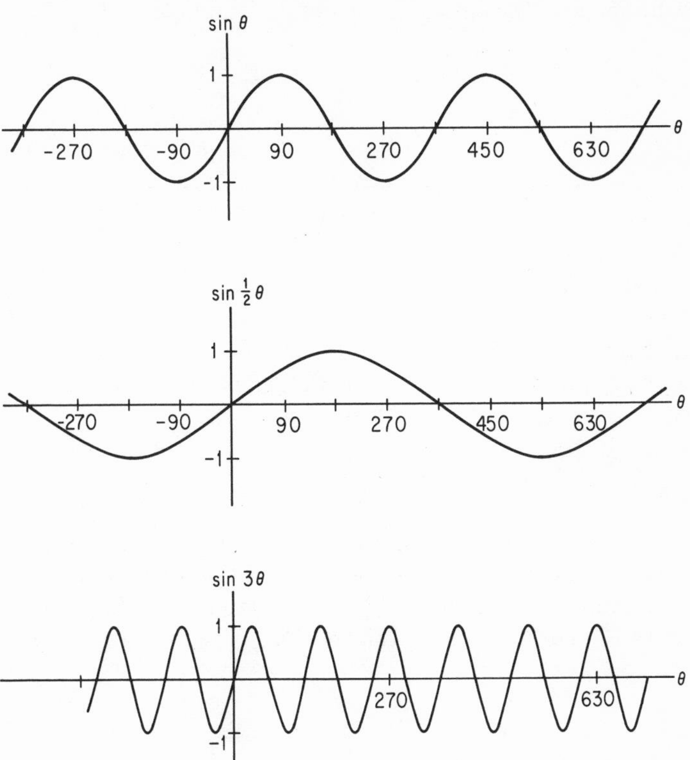

FIG. 6.22

of these two functions oscillates *more slowly* than the "ordinary" sine function, while the second oscillates *faster*.

If we want to *shift* the entire curve to the right or to the left, we can accomplish this by adding to, or subtracting from, θ a suitable constant; for instance, Figure 6.23 gives the graph of

$$f(\theta) = \sin\left(\theta + \frac{\pi}{6}\right)$$

and it can be seen that the entire curve has been moved to the left through a distance of $\pi/6$, where the θ-units are now radians.

There is no reason why we cannot combine all these modifications, that is, shift the curve to the left or to the right and *at the same time* move it up or down, change the length of each cycle, and expand or contract the height of each wave. In that case we would get an equation of the form

$$f(\theta) = k + a \cdot \sin(b\theta + c)$$

where k, a, b, and c are appropriate numerical constants. For instance, if we want to move the entire sine curve up 2 units, shift it $\pi/8$ units to the right, change the period to π radians, and give each wave an amplitude of 4, we get the graph shown in Figure 6.24, and as the reader will be asked to verify in Exercise 4 on page 191, its equation is

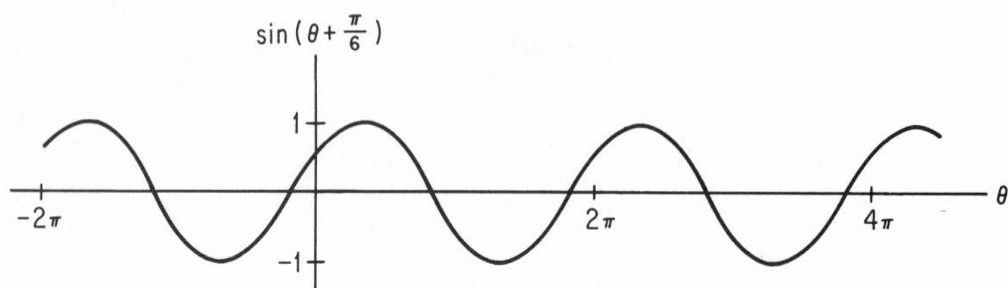

FIG. 6.23

$$f(\theta) = 2 + 4 \cdot \sin\left(2\theta - \frac{\pi}{4}\right)$$

Needless to say, the modifications we have discussed here in connection with the sine function can also be made in the cosine function, or in the other trigonometric functions which we studied in Section 6.2 and in Exercises 10 and 11 on pages 177 and 178.

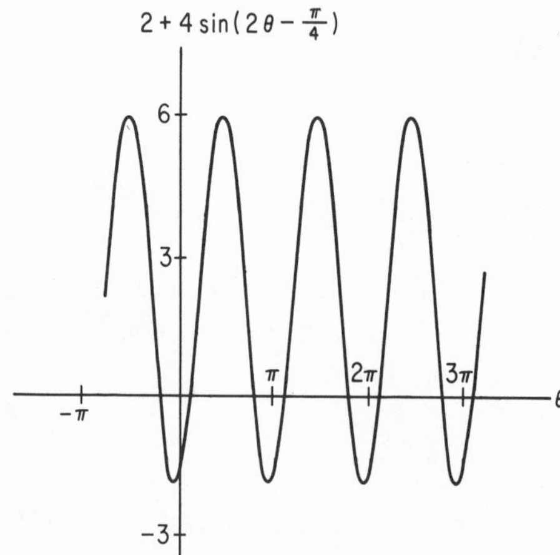

FIG. 6.24

There are numerous other ways of modifying the trigonometric functions. A very important one is illustrated in Figure 6.25, where we

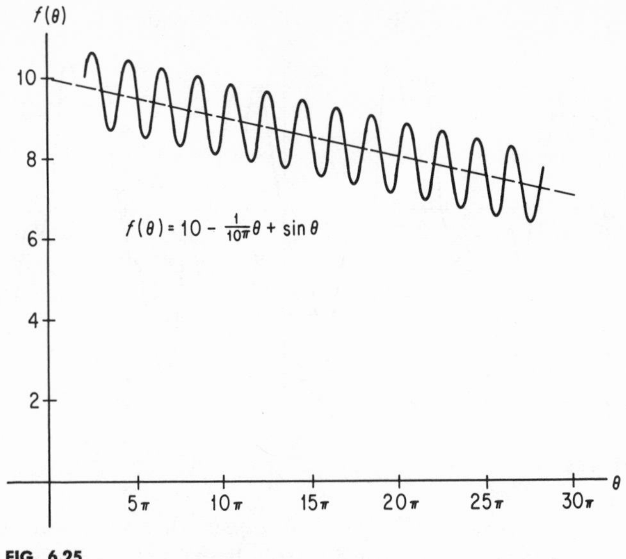

FIG. 6.25

have, so to speak, *wound* the sine waves around the line $y = 10 - \frac{1}{10\pi}\theta$; the equation of this function is

$$f(\theta) = 10 - \frac{1}{10\pi}\theta + \sin\theta$$

where the θ-units are radians. Comparing the graphs of Figures 6.25 and 6.1, we find that this function comes *pretty close* to providing a mathematical model for farm employment in the United States.

To describe periodic phenomena which lead to graphs that are not quite as regularly shaped as those of sine and cosine waves, we usually *combine* the values of several trigonometric functions. For instance, Figure 6.26 gives the graph of

$$f(\theta) = 3(\sin\theta) - \cos 4\theta - \frac{1}{2}\left(\sin\frac{\theta}{2}\right)$$

and it is of interest to note that it took only 14 seconds of actual machine time on a Control Data Corporation 3400 Computer to determine the values of this function for one complete cycle (namely, for $\theta = 0, \frac{1}{50}\pi, \frac{2}{50}\pi, \frac{3}{50}\pi, \ldots$, and 4π).

Generally speaking, it is possible to approximate any periodic pattern, no matter how irregular, by adding a sufficient number of sine and cosine terms with varying periods and amplitudes. Unfortunately, the technical details of this method (called *Fourier Analysis* when we try to duplicate

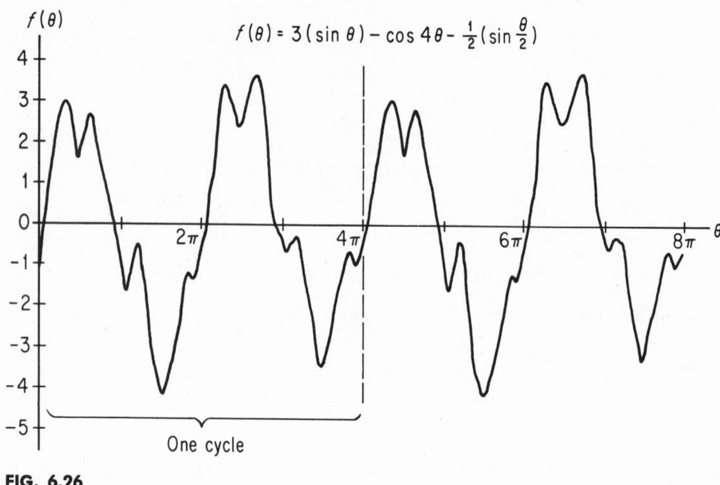

FIG. 6.26

mathematical patterns, and *Harmonic Analysis* when we try to duplicate patterns of observed data) are considerably beyond the scope of this text. All we really hoped to accomplish in this section was to make the reader aware of the *possibility* of modifying and combining trigonometric functions in order to construct models for seasonal variations, business cycles, and other phenomena that are of a periodic nature.

EXERCISES

1. Explain in words what we have to do to the sine or cosine graph of Figure 6.11 so that its equation becomes:

(a) $f(\theta) = -2 + \cos\theta$; (e) $f(\theta) = \frac{1}{3}\cdot\sin\theta$;

(b) $f(\theta) = 5\cdot\cos\theta$; (f) $f(\theta) = \sin(\theta - 180°)$;

(c) $f(\theta) = 7 + \sin\theta$; (g) $f(\theta) = \cos\frac{1}{4}\theta$;

(d) $f(\theta) = \sin 6\theta$; (h) $f(\theta) = \cos\left(\theta + \frac{\pi}{2}\right)$.

[*Hint:* in parts (f) and (h) check for what value of θ we get, respectively, $\sin 0° = 0$ and $\cos 0° = 1$.]

2. Find the equation of the function whose graph is obtained

(a) by shifting the graph of the cosine function 4 units downward;
(b) by expanding the graph of the cosine function so that its amplitude becomes equal to 2;
(c) by contracting the graph of the sine function so that its period becomes 60°;

(d) by shifting the graph of the cosine function π radians to the right;
(e) by expanding the graph of the sine function so that its period becomes 10π radians;
(f) by contracting the graph of the sine function so that its amplitude becomes equal to $1/4$.

3. How do we have to shift or distort the graph of the cosine function to obtain the graph of $f(\theta) = 1 + 3\cdot\cos(\theta - 90°)$?

4. Verify that the modifications suggested on page 188 actually lead to the function whose equation is $f(\theta) = 2 + 4\cdot\sin\left(2\theta - \frac{\pi}{4}\right)$.

5. Referring to Table VI, calculate the values of $f(\theta) = \sin\theta + \cos\theta$ for $\theta = 0°$, $10°, 20°, 30°, \ldots, 340°, 350°$, and $360°$, and use them to plot one complete cycle of the graph of this function.

6. Referring to Table VI, calculate the values of $f(\theta) = 2 - \sin 2\theta + 3\cdot\cos 4\theta$ for $\theta = 0°, 5°, 10°, 15°, \ldots, 175°$, and $180°$, and use them to plot one complete cycle of the graph of this function.

7. Draw a rough sketch of the graph of $f(\theta) = 4 + \frac{\theta}{4\pi} + \cos\theta$ for values of θ from 0 to 8π radians. $\left[\text{\textit{Hint:} wind the cosine waves around the line } f(\theta) = 4 + \frac{\theta}{4\pi}.\right]$

8. Draw a rough sketch of the graph of $f(\theta) = \frac{12\pi}{\theta} + 2\cdot\sin\theta$ for values of θ from 2π to 12π radians. $\left[\text{\textit{Hint:} wind a suitable sine wave around the \textit{hyperbola} } f(\theta) = \frac{12\pi}{\theta}.\right]$

7

SYSTEMS OF LINEAR EQUATIONS AND INEQUALITIES

7.1 INTRODUCTION

On page 94 we referred to $cx + dy = e$ as the *standard form* of the equation of a straight line, and we indicated that it can easily be generalized to handle situations where there are more than two variables. Indeed, we refer to

$$2x + 4y + 3z = 8, \quad 12p + 9q - 5r = 30,$$

and

$$u - v - w = 3$$

as *linear equations in three variables*, we refer to

$$x - y + z - u = 5 \quad \text{and} \quad x_1 - 3x_2 + 2x_3 - x_4 = 6$$

as *linear equations in four variables*, and we refer to

$$2x_1 + 3x_2 - x_3 + 4x_4 + 7x_5 = 12$$

and

$$r - 2s + 5t + u - 3v + w = 15$$

respectively, as *linear equations in five and six variables*. In two of these examples we used *subscripts* to distinguish between the variables, and it should be apparent that this is a very good idea, particularly, when the number of variables is large.

Even though we refer to all of the above equations as *linear*, it should be understood that when there are more than two variables they do not represent straight lines. For three variables they represent *planes* (see discussion on page 86), and when there are more than three variables we refer to their graphs, which cannot be visualized, as *hyperplanes*.

In Section 7.2 we shall study a very elementary method of *solving* systems of linear equations, namely, a method of finding the values of the variables which *at the same time* satisfy (are the solutions of) several linear equations. Later, in Chapter 9, we shall treat the same kind of problem by more advanced techniques involving *matrices* and *determinants*, and it should not come as a surprise that all this work is referred to under the general heading of *linear mathematics*.

Sections 7.3 and 7.4 are devoted to *linear inequalities*, which arise when the equal sign of a linear equation is replaced with $<$, $>$, $\leqslant$, or $\geqslant$, standing, respectively, for "less than," "greater than," "less than or equal to," and "greater than or equal to." As the reader will see from the applications discussed in these two sections and also in Chapters 8 and 10, linear inequalities arise in a great many practical situations.

7.2 SYSTEMS OF LINEAR EQUATIONS

We first met the problem of how to solve a system of two linear equations in two variables in Section 4.8. In a *break-even analysis* we had a cost function given by the linear equation

$$y = 12{,}000 + 80x$$

and a receipts function given by the linear equation

$$y = 120x$$

where x is in each case the number of television sets produced, and cost as well as receipts are in dollars. To solve the problem, we looked for the value of x for which *cost equals receipts*, and we obtained $x = 300$, corresponding to which the cost as well as the receipts total $y = \$36{,}000$.

The solution of this problem was especially easy because both equations were given in *explicit form* (solved for y) — all we had to do was equate the two expressions which represent cost and receipts, and solve for x. Now suppose that we are given the two linear equations

$$\begin{aligned} 2x + 3y &= 5 \\ -5x - 2y &= 4 \end{aligned}$$

which are both in *implicit form*, namely, solved for neither x nor y, and that we are asked to find the values of x and y which satisfy (are solutions of) both equations. Geometrically speaking, we are asked to find the coordinates of the point in which the corresponding lines intersect (see Figure 7.1).

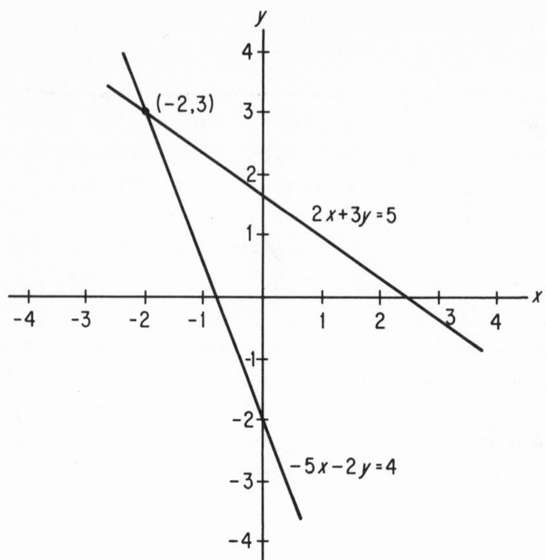

FIG. 7.1

If we wanted to proceed as in the first example of Section 4.8, we could solve each equation for y, getting

$$y = \frac{5 - 2x}{3} \quad \text{and} \quad y = \frac{4 + 5x}{-2}$$

Then, if we equate these two expressions for y, we get

$$\frac{5 - 2x}{3} = \frac{4 + 5x}{-2}$$

and this leads to $-2(5 - 2x) = 3(4 + 5x)$, namely, to

$$\begin{aligned} -10 + 4x &= 12 + 15x \\ -11x &= 22 \\ \text{and} \qquad x &= -2 \end{aligned}$$

The corresponding value for y is $\dfrac{4 + 5(-2)}{-2} = 3$, and we can now say that the given system of linear equations has the solution $x = -2$ and $y = 3$; in other words, the two lines intersect in the point $(-2, 3)$.

The method we have illustrated here is only one of many different methods that can be used to solve a system of two linear equations in two variables. The calculations would have been even simpler if we had used the *method of elimination*, which utilizes the fact that we can "multiply equals by equals," "add equals to equals," and "subtract equals from equals." If we wanted to apply this method to the same system of linear equations, namely,

$$\begin{aligned} 2x + 3y &= 5 \\ -5x - 2y &= 4 \end{aligned}$$

we could *eliminate* y by multiplying the expressions on both sides of the first equation by 2, multiplying the expressions on both sides of the second equation by 3, and then adding the expressions on the respective sides of the two equations. This would give us

$$\begin{aligned} 4x + 6y &= 10 \\ -15x - 6y &= 12 \end{aligned}$$

and then $-11x = 22$ and $x = -2$. The value of y can then be obtained by substituting $x = -2$ into either of the *original* equations; substituting $x = -2$ into the first equation we get $2(-2) + 3y = 5$, and this leads to $3y = 9$ and $y = 3$. (To check this result, we substitute $x = -2$ and $y = 3$ into the second original equation, getting $-5(-2) - 2(3) = 10 - 6 = 4$, which checks.)

Had we wanted to *eliminate* x instead of y in this example, we could have multiplied the expressions on both sides of the first equation by 5, those on both sides of the second equation by 2, and then added the expressions on the respective sides of the two equations. This would have given us

$$\begin{aligned} 10x + 15y &= 25 \\ -10x - 4y &= 8 \end{aligned}$$

and then $11y = 33$ and $y = 3$.

Before we apply the method of elimination to the solution of a system of linear equations involving more than two variables, let us first find a general *symbolic solution* for any system of two linear equations in the two variables x_1 and x_2, namely,

$$\begin{aligned} a_{11}x_1 + a_{12}x_2 &= b_1 \\ a_{21}x_1 + a_{22}x_2 &= b_2 \end{aligned}$$

The reason why we refer to the two variables as x_1 and x_2 (instead of x and y) is that we can easily generalize this notation; if there are more than two variables, we denote the others x_3, x_4, x_5, ... Observe also that each *x-coefficient* has *two subscripts;* the first subscript is 1 or 2 depending on whether the coefficient is in the first equation or in the second, and the second subscript is 1 or 2 depending on whether the coefficient goes with x_1 or x_2. The subscript of the *constant terms* on the right-hand side is 1 or 2 depending on the equation. An obvious advantage of this whole notation is that it can easily be generalized to handle more than two linear equations in more than two variables (see Exercise 3 on page 201).

Now, to eliminate x_2 and thus get a solution for x_1, we first multiply the expressions on both sides of the first equation by a_{22} and those on both sides of the second equation by a_{12}. This gives

$$a_{11}a_{22}x_1 + a_{12}a_{22}x_2 = b_1a_{22}$$
$$a_{21}a_{12}x_1 + a_{22}a_{12}x_2 = b_2a_{12}$$

and if we then subtract the expressions on the respective sides of these two equations and factor out x_1, we get

$$a_{11}a_{22}x_1 - a_{21}a_{12}x_1 = b_1a_{22} - b_2a_{12}$$

and

$$x_1(a_{11}a_{22} - a_{21}a_{12}) = b_1a_{22} - b_2a_{12}$$

Dividing by $a_{11}a_{22} - a_{21}a_{12}$, we finally get

$$x_1 = \frac{b_1a_{22} - b_2a_{12}}{a_{11}a_{22} - a_{21}a_{12}}$$

provided that $a_{11}a_{22} - a_{21}a_{12}$ is *not* equal to zero. It will be left to the reader to verify in Exercise 2 on page 201 that if we had eliminated x_1 instead of x_2, we would have obtained the following solution for x_2:

$$x_2 = \frac{a_{11}b_2 - a_{21}b_1}{a_{11}a_{22} - a_{21}a_{12}}$$

provided again that $a_{11}a_{22} - a_{21}a_{12}$ is *not* equal to zero.

With these formulas we can now solve (or at least try to solve) any system of two linear equations in two variables—all we have to do is substitute into the formulas the given coefficients and constant terms. Referring again to the system of equations which we have used as an illustration throughout this section (with x and y replaced by x_1 and x_2), we find that the solution of

$$2x_1 + 3x_2 = 5$$
$$-5x_1 - 2x_2 = 4$$

can be written directly as

$$x_1 = \frac{5(-2) - 4(3)}{2(-2) - (-5)3} = \frac{-22}{11} = -2$$

and

$$x_2 = \frac{2(4) - (-5)5}{2(-2) - (-5)3} = \frac{33}{11} = 3$$

Since the method of elimination is very easy and straightforward, it would hardly seem worthwhile to memorize the above formulas for x_1 and x_2. Indeed, we have given them partly for future reference (see page 271), and partly to find the conditions under which the method of elimination will not work. Since we cannot divide by zero, the method fails when $a_{11}a_{22} - a_{21}a_{12} = 0$; this can also be written as $a_{11}a_{22} = a_{21}a_{12}$ or as

$$\frac{a_{11}}{a_{12}} = \frac{a_{21}}{a_{22}}$$

and we thus find that the method of elimination fails when the x_1- and x_2-coefficients of the two equations are proportional. Geometrically speaking, this means that the method of elimination fails *when the two lines have the same slope*, as can be seen by rewriting the two equations in *explicit form* solved for x_2 (taking the place of y), namely, as

$$x_2 = \frac{b_1}{a_{12}} - \frac{a_{11}}{a_{12}}x_1 \qquad \text{and} \qquad x_2 = \frac{b_2}{a_{22}} - \frac{a_{21}}{a_{22}}x_1$$

This whole argument certainly stands to reason—we will not get a unique solution (one value for x_1 and one value for x_2) unless the two lines intersect as in Figure 7.1, and this means that they cannot possibly have the same slope.

When two lines do have the same slope, there are two possibilities: *either the lines are parallel and do not intersect, or they coincide and have infinitely many points in common.* To illustrate the first possibility, consider the system

$$\begin{aligned} 2x_1 - 3x_2 &= 6 \\ 4x_1 - 6x_2 &= -18 \end{aligned}$$

where the x_1- and x_2-coefficients are evidently proportional. If we tried to use the method of elimination and multiplied both sides of the first equation by 2, we would get

$$\begin{aligned} 4x_1 - 6x_2 &= 12 \\ 4x_1 - 6x_2 &= -18 \end{aligned}$$

and "subtracting equals from equals" we get $0 = 30$, which obviously cannot be correct. Thus, the system of equations has no solution and we say that the equations are *inconsistent;* as can be seen from Figure 7.2, the two lines are parallel and have no points in common.

To illustrate the other possibility, consider the system

$$\begin{aligned} 2x_1 - 3x_2 &= 6 \\ 10x_1 - 15x_2 &= 30 \end{aligned}$$

where the x_1- and x_2-coefficients are again proportional. This time, however, the equations are *not inconsistent;* in fact, if we multiply the expressions on both sides of the first equation by 5, we get $10x_1 - 15x_2 = 30$, and it can be seen that the two equations are actually *equivalent.* They represent the same line, or to put it differently, the two lines coincide. In this case there are infinitely many solutions and the coordinates of any point on the line $2x_1 - 3x_2 = 6$ is automatically a solution of the system

$$\begin{aligned} 2x_1 - 3x_2 &= 6 \\ 10x_1 - 15x_2 &= 30 \end{aligned}$$

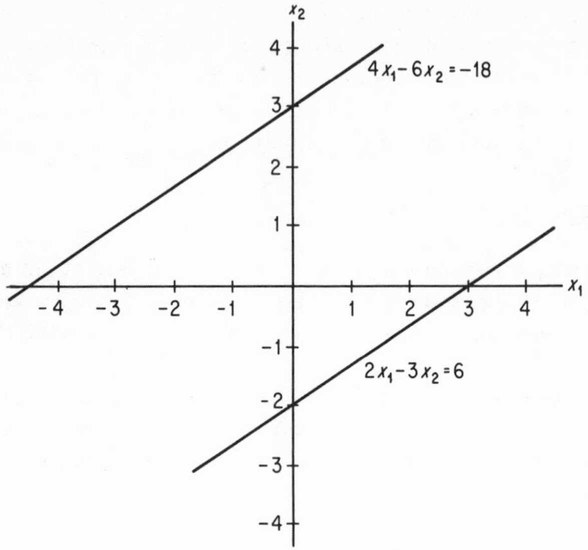

FIG. 7.2

As can be seen from Figure 7.3, where we have plotted the graph of the line $2x_1 - 3x_2 = 6$, the infinite set of solutions includes $x_1 = 3$ and $x_2 = 0$, $x_1 = 0$ and $x_2 = -2$, and $x_1 = 6$ and $x_2 = 2$.

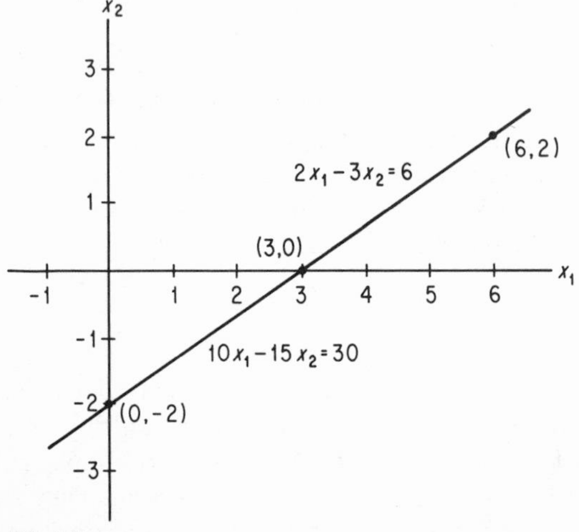

FIG. 7.3

The method of elimination can also be used to solve a system of three linear equations in three variables, a system of four linear equations in four variables, and so on. To illustrate how it works for a system of three linear equations in three variables, let us consider the system

$$\begin{aligned} x_1 - 2x_2 + x_3 &= 8 \\ 3x_1 + 5x_2 + 7x_3 &= 6 \\ 2x_1 - 3x_2 - 5x_3 &= 7 \end{aligned}$$

The first step is to eliminate one of the variables, thus reducing the problem to that of having to solve a system of two linear equations in the other two variables. To this end we choose *two pairs* of equations (including each equation at least once) and eliminate the chosen variable from each pair. For instance, to eliminate x_1 and thus obtain a system of two linear equations in x_2 and x_3, let us eliminate x_1 from the first two equations and also from the first and third. Multiplying the expressions on both sides of the first equation by 3 and leaving the second equation as is, we get

$$\begin{aligned} 3x_1 - 6x_2 + 3x_3 &= 24 \\ 3x_1 + 5x_2 + 7x_3 &= 6 \end{aligned}$$

and then, by subtraction,

$$-11x_2 - 4x_3 = 18$$

Similarly, to eliminate x_1 from the first and third equations we multiply the expressions on both sides of the first equation by 2, leave the third equation as is, and get

$$\begin{aligned} 2x_1 - 4x_2 + 2x_3 &= 16 \\ 2x_1 - 3x_2 - 5x_3 &= 7 \end{aligned}$$

Then, subtracting "equals from equals," we obtain

$$-x_2 + 7x_3 = 9$$

and this leaves us with the following system of two linear equations in x_2 and x_3:

$$\begin{aligned} -11x_2 - 4x_3 &= 18 \\ -x_2 + 7x_3 &= 9 \end{aligned}$$

Now we are on familiar grounds, and we can continue the method of elimination, say, by multiplying the expressions on both sides of the second equation by 11, leaving the first equation as is, and then subtracting "equals from equals." This gives

$$\begin{aligned} -11x_2 - 4x_3 &= 18 \\ -11x_2 + 77x_3 &= 99 \end{aligned}$$

and

$$-81x_3 = -81$$

Hence, $x_3 = 1$, and if we substitute this result into the equation $-x_2 + 7x_3 = 9$, we get $-x_2 + 7(1) = 9$ and $x_2 = -2$. Finally, substituting $x_2 = -2$ and $x_3 = 1$ into any one of the original equations we get $x_1 = 3$, and we have thus shown that the given system of equations has the unique solution $x_1 = 3$, $x_2 = -2$, and $x_3 = 1$. It is a sound practice to check results like this by substituting the values obtained into the original equations. For our example we thus get

$$\begin{aligned} (3) - 2(-2) + (1) &= 3 + 4 + 1 = 8 \\ 3(3) + 5(-2) + 7(1) &= 9 - 10 + 7 = 6 \\ 2(3) - 3(-2) - 5(1) &= 6 + 6 - 5 = 7 \end{aligned}$$

which checks.

When we deal with a system of three linear equations in three variables it can also happen that there are no solutions or that there are infinitely many. Geometrically speaking, we are now dealing with three *planes*, and there are all sorts of possibilities: the three planes may have only one point in common as in our example, and there is a unique solution; the three planes may have infinitely many points in common, which happens when they all intersect in a line or when they all coincide; or they may be *inconsistent* and have no points in common, which happens when all three planes are parallel or when the line in which two of the planes intersect is parallel to (does not intersect) the third plane. These various possibilities are illustrated in Exercise 5 on page 201.

When we apply the method of elimination to the solution of a system of linear equations, we usually begin by eliminating the variable whose coefficients are the smallest numbers (or, at least, the numbers that are easiest to work with). This is why we began by eliminating x_1 in our last illustration, although we could just as well have begun by eliminating x_2 or x_3. A more systematic (though not necessarily easier) way of applying the method of elimination is indicated in Exercise 6 on page 202.

To apply the method of elimination to situations involving more than three linear equations in as many variables, we simply eliminate one variable at a time. In each step we reduce *by one* the number of variables as well as the number of equations, and if we were asked to solve a system of four linear equations in four variables, we would begin by first eliminating one of the variables from three different pairs of these equations. This would leave a system of three linear equations in three variables which can be solved by applying the method of elimination (as in our last illustration). Generally speaking, though, the method of elimination becomes rather tedious when there are more than three variables, and it is preferable in that case to use one of the alternate techniques which we shall discuss in Chapter 9; as we shall see, these methods have the added advantage that they lend themselves more readily to computer applications.

EXERCISES

1. Use the method of elimination to solve each of the following systems of linear equations:

(a) $x + y = 7$
$x - y = 1$

(b) $2x - y = 3$
$x + 2y = 5$

(c) $3u - 2v = 21$
$4u + 5v = 5$

(d) $x_1 - 2x_2 = 2$
$6x_1 + 8x_2 = 5$

(e) $x + 3y - 2z = 7$
$3x - y - 2z = 7$
$2x + 2y + z = 5$

(f) $2x_1 + 5x_2 + 8x_3 = 1$
$3x_1 - 4x_2 - 3x_3 = 5$
$4x_1 - 6x_2 - 2x_3 = 4$

2. Duplicating the method used in the text, verify the symbolic solution for x_2 given on page 196. Also use these formulas for x_1 and x_2 to check the results obtained in parts (a), (b), (c), and (d) of Exercise 1.

3. Generalizing the notation on page 195, write each of the following systems of equations in symbolic form:

(a) three linear equations in x_1, x_2, and x_3;
(b) four linear equations in x_1, x_2, x_3, and x_4.

4. Check whether the following pairs of lines have the same slope. If they do have the same slope, check also whether the lines are *parallel* (namely, whether the equations are *inconsistent* and have no common solutions) or whether they *coincide* (namely, whether the equations are *equivalent* and have infinitely many common solutions); if the lines do not have the same slope, find their point of intersection.

(a) $2x - 3y = 5$
$6x - 9y = 8$

(b) $3x + 5y = 2$
$21x + 35y = 14$

(c) $2x + 5y = 11$
$2x - 5y = 1$

(d) $3x + 12y = -9$
$-2x - 8y = 6$

(e) $2x + 3y = 4$
$3x + 2y = 11$

(f) $3x - 6y = 8$
$-5x + 10y = 12$

5. Verify the following assertions concerning the respective systems of three linear equations in three variables and the planes which they represent:

(a) The planes represented by $x - 2y + 3z = 5$, $2x - 4y + 6z = 7$, and $-3x + 6y - 9z = 13$ are *all parallel*; that is, all possible pairs of equations are *inconsistent.*

(b) The planes represented by $4x - 6y + 10z = 8$, $8x - 12y + 20z = 16$, and $-6x + 9y - 15z = -12$ coincide; the system of equations has infinitely many solutions including $x = 1$, $y = 1$, $z = 1$, and also $x = 5$, $y = 2$, $z = 0$, and $x = 5$, $y = -3$, and $z = -3$, as can be checked by substitution.

(c) The equations $x - 2y + z = 5$, $x + 3y - 3z = 1$, and $2x + y - 2z = 3$

are *inconsistent*, but the planes which they represent are not all parallel. (*Hint:* to show that the equations are inconsistent, add the expressions on the respective sides of the first two equations and compare the result with the third equation; to show that they are not all parallel, verify that the point (4, 0, 1) lies on the first two planes, that the point (4, 1, 3) lies on the first and the third, and that the point (1, −1, −1) lies on the second and the third.)

6. A systematic way of applying the method of elimination to the solution of a system of k linear equations in k variables is to eliminate the first variable from the second equation, the first two variables from the third equation, the first three variables from the fourth equation, and so on. The value of the kth variable x_k can then be read off the kth equation, and, working backwards, substitution of the value of x_k into the $(k - 1)$th equation gives the value of x_{k-1}, substitution of the values of x_k and x_{k-1} into the $(k - 2)$th equation gives the value of x_{k-2}, and so on. Use this method to solve the following system of linear equations:

$$\begin{aligned} x_1 - 3x_2 + 5x_3 &= 2 \\ 2x_1 + 2x_2 - 3x_3 &= 2 \\ 3x_1 - x_2 + 4x_3 &= 8 \end{aligned}$$

7. In Section 4.3 we used the *two-point formula* to find the equation of the line which passes through two given points. An alternate way is to write the equation of the line as $y = a + bx$, substitute *separately* the coordinates of each point, and then solve the resulting system of equations for a and b.

   (a) Use this alternate method to find the equation of the line which passes through the points (3, 2) and (5, 3), and compare the result with that obtained for part (c) of Exercise 8 on page 102.
   (b) Use this alternate method to find the equation of the line which passes through the points (−1, 2) and (3, 8), and compare the result with that obtained for part (d) of Exercise 8 on page 102.

8. A bakery sells two kinds of cakes for which it charges p_1 dollars a piece and p_2 dollars a piece, respectively. If the supply and the demand for the first kind of cake are given by

$$S_1 = 58 + 20p_1 - 5p_2 \quad \text{and} \quad D_1 = 100 - 10p_1 + 5p_2$$

while the supply and the demand for the second kind of cake are given by

$$S_2 = 152 - 15p_1 + 40p_2 \quad \text{and} \quad D_2 = 200 + 5p_1 - 30p_2$$

how should they price the two kinds of cake so that the market for both kinds of cake will be in *equilibrium*, namely, so that for each kind of cake supply equals demand? (*Hint:* equate S_1 to D_1 and S_2 to D_2, and solve the resulting system of equations for p_1 and p_2.)

9. A company makes two kinds of machine parts. The first kind requires 4 hours of labor, 2.5 pounds of raw material, and can be produced at a cost of \$18.80; the second kind requires 3 hours of labor, 4 pounds of raw material, and can be

produced at a cost of \$19.20. What is the cost of labor per hour and the cost of the raw material per pound?

10. FITTING A PARABOLA THROUGH THREE POINTS. To find the equation of the parabola $y = a + bx + cx^2$ which passes through three given points, we have only to substitute *separately* the coordinates of each point, and then solve the resulting system of equations for a, b, and c. Using this method to find the equation of the parabola which passes through the points (19, 26), (21, 16), and (22, 14), solve the system of equations

$$\begin{aligned} 26 &= a + 19b + 361c \\ 16 &= a + 21b + 441c \\ 14 &= a + 22b + 484c \end{aligned}$$

and thus verify the equation given on page 111.

11. LEAST SQUARES CURVE FITTING. If the overall pattern of a set of points representing observed data can be described by means of a straight line, the equation of the line *which best fits the given data* is generally found by the *method of least squares.* The theory which underlies this method will be discussed near the end of Chapter 13; for the present, let us merely state the result that the constants a and b in $y = a + bx$ are obtained by solving the system of linear equations

$$\begin{aligned} \textstyle\sum y &= a \cdot n + b(\textstyle\sum x) \\ \textstyle\sum xy &= a(\textstyle\sum x) + b(\textstyle\sum x^2) \end{aligned}$$

Here n is the number of points, $\sum x$ stands for the sum of their x-coordinates, $\sum x^2$ stands for the sum of the squares of their x-coordinates, $\sum y$ stands for the sum of the y-coordinates of the n points, and $\sum xy$ stands for the sum of the products obtained by multiplying the x- and y-coordinates of each point.

(a) Referring to the income and clothing data on page 78, verify that $n = 8$, $\sum x = 47{,}500$, $\sum x^2 = 321{,}790{,}000$, $\sum y = 3970$, and $\sum xy = 26{,}632{,}000$.

(b) Solve the resulting system of equations

$$\begin{aligned} 3{,}970 &= 8a + 47{,}500b \\ 26{,}632{,}000 &= 47{,}500a + 321{,}790{,}000b \end{aligned}$$

for a and b, and thus verify the equation of the *least-squares line* given on page 79.

12. LEAST SQUARES CURVE FITTING, CONTINUED. The total cost of magazine advertising placed during the years 1955 through 1962 was 657, 692, 739, 693, 784, 854, 836, and 876 million dollars.

(a) Coding the years so that 1955 corresponds to $x = -3$, 1956 corresponds to $x = -2$, 1957 corresponds to $x = -1$, . . . , and 1962 corresponds to $x = 4$, show that for these $n = 8$ data points $\sum x = 4$, $\sum x^2 = 44$, $\sum y = 6{,}131$, and $\sum xy = 4{,}410$.

(b) Substituting the appropriate quantities into the two equations of

Exercise 11 and solving for a and b, show that the equation of the line which best fits the given data is

$$y = 750 + 32x$$

(c) Plot the original data and the line obtained in part (b) in one diagram, and judge (by eye) how well the line fits the given data.
(d) Use the equation obtained in part (b) to predict the total cost of magazine advertising for the year 1970. (*Hint:* be careful to substitute the correct coded value of x.)

The reason why the method of least squares is used in problems of this kind is explained in Section 13.4.

13. Suppose that the SEC wants to untangle the interlocking directorate of three utility companies on the basis of the following information: the first company has 20 directors, the second has 16, and the third has 19; 7 of these directors serve only on the Board of the first company, 6 serve only on the Board of the second company, 4 serve only on the Board of the third company, and 2 serve on the Board of all three companies.

(a) if x of the directors serve only on the Board of the first and third companies, y of the directors serve only on the Board of the first and second companies, while z of the directors serve only on the Board of the second and third companies, show that these three variables must satisfy the system of equations

$$\begin{aligned} x + y \quad\quad &= 11 \\ y + z &= 8 \\ x \quad\quad + z &= 13 \end{aligned}$$

(*Hint:* draw a Venn diagram like that of Figure 1.5 on page 13, with the three circles representing the three Boards of Directors, and then proceed as in the illustrations on pages 13 and 14.)
(b) Solve the system of equations of part (a).
(c) How many of the directors of the first company serve also on the Board of the third company, and how many of the directors of the third company serve also on the Board of the second company?

7.3 INEQUALITIES

An important property of the real numbers is that they are *ordered.* In Chapter 2 we pictured this ordering along a line as in Figure 2.2, with the greater number always to the right and the smaller one to the left. As we also pointed out on page 38, one (and only one) of the following must be true for any two elements of an *ordered field,* and, hence, for any two real numbers a and b:

a equals b, which we write as $a = b$; a is greater than b, which we write as $a > b$; or a is less than b, which we write as $a < b$.

To check whether a real number a is less than, equal to, or greater than a real number b we have only to observe their difference; if $a - b$ is *negative* then a is less than b, if $a - b$ is *zero* then a equals b, and if $a - b$ is *positive* then a is greater than b. Thus, -10 is less than -7 since $-10 - (-7) = -3$, which is *negative;* of course, this is also apparent from a diagram like that of Figure 2.2, where -10 lies to the left of -7.

Many of the rules which apply to *equalities* apply also to *inequalities*, that is, to expressions involving $<$ and $>$. For example, where $a = b$ and $b = c$ implies that $a = c$ for any real numbers a, b, and c, we now have

Rule 1: *If $a > b$ and $b > c$, then $a > c$.*

Thus, if Mr. Jones makes more money than Mr. Brown and Mr. Brown more money than Mr. Smith, then Mr. Jones makes more money than Mr. Smith.

So far as *adding equals to equals* is concerned, we can also add *equals to unequals* by making use of the fact that

Rule 2: *If $a > b$, then $a + c > b + c$.*

For instance, if one car is more expensive than another but the license fee is the same, then the total amount spent for the first car exceeds that spent for the second. We can also add *unequals to unequals* provided the two inequalities have the *same sense* (go in the same direction); to this end we make use of

Rule 3: *If $a > b$ and $c > d$, then $a + c > b + d$.*

Thus, if Mr. White is older than Mrs. White and Mr. Adams is older than Mrs. Adams, then the sum of the ages of the two men exceeds that of the ages of the two women. Observe, however, that we cannot say whether the sum of the ages of Mr. and Mrs. White exceeds that of the ages of Mr. and Mrs. Adams, and we cannot compare the sum of the ages of Mr. White and Mrs. Adams with that of the ages of Mr. Adams and Mrs. White.

Although we phrased Rule 2 so that it applies to the *addition of equals to unequals*, it applies also to the *subtraction of equals from unequals.* To demonstrate this we have only to point out that subtracting 3 or -5, for example, is the same as adding -3 or $+5$. Thus, if Mr. Green makes more money than Mr. Peters but their payroll deductions are the same, then Mr. Green's take-home pay will exceed that of Mr. Peters. So far as Rule 3 is concerned, it is easy to make up examples which demonstrate that this kind of argument will *not* work; for instance, $10 > 5$ and $12 > 2$, but $10 - 12$ is *not* greater than $5 - 2$.

So far as the *multiplication of equals by equals* is concerned, we have to be careful when it comes to inequalities. To *multiply unequals by equals*, we use

Rule 4: *If $a > b$, then $ac > bc$ when c is positive and $ac < bc$ when c is negative.*

Observe that when c is positive the sense (direction) of the inequality remains the same, but when c is negative the sense of the inequality is reversed. For example, whereas $13 > 5$ implies that $13 \cdot 2 > 5 \cdot 2$ (or $26 > 10$), it also implies that $13(-2) < 5(-2)$, namely, that $-26 < -10$. Also, if a share of IBM costs more than a share of GE, then 50 shares of IBM will cost more than 50 shares of GE; on the other hand, if someone has ordered (but not yet paid for) these shares, then 50 shares of IBM will leave him with less money in the bank than 50 shares of GE.

We can also multiply *unequals by unequals*, provided the numbers are all positive and the inequalities have the same sense (go in the same direction); in that case we have

Rule 5: *If a, b, c, and d are all positive and $a > b$ and $c > d$, then $ac > bd$.*

For example, if a pound of butter costs more than a pound of margarine, then 5 pounds of butter cost more than 2 pounds of margarine. Note, however, that we cannot tell whether 2 pounds of butter cost more than 5 pounds of margarine. Also, $4 > 2$ and $-2 > -3$ does *not* imply that $4(-2) > 2(-3)$; in fact, -8 is *less than* -6.

Although we phrased Rule 4 so that it applies to the *multiplication of unequals by equals*, it applies also to the *division of unequals by equals*. To demonstrate this we have only to point out that dividing by 4 or -7, for example, is the same as multiplying by $1/4$ or $-1/7$. Thus, if one house costs more than another, then a one third down-payment on the first will cost more than a one third down-payment on the other. So far as Rule 5 is concerned, we can easily make up examples which demonstrate that this kind of argument will *not* work; for instance, $15 > 10$ and $5 > 2$, but $15 \div 5$ is *not* greater than $10 \div 2$.

There are many other rules about inequalities which are immediate consequences of the five rules which we have discussed (see Exercise 3 on page 211). Above all, it should be observed that Rules 1 through 5 hold also when we substitute $<$ for $>$ and *vice versa*.

It is customary to refer to $a > b$ and $a < b$ as *strict* (or *strong*) inequalities and to $a \geqslant b$ (which reads "a is greater than or equal to b") and $a \leqslant b$ (which reads "a is less than or equal to b") as the corresponding *weak* inequalities. This notation makes it possible to simplify (abbreviate) certain statements involving inequalities. For instance, the statement "the bank pays at least 4 percent interest" can be written as $i \geqslant 4\%$ instead of $i > 4\%$ *or* $i = 4\%$. Similarly, if a job is open to anyone who is at most 45 years old, we can express this by writing $y \leqslant 45$ (where y is a person's age) instead of $y < 45$ *or* $y = 45$.

So far as the manipulation of weak inequalities is concerned, it can easily be shown that all the rules which apply to $>$ and $<$ apply also to $\geqslant$ and $\leqslant$. We have to be careful, though, when we *combine* weak and strong inequalities; for instance, if $a \geqslant b$, $b > c$, $c > d$, and $d \geqslant e$, all we can say about a and e is that $a > e$.

Inequalities such as $3 > 2$, $5 < 7$, and $x + 1 > x$ are referred to as *absolute inequalities*—the first two simply express true relationships between numbers, and the other one holds regardless of what value we might substitute for x. In contrast, $x > 3$, $2x - 5 < 7$, and $x^2 > 4$ are referred to as *conditional inequalities*—they hold for some, but not all, values of x. Among infinitely many other possibilities, $x > 3$ holds for $x = 5$ or $x = 11$ but not for $x = 0$ or $x = -3$; $2x - 5 < 7$ holds for $x = 1$ or $x = 2$ but not for $x = 6$ or $x = 10$; and $x^2 > 4$ holds for $x = -5$ or $x = 3$, but not for $x = 1$ or $x = -1/2$.

In the remainder of this chapter we shall be concerned mostly with conditional inequalities; in particular, we shall learn how to *solve* conditional inequalities, namely, how to determine for what values of the variable (or the variables) given inequalities are true. To give an example, suppose that a used-car dealer budgets \$500 for television advertising, and that a local television station charges \$80 for a one-minute commercial during the late late show. The question is, *how many of these commercials can the dealer afford*? If we denote the unknown number of commercials with the letter x, their cost is $80x$, and we obtain the inequality

$$80x \leqslant 500$$

which expresses the fact that the cost of the commercials cannot exceed but could equal \$500. If we now multiply the expressions on both sides of this inequality by $1/80$ (or divide by 80), we get

$$x \leqslant \frac{500}{80} \qquad \text{or} \qquad x \leqslant 6\frac{1}{4}$$

and we find that the used-car dealer can afford at most 6 commercials.

To consider another example, suppose that Mr. Black, who has \$4,000 in his savings account, wants to use some of his money to buy a certain kind of stock which sells for \$62 a share, but he does not want the balance of his savings account to go below \$1,500. If he buys x shares, he will have to take $62x$ dollars out of his savings account, which leaves him a balance of $4{,}000 - 62x$; since this balance is not supposed to go below \$1,500, we can write

$$4{,}000 - 62x \geqslant 1{,}500$$

and the problem is to solve this inequality for x. If we subtract 4,000 from the expressions on both sides of the inequality (or add $-4{,}000$ in accordance with Rule 2), we get

$$-62x \geqslant -2{,}500$$

and if we then divide the expressions on both sides of the inequality by -62 (or multiply by $-1/62$ in accordance with Rule 4), we get

$$x \leqslant \frac{-2{,}500}{-62} \qquad \text{or} \qquad x \leqslant 40\frac{20}{62}$$

This means that he can buy at most 40 shares. Observe that the *sense* (or direction) of the inequality became reversed when we divided by -62.

To simplify our notation, we sometimes write two inequalities as one, and call it a *double inequality*. For instance, if x, the asking-price for a piece of property, exceeds \$12,000 but is not more than \$15,000, we can express this by writing

$$\$12{,}000 < x \leqslant \$15{,}000$$

instead of $x > \$12{,}000$ *and* $x \leqslant \$15{,}000$. This is simply a short-hand notation, and we can still apply the various rules so long as we keep in mind that we are actually dealing with two inequalities. To illustrate, suppose that an opinion poll estimates on the basis of sample data that a certain candidate will get 55.6 percent of the vote, and that the research workers conducting the poll are *practically certain* that the error of this estimate is less than 4.5 percent. Now, if p denotes the *true* percentage of the votes the candidate will actually get, their error is given by the difference $55.6 - p$, and the double inequality

$$-4.5 < 55.6 - p < 4.5$$

expresses the fact that their error is less than 4.5 percent either way. (If their estimate is too high, $55.6 - p$ will be positive but less than 4.5, and if their estimate is too low, $55.6 - p$ will be negative but greater than -4.5.) If we now multiply -4.5, $55.6 - p$, as well as 4.5 by -1, we get

$$4.5 > p - 55.6 > -4.5$$

according to Rule 4, and if we then add 55.6 to each term we get

$$60.1 > p > 51.1$$

according to Rule 2. Rewriting this double inequality as

$$51.1 < p < 60.1$$

with the smallest term on the left and the largest term on the right, we find that the persons conducting the poll can be *practically certain* that the candidate will get between 51.1 and 60.1 percent of the vote.

Geometrically, this result may be indicated as in the first diagram of Figure 7.4. Had the operators of the poll claimed that their error is at most 4.5 percent, then the solution for the true percentage (of votes the candidate will get) would have been

$$51.1 \leqslant p \leqslant 60.1$$

and we could have indicated this geometrically as in the second diagram of Figure 7.4, where the heavy dots are meant to indicate that the endpoints

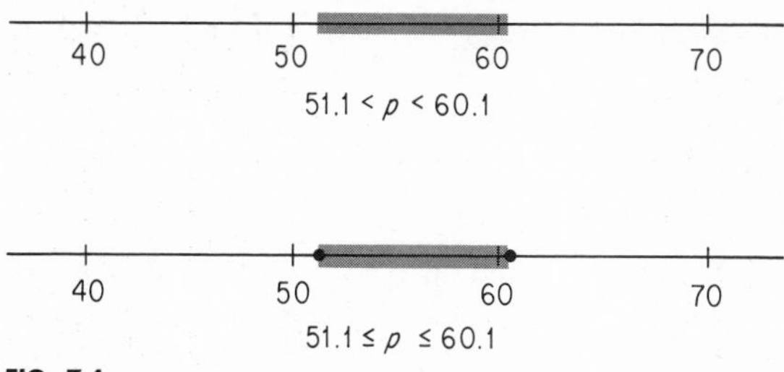

FIG. 7.4

of the interval are included. Actually, there are various ways of indicating whether or not an endpoint is included; two ways of indicating that the asking-price for a piece of property exceeds \$12,000 but is not more than \$15,000 are shown in Figure 7.5.

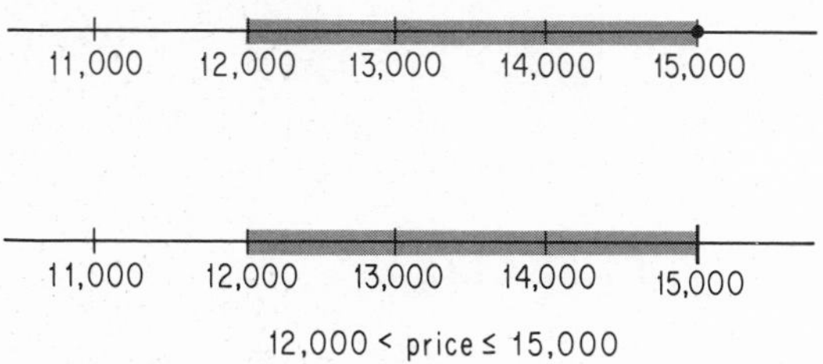

FIG. 7.5

Inequalities can also be simplified at times by using *absolute values*. As we indicated in Exercise 9 on page 81, the absolute value of any real number x is denoted $|x|$, and $|x| = x$ when x is positive or zero, while $|x| = -x$ when x is negative. For example, $|13| = 13$, $|-7| = 7$, and $|-22| = -(-22) = 22$, and it is worth noting that we use absolute values whenever we are interested in the *magnitude* of a quantity and not in its sign. With reference to the example on page 208, we could thus have expressed the pollster's claim (that the error of his estimate is less than 4.5 percent) by writing

$$|55.6 - p| < 4.5$$

The error is given by the difference between the estimate of 55.6 and the true value p, and the inequality asserts that the *magnitude* of this error is less than 4.5.

In general, if a is a positive real number, then $|x| < a$ means that x is *numerically less* than a, namely, that x falls *inside of* the interval from $-a$ to a; symbolically, $|x| < a$ is thus equivalent to $-a < x < a$. By the same token, $|x| > a$ means that x is *numerically greater* than a, namely, that x falls *outside of* the interval from $-a$ to a; symbolically, $|x| > a$ is thus equivalent to $x < -a$ *or* $x > a$. For example, $|x - 2| < 3$ is equivalent to $-3 < x - 2 < 3$, and, hence, to

$$-1 < x < 5$$

and $|x + 4| \geqslant 2$ is equivalent to $x + 4 \leqslant -2$ *or* $x + 4 \geqslant 2$, and, hence, to

$$x \leqslant -6 \quad \text{or} \quad x \geqslant -2$$

Geometrically, the values of x for which $|x - 2| < 3$ and $|x + 4| \geqslant 2$ are represented by the intervals shaded in the two diagrams of Figure 7.6.

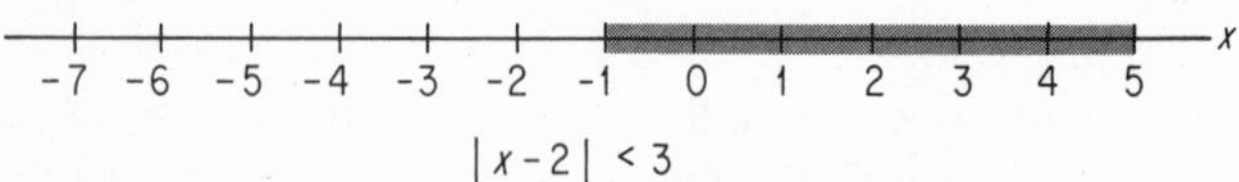

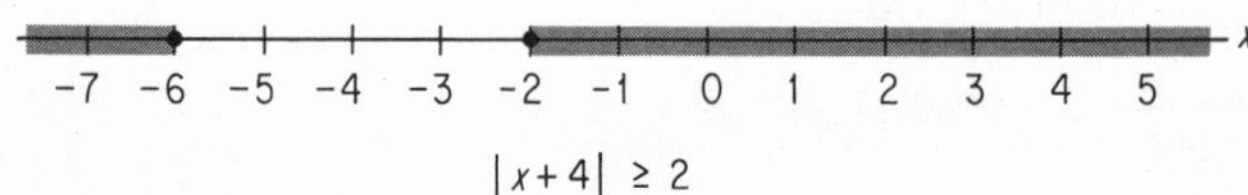

FIG. 7.6

EXERCISES

1. Which of the following inequalities are true and which are false:

(a) $12 > -9$; (d) $3 \geqslant 3$; (g) $2/5 < 3/6$;
(b) $13 < 10$; (e) $-6 > -8$; (h) $-1 \geqslant -1$;
(c) $5/4 > 4/3$; (f) $-5 > -3$; (i) $-2 \geqslant 0$.

2. Perform each of the following operations:

(a) Add 12 to the expressions on both sides of the inequality $x - 12 > 3$;

(b) Multiply the expressions on both sides of the inequality $\frac{1}{2}x < 4$ by 2;

(c) Multiply the expressions on both sides of the inequality $-3x \leqslant 6$ by $-1/3$;

(d) Subtract 4 from the expressions on both sides of the inequality $2x + 4 > 7$;
(e) Divide the expressions on both sides of the inequality $-5x < 15$ by -5.

3. Use the five rules on pages 205 and 206 to prove:

(a) If $a > b$, then $-a < -b$;

(b) If a and b are positive real numbers and $a > b$, then $\frac{1}{b} > \frac{1}{a}$; (*Hint:* divide the expressions on both sides of the inequality $a > b$ by ab.)

(c) Use the result of part (b) to show that if a, b, and c are positive real numbers and $a > b$, then $c/a < c/b$.

(d) If a and b are positive real numbers and $a > b$, then $a^2 > b^2$. (*Hint:* multiply the expressions on both sides of the inequality $a > b$ by a, also multiply them by b, and combine the two results with the use of Rule 1 on page 205.)

4. When a variable must satisfy two inequalities, it can happen that the inequalities are *inconsistent* (that is, no value of x can satisfy both) or that one of them is *redundant* (that is, one of the inequalities automatically takes care of the other). Check whether either of these situations arises in the following examples:

(a) $x > 3$ and $x > 2$;
(b) $x \geqslant 2$ and $x \leqslant 4$;
(c) $x < 5$ and $x \geqslant 7$;
(d) $x < -1$ and $x > 1$;
(e) $x \leqslant -1$ and $x \geqslant -3$;
(f) $x > -10$ and $x \leqslant 12$.

5. Solve the following inequalities and indicate the result graphically as in Figures 7.4 and 7.5:

(a) $2x - 3 > 5$:
(b) $3x + 2 \leqslant 14$;
(c) $\frac{1}{2}x - 2 > \frac{3}{2}$;
(d) $5 - 2x > 3$;
(e) $3 + \frac{x}{3} \geqslant 1$;
(f) $\frac{2}{x} > \frac{3}{4}$;

[*Hint:* note that x cannot be negative or zero in part (f).]

6. An automatic freight elevator designed to carry a maximum load of 4,000 pounds is being used to lift pianos weighing 320 pounds each. Set up an inequality that must be satisfied by x, the number of pianos which the elevator can lift at one time. What is the greatest number of pianos the elevator can lift?

7. A certain health ordinance requires that there be at least 130 cubic feet of "breathing space" per customer in the banquet room of a hotel. Set up an inequality that must be satisfied by x, the number of customers allowed in a banquet room which is 50 feet long, 40 feet wide, and 12 feet high. What is the greatest number of customers allowed in this banquet room?

8. The sales manager of a department store predicts that the store's 1970 sales will be within \$200,000 of \$3,000,000. Set up inequalities for x, the store's actual 1970 sales,

(a) using absolute values;
(b) without using absolute values.

9. A stockbroker claims that during the next six months the price of a certain stock will stay within \$2.50 of its current price of \$58.25. Express the broker's claim in terms of inequalities for x, the price of the stock,

(a) using absolute values;
(b) without using absolute values.

10. Rewrite the following inequalities without absolute values, and indicate the results graphically as in Figure 7.6:

(a) $|x| < 4$; (c) $|2x - 5| \leqslant 3$;
(b) $|x + 5| \geqslant 1$; (d) $|3x + 1| > 4$.

7.4 SYSTEMS OF LINEAR INEQUALITIES

Every line divides the plane into *two regions*. The graph of $3x + 4y = 24$, for example, divides the plane into the two regions shown in Figure 7.7—the one that is shaded represents the inequality $3x + 4y > 24$, which means that the coordinates of any point in that region satisfy (are a solution of) the inequality $3x + 4y > 24$; the other region correspondingly represents the inequality $3x + 4y < 24$. It is customary to refer to the shaded region of Figure 7.7 as the *graph* (or the *solution set*) of the inequality $3x + 4y > 24$, and to the other region as the *graph* (or the *solution set*) of the inequality $3x + 4y < 24$.

If the equality sign of a linear equation is replaced by $<$, $>$, $\leqslant$, or $\geqslant$, we refer to the resulting inequality as a *linear inequality*. For two variables, the graph of a linear inequality consists of one of the two regions into which the line representing the corresponding equation divides the plane, and whether or not the line, itself, is included depends on whether the inequality is weak or strong. Thus, the graph of $3x + 4y \geqslant 24$ consists of the shaded region of Figure 7.7 as well as the line $3x + 4y = 24$.

To plot the graph of a linear inequality in two variables, we first draw the line which represents the corresponding equality, and then we decide which of the two regions corresponds to the original inequality, and whether the line, itself, is to be included. For instance, to plot the graph of $x - y - 1 \geqslant 0$, we first draw the line $x - y - 1 = 0$ as in Figure 7.8. Then we take an arbitrary point that is *easy to plot* (the origin, for example, provided it does not lie on the line) and check whether its coordinates satisfy the inequality—this enables us to decide which of the two regions belongs to the graph of the given inequality. Since $x = 0$ and $y = 0$ obviously do *not* satisfy the inequality $x - y - 1 \geqslant 0$, we conclude that the region which does *not* contain the origin, namely, the shaded region of

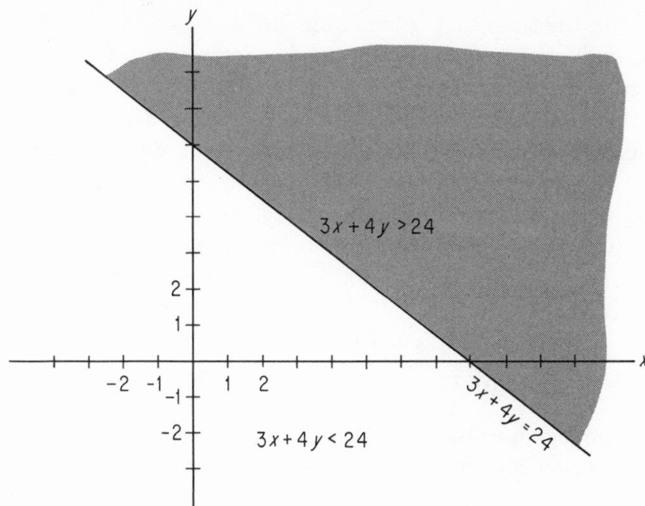

FIG. 7.7

Figure 7.8, belongs to the graph of $x - y - 1 \geqslant 0$. To indicate that the line, itself, is also part of the graph, we have drawn it heavier than the other lines.

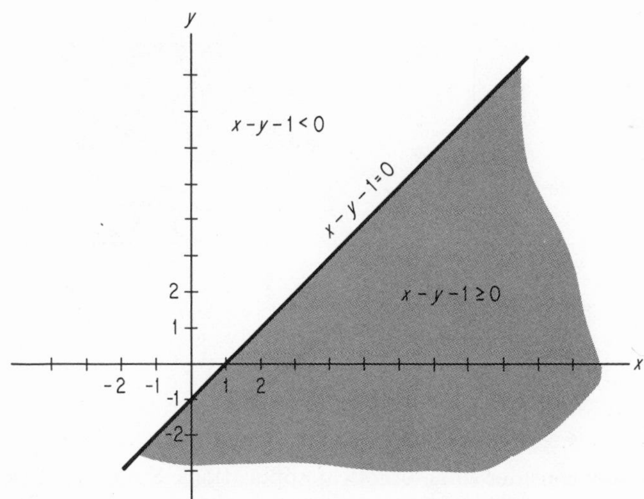

FIG. 7.8

In business and economics, there are many applied problems in which several conditions expressed as linear inequalities must be satisfied at the same time. These conditions may be due to the scarcity of raw materials, restrictions on the time that is available for the manufacture of a product, limited capitalization, shortages in the labor force that can perform a given task, and so on. In general, when we ask for the *solution set* (or the *common solution*) of a system of linear inequalities, we are asking for the set of points whose coordinates satisfy (are solutions of) *all* of the inequalities. In practice, this means that we must find the *intersection* of the solution sets of the individual inequalities, namely, *the region which their graphs have in common*. For instance, if we combine the two inequalities with which we have worked so far in this section, we find that the solution of the system of linear inequalities

$$3x + 4y > 24$$
$$x - y - 1 \geqslant 0$$

is given by the region common to the shaded regions of Figures 7.7 and 7.8. Thus, the solution of this system of inequalities is given by the shaded region of Figure 7.9, where the heavy line serves to indicate that the solution includes the upper portion of the line $x - y - 1 = 0$.

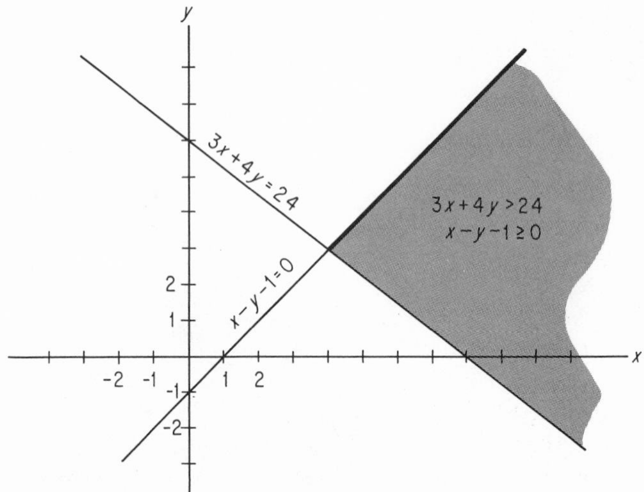

FIG. 7.9

Let us now consider some practical applications. Suppose, for example, that a company makes two kinds of dietary animal food, A and B, which (among other ingredients) contain two important food supplements. Specifically, it takes 2 pounds of the first supplement and 1 pound of the second supplement to make a dozen cans of animal food A, and 4 pounds of the first supplement and 5 pounds of the second supplement to make a dozen cans of animal food B. Now, on a given day 80 pounds of the first supplement and 70 pounds of the second supplement are on hand (but need not all be used up), and the production manager of the company has to decide how many dozen cans of each kind of animal food he should schedule for that day.

So far as the work of this chapter is concerned, we shall merely investigate what kind of scheduling is *feasible*. Obviously, 50 dozen cans of animal food A would not be feasible since this would require too much of the first supplement, and 12 dozen cans of each kind of animal food would not be feasible since this would require too much of the second supplement. On the other hand, 10 dozen cans of each kind of animal food would be feasible, and so would be 5 dozen cans of the first kind and 12 dozen cans of the other; observe, however, that in neither case would all of the food supplements be used up. In Chapter 8 we shall also consider the *profit* which the company makes on each of these two kinds of animal food, and (combining this information with the results obtained here) we will be able to decide which kind of scheduling is actually the *most profitable.*

If we let x and y denote the dozens of cans of animal foods A and B which the production manager schedules for the given day, the restrictions imposed on x and y by the conditions of the problem are given by the four inequalities

$$\begin{aligned} &x \geqslant 0 \\ &y \geqslant 0 \\ &2x + 4y \leqslant 80 \\ &x + 5y \leqslant 70 \end{aligned}$$

The first two inequalities simply state that the quantities of animal food produced cannot be negative; the third inequality expresses the fact that only 80 pounds of the first supplement are available, while the fourth inequality expresses the fact that only 70 pounds of the second food supplement are available. Clearly, $2x + 4y$ pounds of the first food supplement and $x + 5y$ pounds of the second food supplement are needed to make x dozen cans of animal food A and y dozen cans of animal food B.

We thus have a system of *four* linear inequalities in two variables, and to solve it we must find the region which their respective graphs have in common. The first two inequalities tell us that we are limited to points to the right of (or on) the y-axis, and above (or on) the x-axis; in other words, we are restricted to the *first quadrant*. So far as the other two inequalities are concerned, we simply plot the lines $2x + 4y = 80$ and $x + 5y = 70$ as in Figure 7.10, and since $x = 0$ and $y = 0$ (the coordinates of the origin) satisfy both inequalities, we conclude that their respective graphs are the regions which lie below (or on) these two lines. Thus, the solution of the whole system of linear inequalities is given by the shaded region of Figure 7.10, and it includes the boundary, as is indicated by means of the heavy lines.

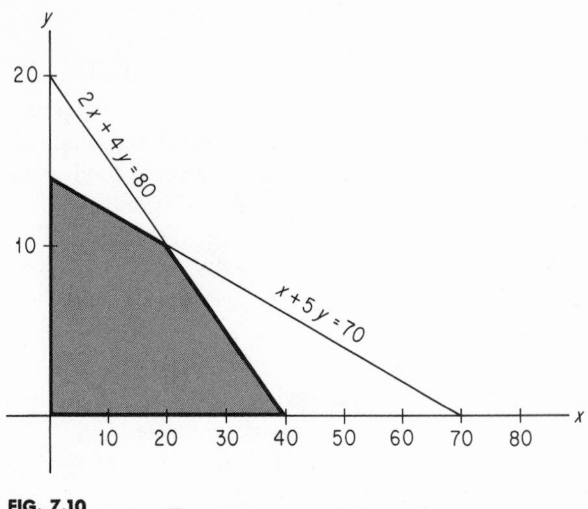

FIG. 7.10

As can be seen from the diagram of Figure 7.10, the points (10, 10) and (5, 12) are among those falling *inside* of the shaded region, and this means that the production manager could schedule the production of 10 dozen cans of each kind of animal food, or 5 dozen cans of animal food A and 12 dozen cans of animal food B. It can also be seen from this diagram that he *cannot* schedule the production of 50 dozen cans of animal food A or 12 dozen cans of each kind, for both points, (50, 0) and (12, 12), lie *outside* of the shaded region of Figure 7.10. This is as far as we shall go for now; to single out a particular point within the shaded region of feasible solutions requires further considerations, say, about the company's profit or the demand for the two products.

The solution of systems of linear inequalities also plays an important role in problems of *allocation*, namely, in problems connected with the distribution or transportation of raw materials, labor, and finished products. Consider, for example, a distributor of major appliances, who supplies retail outlets in three cities, C_1, C_2, and C_3, from two different warehouses, W_1 and W_2. Suppose, furthermore, that he has 9 food freezers in warehouse stock, 5 in warehouse W_1 and 4 in warehouse W_2, and that he must somehow deliver 3 of the freezers to retail outlets in city C_1, 4 to retail outlets in city C_2, and the other 2 to retail outlets in city C_3. Thus, the distributor must decide *how many of the freezers to ship from each warehouse to each city*, and given the cost of delivery he may well want to plan the whole operation so as to minimize his cost. For the time being, we shall merely examine the various ways in which delivery can be made, but in Section 8.2 we shall return to this problem and determine the particular allocation of the freezers which will minimize the distributor's cost. Of course, this will require knowledge of the cost of shipping a freezer from each warehouse to each city.

If x_1 freezers are shipped from W_1 to C_1 and x_2 freezers from W_1 to C_2, this means that the other $3 - x_1$ freezers needed in C_1 and the other $4 - x_2$ freezers needed in C_2 will have to come from W_2. This provides a total of 3 freezers for C_1 and 4 freezers for C_2, and it leaves $5 - x_1 - x_2$ freezers in warehouse W_1 and

$$4 - (3 - x_1) - (4 - x_2) = x_1 + x_2 - 3$$

freezers in warehouse W_2, which are all shipped to C_3 (see Figure 7.11).

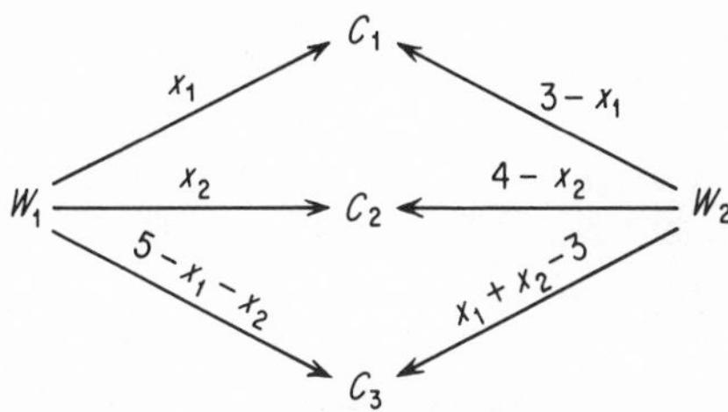

FIG. 7.11

Since the number of freezers shipped from a warehouse to a city cannot be negative, we find that the allocation of the freezers must satisfy the six inequalities

$$\begin{aligned} x_1 &\geqslant 0 \\ 3 - x_1 &\geqslant 0 \\ x_2 &\geqslant 0 \\ 4 - x_2 &\geqslant 0 \\ 5 - x_1 - x_2 &\geqslant 0 \\ x_1 + x_2 - 3 &\geqslant 0 \end{aligned}$$

The first two inequalities limit us to the region between the two vertical lines $x_1 = 0$ and $3 - x_1 = 0$ (namely, $x_1 = 3$), and the next two inequalities limit us to the region between the two horizontal lines $x_2 = 0$ and $4 - x_2 = 0$ (namely, $x_2 = 4$). Together, these four inequalities limit us to the rectangle $ABCD$ of Figure 7.12, including its boundary. The two remaining inequalities can be written as

$$x_1 + x_2 \leqslant 5 \qquad \text{and} \qquad x_1 + x_2 \geqslant 3$$

and they restrict us to the region which falls *between* the lines $x_1 + x_2 = 3$ and $x_1 + x_2 = 5$. Thus, the solution of the whole system of linear inequalities is given by the shaded region of Figure 7.12, including the boundary.

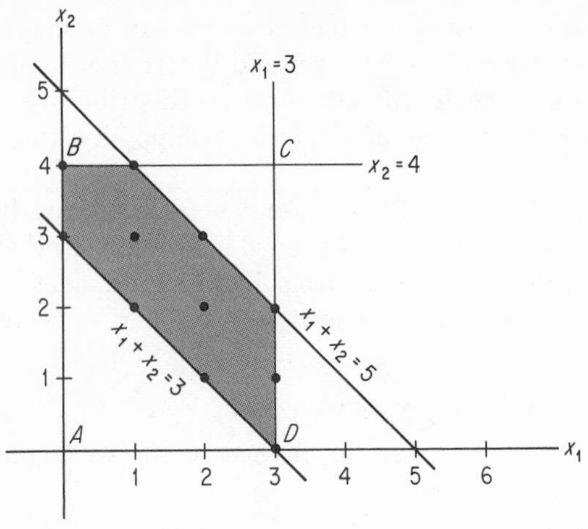

FIG. 7.12

Actually, the solution to this problem is given by the *eleven points* marked in Figure 7.12, not the entire shaded region, and this is due to the fact that x_1 and x_2 must both be *positive integers or zero*. Thus, the eleven points represent all feasible ways of distributing the nine freezers. For instance, the point (2, 3) represents the case where 2 freezers are shipped from W_1 to C_1, 3 from W_1 to C_2, $5 - 2 - 3 = 0$ from W_1 to C_3, $3 - 2 = 1$ from W_2 to C_1, $4 - 3 = 1$ from W_2 to C_2, and $2 + 3 - 3 = 2$ from W_2 to C_3. Similarly, (1, 4) represents the case where 1 freezer is shipped from W_1 to C_1, 4 from W_1 to C_2, $5 - 1 - 4 = 0$ from W_1 to C_3, $3 - 1 = 2$ from W_2 to C_1, $4 - 4 = 0$ from W_2 to C_2, and $1 + 4 - 3 = 2$ from W_2 to C_3.

Finally, let us consider an example involving linear inequalities in three variables, which we shall denote x_1, x_2, and x_3 (although we could just as well denote them x, y, and z, or u, v, and w). Suppose that a manufacturer of a line of patent medicines is preparing a production run on Medicines A, B, and C. There are sufficient ingredients on hand to make 30,000 bottles of A, 40,000 bottles of B, and 20,000 bottles of C, but the time for the production run is limited to a maximum of 190 hours. This imposes certain restrictions, as it takes 3 hours to prepare enough material to fill a thousand bottles of Medicine A, 2 hours to prepare enough material to fill a thousand bottles of Medicine B, and 4 hours to prepare enough material to fill a thousand bottles of Medicine C.

If the manufacturer plans to prepare x_1 thousand bottles of Medicine A, x_2 thousand bottles of Medicine B, and x_3 thousand bottles of Medicine C, the three variables, x_1, x_2, and x_3, must satisfy the seven inequalities

$$
\begin{array}{ll}
x_1 \geqslant 0 & x_1 \leqslant 30 \\
x_2 \geqslant 0 & x_2 \leqslant 40 \\
x_3 \geqslant 0 & x_3 \leqslant 20
\end{array}
$$

and

$$3x_1 + 2x_2 + 4x_3 \leqslant 190$$

The first six inequalities require that $0 \leqslant x_1 \leqslant 30$, $0 \leqslant x_2 \leqslant 40$, $0 \leqslant x_3 \leqslant 20$, and, geometrically speaking, this means that we are restricted to the inside or boundary of the brick-shaped solid of Figure 7.13. The seventh inequality limits us to points falling *behind* the plane shown (at least in part) in Figure 7.14. The equation of this plane is $3x_1 + 2x_2 + 4x_3 = 190$, and it cuts the coordinate axes at the points $(63\frac{1}{3}, 0, 0)$, $(0, 95, 0)$, and $(0, 0, 47\frac{1}{2})$. Now, if we combine Figures 7.13 and 7.14, we find that the plane of Figure 7.14 slices a corner off the brick-shaped solid of Figure 7.13, as shown in Figure 7.15. Thus, the solution of the seven inequalities is given by the three-dimensional configuration whose sides we shaded in Figure 7.15; any point inside or on the surface of this "brick-shaped solid minus a corner" represents a feasible way of scheduling the production of the three medicines. For instance, the point (25, 10, 15) belongs to the solution—there are enough bottles and it takes $3 \cdot 25 + 2 \cdot 10 + 4 \cdot 15 = 155$ hours. This means that they *can* schedule the production of 25,000 bottles of Medicine A, 10,000 bottles of Medicine B, and 15,000 bottles of Medicine C; it does *not* use up all of the time that is available, but all we said was that the operation should take *at most* 190 hours. Observe, also, that (25, 10, 48) is *not* a feasible solution because there would not be enough bottles for Medicine C, that (28, 17, 20) is *not* a feasible solution because the production run would take too long, and that (30, 40, 5) *is* a feasible solution which actually uses up all of the available time. So far, our analysis

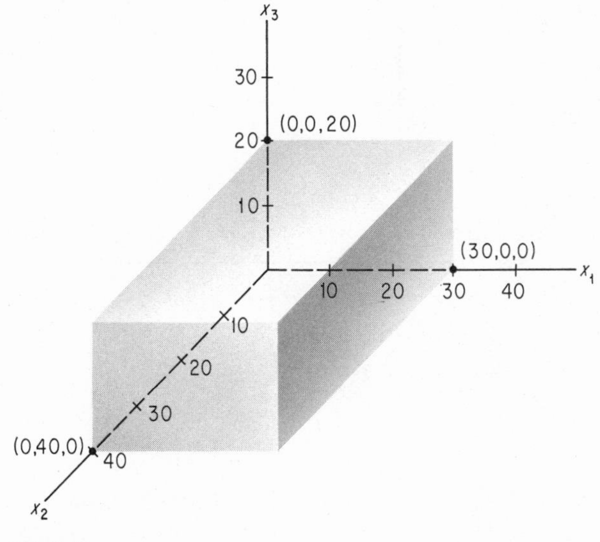

FIG. 7.13

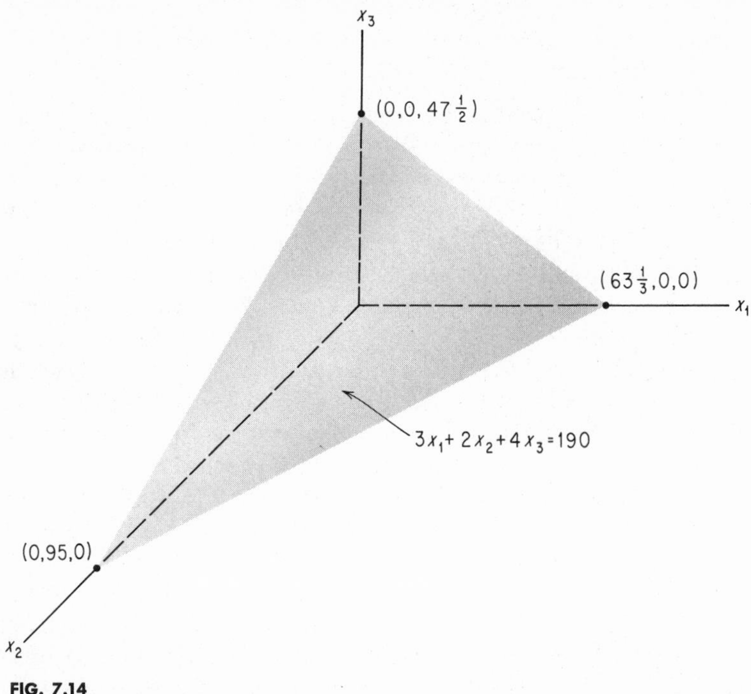

FIG. 7.14

has shown only what kind of production scheduling is feasible under the stated conditions. In Section 8.2 we shall go one step further and decide which scheduling is *best* (namely, *most profitable*), and we shall base this

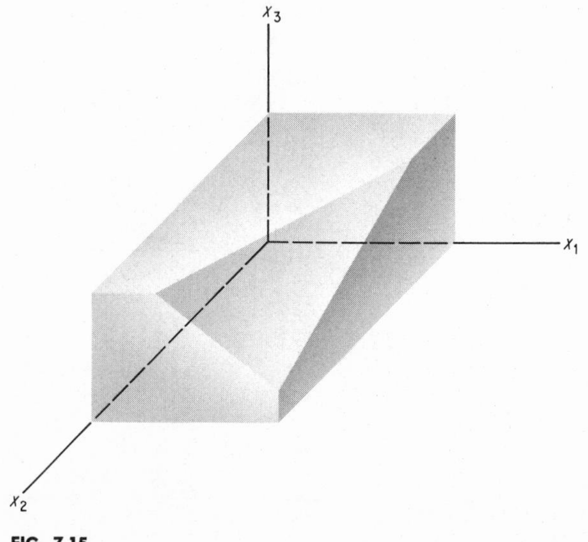

FIG. 7.15

on additional information concerning the profits associated with the three kinds of medicine.

EXERCISES*

1. Draw graphs of the regions which represent the following inequalities:

(a) $x + 2y > 6$; (c) $2x + 5y \geqslant 20$;
(b) $3x - 4y \leqslant 12$; (d) $3x + 4y < -12$.

2. Draw graphs of the solutions sets of the following systems of linear inequalities:

(a) $x - y > 0$
$x + y > 4$

(b) $4x - y \leqslant -2$
$x + 2y > 1$

(c) $y - x > 1$
$2y - 3x < 2$
$x \leqslant 2$

(d) $4x - 3y + 11 > 0$
$3x + 5y + 1 \geqslant 0$

(e) $x + y < 5$, $x + y \geqslant 2$,
$x \leqslant 4$, and $y < 2$

(f) $x \geqslant 0$, $y \geqslant 0$,
$x \leqslant 5$, $y \leqslant 8$,
$3x + 2y < 19$

3. Draw graphs of the regions which represent the solutions of the following systems of linear inequalities:

(a) $x \geqslant 0$, $y \geqslant 0$, $z \geqslant 0$, $x \leqslant 5$, $y \leqslant 3$, and $2x + 3y + z \leqslant 24$. (*Hint:* draw the plane $2x + 3y + z = 24$ by joining the points at which it cuts the coordinate axes.)

(b) $x \geqslant 0$, $y \geqslant 0$, $z \geqslant 0$, $x + y + 2z \leqslant 6$, and $x + z \leqslant 3$. (*Hint:* draw the plane $x + y + 2z = 6$ by joining the points at which it cuts the coordinate axes, and draw the plane $x + z = 3$ by joining the points at which it cuts the x- and z-axes, and then drawing lines through these points which are parallel to the y-axis.)

4. In a 30-minute "Special" shown on television, anywhere from 3 to 5 minutes are devoted to commercials, the master of ceremonies performs for at least 10 minutes, and the remainder of the time is devoted to musical numbers.

(a) If x is the number of minutes taken up by the master of ceremonies and y is the number of minutes devoted to musical numbers, give the four inequalities which completely determine what values can be assumed by x and y.

(b) Sketch the region of feasible solutions, and check whether it contains the points (20, 3), (22, 4), (26, 5), (12, 13), (8, 16), and (13, 14).

5. Mr. Jones is told by his doctor that he should supplement his daily diet with *at least* 50 mg of calcium and 8 mg of iron. He cannot buy these minerals separately, but 5 mg of calcium and 2 mg of iron are contained in each vitamin pill Q, while 10 mg of calcium and 1 mg of iron are contained in each vitamin pill R.

---

* If the reader has had no previous experience in drawing three-dimensional figures, he may have some difficulties with Exercise 3 and with parts (b) of Exercises 8 and 9.

(a) If Mr. Jones takes x vitamin pills Q and y vitamin pills R per day, what linear inequalities must be satisfied by x and y in addition to $x \geqslant 0$ and $y \geqslant 0$ so that he will get enough of these mineral supplements?

(b) Sketch the region of feasible solutions, and check whether it contains the points (9, 1), (1, 5), (5, 2), and (6, 3).

6. Among the three secretaries working for the president of a company, Rose takes 2 minutes to answer a certain kind of form letter, Betty takes 3 minutes, and Jane takes 4 minutes.

(a) If only one typewriter is in working condition and 8 of these letters have to be answered within a maximum time of 20 minutes, what inequalities must be satisfied by x, y, and $8 - x - y$, the number of letters answered, respectively, by Rose, Betty, and Jane.

(b) Sketch the region of feasible solutions. Also, since x and y must be positive integers or zero, give the coordinates of all feasible points and indicate in each case how many letters are answered by Rose, by Betty, and by Jane.

7. A manufacturer makes two kinds of glass trays. The more solid ones cost \$5.00 to produce and \$0.20 to ship, while the more flimsy ones cost \$2.00 to produce and \$0.40 to ship.

(a) If the manufacturer schedules the production of x of the more solid trays and y of the more flimsy trays, what inequalities must be satisfied by x and y if the total production cost must not exceed \$3,000 and the total shipping cost must not exceed \$160?

(b) Sketch the region of feasible solutions, and check whether it contains the points (500, 150), (580, 110), and (400, 210).

8. A jeweler buys gold from three different suppliers, among which the first can sell him at most 30 ounces, the second can sell him at most 50 ounces, and the third can sell him all he wants.

(a) If x, y, and z denote the number of ounces the jeweler orders from each of these suppliers, what inequalities must be satisfied by x, y, and z if the jeweler's order does not exceed 120 ounces?

(b) Sketch the region of feasible solutions. (*Hint:* draw the plane $x + y + z = 120$ by joining the points at which the plane cuts the coordinate axes; also find the point on this plane for which $x = 30$ and $y = 50$.)

9. The manager of a supermarket has a maximum of 3,800 cubic feet of storage space available for three kinds of merchandise, for which he can spend at most \$19,000. The first kind of merchandise comes in 5-cubic-foot cartons costing \$20 a piece, the second kind comes in 3-cubic-foot cartons costing \$50 a piece, and the third kind comes in 4-cubic-foot cartons costing \$20 a piece.

(a) If the manager of the supermarket orders x cartons of the first kind of merchandise, y cartons of the second kind, and z cartons of the third kind, what inequalities must be satisfied by x, y, and z?

(b) Sketch the region of feasible solutions. (*Hint:* draw each plane by joining the points at which it cuts the coordinate axes.)

(c) Check whether the following points are in the region of feasible solutions: (600, 120, 50), (500, 200, 20), (550, 150, 40), and (608, 0, 190).

8

LINEAR PROGRAMMING

8.1 INTRODUCTION

In recent years, much progress has been made with problems relating to the allocation of limited resources so as to meet desired goals. Characteristically, the primary objective of all these problems is to plan (or *program*) activities so that a required job can be done most efficiently with a given labor force, goods can be manufactured most economically with given ingredients, merchandise can be distributed at a minimum cost with existing facilities, and so on. The *programming models* we shall discuss in this chapter (and more rigorously in Chapter 10) are all *linear models*; that is, we shall be interested in *maximizing* (or *minimizing*) linear expressions of the form*

$$c_1x_1 + c_2x_2 + \cdots + c_kx_k$$

where the x's are variables and the c's are known constants, and where the x's are subject to restrictions (limitations, or constraints) expressed in terms of linear equations or linear inequalities. Hence, we refer to these methods as *linear programming.*

---

* The linear expressions we try to maximize or minimize are often referred to as values of the corresponding *objective functions,* for these functions pertain to the *objectives* we are trying to achieve.

8.2 GEOMETRICAL SOLUTIONS

A large class of linear programming problems consists of so-called "mixing" problems—they require that given resources be combined, or "mixed," so as to produce specified outputs in the most efficient way. To illustrate, let us return to the example on page 215, where we considered the problem of mixing two kinds of food supplements in the preparation of two dietary animal foods, A and B. Under the conditions of the problem, 80 pounds of the first supplement and 70 pounds of the second supplement are available, and we were told that it takes 2 pounds of the first supplement and 1 pound of the second supplement to produce a dozen cans of animal food A, and 4 pounds of the first supplement and 5 pounds of the second supplement to produce a dozen cans of animal food B. Using the letters x and y to denote the dozens of cans of animal foods A and B scheduled for production, we expressed the restrictions imposed on these variables as

$$x \geqslant 0, \quad y \geqslant 0, \quad 2x + 4y \leqslant 80, \quad \text{and} \quad x + 5y \leqslant 70$$

and we showed that the solution of this system of linear inequalities is given by the shaded region of Figure 7.10 on page 216.

Adding the information that the company makes a profit of \$3.00 on a dozen cans of animal food A and a profit of \$10.00 on a dozen cans of animal food B, we can now ask for the values of x and y which will *maximize the company's profit*, namely, the values of x and y for which

$$3x + 10y$$

is a *maximum*.

At a first glance it may seem that the production manager should forget about animal food A and concentrate on animal food B, and this would be correct if there were an *unlimited supply* of all the necessary ingredients. Note, however, that if he limits the production to animal food B, he cannot schedule the production of more than 14 dozen cans; this would use up *all* of the second food supplement and yield a profit of \$140, but $80 - 14(4) = 24$ pounds of the first supplement would be left over.

Since animal food A uses more of the first supplement (per dozen cans) than animal food B, it suggests itself that it may be more profitable, perhaps, to produce a few dozen cans of animal food A and fewer than 14 dozen cans of animal food B. Indeed, before we start looking for the *most profitable* way of scheduling the production of these two dietary animal foods, let us see whether it might be possible to arrange things so that the company's profit will be increased to, say, \$150. This means that we must choose x and y so that

$$3x + 10y = 150$$

while, at the same time, $x \geqslant 0$, $y \geqslant 0$, $2x + 4y \leqslant 80$, and $x + 5y \leqslant 70$.

Geometrically speaking, this means that we must look for a point which lies on the line

$$3x + 10y = 150$$

and which is also in the shaded region (of feasible solutions) of Figure 7.10. If we combine the two as in Figure 8.1, it can be seen that the line cuts the shaded region; in fact, any point on the line segment PQ satisfies *all* of the conditions. Among them are the points (20, 9) and (10, 12),

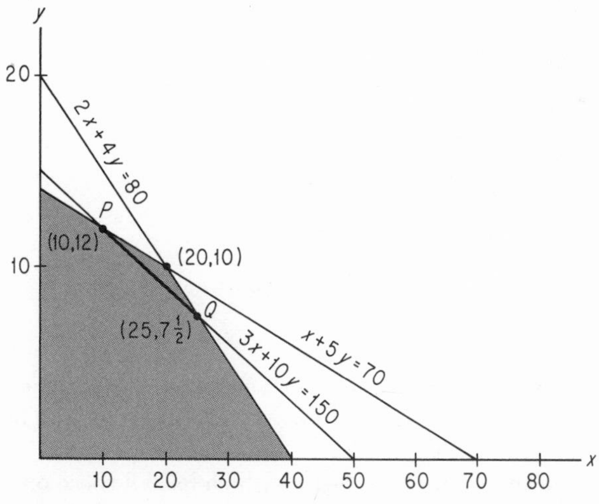

FIG. 8.1

for example, and it can easily be checked that the production of 20 dozen cans of animal food A and 9 dozen cans of animal food B, or 10 dozen cans of animal food A and 12 dozen cans of animal food B, meets all of the conditions. As the reader will be asked to verify in Exercise 7 on page 233, however, some of the first supplement will be left over in each case, and some of the second supplement will also be left over in the first case.

Instead of asking for a production schedule which will yield a profit of \$150, we could have asked for a production schedule which will yield a profit of \$50, a profit of \$100, a profit of \$200, and so on. This means that we would have had to look for points on the lines $3x + 10y = 50$, $3x + 10y = 100$, $3x + 10y = 200$, ..., which are all shown in Figure 8.2 together with the line $3x + 10y = 150$. An important feature of these lines is that they are *all parallel*; in fact, we will get a line parallel to $3x + 10y = 150$ no matter what profit we substitute for \$150, since the x- and y-coefficients (which determine the slope) are always the same. It can also be seen from Figure 8.2 that *when the profit is decreased the line will move closer to the origin* and *when the profit is increased the line will move further away*. This suggests that we look for the line which is *parallel to the line* $3x + 10y = 150$, which is *as far away from the origin as possible,*

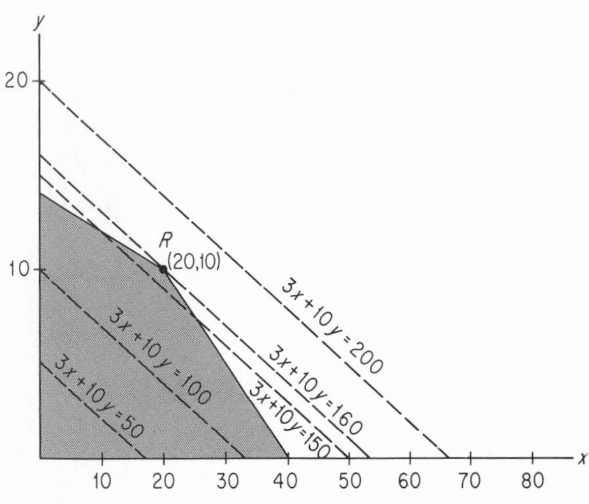

FIG. 8.2

and which has *at least one point in common with the region of feasible solutions.* Clearly, any point which lies on this line and also in the region of feasible solutions will yield a *maximum profit.*

As can be seen from Figure 8.2, the line which has all these properties is the one we have drawn parallel to $3x + 10y = 150$ through the point (20, 10), namely, through the point R in which the two lines $2x + 4y = 80$ and $x + 5y = 70$ intersect. We have thus solved the problem of scheduling the company's production—its profit will be a *maximum* (in fact, it will equal $3 \cdot 20 + 10 \cdot 10 = \$160$) on the sales of 20 dozen cans of animal food A and 10 dozen cans of animal food B. Observe that the point (20, 10) lies on the *boundary* of the region of feasible solutions, and that *all* the available amounts of the two food supplements ($20 \cdot 2 + 10 \cdot 4 = 80$ pounds of the first supplement and $20 \cdot 1 + 10 \cdot 5 = 70$ pounds of the second supplement) will be used up.

Let us now give the same kind of treatment to the allocation problem of Section 7.4, where a distributor of major appliances had to deliver freezers from warehouses W_1 and W_2 to cities C_1, C_2, and C_3. Letting x_1 and x_2 denote the number of freezers he ships from warehouse W_1 to C_1 and C_2, we showed that he must ship $5 - x_1 - x_2$ freezers from W_1 to C_3, $3 - x_1$ freezers from W_2 to C_1, $4 - x_2$ freezers from W_2 to C_2, and $x_1 + x_2 - 3$ freezers from W_2 to C_3, and that the variables x_1 and x_2 must, therefore, satisfy the inequalities

$$x_1 \geqslant 0, \quad 3 - x_1 \geqslant 0, \quad x_2 \geqslant 0, \quad 4 - x_2 \geqslant 0,$$
$$5 - x_1 - x_2 \geqslant 0, \quad \text{and} \quad x_1 + x_2 - 3 \geqslant 0$$

The corresponding region of feasible solutions is shown in Figure 7.12 on page 218.

To continue the analysis of this problem, let us suppose that it costs \$4.50 to deliver one of these freezers from W_1 to C_1, \$1.50 to deliver one from W_1 to C_2, \$2.50 to deliver one from W_1 to C_3, and that the corresponding figures for delivery from warehouse W_2 are \$6.00, \$1.00, and \$5.00. The total cost of delivering the nine freezers is thus given by

$$\begin{aligned} 4.50x_1 + 1.50x_2 + 2.50(5 - x_1 - x_2) + 6.00(3 - x_1) \\ + 1.00(4 - x_2) + 5.00(x_1 + x_2 - 3) \\ = x_1 + 3x_2 + 19.50 \end{aligned}$$

and we can now ask for the values of x_1 and x_2 which will *minimize* this expression.

If we let c stand for the total cost of delivering the nine freezers, then $x_1 + 3x_2 + 19.50 = c$ represents a straight line like that of Figure 8.3, in which we have also reproduced the region of feasible solutions from Figure 7.12 on page 218. Of course, we will get different lines for different values of

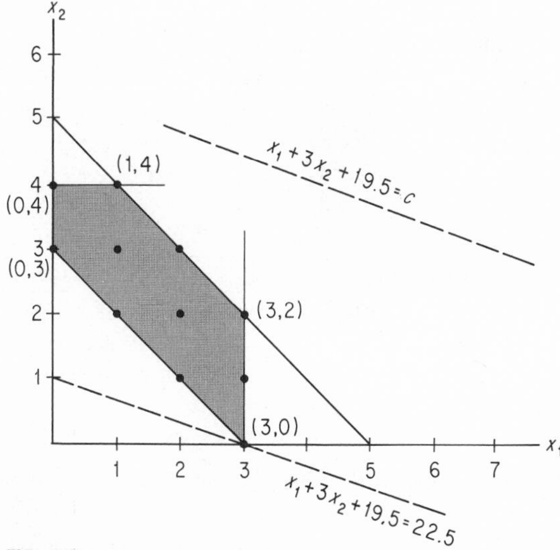

FIG. 8.3

c, but they are all *parallel* to the line which we have drawn. If we actually plotted some of these lines for assorted positive values of c, we would find that the smallest value of c corresponds to the line which is *closest to the origin*. To *minimize* the cost of delivering the nine freezers, we must, therefore, look for the line which is *parallel to the one we have drawn,* which is *as close as possible to the origin,* yet which *intersects, or at least touches, the shaded region of feasible solutions.* Evidently, the line we are looking for is the dashed line of Figure 8.3, namely, the one which passes through the point (3, 0). This means that the cost of delivering the freezers is least when the distributor ships $x_1 = 3$ of the 5 freezers in warehouse W_1 to C_1 and $x_2 = 0$ to C_2, and it follows that he must ship the other $5 - x_1 - x_2 = 5 - 3 - 0 = 2$ freezers in W_1 to C_3, $3 - x_1 = 3 - 3 = 0$ of the 4 freezers in warehouse W_2 to C_1, $4 - x_2 = 4 - 0 = 4$ to C_2, and $x_1 + x_2 - 3 = 3 + 0 - 3 = 0$ to C_3. Also, if the freezers are distributed in this way, their delivery will cost

$$x_1 + 3x_2 + 19.50 = 3 + 3(0) + 19.50 = \$22.50$$

and if the reader does not believe that this is actually a minimum, he has only to calculate the total cost of delivering the freezers for each of the other ten points (feasible solutions) marked in Figure 8.3.

Both of the examples we have considered so far in this section have been in two variables, and (counting the fact that the variables had to be greater than or equal to zero) the first example involved 4 restrictions on x and y, while the second example involved 6 restrictions on x_1 and x_2. Of course, all these restrictions were expressed in terms of *linear inequalities,* for this is characteristic of problems in which linear programming methods can be applied. Before we turn to problems involving three variables, like the bottling problem of Section 7.4, let us study one more problem in two variables, which is different in that *the solution is not unique.* Thus, consider a company which manufactures two kinds of wine racks, a standard model and a de luxe model. It processes these racks on three different machines, *I, II,* and *III*; specifically, it takes 2.0, 1.2, and 2.4 hours on machines *I, II,* and *III* to make a standard rack, and 2.0, 2.4, and 0.8 hours on machines *I, II,* and *III* to make a de luxe rack. The profit which the company makes on these racks is \$2.40 for each standard model and \$4.80 for each de luxe model, and the problem is to determine *how many racks of each kind they should schedule so as to maximize the total profit from a production run during which 48 hours are available on each machine.*

If the company schedules the production of x_1 standard racks and x_2 de luxe racks, we must have $x_1 \geqslant 0$ and $x_2 \geqslant 0$, and these variables must also satisfy the inequalities

$$\begin{aligned} 2.0x_1 + 2.0x_2 &\leqslant 48 \\ 1.2x_1 + 2.4x_2 &\leqslant 48 \\ 2.4x_1 + 0.8x_2 &\leqslant 48 \end{aligned}$$

since $2.0x_1 + 2.0x_2$ hours will be required on machine *I*, $1.2x_1 + 2.4x_2$ hours will be required on machine *II*, and $2.4x_1 + 0.8x_2$ hours will be required on machine *III*. The quantity we shall want to *maximize* is the company's *total profit* on the sales of x_1 standard racks and x_2 de luxe racks, namely,

$$2.40x_1 + 4.80x_2$$

Now, if we consider the above inequalities together with $x_1 \geqslant 0$ and $x_2 \geqslant 0$, we obtain the region of feasible solutions which we shaded in Figure 8.4; it is bounded by the lines $2.0x_1 + 2.0x_2 = 48$, $1.2x_1 + 2.4x_2 = 48$, and $2.4x_1 + 0.8x_2 = 48$, and the x_1- and x_2-axes. To find the most profitable solution, let p denote the company's profit on the sales of x_1 standard racks and x_2 de luxe racks, and let us plot the graph of the line

$$2.40x_1 + 4.80x_2 = p$$

for some arbitrary value of p (see Figure 8.4). As in our previous examples, we will get different *parallel* lines for different values of p, with the larger

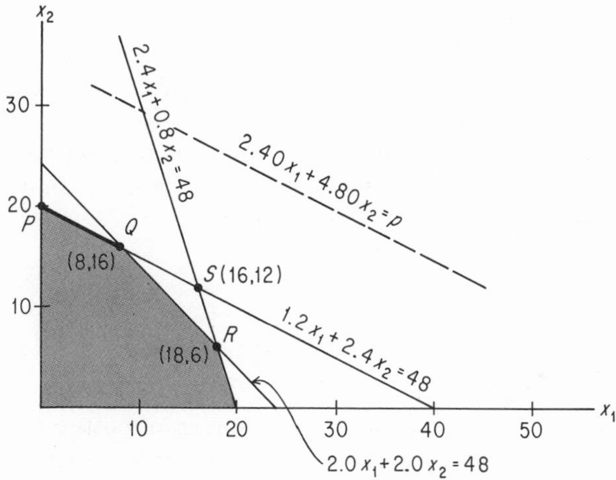

FIG. 8.4

values of p corresponding to the lines which are further away from the origin. To solve the problem, we shall thus have to look for the line which is *parallel to the one we have drawn*, which is *as far away from the origin as possible* (so as to maximize p), yet which *intersects, or at least touches, the shaded region of feasible solutions.* This is not hard, for inspection of Figure 8.4 shows that the line we are looking for is the line

$$1.2x_1 + 2.4x_2 = 48$$

which has already been drawn as part of the boundary of the region of feasible solutions. (This follows from the fact that the x_1- and x_2-coefficients in $2.40x_1 + 4.80x_2 = p$ and $1.2x_1 + 2.4x_2 = 48$ are *proportional*, and, hence, the lines are parallel.) Thus, any point on the line $1.2x_1 + 2.4x_2 = 48$

between the points P and Q of Figure 8.4 constitutes a solution—it satisfies all of the inequalities and it maximizes the profit. The coordinates of points P and Q are (0, 20) and (8, 16), as can easily be verified by substituting $x_1 = 0$ into $1.2x_1 + 2.4x_2 = 48$ and solving for x_2, and by solving the system of linear equations

$$\begin{aligned} 1.2x_1 + 2.4x_2 &= 48 \\ 2.0x_1 + 2.0x_2 &= 48 \end{aligned}$$

If it were not for the fact that x_1 and x_2 must be integers, there would be *infinitely many solutions*; actually, there are only the five solutions $x_1 = 0$ and $x_2 = 20$, $x_1 = 2$ and $x_2 = 19$, $x_1 = 4$ and $x_2 = 18$, $x_1 = 6$ and $x_2 = 17$, and $x_1 = 8$ and $x_2 = 16$. It will be left to the reader to verify in Exercise 9 on page 233 that in each case the company's profit is \$96.00.

The only problem in three variables which we considered in Section 7.4 was the one concerning the bottling of three kinds of medicine—there was a limited supply of bottles and at most 190 hours were available for the whole operation. If we now add the information that the manufacturer makes a profit of \$24 on a thousand bottles of Medicine A, a profit of \$35 on a thousand bottles of Medicine B, and a profit of \$18 on a thousand bottles of Medicine C, we can continue the problem and ask for the most profitable way of scheduling the operation. Using the same notation as on page 218, we shall thus have to *maximize* the quantity

$$24x_1 + 35x_2 + 18x_3$$

subject to the restrictions

$$\begin{aligned} &x_1 \geqslant 0, \quad x_1 \leqslant 30, \quad x_2 \geqslant 0, \quad x_2 \leqslant 40, \quad x_3 \geqslant 0, \\ &x_3 \leqslant 20, \quad \text{and} \quad 3x_1 + 2x_2 + 4x_3 \leqslant 190 \end{aligned}$$

where x_1, x_2, and x_3 are (in thousands) the number of bottles prepared of each kind of medicine. The region of feasible solution was originally shown in Figure 7.15 on page 220, and we have reproduced it here in Figure 8.5, which also contains the graph of the plane

$$24x_1 + 35x_2 + 18x_3 = p$$

for some arbitrary positive value of the manufacturer's profit, p. This profit becomes smaller when the plane is moved *parallel to itself* toward the origin, and to keep it as large as possible while satisfying the seven restrictions (linear inequalities) involving x_1, x_2, and x_3, we shall have to move the plane parallel to itself toward the origin until it first makes contact with (touches) the shaded region of feasible solutions. Although it may be difficult to visualize this without actually constructing a three-dimensional model (perhaps, with pieces of cardboard or paper representing the various planes), the first contact occurs at the point (30, 40, 5), namely, the point in which the planes $x_1 = 30$, $x_2 = 40$, and $3x_1 + 2x_2 + 4x_3 = 190$ intersect.

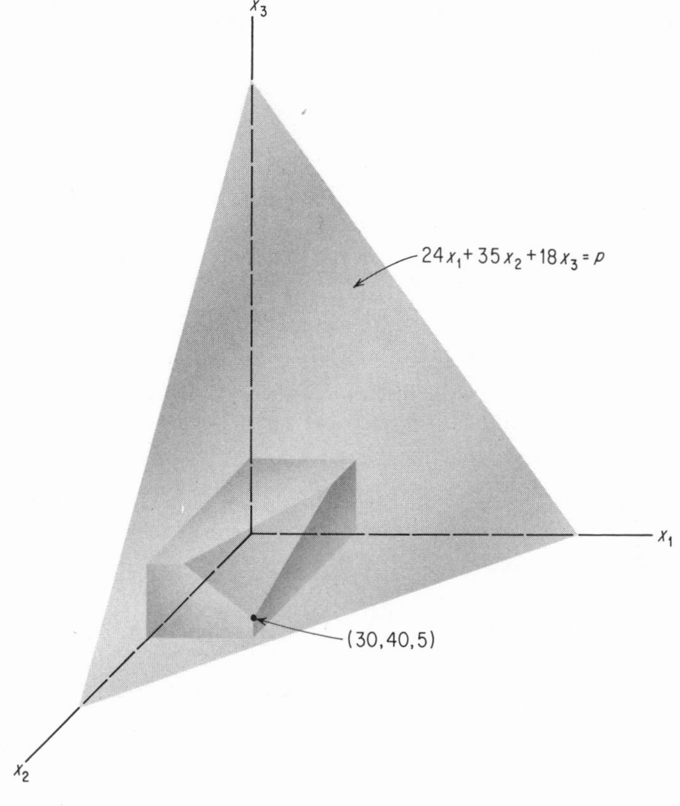

FIG. 8.5

Thus, $x_1 = 30$, $x_2 = 40$, and $x_3 = 5$ is the solution of the problem, and the manufacturer will realize the maximum profit of

$$24(30) + 35(40) + 18(5) = \$2{,}210$$

on the sales of 30,000 bottles of Medicine A, 40,000 bottles of Medicine B, and 5,000 bottles of Medicine C. The solution which we obtained here is *unique*, but this would not have been the case, for example, if the profit on Medicine B had been \$9 per thousand bottles instead of \$35. As the reader will be asked to show in Exercise 13 on page 233, there would then be many different solutions which all lead to a maximum profit of \$1,170.

The geometrical, or graphical, method of solving linear programming problems works nicely for two variables, but it may involve configurations which are difficult to picture when there are three variables, and it cannot be used when there are four variables or more. Thus, there is a need for alternate methods of solving linear programming problems. The one which we shall study in Section 8.3 is a simple algebraic method which can be used regardless of the number of variables, and which reduces the problem to that of solving systems of linear equations.

EXERCISES

1. How should the manufacturer of Exercise 7 on page 222 schedule the production of the glass trays, if he makes a profit of $2.00 on each standard tray, a profit of $2.40 on each de luxe tray, and he wants to *maximize his total profit*? What is this maximum profit?

2. How would Mr. Jones of Exercise 5 on page 221 *minimize the cost* of adding the necessary minerals to his diet if

   (a) each vitamin pill Q costs 3 cents and each vitamin pill R costs 4 cents;
   (b) each vitamin pill Q costs 3 cents and each vitamin pill R costs 6 cents?

   Also find the corresponding minimum costs.

3. How should the letters be assigned to the three secretaries of Exercise 6 on page 222 so as to *minimize the cost* of answering the 8 letters, if

   (a) Rose gets $3.60 an hour, Betty gets $2.80 an hour, and Jane gets $1.50 an hour;
   (b) Rose gets $3.90 an hour, Betty gets $2.20 an hour, and Jane gets $1.50 an hour;
   (c) Rose gets $3.60 an hour, Betty gets $2.20 an hour, and Jane gets $1.50 an hour;
   (d) Rose gets $2.40 an hour, Betty gets $2.40 an hour, and Jane gets $1.50 an hour?

   [*Hint:* in each case determine first how much each secretary is paid to answer one of the form letters; in part (d) plot the lines which correspond to total costs of 70, 80, and 90 cents, and use them as guides to find the line which corresponds to the minimum cost.]

4. A wholesale distributor of art reproductions manufactures his own wooden frames, two kinds, which he gives away free with the paintings. It takes 20, 10, and 10 minutes to *cut, assemble,* and *finish* the first kind of frame which costs him $1.20 a piece, and 10, 20, and 60 minutes to *cut, assemble,* and *finish* the other kind of frame which costs him $3.60 a piece. If a certain production run calls for at least 8 hours of cutting, at least 10 hours of assembling, and at least 18 hours of finishing, how many frames of each kind should he schedule so as to *minimize his cost*? What is the minimum cost?

5. What would have been the answer to Exercise 4 if the cost of the frames had been $2.70 and $1.80, respectively?

6. Referring to the illustration on page 224, suppose that the company which makes the dietary animal food decides to add a third food supplement, of which 1.4 pounds are required for a dozen cans of animal food A, 4 pounds are required for a dozen cans of animal food B, and 65 pounds are available on that

day. Assuming that the profit figures remain unchanged, how many dozen cans of each kind of animal food should the production manager schedule for that day so as to *maximize the company's profit*? What is this maximum profit?

7. With reference to the example on page 225, determine the amount of each food supplement that is left over when they produce 20 dozen cans of animal food A and 9 dozen cans of animal food B, and when they produce 10 dozen cans of animal food A and 12 dozen cans of animal food B.

8. Referring to Figure 8.3 on page 227, calculate the total cost of delivering the nine freezers for each of the other ten points (feasible solutions) marked in the diagram.

9. Referring to the illustration on page 230, verify that the company's profit is $96.00 for each of the five solutions.

10. With reference to Exercise 9 on page 222, how many cartons of each kind of merchandise should the supermarket manager order so as to *maximize his total profit*, if

    (a) his profits on a carton of each of the three kinds of merchandise are, respectively, $20, $10, and $15;
    (b) his profits on a carton of each of the three kinds of merchandise are, respectively, $10, $20, and $8?

    Also find the corresponding total profits.

11. A company has the capacity to manufacture a maximum of 240 radios per day. The three kinds it makes require, respectively, 9 ounces, 6 ounces, and 2 ounces of copper wire, and they yield profits of $6, $2, and $2. If 900 ounces of copper wire are available on a certain day, how many radios of each kind should they produce so as to maximize their profit? What is this maximum profit?

12. What would have been the answer to Exercise 11 if the profits on the three kinds of radios had been $4, $4, and $2?

13. Rework the medicine-bottling example on page 230, making the profit on Medicine B $9 per thousand bottles instead of $35, and show that there will then be many possible solutions, which all lead to a maximum profit of $1,170. How many solutions would there be if x_1, x_2, and x_3 had to be integers?

8.3 INSPECTION OF VERTICES

The reader may have noticed that in all of our examples the solution was given by a point, or points, on the *boundary* (namely, the outside edge, or surface) of the region of feasible solutions. In fact, when there was a unique solution, it was given by a *vertex*, or corner, of the region of feasible solutions—that is, for two variables the solution was given by the point of intersection of two lines, and for three variables it was given by the point of intersection of three planes. This result can be generalized to linear programming problems involving any number of variables, and it can also be shown that *if the solution is not unique,* at least two solutions must correspond to vertices of the region of feasible solutions, and every point on the line segment joining them is also a solution. This is what happened in the wine-rack example illustrated in Figure 8.4, where the solution included the points P and Q, and it would also have included every point on the line segment PQ had it not been for the fact that x_1 and x_2 had to be integers.

Using these results (which are treated much more formally in the books referred to at the end of this chapter), we can now solve any linear programming problem by listing all of the vertices of the region of feasible solutions, calculating the corresponding values of the *objective function* (namely, the corresponding values of the linear expression which is to be maximized or minimized), and then choosing the vertex, or the vertices, at which it is a maximum or a minimum. Referring to the second illustration of Section 8.2, for example, the one which dealt with the delivery of nine freezers, we find from Figure 8.3 on page 227 that the vertices of the region of feasible solutions are the points (0, 3), (0, 4), (1, 4), (3, 0), and (3, 2). The cost of delivering the freezers was given by $x_1 + 3x_2 + 19.5$, and if we now calculate the value of this expression for each of the five vertices, we get

Vertex	$x_1 + 3x_2 + 19.5$
(0, 3)	28.5
(0, 4)	31.5
(1, 4)	32.5
(3, 0)	22.5 ⟵ *minimun*
(3, 2)	28.5

As can be seen from this table, the solution is given by $x_1 = 3$ and $x_2 = 0$, and the corresponding cost of delivering the nine freezers is \$22.50; this agrees with the results obtained on page 228.

To apply this method to the third illustration of Section 8.2, which involved the scheduling of the production of two kinds of wine racks on three machines, we have only to investigate what happens at the five vertices of the shaded region of Figure 8.4. Starting at the origin and going *clockwise* along the boundary of the shaded region, we find that the next vertex is the point P at which the line $1.2x_1 + 2.4x_2 = 48$ cuts the x_2-axis, namely, the point (0, 20). Then comes the point of intersection of the lines $2.0x_1 + 2.0x_2 = 48$ and $1.2x_1 + 2.4x_2 = 48$, namely, the point Q, and it can easily be checked by the method of elimination that its coordinates are $x_1 = 8$ and $x_2 = 16$. The next vertex is the point of intersection of the lines $2.0x_1 + 2.0x_2 = 48$ and $2.4x_1 + 0.8x_2 = 48$, namely, the point R of Figure 8.4, and the method of elimination yields $x_1 = 18$ and $x_2 = 6$.

Finally, the fifth vertex is the point at which the line $2.4x_1 + 0.8x_2 = 48$ cuts the x_1-axis, and its coordinates are $x_1 = 20$ and $x_2 = 0$. The expression which we want to maximize in this example, the company's profit, is given by

$$2.40x_1 + 4.80x_2$$

and if we calculate its value for each vertex, we obtain

Vertex	$2.40x_1 + 4.80x_2$	
(0, 0)	0	
(0, 20)	96 ⟵	*maximum*
(8, 16)	96 ⟵	*maximum*
(18, 6)	72	
(20, 0)	48	

As can be seen from this table, the company's profit is a maximum at the points (0, 20) and (8, 16), and, in accordance with the observation we made on page 234, it follows that the company's profit will also be a maximum for any point which lies on the line segment joining (0, 20) and (8, 16). (Since x_1 and x_2 have to be integers in this example, there are actually only the five solutions which we gave on page 230.)

In this last example we found the coordinates of the vertices by systematically going around the region of feasible solutions, which was shown in Figure 8.4 on page 229. Had we not looked at the region of feasible solutions, we might have tried to find a vertex by determining the point of intersection of the lines $1.2x_1 + 2.4x_2 = 48$ and $2.4x_1 + 0.8x_2 = 48$. Even though both of these lines are part of the boundary of the region of feasible solutions, their point of intersection (point S of Figure 8.4) does *not* represent a feasible solution. Its coordinates are $x_1 = 16$ and $x_2 = 12$, and the inequality $2.0x_1 + 2.0x_2 \leqslant 48$ is not satisfied at this point, since

$$2.0(16) + 2.0(12) = 56 > 48$$

This illustrates why we have to be very careful when we look for the vertices of the region of feasible solutions, particularly, when we do so without looking at an appropriate diagram.

Let us now return to the medicine-bottling problem in three variables (treated first on page 219 and then again on page 230), and let us determine the coordinates of the *ten* vertices of the solid which contains all feasible solutions. Referring to Figure 8.6, in which we have reproduced the region of feasible solutions from Figure 7.15 on page 220, the seven vertices which correspond to corners of the original "brick" of Figure 7.13 on page 219 are easily determined. First, there is the origin (0, 0, 0); then, on the coordinate axes there are the points (30, 0, 0), (0, 40, 0), and (0, 0, 20), as indicated in Figure 7.13; finally, on the *coordinate planes* (namely, the planes which contain, respectively, the x_1-axis and the x_2-axis, the x_1-axis and the x_3-axis, and the x_2-axis and the x_3-axis) there are the points (30, 40, 0), (30, 0, 20), and (0, 40, 20). So far as the other three vertices are concerned (namely, the ones which we labeled P, Q, and R), observe that each one is the point of

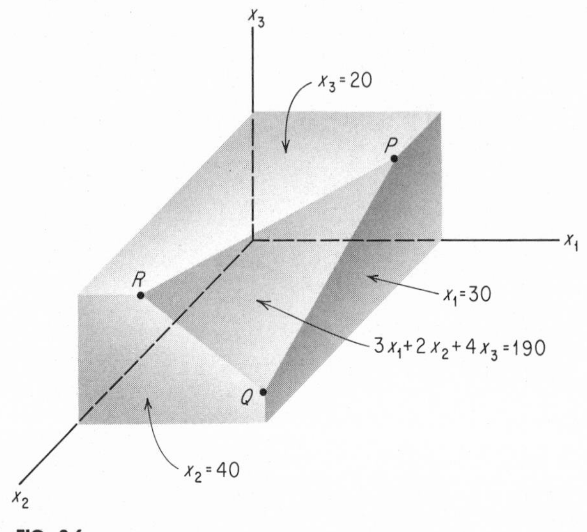

FIG. 8.6

intersection of *three planes*. Point P, for example, is the point of intersection of the planes

$$x_1 = 30, \quad x_3 = 20, \quad \text{and} \quad 3x_1 + 2x_2 + 4x_3 = 190$$

where $x_1 = 30$ is the plane which contains the points P and Q of Figure 8.6, and which is parallel to the x_2x_3-plane, namely, the plane which contains the x_2- and x_3-axes. Similarly, $x_3 = 20$ is the plane which contains the points P and R of Figure 8.6, and which is parallel to the x_1x_2-plane.* If we now substitute $x_1 = 30$ and $x_3 = 20$ into the third equation, we obtain

$$3(30) + 2x_2 + 4(20) = 190$$

and it follows that $2x_2 = 190 - 90 - 80 = 20$ and $x_2 = 10$, and, hence, that the coordinates of point P are (30, 10, 20). To find the coordinates of point Q we have to solve the system of equations

$$x_1 = 30, \quad x_2 = 40, \quad \text{and} \quad 3x_1 + 2x_2 + 4x_3 = 190$$

(representing the three planes of Figure 8.6 which intersect in point Q), and

* Note that $x_1 = 30$ may be looked upon as the equation of the plane which consists of all the points whose x_1-coordinate is 30, and that $x_3 = 20$ may be looked upon as the equation of the plane which consists of all the points whose x_3-coordinate is 20.

to find the coordinates of point R we have to solve the system of equations

$$x_2 = 40, \quad x_3 = 20, \quad \text{and} \quad 3x_1 + 2x_2 + 4x_3 = 190$$

(representing the three planes of Figure 8.6 which intersect in point R). Leaving the details to the reader in Exercise 8 on page 242, let us merely state the result that the coordinates of points Q and R are, respectively, (30, 40, 5) and (10, 40, 20).

The expression which we have to maximize in this problem is the company's profit on the sales of x_1 thousand bottles of Medicine A, x_2 thousand bottles of Medicine B, and x_3 thousand bottles of Medicine C, namely,

$$24x_1 + 35x_2 + 18x_3$$

and if we calculate its value for each of the ten vertices, we get

Vertex	$24x_1 + 35x_2 + 18x_3$	
(0, 0, 0)	0	
(30, 0, 0)	720	
(0, 40, 0)	1,400	
(0, 0, 20)	360	
(30, 40, 0)	2,120	
(30, 0, 20)	1,080	
(0, 40, 20)	1,760	
(30, 10, 20)	1,430	
(30, 40, 5)	2,210 ⟵	*maximum*
(10, 40, 20)	2,000	

Thus, it can be seen that the maximum profit is \$2,210, and that it is attained on the sales of 30,000 bottles of Medicine A, 40,000 bottles of Medicine B, and 5,000 bottles of Medicine C.

Let us now consider an example in which we cannot picture the region of feasible solutions because it is in *four dimensions;* in other words, let us consider a problem which involves *four variables.* Suppose, for instance, that the manager of an oil refinery has to schedule the blending of four kinds of gasoline, A, B, C, and D. The refinery's facilities permit the blending of *at most* ten million gallons during the period under consideration, and there is the further restriction that only 2,000 pounds of a secret anti-knock ingredient are available. It takes 200 pounds of this ingredient to blend a million gallons of gasoline A, 100 pounds for a million gallons of gasoline B, 400 pounds for a million gallons of gasoline C, and 100 pounds for a million gallons of gasoline D. Now, if the refinery makes a profit of 2.4 cents per gallon on gasoline A, 3.0 cents per gallon on gasoline B, 4.8 cents per gallon on gasoline C, and 3.6 cents per gallon on gasoline D, the question is *how should the manager schedule the production of the four gasolines so as to maximize the refinery's profit?*

If he schedules the blending of x_1 million gallons of gasoline A, x_2 million gallons of gasoline B, x_3 million gallons of gasoline C, and x_4 million gallons of gasoline D, the problem is to maximize

$$24{,}000x_1 + 30{,}000x_2 + 48{,}000x_3 + 36{,}000x_4$$

since a million gallons of gasolines A, B, C, and D yield respective profits of \$24,000, \$30,000, \$48,000, and \$36,000. The variables x_1, x_2, x_3, and x_4 must all be *non-negative,* they must satisfy the inequality

$$x_1 + x_2 + x_3 + x_4 \leqslant 10$$

since the total production cannot exceed 10 million gallons, and they must satisfy the inequality

$$200x_1 + 100x_2 + 400x_3 + 100x_4 \leqslant 2{,}000$$

since only 2,000 pounds of the anti-knock ingredient is available. Note that the last inequality can be simplified by dividing each term by 100, so that it becomes

$$2x_1 + x_2 + 4x_3 + x_4 \leqslant 20$$

Now that we have formulated this linear programming problem in mathematical terms, the method of this section requires that we locate all of the vertices of the region of feasible solutions. To this end, let us point out that the boundary of the region of feasible solutions consists of *six* geometrical configurations, called *hyper-planes,* which are given by the equations

$$x_1 = 0, \quad x_2 = 0, \quad x_3 = 0, \quad x_4 = 0,$$
$$x_1 + x_2 + x_3 + x_4 = 10 \quad \text{and} \quad 2x_1 + x_2 + 4x_3 + x_4 = 20$$

This is a generalization of what happened when we dealt with two or three variables. In the *two-variable case,* the boundary of the region of feasible solutions consisted of lines, which were obtained by substituting equal signs for the inequality signs in the restrictions (linear inequalities) imposed on the two variables. Furthermore, each vertex of the region of feasible solutions was a point of intersection of two of these lines, and its coordinates were obtained by solving the corresponding system of two linear equations in the two variables. In the *three-variable case,* the boundary of the region of feasible solutions consisted of planes, which were obtained by substituting equal signs for the inequality signs in the restrictions (linear inequalities) imposed on the three variables. Furthermore, each vertex of the region of feasible solutions was a point of intersection of three of these planes, and its coordinates were obtained by solving a corresponding system of three linear equations in the three variables.

Generalizing this procedure to the *four-variable case,* we can say that in the given example the coordinates of each vertex of the region of feasible solutions must be the solution of a system of four linear equations in the four variables, chosen from among the six linear equations $x_1 = 0$, $x_2 = 0$, $x_3 = 0$, $x_4 = 0$, $x_1 + x_2 + x_3 + x_4 = 10$, and $2x_1 + x_2 + 4x_3 + x_4 = 20$. As the reader will be asked to show in Exercise 16 on page 449, there are altogether 15 different ways in which we can choose 4 of 6 linear equations, and, hence, there are *potentially* 15 vertices. Actually, there are only 7 different vertices in this example, since some of the systems of four linear equations have the same solution, one has no solution, and three have solutions which must be ruled out because they do not satisfy all of the inequalities.

If we take the *first four equations*, namely, $x_1 = 0$, $x_2 = 0$, $x_3 = 0$, and $x_4 = 0$, we obtain the point (0, 0, 0, 0), the origin, which *is* a vertex since these values of the four variables also satisfy the inequalities

$$x_1 + x_2 + x_3 + x_4 \leqslant 10 \quad \text{and} \quad 2x_1 + x_2 + 4x_3 + x_4 \leqslant 20$$

If we take the *first three equations together with the fifth equation*, we have to solve the following system of linear equations

$$x_1 = 0, \quad x_2 = 0, \quad x_3 = 0, \quad \text{and} \quad x_1 + x_2 + x_3 + x_4 = 10$$

As can be verified by substituting $x_1 = 0$, $x_2 = 0$, and $x_3 = 0$ into the other equation, the solution is $x_1 = 0$, $x_2 = 0$, $x_3 = 0$, and $x_4 = 10$, and the point (0, 0, 0, 10) *is* a vertex of the region of feasible solutions, since these values of the four variables also satisfy the inequalities

$$x_4 \geqslant 0 \quad \text{and} \quad 2x_1 + x_2 + 4x_3 + x_4 \leqslant 20$$

If we take the *first three equations together with the sixth equation*, we have to solve the following system of linear equations

$$x_1 = 0, \quad x_2 = 0, \quad x_3 = 0, \quad \text{and} \quad 2x_1 + x_2 + 4x_3 + x_4 = 20$$

The solution is $x_1 = 0$, $x_2 = 0$, $x_3 = 0$, and $x_4 = 20$, but the point (0, 0, 0, 20) is *not* a vertex of the region of feasible solutions; in fact, it does not even belong to it, since these values of the four variables do *not* satisfy the inequality

$$x_1 + x_2 + x_3 + x_4 \leqslant 10$$

If we take the *first, third, fifth, and sixth equations*, we have to solve the following system of linear equations

$$x_1 = 0, \quad x_3 = 0, \quad x_1 + x_2 + x_3 + x_4 = 10,$$
$$\text{and} \quad 2x_1 + x_2 + 4x_3 + x_4 = 20$$

Substituting $x_1 = 0$ and $x_3 = 0$ into the other two equations, we obtain the *inconsistent* system

$$x_2 + x_4 = 10$$
$$x_2 + x_4 = 20$$

and, hence, there is *no vertex* corresponding to this choice of four of the six linear equations.

To consider one more case, let us take the *first, fourth, fifth, and sixth equations,* so that we have to solve the following system of linear equations

$$x_1 = 0, \quad x_4 = 0, \quad x_1 + x_2 + x_3 + x_4 = 10,$$
$$\text{and} \quad 2x_1 + x_2 + 4x_3 + x_4 = 20$$

Substituting $x_1 = 0$ and $x_4 = 0$ into the other two equations, we obtain

$$x_2 + x_3 = 10$$
$$x_2 + 4x_3 = 20$$

and it can easily be seen that the solution of this system of linear equations is $x_2 = \frac{20}{3}$ and $x_3 = \frac{10}{3}$. The point $(0, \frac{20}{3}, \frac{10}{3}, 0)$ *is* a vertex of the region of feasible solutions since these values of the four variables also satisfy the inequalities $x_2 \geqslant 0$ and $x_3 \geqslant 0$.

Continuing in this way (see Exercise 9 on page 242), we obtain the seven vertices given in the following table, which also shows the corresponding values of $24{,}000x_1 + 30{,}000x_2 + 48{,}000x_3 + 36{,}000x_4$, representing the refinery's profit:

Vertex	*Profit*	
(0, 0, 0, 0)	0	
(0, 0, 0, 10)	\$360,000	
(0, 0, 5, 0)	\$240,000	
$\left(0, 0, \frac{10}{3}, \frac{20}{3}\right)$	\$400,000	← *maximum*
(0, 10, 0, 0)	\$300,000	
$\left(0, \frac{20}{3}, \frac{10}{3}, 0\right)$	\$360,000	
(10, 0, 0, 0)	\$240,000	

Thus, the maximum profit is \$400,000 on the sales of $3\frac{1}{3}$ million gallons of gasoline C and $6\frac{2}{3}$ million gallons of gasoline D.

The method of this section has the advantage that it is *systematic* (which is a requirement for the use of computers), and that it involves only relatively simple algebra. Its main disadvantage is that it can involve a tremendous amount of algebraic detail. As the reader will be asked to verify in Exercise 16 on page 449, in a linear programming problem involving 5 variables which must be non-negative and satisfy 4 other linear inequalities, the region of feasible solutions has potentially 126 vertices, and in a linear programming problem involving 6 variables which must be non-negative and satisfy 5 other linear inequalities, the region of feasible solutions has potentially 462 vertices. To use the method of this section, we would thus have to solve 126 systems of five linear equations in five variables in the first case, and 462 systems of six linear equations in six variables in the second case. A good deal of this work can be avoided by using an alternate algebraic method, called the *Simplex method,* which we shall study in Chapter 10. Had we used this method in the gasoline-blending problem on page 237, we would have had to solve only *one* system of six linear equations in six variables instead of 15 systems of four linear equations in four variables. Similarly, to handle the two problems referred to earlier in this paragraph, the Simplex method requires that we solve *one* system of nine linear equations in nine variables instead of 126 systems of five linear equations in five variables, and *one* system of eleven linear equations in eleven variables instead of 462 systems of six linear equations in six variables. This still does not look very inviting, but as we shall see in Chapter 10, the Simplex method does provide considerable simplifications.

The examples of this chapter have served to illustrate the great variety of problems which come under the general heading of linear programming. So far as the exercises are concerned, the reader has the enormous advantage of *knowing for sure* that they pertain to linear programming situations, for one of the greatest difficulties faced by most beginners is that of *recognizing* problems which can be solved by linear programming techniques. Although the subject of linear programming has continually grown in importance and it has found many applications in business and economics, it is by no means the "last word" in management science. A good deal of current research is devoted to *non-linear programming,* which applies when the quantity to be maximized or minimized need not be the value of a linear function and the restrictions on the variables need not be expressed in terms of linear inequalities. A considerable amount of research is also being done in *dynamic programming,* which applies to situations in which a *sequence* of decisions has to be made so as to maximize or minimize the values of an objective function, and in *stochastic programming,* where corresponding decisions are based on anticipations concerning the probable values of various relevant factors.

EXERCISES

1. Repeat Exercise 1 on page 232 by listing the vertices of the region of feasible solutions, calculating the manufacturer's total profit for each vertex, and thus determining the number of trays of each kind that should be produced so as to maximize the total profit.
2. Rework both parts of Exercise 2 on page 232 by calculating Mr. Jones' cost for each vertex of the region of feasible solution, and thus determining optimum conditions.
3. Rework all four parts of Exercise 3 on page 232 by the method of this section.
4. Solve the linear programming problem of Exercise 4 on page 232 by the method of this section, namely, by calculating the wholesale distributor's cost for each vertex of the region of feasible solutions.

5. Repeat Exercise 6 on page 232 by the method of this section, that is, by determining the company's profit for each vertex of the region of feasible solutions.

6. Solve both parts of the linear programming problem of Exercise 10 on page 233 by the method of this section.

7. Solve the linear programming problem of Exercise 11 on page 233 by the method of this section.

8. Verify that the coordinates of points Q and R of Figure 8.6 are (30, 40, 5) and (10, 40, 20).

9. On pages 239 and 240 we investigated five of the fifteen *potential* vertices of the region of feasible solutions for the gasoline-blending example. Investigating the other ten possibilities and calculating the refinery's profit for each vertex, verify the results given in the table on page 240.

10. Use the method of this section to find the maximum value of $3.5x + 2.0y$, where x and y must be non-negative and satisfy the inequalities $x + y \leqslant 6$, $5x + 3y \leqslant 20$, and $x - y \leqslant 1$.

11. Use the method of this section (that is, investigate all 20 potential vertices of the region of feasible solutions) to find the maximum value of $28x_1 + 21x_2 + 10x_3$, where x_1, x_2, and x_3 must satisfy the inequalities

$$x_1 \geqslant 0, \quad x_2 \geqslant 0, \quad x_3 \geqslant 0, \quad 3x_1 + 2x_2 + 4x_3 \leqslant 12,$$
$$x_1 + 2x_2 + 4x_3 \leqslant 8, \quad \text{and} \quad x_1 + 3x_2 + 2x_3 \leqslant 6$$

12. Referring to the illustration on page 224, suppose that the company wants to expand its line by including two other animal foods, C and D. A dozen cans of animal food C require 3 pounds of each food supplement, while a dozen cans of animal food D require 5 pounds of the first food supplement and 2 pounds of the second. If all other figures are the same as before, and a dozen cans of animal foods C and D yield respective profits of $8.00 and $9.00, how should one schedule the production of the four animal foods so as to maximize the company's profit?

REFERENCES

Barson, A. S., *What Is Linear Programming?* Boston: D. C. Heath and Co., 1964.

Bennion, E. G., *Elementary Mathematics of Linear Programming and Game Theory*. East Lansing, Mich.: Bureau of Business and Economic Research, Michigan State University, 1960.

Glicksman, A. M., *An Introduction to Linear Programming and the Theory of Games*. New York: John Wiley & Sons, Inc., 1963.

Smythe, W. R., Jr., and Johnson, L. A., *Introduction to Linear Programming with Applications*. Englewood Cliffs, N.J.: Prentice-Hall, Inc., 1966.

Thompson, W. W., Jr., *Operations Research Techniques*. Columbus, Ohio: Charles E. Merrill Books, Inc., 1967.

9

MATRIX ALGEBRA

9.1 INTRODUCTION

Very often a single number is all that matters in the description of a given situation—a sports writer may be interested only in the fact that 16,483 persons attended a certain baseball game, and an ad writer may have all the information he needs, if he is told that a given merchant will reduce the price of all of the 117 television sets he has in stock. Things would be quite different, however, if the business manager of the baseball team had to report attendance figures to his accountant, or the merchant had to place an order to replenish his stock of television sets. In that case, the business manager of the baseball team might report that 1,255 persons bought box seats, 6,719 bought reserved seats, 7,914 bought general admissions, and 595 were admitted free, and (assuming that he stocks only one brand of television sets) the merchant might be interested in the fact that his inventory consists of 6 color consoles, 15 black and white consoles, 48 color table models, 30 color portables, and 18 black and white portables. In abbreviated form, the figures which the business manager of the baseball team supplies to his accountant could be written as

$$(1{,}255,\ 6{,}719,\ 7{,}914,\ 595)$$

and the information which describes the merchant's inventory could be presented as

$$(6,\ 15,\ 48,\ 30,\ 18)$$

In mathematics, we refer to arrays of numbers like these as *row vectors*, or simply as *vectors;* the numbers are enclosed by parentheses and separated by commas. The individual numbers are referred to as the *components*, or the *elements*, of the vector, and each component has a special significance (in any given problem) which must be clearly understood. Evidently, the vector (1,255, 6,719, 7,914, 595) would be of no value to the accountant unless he knew exactly what each component represents, and the vector (6, 15, 48, 30, 18) would be of no value to the merchant unless he knew precisely what kind of television set each figure represents.

It is of interest to note that we have already used the vector notation in connection with points in the plane and in three-dimensional space. We can now say that a point in the plane is represented by the vector (x, y), where x and y are its coordinates as shown in Figure 3.6 on page 74, and that a point in space is represented by the vector (x, y, z), where x, y, and z are its coordinates as shown in Figure 3.14 on page 85. Incidentally, this explains why we refer to the number of components of a vector as its *dimension*. This geometrical interpretation of vectors is very important, it leads to models for many concepts of physics (velocity, acceleration, and force, for example), and we shall elaborate on it in Exercise 12 on page 252.

If the components of a vector are written one beneath the other, we refer to it as a *column vector*. Thus, the figures in our two numerical examples could have been represented by the column vectors

$$\begin{pmatrix} 1{,}255 \\ 6{,}719 \\ 7{,}914 \\ 595 \end{pmatrix} \quad \text{and} \quad \begin{pmatrix} 6 \\ 15 \\ 48 \\ 30 \\ 18 \end{pmatrix}$$

where the numbers are again enclosed by parentheses, but no commas are needed to keep them apart. Whether we use a row vector or a corresponding column vector in a given problem will depend on what we intend to do with the vector.

It may have occurred to the reader that if the merchant of our example had carried several brands of television sets, the inventory vector (6, 15, 48, 30, 18) would not have provided an adequate description. Supposing that he carries two brands, X and Y, he could give a separate inventory vector for each brand, say, (6, 12, 25, 8, 11) for brand X and (0, 3, 23, 22, 7) for brand Y. This means that his inventory consists of 6 color consoles of brand X and none of brand Y, 12 black and white consoles of brand X and 3 of brand Y, 25 color table models of brand X and 23 of brand Y, and so on. He could also have conveyed this information by means of the following kind of array, called a *matrix*

$$\begin{pmatrix} 6 & 12 & 25 & 8 & 11 \\ 0 & 3 & 23 & 22 & 7 \end{pmatrix}$$

Here, the numbers in the first row pertain to brand X, those in the second row pertain to brand Y, and (as before) the first number in each row is the number of color consoles, the second number is the number of black and white consoles, . . . , and the fifth number is the number of black and white portables. Again, the numbers are enclosed by parentheses, but no commas are used to separate the numbers in the different rows and columns.

Referring to the baseball example, we might similarly use a matrix to represent the attendance figures, say, for four consecutive games. Assuming that the original data pertained to the first of these games, this matrix might look as follows:

$$\begin{pmatrix} 1{,}255 & 6{,}719 & 7{,}914 & 595 \\ 2{,}305 & 8{,}501 & 10{,}513 & 1{,}006 \\ 1{,}864 & 5{,}967 & 8{,}445 & 870 \\ 3{,}059 & 11{,}487 & 14{,}566 & 1{,}712 \end{pmatrix}$$

The four games are represented by the four rows, box seats by the numbers in the first column, reserved seats by the numbers in the second column, general admissions by the numbers in the third column, and free admissions by those in the fourth column.

In general, a *matrix* is a rectangular (or square) array of numbers arranged in rows and columns. If a matrix has m rows and n columns, it is said to be of *order* $m \times n$ (which is read "m by n," and where the number of rows always comes first); the order of a matrix is also referred to as its *dimensions*. To distinguish matrices from other kinds of mathematical objects (real numbers or functions, for example), we denote them by capital letters in boldface type. Thus, we might refer to the 2×5 matrix of the television-set-inventory example as matrix $\mathbf{R}$, and to the 4×4 matrix of the baseball-admissions example as matrix $\mathbf{D}$. Note that the second of these two matrices has as many rows as columns, which makes it a *square matrix*.

The individual entries of a matrix are referred to as its *elements*, and in both of our examples the elements of the respective matrices were numbers. (In more advanced work in mathematics, the elements of a matrix can also be functions or other kinds of mathematical objects; in fact, the elements of a matrix can, themselves, be matrices. So far as the work in this book is concerned, we shall consider only matrices whose elements are real numbers.) As we have already pointed out in connection with vectors, the position of each element within a matrix attaches to it a special significance (in any given problem), and it should be noted that

$$\begin{pmatrix} -3 & 5 \\ 7 & 1 \end{pmatrix} \quad \begin{pmatrix} 5 & -3 \\ 1 & 7 \end{pmatrix}$$

are *different* matrices even though they contain the same numbers.

It is customary to denote the elements of a matrix with the same letter as the matrix, though in lower case and in ordinary (lightface) type. Furthermore, we use *double subscripts* to designate the position of each element within a matrix, with the first subscript designating the row and the second subscript designating the column. Thus, a_{11} is the element in the first row and the first column of matrix **A**, a_{23} is the element in its second row and third column, a_{74} is the element in its seventh row and fourth column, and so on. Similarly, b_{45} is the element in the fourth row and the fifth column of matrix **B**, and c_{36} is the element in the third row and sixth column of matrix **C**.* In general, if **A** is an $m \times n$ matrix, we write

$$\mathbf{A} = \begin{pmatrix} a_{11} & a_{12} & \dots & a_{1n} \\ a_{21} & a_{22} & \dots & a_{2n} \\ \dots & \dots & \dots & \dots \\ a_{m1} & a_{m2} & \dots & a_{mn} \end{pmatrix}$$

and if we want to talk about an element of this matrix without being specific, we refer to it as a_{ij}, where i can be 1, 2, 3, . . . , or m, and j can be 1, 2, 3, . . . , or n.

Having defined vectors on page 243 and matrices on page 245, let us point out that there is really no need to treat them separately. After all, a row vector with k components is a $1 \times k$ matrix, and a column vector with k components is a $k \times 1$ matrix. The terms "element" and "component" are also used interchangeably.

The next few sections of this chapter will be devoted to *matrix algebra*, namely, to the rules according to which matrices are combined. As we shall see, matrices of the same order can be added and subtracted, some matrices can be multiplied, and some can even be divided. Matrix algebra has many important applications in all branches of science; above all, it is used whenever one has to deal with large systems of linear equations in many variables. Since this is generally the case when the *Simplex method* is used in linear programming, we shall devote a whole chapter, Chapter 10, to this important application.

9.2 MATRIX ADDITION AND SUBTRACTION

To begin our study of matrix algebra, let us state formally what we mean by the *equality* of two matrices: two $m \times n$ matrices **A** and **B** are equal, and we write **A** = **B**, if and only if all their corresponding elements are equal. In other words, if the elements of two $m \times n$ matrices are denoted a_{ij} and b_{ij},

---

* If a matrix has more than nine rows or columns, the two subscripts are separated by a comma to avoid confusion; for instance, $a_{12,3}$ is the element in the twelfth row and the third column of matrix **A**.

the matrices are equal if and only if $a_{ij} = b_{ij}$ for each possible pair of subscripts i and j. For example, if

$$\mathbf{A} = \begin{pmatrix} 3 & -7 & 4 \\ 0 & 1 & 5 \end{pmatrix}, \quad \mathbf{B} = \begin{pmatrix} 3 & 4 & -7 \\ 0 & 5 & 1 \end{pmatrix},$$

$$\mathbf{C} = \begin{pmatrix} 3 & -7 & 4 \\ 0 & 1 & 5 \end{pmatrix}, \quad \mathbf{D} = \begin{pmatrix} 0 & 1 & 5 \\ 3 & -7 & 4 \end{pmatrix}$$

then **A** is equal to **C**, but neither **A** nor **C** nor **D** is equal to **B**, and neither **A** nor **B** nor **C** is equal to **D**. Note that we can speak of the equality of two matrices only if they are of the same order, namely, if they have the same dimensions. Observe, also, that two matrices need not be equal even though they contain the same numbers; this is apparent from matrices **A**, **B**, and **D**, which contain the same numbers but *not in the same positions.*

As might be expected, we add two matrices by simply adding their corresponding elements. More formally, if **A** and **B** are $m \times n$ matrices with the elements a_{ij} and b_{ij}, then $\mathbf{A} + \mathbf{B}$ is the $m \times n$ matrix whose elements are $a_{ij} + b_{ij}$. For example, if

$$\mathbf{A} = \begin{pmatrix} 2 & 1 & 5 \\ 7 & 4 & -1 \\ 1 & 6 & 8 \end{pmatrix} \quad \text{and} \quad \mathbf{B} = \begin{pmatrix} -3 & 2 & 4 \\ 0 & 7 & 1 \\ -4 & -2 & 3 \end{pmatrix}$$

then

$$\mathbf{A} + \mathbf{B} = \begin{pmatrix} 2 + (-3) & 1 + 2 & 5 + 4 \\ 7 + 0 & 4 + 7 & -1 + 1 \\ 1 + (-4) & 6 + (-2) & 8 + 3 \end{pmatrix} = \begin{pmatrix} -1 & 3 & 9 \\ 7 & 11 & 0 \\ -3 & 4 & 11 \end{pmatrix}$$

where we have added each element of **B** to the corresponding element of **A**. As is apparent from this definition, *two matrices can be added only if they are of the same order.*

To give an applied example in which it is meaningful to speak of a matrix sum, let us refer again to the television-set-inventory illustration on page 244, where the merchant's inventory was given by the matrix

$$\mathbf{R} = \begin{pmatrix} 6 & 12 & 25 & 8 & 11 \\ 0 & 3 & 23 & 22 & 7 \end{pmatrix}$$

Suppose now that the merchant places an order with a local distributor, and that this order is represented by the matrix

$$\mathbf{S} = \begin{pmatrix} 4 & 3 & 0 & 10 & 5 \\ 12 & 10 & 0 & 0 & 10 \end{pmatrix}$$

where the rows and columns have the same significance as before; in other words, he orders 4 color consoles of brand X and 12 of brand Y, 3 black and white consoles of brand X and 10 of brand Y, no color table models, and so on. If this order is filled before any of the sets the merchant has in stock are sold, his new inventory matrix $\mathbf{T}$ is given by the *matrix sum*

$$\mathbf{T} = \mathbf{R} + \mathbf{S} = \begin{pmatrix} 6+4 & 12+3 & 25+0 & 8+10 & 11+5 \\ 0+12 & 3+10 & 23+0 & 22+0 & 7+10 \end{pmatrix}$$

$$= \begin{pmatrix} 10 & 15 & 25 & 18 & 16 \\ 12 & 13 & 23 & 22 & 17 \end{pmatrix}$$

To continue this example, suppose that after the inventory has been replenished, the merchant holds a special two-week sale, for which his sales of television sets are given by the matrix

$$\mathbf{U} = \begin{pmatrix} 4 & 11 & 16 & 9 & 7 \\ 7 & 13 & 18 & 14 & 15 \end{pmatrix}$$

Now then, at the end of this two-week sale his inventory is reduced to

$$\mathbf{V} = \begin{pmatrix} 10-4 & 15-11 & 25-16 & 18-9 & 16-7 \\ 12-7 & 13-13 & 23-18 & 22-14 & 17-15 \end{pmatrix}$$

$$= \begin{pmatrix} 6 & 4 & 9 & 9 & 9 \\ 5 & 0 & 5 & 8 & 2 \end{pmatrix}$$

and it would seem only reasonable to refer to this matrix as the *difference* between $\mathbf{T}$ and $\mathbf{U}$, and write it as $\mathbf{V} = \mathbf{T} - \mathbf{U}$. Indeed, this is how the difference between two matrices is defined: *we simply subtract the corresponding elements*. More formally, if $\mathbf{A}$ and $\mathbf{B}$ are $m \times n$ matrices with the elements a_{ij} and b_{ij}, then their difference is the $m \times n$ matrix $\mathbf{A} - \mathbf{B}$ whose elements are $a_{ij} - b_{ij}$. As in addition, we can speak of the difference between two matrices only if they are of the same order.

If we subtract an $m \times n$ matrix $\mathbf{A}$ from itself, we obtain the $m \times n$ matrix $\mathbf{A} - \mathbf{A}$ whose elements are all zeros. Such a matrix is referred to as a *zero matrix*, or *null matrix*, and it serves the same function as the number zero in "ordinary" arithmetic—as can easily be verified, $\mathbf{A} + \mathbf{0} = \mathbf{0} + \mathbf{A} = \mathbf{A}$ for any $m \times n$ matrix $\mathbf{A}$ and the corresponding zero matrix of order $m \times n$. As this discussion suggests, there is more than one zero matrix; in fact, there is one for each possible order. The following are some examples, namely, the zero matrices of order 2×2, 4×1, and 3×5:

$$\begin{pmatrix} 0 & 0 \\ 0 & 0 \end{pmatrix}, \quad \begin{pmatrix} 0 \\ 0 \\ 0 \\ 0 \end{pmatrix}, \quad \text{and} \quad \begin{pmatrix} 0 & 0 & 0 & 0 & 0 \\ 0 & 0 & 0 & 0 & 0 \\ 0 & 0 & 0 & 0 & 0 \end{pmatrix}$$

EXERCISES

1. Give the order of each of the following matrices, and also state whether it is a row vector, a column vector, a square matrix, or none of these:

(a) $\begin{pmatrix} 3 & 2 & -4 \\ 2 & -1 & 5 \end{pmatrix}$

(e) $\begin{pmatrix} 2 \\ 3 \end{pmatrix}$

(b) $\begin{pmatrix} -3 & 5 & 0 \\ 0 & 1 & -1 \\ 2 & -4 & 3 \end{pmatrix}$

(f) $\begin{pmatrix} 2 & 4 & 0 & -1 \\ -1 & 3 & 2 & 0 \\ 5 & -2 & 4 & -3 \\ 6 & 0 & 1 & 2 \end{pmatrix}$

(c) $(1, -3, 5, 0, 2)$

(g) $\begin{pmatrix} 1 \\ -1 \\ 1 \\ 0 \end{pmatrix}$

(d) $\begin{pmatrix} 1 & -1 \\ 0 & 3 \\ 2 & -1 \\ 4 & 3 \end{pmatrix}$

(h) $\begin{pmatrix} 1 & 5 & -2 & 3 & -1 \\ 0 & 4 & 3 & -2 & 0 \end{pmatrix}$

2. Given

$$\begin{pmatrix} x & 3 & -1 \\ 0 & -2 & 0 \\ 1 & u & t \\ 5 & -7 & 6 \end{pmatrix} = \begin{pmatrix} 5 & 3 & -1 \\ 0 & y & 0 \\ 1 & 4 & -5 \\ s & -7 & z \end{pmatrix}$$

find the values of s, t, u, x, y, and z.

3. Given

$$\begin{pmatrix} 3 & a & 4 & 0 \\ -1 & 2 & b & 3 \end{pmatrix} = \begin{pmatrix} 3 & -2 & c & 0 \\ d & 2 & 0 & 3 \end{pmatrix}$$

find a, b, c, and d.

4. Find $\mathbf{A} + \mathbf{B}$ and $\mathbf{A} - \mathbf{B}$ for each part of this exercise, provided, of course, that these quantities exist:

(a) $\mathbf{A} = \begin{pmatrix} -3 & 2 \\ 6 & -1 \end{pmatrix}$, $\mathbf{B} = \begin{pmatrix} 2 & -2 \\ -4 & 3 \end{pmatrix}$;

(b) $\mathbf{A} = (0, 3, -4, 7, 2)$, $\mathbf{B} = (-1, 2, 5, -4, 3)$;

(c) $\mathbf{A} = \begin{pmatrix} 4 & 0 & -2 \\ -1 & 3 & 5 \end{pmatrix}$, $\mathbf{B} = \begin{pmatrix} 3 & -1 & 1 \\ -1 & 2 & -4 \end{pmatrix}$

(d) $\mathbf{A} = \begin{pmatrix} 3 \\ 2 \\ -1 \end{pmatrix}$, $\mathbf{B} = \begin{pmatrix} -1 \\ 0 \\ 5 \\ 2 \end{pmatrix}$;

(e) $\mathbf{A} = \begin{pmatrix} 2 & 0 & -1 \\ 0 & -3 & 4 \\ 5 & -1 & 0 \\ 1 & 6 & 2 \end{pmatrix}$, $\mathbf{B} = \begin{pmatrix} 3 & -1 & 1 \\ 0 & -2 & 1 \\ 2 & 1 & 3 \\ -1 & 4 & -1 \end{pmatrix}$;

5. If

$$\begin{pmatrix} 2 \\ 3 \\ -1 \end{pmatrix} + \begin{pmatrix} x \\ y \\ z \end{pmatrix} = \begin{pmatrix} 4 \\ 1 \\ -1 \end{pmatrix}$$

find x, y, and z.

6. Like "ordinary" addition, matrix addition is *commutative* and *associative.* Verify this for the matrices

$$\mathbf{A} = \begin{pmatrix} -3 & 2 \\ 4 & 1 \end{pmatrix}, \mathbf{B} = \begin{pmatrix} 2 & -2 \\ 3 & -1 \end{pmatrix}, \text{ and } \mathbf{C} = \begin{pmatrix} 1 & 2 \\ 1 & 3 \end{pmatrix}$$

by showing that $\mathbf{A} + \mathbf{B} = \mathbf{B} + \mathbf{A}$ and $\mathbf{A} + (\mathbf{B} + \mathbf{C}) = (\mathbf{A} + \mathbf{B}) + \mathbf{C}$.

7. An airline reports the number of seats occupied on its flights by means of a 1×4 row vector—the first component represents the number of seats occupied by first class passengers, the second component represents those occupied by coach passengers, the third component represents those occupied by students traveling at reduced rates, and the fourth component represents those occupied by non-paying passengers.

(a) If (15, 27, 4, 3) represents the seats occupied on a flight as it leaves Los Angeles for New York via Chicago, and (3, −4, 5, −1) represents the change which takes place in Chicago, find the 1×4 vector which represents the seats occupied on this flight as it arrives in New York.

(b) If (14, 30, 7, 2) represents the seats occupied on a flight as it leaves Phoenix for Dallas via El Paso, and (19, 21, 8, 2) represents the seats occupied as the plane arrives in Dallas, find the 1×4 vector which represents the change which took place in El Paso.

8. A Plymouth-Chrysler-Imperial dealer represents his inventory of new cars by means of a 3×4 matrix—the numbers in the three rows pertain, respectively, to Plymouths, Chryslers, and Imperials, and the numbers in the four columns pertain, respectively, to four-door sedans, two-door sedans, convertibles, and station wagons.

(a) Explain in words what new cars he has on hand, if on January 1, 1969, his inventory is given by the matrix

$$\mathbf{K} = \begin{pmatrix} 8 & 12 & 4 & 5 \\ 3 & 5 & 2 & 3 \\ 4 & 2 & 0 & 0 \end{pmatrix}$$

(b) If his January sales are given by the matrix

$$\mathbf{L} = \begin{pmatrix} 5 & 8 & 2 & 3 \\ 1 & 3 & 1 & 2 \\ 2 & 1 & 0 & 0 \end{pmatrix}$$

and no new cars were added to his stock, what is his inventory on February 1, 1969?

(c) If the new cars he receives during February are given by the matrix

$$\mathbf{M} = \begin{pmatrix} 6 & 5 & 3 & 5 \\ 4 & 3 & 2 & 5 \\ 5 & 2 & 0 & 0 \end{pmatrix}$$

and his February sales are given by the matrix

$$\mathbf{N} = \begin{pmatrix} 4 & 7 & 4 & 3 \\ 3 & 2 & 3 & 2 \\ 3 & 2 & 0 & 0 \end{pmatrix}$$

what is his inventory on March 1, 1969?

9. SCALAR MULTIPLICATION. In matrix algebra, "ordinary" numbers are referred to as *scalars*, and when we multiply a matrix by a scalar, this means that each element of the matrix is multiplied by that scalar; for instance,

$$\text{if } \mathbf{A} = \begin{pmatrix} 2 & -2 \\ 1 & 4 \end{pmatrix}, \text{ then } 3\mathbf{A} = \begin{pmatrix} 3\cdot 2 & 3(-2) \\ 3\cdot 1 & 3\cdot 4 \end{pmatrix} = \begin{pmatrix} 6 & -6 \\ 3 & 12 \end{pmatrix}.$$

(a) Referring to part (a) of Exercise 4, find $2\mathbf{A}$, $5\mathbf{B}$, and $2\mathbf{A} + 5\mathbf{B}$;
(b) Referring to part (c) of Exercise 4, find $3\mathbf{A}$, $2\mathbf{B}$, and $3\mathbf{A} - 2\mathbf{B}$;
(c) If

$$3\begin{pmatrix} x \\ 1 \\ 4 \end{pmatrix} - 2\begin{pmatrix} 1 \\ y \\ 5 \end{pmatrix} + \begin{pmatrix} 0 \\ 1 \\ z \end{pmatrix} = \begin{pmatrix} 13 \\ 0 \\ 6 \end{pmatrix}$$

find x, y, and z.

(d) The *negative*, or *additive inverse* (see page 36), of matrix $\mathbf{A}$ is denoted by $-\mathbf{A}$ and it is characterized by the property that $\mathbf{A} + (-\mathbf{A}) = (-\mathbf{A}) + \mathbf{A} = \mathbf{0}$ where $\mathbf{0}$ is the zero matrix of the same order as $\mathbf{A}$. Express $-\mathbf{A}$ as the product of $\mathbf{A}$ and a suitable scalar, and find the negative of each of the matrices of parts (a), (b), (c), and (d) of Exercise 1.

10. THE TRANSPOSE OF A MATRIX. The *transpose* of matrix $\mathbf{A}$, written $\mathbf{A}'$, is the matrix whose first row is the same as the first column of $\mathbf{A}$, whose second row is the same as the second column of $\mathbf{A}$, and so on.

(a) If matrix $\mathbf{A}$ is of order $m \times n$, what is the order of $\mathbf{A}'$?
(b) If $\mathbf{B}$ is a $1 \times k$ row vector, what kind of a special matrix is $\mathbf{B}'$?
(c) Find the transpose of each of the matrices of parts (a), (b), (c), (e), and (h) of Exercise 1.
(d) Find x, y, and z, given that

$$\begin{pmatrix} 1 & -2 & x \\ y & 3 & 0 \\ 4 & z & 2 \end{pmatrix}' = \begin{pmatrix} 1 & 5 & 4 \\ -2 & 3 & -1 \\ 4 & 0 & 2 \end{pmatrix}$$

(e) Verify the rule $(\mathbf{A} + \mathbf{B})' = \mathbf{A}' + \mathbf{B}'$ for the two matrices of part (a) of Exercise 4.

11. VECTORS AND COMPLEX NUMBERS. It is possible to look at complex numbers as 1×2 row vectors—if x and y are real numbers, we simply identify the complex number $x + iy$ with the vector (x, y).

(a) What complex numbers are represented by the following vectors: (2, 2), (0, −1), (1, 0), (−3, −2), and (3, 4)?
(b) Write each of the following complex numbers as vectors: i, $1 + i$, 0, -1, $2 + 3i$, $2 - i$, and $7 - 5i$.
(c) Can we add complex numbers by adding the corresponding vectors in accordance with the rule for matrix addition on page 247?

12. VECTORS AND DIRECTED DISTANCES. As we saw on page 244, 1×2 and 1×3 vectors can be identified with points in the plane and points in space. Very similar is the interpretation in which we identify vectors with *directed*

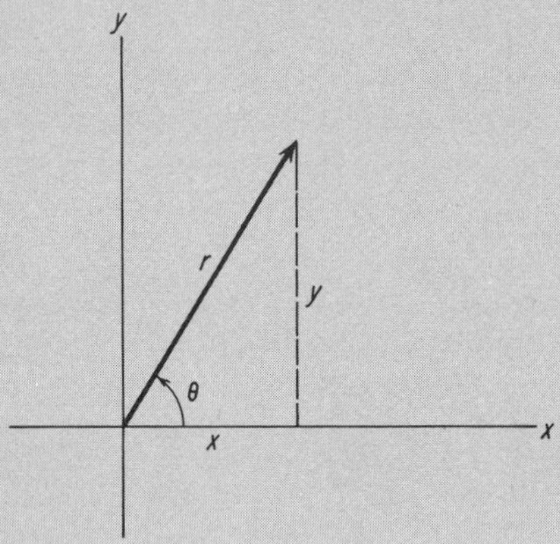

FIG. 9.1

distances (namely, with quantities having magnitude as well as direction) as is indicated in Figures 9.1 and 9.2. In both cases, the length of the arrow represents the *magnitude* of the vector, and the *direction* of the vector is simply that of the arrow, itself.

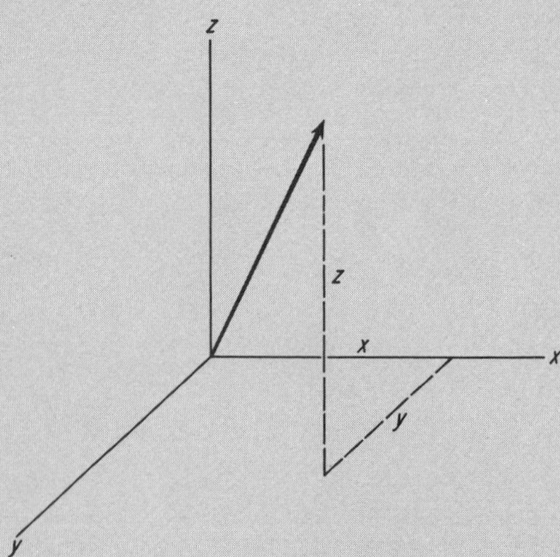

FIG. 9.2

(a) Draw in one diagram the arrows (directed distances) which correspond to the following 1×2 vectors: $(3, 0)$, $(1, 5)$, $(-2, -4)$, $(0, -3)$, and $(2, -3)$.

(b) Give a *geometrical rule* for finding the sum of two 1×2 vectors. (*Hint:* see part (b) of Exercise 24 on page 127.)

(c) Draw in one diagram the arrows (directed distances) which correspond to the following 1×3 row vectors: $(3, 2, 0)$, $(0, 0, 4)$, $(1, 4, -3)$, and $(4, -2, 1)$.

(d) Given the components of a 1×2 vector, we can calculate its magnitude and its direction by means of the formulas of Exercise 14 on page 182, namely,

$$r = \sqrt{x^2 + y^2} \qquad \text{and} \qquad \tan \theta = \frac{y}{x}$$

where r is always *positive* and θ is given by the appropriate value on the interval from 0° to 360°. Find the magnitude and the direction of each of the following vectors: $(3, 4)$, $(12, 5)$, $(-2, 2)$, and $(-1, -\sqrt{3})$. (*Hint:* for the first two vectors use Table VI, and for the other two refer to Figures 6.10 and 6.19.)

(e) If r is the magnitude of a 1×2 vector and θ measures its direction as in Figure 9.1, we find from Figure 6.14 on page 178 that the two components of the vector are given by $x = r \cdot \cos \theta$ and $y = r \cdot \sin \theta$. Find the components of each of the following 1×2 vectors: $r = 3$ and $\theta = 180°$, $r = 5$ and $\theta = 270°$, $r = 4$ and $\theta = 45°$, and $r = 10$ and $\theta = 240°$. (*Hint:* for the last two vectors refer to Figures 6.10 and 6.19.)

(f) In physics, we use vectors to represent velocities, forces, accelerations, and other quantities which have magnitude as well as direction. Using the rules of vector (or matrix) addition and subtraction, we can thus combine velocities, forces, etc., as in the solution of the following problem: *if a motorboat is moving on its own power at 20 miles per hour in a northeasterly direction and the current is moving it 5 miles per hour in a southerly direction, what is its actual (resultant) motion?* Since the ship's own motion is given by the vector $(14.14, 14.14)$, where we made use of the fact that $\cos 45° = \sin 45° = 0.7071$ and rounded to two decimals, and since the motion of the current is given by the vector $(0, -5)$, we find that the boat's overall motion is given by the vector

$$(14.14, 14.14) + (0, -5) = (14.14, 9.14)$$

Its magnitude is $r = \sqrt{14.14^2 + 9.14^2} = 16.8$ miles per hour (approximately), and its direction is given by the angle θ for which $\tan \theta = \frac{9.14}{14.14} = 0.646$, namely, $\theta = 33°$ according to Table VI. Use this method to find the resultant (actual) motion of an airplane approaching a landing strip at a speed of 96 miles per hour pointed due west, if the wind is blowing at 40 miles per hour due southeast.

(g) If an object is acted on simultaneously by several forces, the overall effect is that of a single force, called the *resultant* force, which is given

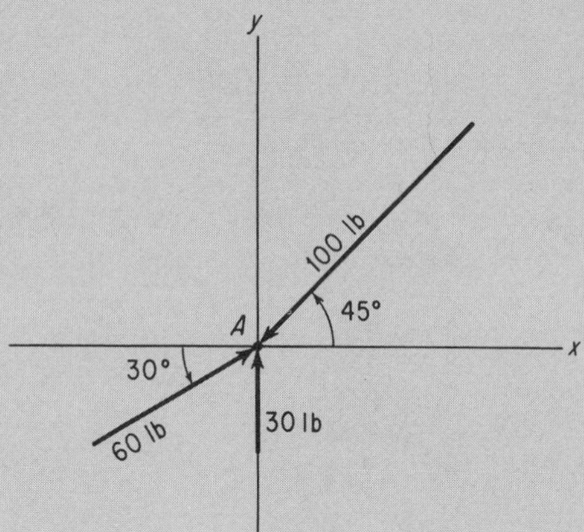

FIG. 9.3

by the sum of the vectors representing the individual forces. Find the magnitude and the direction of the resultant of the forces acting on point A of Figure 9.3, and also find the magnitudes of forces F and G of Figure 9.4 so that the resultant of the three forces will be the vector $(0, 0)$, namely, so that the three forces will be *in equilibrium*.

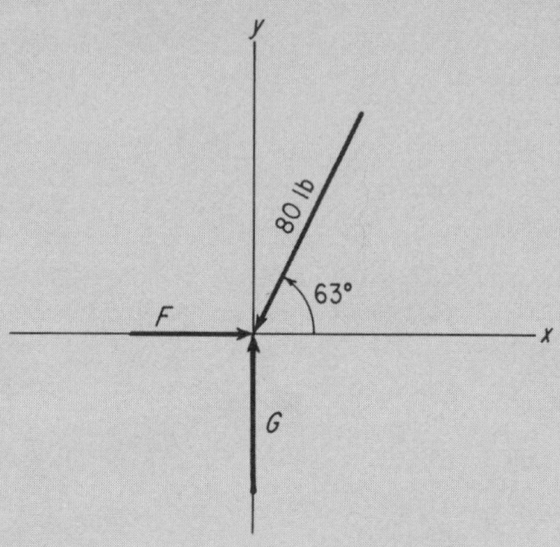

FIG. 9.4

9.3 MATRIX MULTIPLICATION

Continuing the discussion of the preceding section, we might be led to define the product of two $m \times n$ matrices as the matrix which would be obtained by pairwise multiplying their respective elements. This could be done, of course, but we shall give an entirely different definition which leads to a much more *useful* concept of a matrix product. Since this definition is fairly complicated, let us illustrate it first in connection with a $1 \times k$ matrix and a $k \times 1$ matrix, namely, in connection with a row vector and a column vector having the same dimension. Returning to the first example on page 243, where we represented the attendance figures for a baseball game by means of the vector

$$(1{,}255,\ 6{,}719,\ 7{,}914,\ 595)$$

let us suppose now that we are interested in the *total receipts*. If a box seat costs \$4.00, a reserved seat costs \$2.50, and a general admission costs \$1.25, we can represent this information by means of the column vector

$$\begin{pmatrix} 4.00 \\ 2.50 \\ 1.25 \\ 0.00 \end{pmatrix}$$

where the bottom value represents the price of a free admission. Since the total amounts received for box seats, reserved seats, general admissions, and free admissions, are, respectively, 1,255(\$4.00), 6,719(\$2.50), 7,914(\$1.25), and 595(\$0.00), the total receipts for the game are

$$1{,}255(4.00) + 6{,}719(2.50) + 7{,}914(1.25) + 595(0.00) = \$31{,}710$$

Note that this total is the sum of the products obtained by multiplying the *first* element of the row vector by the *first* element of the column vector, the *second* element of the row vector by the *second* element of the column vector, the *third* element of the row vector by the *third* element of the column vector, and the *fourth* element of the row vector by the *fourth* element of the column vector.

Since sums of products like this arise in many applications (see also Exercises 4 and 5 on page 259), we shall let it *define* the product of a row vector and a column vector having the same dimension. Aside from the fact that this kind of vector product has important applications, it also serves to define the product of two matrices in the following way:

If $\mathbf{A}$ *is an* $m \times n$ *matrix and* $\mathbf{B}$ *is an* $n \times r$ *matrix, then their product* $\mathbf{C} = \mathbf{A} \cdot \mathbf{B}$ *is the* $m \times r$ *matrix whose elements are*

$$c_{ij} = (a_{i1}, a_{i2}, \ldots, a_{in}) \begin{pmatrix} b_{1j} \\ b_{2j} \\ \vdots \\ b_{nj} \end{pmatrix}$$

$$= a_{i1}b_{1j} + a_{i2}b_{2j} + \ldots + a_{in}b_{nj}$$

where the a's and the b's are the respective elements of matrices $\mathbf{A}$ and $\mathbf{B}$. In words, the element c_{ij} in the ith row and the jth column of the product matrix **C** is obtained by "multiplying" the ith row of **A** (looked upon as a row vector) by the jth column of **B** (looked upon as a column vector). Before we give any numerical examples, let us make it very clear that with this definition we can speak of $\mathbf{A}\cdot\mathbf{B}$, the product of two matrices **A** and **B**, if and only if *the number of columns in* **A** *equals the number of rows in* **B**.

The following is an example in which we multiply a 2×3 matrix by a 3×2 matrix, which is possible because the first matrix has three columns and the second has three rows. Using the matrices

$$\mathbf{A} = \begin{pmatrix} 2 & 3 & -1 \\ 4 & 1 & 5 \end{pmatrix} \quad \text{and} \quad \mathbf{B} = \begin{pmatrix} 1 & -2 \\ 3 & -3 \\ 2 & 6 \end{pmatrix}$$

we can write

$$\mathbf{A}\cdot\mathbf{B} = \begin{pmatrix} 2 & 3 & -1 \\ 4 & 1 & 5 \end{pmatrix}\begin{pmatrix} 1 & -2 \\ 3 & -3 \\ 2 & 6 \end{pmatrix} = \begin{pmatrix} c_{11} & c_{12} \\ c_{21} & c_{22} \end{pmatrix} = \mathbf{C}$$

and, "multiplying" the *first* row of **A** by the *first* column of **B**, we get

$$c_{11} = 2\cdot 1 + 3\cdot 3 + (-1)2 = 9$$

Similarly, "multiplying" the *first* row of **A** by the *second* column of **B**, the *second* row of **A** by the *first* column of **B**, and the *second* row of **A** by the *second* column of **B**, we obtain

$$c_{12} = 2(-2) + 3(-3) + (-1)6 = -19$$

$$c_{21} = 4\cdot 1 + 1\cdot 3 + 5\cdot 2 = 17$$

$$c_{22} = 4(-2) + 1(-3) + 5\cdot 6 = 19$$

and, hence,

$$\mathbf{A}\cdot\mathbf{B} = \begin{pmatrix} 2 & 3 & -1 \\ 4 & 1 & 5 \end{pmatrix}\begin{pmatrix} 1 & -2 \\ 3 & -3 \\ 2 & 6 \end{pmatrix} = \begin{pmatrix} 9 & -19 \\ 17 & 19 \end{pmatrix} = \mathbf{C}$$

To give another illustration of matrix multiplication, let us refer again to the baseball-attendance example on page 245, and let us now calculate the total receipts for *each* of the four games on the basis of the attendance matrix **D** on page 245, and the column vector of ticket prices on page 255, which we shall now denote with the letter **E**. The total receipts are given by the product matrix $\mathbf{F} = \mathbf{D}\cdot\mathbf{E}$, for which we get

$$\mathbf{D}\cdot\mathbf{E} = \begin{pmatrix} 1{,}255 & 6{,}719 & 7{,}914 & 595 \\ 2{,}305 & 8{,}501 & 10{,}513 & 1{,}006 \\ 1{,}864 & 5{,}967 & 8{,}445 & 870 \\ 3{,}059 & 11{,}487 & 14{,}566 & 1{,}712 \end{pmatrix}\begin{pmatrix} 4.00 \\ 2.50 \\ 1.25 \\ 0.00 \end{pmatrix}$$

$$= \begin{pmatrix} 31{,}710.00 \\ 43{,}613.75 \\ 32{,}929.75 \\ 59{,}161.00 \end{pmatrix} = \mathbf{F}$$

where the first total was already obtained on page 255. The total receipts for the second game are

$$2{,}305(4.00) + 8{,}501(2.50) + 10{,}513(1.25) + 1{,}006(0.00) = \$43{,}613.75$$

while those for the third and fourth game are, respectively,

$$1{,}864(4.00) + 5{,}967(2.50) + 8{,}445(1.25) + 870(0.00) = \$32{,}929.75$$

and

$$3{,}059(4.00) + 11{,}487(2.50) + 14{,}566(1.25) + 1{,}712(0.00) = \$59{,}161.00$$

To continue with this baseball example, suppose we are also interested in the combined attendance figures for the four games, namely, the total sales of box seats, the total sales of reserved seats, and so on. It will be left to the reader to verify in Exercise 9 on page 260 that these totals are, in fact, the elements of the product matrix obtained by multiplying the row vector (1, 1, 1, 1) by the attendance matrix **D** for the four games, namely, the elements of

$$(1, 1, 1, 1)\begin{pmatrix} 1{,}255 & 6{,}719 & 7{,}914 & 595 \\ 2{,}305 & 8{,}501 & 10{,}513 & 1{,}006 \\ 1{,}864 & 5{,}967 & 8{,}445 & 870 \\ 3{,}059 & 11{,}487 & 14{,}566 & 1{,}712 \end{pmatrix} = (8{,}483, 32{,}674, 41{,}438, 4{,}183)$$

Thus, they sold a total of 8,483 box seats, 32,674 reserved seats, and 41,438 general admissions, and there were 4,183 free admissions. Note that it is true in general that *if an $m \times n$ matrix* **A** *is multiplied on the left by the $1 \times m$ row vector whose elements are all 1's, the result is a $1 \times n$ row vector whose elements are the sums of the elements in the corresponding columns of matrix* **A** (see also Exercise 9 on page 260).

Matrix multiplication is often used to illustrate a mathematical operation for which the *commutative law* does not hold. As we pointed out on page 256, two matrices can be multiplied only when the first has as many columns as the second has rows. Thus, if **A** is a 2×3 matrix and **B** is a 3×5 matrix, then $\mathbf{A} \cdot \mathbf{B}$ is a 2×5 matrix, but $\mathbf{B} \cdot \mathbf{A}$ is not defined since **B** has 5 columns while **A** has only 2 rows. Even if both products exist, however, they need not be equal. Referring to the illustration on page 256, for example, where we calculated the product $\mathbf{A} \cdot \mathbf{B}$ for the two matrices

$$\mathbf{A} = \begin{pmatrix} 2 & 3 & -1 \\ 4 & 1 & 5 \end{pmatrix} \quad \text{and} \quad \mathbf{B} = \begin{pmatrix} 1 & -2 \\ 3 & -3 \\ 2 & 6 \end{pmatrix}$$

similar calculations would show that

$$\mathbf{B}\cdot\mathbf{A} = \begin{pmatrix} 1 & -2 \\ 3 & -3 \\ 2 & 6 \end{pmatrix}\begin{pmatrix} 2 & 3 & -1 \\ 4 & 1 & 5 \end{pmatrix} = \begin{pmatrix} -6 & 1 & -11 \\ -6 & 6 & -18 \\ 28 & 12 & 28 \end{pmatrix}$$

This is a 3×3 matrix which is most certainly not equal to the 2×2 matrix **C** obtained on page 256. Finally, even if two matrices **P** and **Q** are $m \times m$ *square matrices,* the two products $\mathbf{P}\cdot\mathbf{Q}$ and $\mathbf{Q}\cdot\mathbf{P}$ need not be equal; this is illustrated in Exercise 6 on page 260.

At the end of Section 9.2 we defined *zero matrices,* or *null matrices,* whose elements are all zeros, and which play the same role as the number zero in ordinary arithmetic. Correspondingly, let us now define so-called *identity matrices,* which, for matrix multiplication, play the role of the number 1. An identity matrix is a *square matrix* for which the elements on the diagonal from upper left to lower right are 1's and all other elements are 0's. The following are some examples, namely, the identity matrices of order 2×2, 3×3, and 4×4:

$$\begin{pmatrix} 1 & 0 \\ 0 & 1 \end{pmatrix}, \quad \begin{pmatrix} 1 & 0 & 0 \\ 0 & 1 & 0 \\ 0 & 0 & 1 \end{pmatrix}, \quad \text{and} \quad \begin{pmatrix} 1 & 0 & 0 & 0 \\ 0 & 1 & 0 & 0 \\ 0 & 0 & 1 & 0 \\ 0 & 0 & 0 & 1 \end{pmatrix}$$

It is easy to verify that if **A** is an $n \times n$ matrix and **I** is the identity matrix of order $n \times n$, then $\mathbf{A}\cdot\mathbf{I} = \mathbf{I}\cdot\mathbf{A} = \mathbf{A}$; this is the property which characterizes the number 1 in "ordinary" arithmetic, where $a\cdot 1 = 1\cdot a = a$ for any real number a. For instance, for a 2×2 matrix,

$$\begin{aligned} \mathbf{I}\cdot\mathbf{A} = \begin{pmatrix} 1 & 0 \\ 0 & 1 \end{pmatrix}\begin{pmatrix} a_{11} & a_{12} \\ a_{21} & a_{22} \end{pmatrix} &= \begin{pmatrix} 1\cdot a_{11}+0\cdot a_{21} & 1\cdot a_{12}+0\cdot a_{22} \\ 0\cdot a_{11}+1\cdot a_{21} & 0\cdot a_{12}+1\cdot a_{22} \end{pmatrix} \\ &= \begin{pmatrix} a_{11} & a_{12} \\ a_{21} & a_{22} \end{pmatrix} \\ &= \mathbf{A} \end{aligned}$$

EXERCISES

1. For each of the following pairs of matrices check whether it is possible to calculate $\mathbf{A}\cdot\mathbf{B}$, $\mathbf{B}\cdot\mathbf{A}$, both, or neither:

   (a) **A** is a 2×5 matrix and **B** is a 5×2 matrix;
   (b) **A** is a 3×4 matrix and **B** is a 2×3 matrix;
   (c) **A** is a 3×5 matrix and **B** is a 3×5 matrix;
   (d) **A** is a 4×2 matrix and **B** is a 2×4 matrix;
   (e) **A** is a 3×5 matrix and **B** is a 5×6 matrix;
   (f) **A** is a 3×4 matrix and **B** is a 2×5 matrix.

2. Evaluate each of the following matrix products:

(a) $(2, -1, 3)\begin{pmatrix} 1 \\ 4 \\ -2 \end{pmatrix}$;

(b) $\begin{pmatrix} 3 & -2 \\ 2 & 1 \end{pmatrix}\begin{pmatrix} 1 & 5 \\ -3 & 4 \end{pmatrix}$;

(c) $\begin{pmatrix} 3 & 0 & -1 & 2 \\ 1 & -2 & 0 & 3 \end{pmatrix}\begin{pmatrix} 1 & 0 & -2 \\ 3 & 1 & 0 \\ -1 & 2 & 3 \\ 2 & -3 & 1 \end{pmatrix}$

(d) $\begin{pmatrix} 2 \\ -1 \\ 3 \end{pmatrix}(1, 5, -2)$;

(e) $\begin{pmatrix} 1 & 2 \\ 0 & -3 \\ 1 & -1 \end{pmatrix}\begin{pmatrix} 1 & 0 & 4 & -2 & 1 \\ 0 & -1 & -1 & 3 & 0 \end{pmatrix}$

(f) $\begin{pmatrix} -2 & 1 & 1 \\ 1 & 0 & 3 \\ 5 & -1 & 0 \end{pmatrix}\begin{pmatrix} 1 & -1 & 1 \\ 0 & 3 & -2 \\ 4 & -3 & 5 \end{pmatrix}$

3. Referring to the television-set-inventory example on page 244, suppose that the prices at which the merchant sells the five kinds of sets (regardless of brand) are given by the corresponding elements of the column vector

$$\begin{pmatrix} \$499 \\ \$265 \\ \$349 \\ \$289 \\ \$139 \end{pmatrix}$$

Multiply the inventory matrix **R** on page 244 by this column vector, and explain what the resulting figures represent.

4. The elements of the following row vector are the prices (in cents) which a supermarket charges for a pound of butter, a dozen eggs, a loaf of bread, a pound of coffee, and a quart of milk:

$$\mathbf{P} = (86, 53, 34, 69, 28)$$

If the corresponding amounts of butter, eggs, bread, coffee, and milk, which a housewife buys are given by the elements of the column vector

$$\mathbf{Q} = \begin{pmatrix} 1/2 \\ 2 \\ 1 \\ 1 \\ 3 \end{pmatrix}$$

calculate $\mathbf{P}\cdot\mathbf{Q}$ and explain its significance. What product should we have asked for instead of $\mathbf{P}\cdot\mathbf{Q}$, if $\mathbf{Q}$ had been given as a row vector instead of a column vector? (*Hint:* see Exercise 10 on page 251.)

5. The 1957 and 1964 prices received by farmers for wheat, corn, oats, and barley (in dollars per bushel) are given by the respective elements of the two row vectors

$$\mathbf{P}_{57} = (1.93, 1.11, 0.61, 0.89)$$

$$\mathbf{P}_{64} = (1.37, 1.15, 0.63, 0.95)$$

and the corresponding quantities produced in 1957 (in millions of bushels) are given by the respective elements of the column vector

$$\mathbf{Q} = \begin{pmatrix} 956 \\ 3{,}045 \\ 1{,}290 \\ 443 \end{pmatrix}$$

(a) Calculate the value of $\mathbf{P}_{57} \cdot \mathbf{Q}$ and explain what this product represents.
(b) Calculate the value of $\mathbf{P}_{64} \cdot \mathbf{Q}$ and explain what this product represents.
(c) Use the results of parts (a) and (b) to calculate the value of

$$\frac{\mathbf{P}_{64} \cdot \mathbf{Q}}{\mathbf{P}_{57} \cdot \mathbf{Q}} \cdot 100$$

namely, the value of the so-called *Laspeyres index*, which (in this instance) serves to compare the 1964 prices received by farmers for the given commodities with the prices they received in 1957.

6. To demonstrate that the multiplication of square matrices is not necessarily *commutative*, calculate $\mathbf{A} \cdot \mathbf{B}$ as well as $\mathbf{B} \cdot \mathbf{A}$ for the two matrices

$$\mathbf{A} = \begin{pmatrix} -2 & 1 \\ 3 & -1 \end{pmatrix} \quad \text{and} \quad \mathbf{B} = \begin{pmatrix} 0 & -1 \\ 3 & 2 \end{pmatrix}$$

7. The following is an important rule of ordinary algebra (which we used in Exercise 3 on page 123 to solve quadratic equations by factoring): *if the product of two numbers is zero, then one or the other must be zero.* Show that this rule does not hold in matrix algebra by evaluating the product

$$\begin{pmatrix} 1 & -2 \\ -2 & 4 \end{pmatrix} \cdot \begin{pmatrix} 4 & -2 \\ 2 & -1 \end{pmatrix}$$

8. Verify the *associative law* $\mathbf{A} \cdot (\mathbf{B} \cdot \mathbf{C}) = (\mathbf{A} \cdot \mathbf{B}) \cdot \mathbf{C}$ for the matrices

$$\mathbf{A} = \begin{pmatrix} 2 & 0 & -1 \\ -1 & -2 & 2 \end{pmatrix}, \quad \mathbf{B} = \begin{pmatrix} -1 & 0 & 1 \\ 2 & -3 & -1 \\ 3 & 0 & -1 \end{pmatrix}, \quad \text{and} \quad \mathbf{C} = \begin{pmatrix} -1 \\ 1 \\ 2 \end{pmatrix}$$

9. Verify the result obtained on page 257, where we multiplied the vector (1, 1, 1, 1) by the attendance matrix $\mathbf{D}$ for the four baseball games. What would be the significance of the result which we would obtain if we multiplied the attendance matrix $\mathbf{D}$ *on the right* by the 4×1 column vector whose elements are all 1's?

10. Describe what happens in each case to the elements of the matrix

$$\mathbf{A} = \begin{pmatrix} a_{11} & a_{12} & a_{13} \\ a_{21} & a_{22} & a_{23} \\ a_{31} & a_{32} & a_{33} \end{pmatrix}$$

if it is multiplied *on the left* by

(a) $\begin{pmatrix} 3 & 0 & 0 \\ 0 & 1 & 0 \\ 0 & 0 & 1 \end{pmatrix}$; (c) $\begin{pmatrix} 1 & 1 & 0 \\ 0 & 1 & 0 \\ 0 & 0 & 1 \end{pmatrix}$; (e) $\begin{pmatrix} 0 & 0 & 1 \\ 0 & 1 & 0 \\ 1 & 0 & 0 \end{pmatrix}$;

(b) $\begin{pmatrix} 0 & 1 & 0 \\ 1 & 0 & 0 \\ 0 & 0 & 1 \end{pmatrix}$; (d) $\begin{pmatrix} 1 & 0 & 0 \\ 0 & 2 & 0 \\ 0 & 0 & 1 \end{pmatrix}$; (f) $\begin{pmatrix} 1 & 0 & 0 \\ 0 & 1 & -1 \\ 0 & 0 & 1 \end{pmatrix}$.

Generalizing from these results, by what matrix should we multiply matrix **A** *on the left* so that

(g) each element of the third row will be multiplied by 5;
(h) the elements of the second and third rows will be interchanged;
(i) the elements of the third row are added to the corresponding elements of the first row;
(j) the elements of the first row are subtracted from the corresponding elements of the second row?

11. Given the matrices

$$\mathbf{A} = \begin{pmatrix} 0 & 0 & 0 & 1 \\ 1 & 0 & 0 & 0 \\ 0 & 1 & 0 & 0 \\ 0 & 0 & 1 & 0 \end{pmatrix} \qquad \mathbf{B} = \begin{pmatrix} 0 & 0 & 1 & 0 \\ 0 & 0 & 0 & 1 \\ 1 & 0 & 0 & 0 \\ 0 & 1 & 0 & 0 \end{pmatrix}$$

$$\mathbf{C} = \begin{pmatrix} 0 & 1 & 0 & 0 \\ 0 & 0 & 1 & 0 \\ 0 & 0 & 0 & 1 \\ 1 & 0 & 0 & 0 \end{pmatrix} \qquad \mathbf{D} = \begin{pmatrix} 1 & 0 & 0 & 0 \\ 0 & 1 & 0 & 0 \\ 0 & 0 & 1 & 0 \\ 0 & 0 & 0 & 1 \end{pmatrix}$$

fill in the following multiplication table and compare it with the multiplication table for the rotations of sales managers which we gave on page 3:

	A	**B**	**C**	**D**
A				
B				
C				
D				

What is the significance of this result?

12. THE MAGNITUDE OF A VECTOR. Show that if $\mathbf{X}$ is a 1×2 row vector, its magnitude (see Exercise 12 on page 252) is given by $\sqrt{\mathbf{X} \cdot \mathbf{X}'}$, where $\mathbf{X}'$ is the *transpose* of $\mathbf{X}$. Using the quantity $\sqrt{\mathbf{X} \cdot \mathbf{X}'}$ to define the magnitude of any row vector $\mathbf{X}$, find the magnitude of (8, 15), (2, 2, −1), (−2, 6, 3), and (7, −5, 1, 11).

9.4 THE INVERSE OF A MATRIX

The remainder of this chapter will be devoted mostly to the solution of systems of linear equations, and we shall thus continue the work of the first part of Chapter 7. To begin with, let us demonstrate how systems of linear equations can be written in matrix form, using as an example a system of two linear equations in two variables. Following the notation introduced on page 195, we write these equations as

$$a_{11}x_1 + a_{12}x_2 = b_1$$
$$a_{21}x_1 + a_{22}x_2 = b_2$$

where x_1 and x_2 are the two variables, b_1 and b_2 are the constant terms, and the subscripts of the coefficients a_{11}, a_{12}, a_{21}, and a_{22} tell us to which equation and to which variable each coefficient belongs—the first subscript is 1 or 2 depending on the equation, and the second subscript is the same as that of the corresponding variable. An obvious advantage of this notation is that it can easily be extended to n linear equations in n variables (see Exercise 3 on page 201).

To write the above system of linear equations in matrix form, let us introduce the following three matrices, representing, in turn, the variables, the coefficients, and the constant terms:

$$\mathbf{X} = \begin{pmatrix} x_1 \\ x_2 \end{pmatrix}, \quad \mathbf{A} = \begin{pmatrix} a_{11} & a_{12} \\ a_{21} & a_{22} \end{pmatrix}, \quad \mathbf{B} = \begin{pmatrix} b_1 \\ b_2 \end{pmatrix}$$

Calculating the product $\mathbf{A} \cdot \mathbf{X}$, we obtain

$$\mathbf{A} \cdot \mathbf{X} = \begin{pmatrix} a_{11} & a_{12} \\ a_{21} & a_{22} \end{pmatrix} \begin{pmatrix} x_1 \\ x_2 \end{pmatrix} = \begin{pmatrix} a_{11}x_1 + a_{12}x_2 \\ a_{21}x_1 + a_{22}x_2 \end{pmatrix}$$

and it should be observed that the elements of the resulting column vector are precisely the left-hand members of the original equations. Thus, we can substitute for them b_1 and b_2, getting

$$\mathbf{A} \cdot \mathbf{X} = \begin{pmatrix} a_{11}x_1 + a_{12}x_2 \\ a_{21}x_1 + a_{22}x_2 \end{pmatrix} = \begin{pmatrix} b_1 \\ b_2 \end{pmatrix} = \mathbf{B}$$

or simply

$$\mathbf{A} \cdot \mathbf{X} = \mathbf{B}$$

Although $\mathbf{A} \cdot \mathbf{X} = \mathbf{B}$ is *one* matrix equation, it is simply another way of writing the original pair of equations; had we begun with three equations in three variables, $\mathbf{A} \cdot \mathbf{X} = \mathbf{B}$ would have represented the *three* equations

$$a_{11}x_1 + a_{12}x_2 + a_{13}x_3 = b_1$$
$$a_{21}x_1 + a_{22}x_2 + a_{23}x_3 = b_2$$
$$a_{31}x_1 + a_{32}x_2 + a_{33}x_3 = b_3$$

Actually, we already met this idea of representing *several equations* by means of *one matrix equation* on page 256, where the matrix equation $\mathbf{D} \cdot \mathbf{E} = \mathbf{F}$ represented the *four* equations which we used to calculate the total receipts for the four baseball games.

In ordinary algebra, the equation $ax = b$ can be solved by dividing the expressions on both sides of the equation by a, getting $x = b/a$ provided

$a \neq 0$. Alternately, we can obtain this solution by *multiplying* the expressions on both sides of the equation by the *reciprocal* of a, namely, by $1/a$ or a^{-1}, getting

$$a^{-1} \cdot ax = a^{-1} \cdot b$$

$$(a^{-1} \cdot a)x = a^{-1} \cdot b$$

and, hence,

$$x = a^{-1} \cdot b$$

since $a^{-1} \cdot a$ is equal to 1. To extend the concept of a *reciprocal* to matrix multiplication, let us now make the following definition:

> *If* **A** *is a square matrix and there exists a square matrix* **C** *such that* $\mathbf{C} \cdot \mathbf{A} = \mathbf{I}$, *where* **I** *is the identity matrix of the same order as* **A**, *then* **C** *is called the inverse of* **A** *and it is denoted* $\mathbf{A}^{-1}$.

For instance, the inverse of the matrix

$$\mathbf{A} = \begin{pmatrix} 2 & 3 \\ -5 & -2 \end{pmatrix}$$

is the matrix

$$\mathbf{A}^{-1} = \begin{pmatrix} -2/11 & -3/11 \\ 5/11 & 2/11 \end{pmatrix}$$

as can easily be verified by showing that the product $\mathbf{A}^{-1} \cdot \mathbf{A}$ equals the identity matrix

$$\begin{pmatrix} 1 & 0 \\ 0 & 1 \end{pmatrix}$$

Actually performing this multiplication, we get

$$\begin{aligned} \mathbf{A}^{-1} \cdot \mathbf{A} &= \begin{pmatrix} -2/11 & -3/11 \\ 5/11 & 2/11 \end{pmatrix} \begin{pmatrix} 2 & 3 \\ -5 & -2 \end{pmatrix} \\ &= \begin{pmatrix} (-2/11)2 + (-3/11)(-5) & (-2/11)3 + (-3/11)(-2) \\ (5/11)2 + (2/11)(-5) & (5/11)3 + (2/11)(-2) \end{pmatrix} \\ &= \begin{pmatrix} 1 & 0 \\ 0 & 1 \end{pmatrix} \end{aligned}$$

and in Exercise 1 on page 269 the reader will be asked to verify that we would have obtained the same result for $\mathbf{A} \cdot \mathbf{A}^{-1}$.

It follows from our definition that the inverse of a square matrix **A** must be of the same order as **A**, and it can also be shown that if **C** is the inverse of **A**, then **A** is the inverse of **C**, namely, that $\mathbf{A}^{-1} \cdot \mathbf{A} = \mathbf{A} \cdot \mathbf{A}^{-1}$ whenever $\mathbf{A}^{-1}$ exists. Our definition does not tell us, however, how we can check whether any given square matrix has an inverse, and it does not tell us how to find the inverse of a matrix when it does exist. The first of these two problems will be taken up in Section 9.6, where we shall study what is called the *determinant* of a matrix, and the other problem will be treated in Section 9.5.

Let us now return to the problem of solving systems of linear equations, which we left on page 262 after writing the equations in matrix form as $\mathbf{A} \cdot \mathbf{X} = \mathbf{B}$. Supposing that the coefficient matrix $\mathbf{A}$ has the inverse $\mathbf{A}^{-1}$, we can multiply the expressions on both sides of this matrix equation by $\mathbf{A}^{-1}$, getting

$$\mathbf{A}^{-1} \cdot (\mathbf{A} \cdot \mathbf{X}) = \mathbf{A}^{-1} \cdot \mathbf{B}$$

Then, making use of the fact that matrix multiplication is *associative* (see Exercise 8 on page 260), we get

$$(\mathbf{A}^{-1} \cdot \mathbf{A}) \cdot \mathbf{X} = \mathbf{A}^{-1} \cdot \mathbf{B}$$

and, hence,

$$\mathbf{X} = \mathbf{A}^{-1} \cdot \mathbf{B}$$

since $\mathbf{A}^{-1} \cdot \mathbf{A} = \mathbf{I}$ and $\mathbf{I} \cdot \mathbf{X} = \mathbf{X}$. *This tells us that the solutions for the x's are given by the elements of the matrix* $\mathbf{A}^{-1} \cdot \mathbf{B}$.

To illustrate this method of solving a system of linear equations, let us use it to solve the following system of two linear equations in two variables:

$$2x_1 + 3x_2 = 5$$
$$-5x_1 - 2x_2 = 4$$

This is going to be easy, since we do not have to worry about finding the inverse of the coefficient matrix $\mathbf{A}$—as we demonstrated on page 263, its inverse is the matrix

$$\begin{pmatrix} -2/11 & -3/11 \\ 5/11 & 2/11 \end{pmatrix}$$

Thus,

$$\mathbf{A}^{-1} \cdot \mathbf{B} = \begin{pmatrix} -2/11 & -3/11 \\ 5/11 & 2/11 \end{pmatrix} \begin{pmatrix} 5 \\ 4 \end{pmatrix} = \begin{pmatrix} (-2/11)5 + (-3/11)4 \\ (5/11)5 \quad + (2/11)4 \end{pmatrix}$$
$$= \begin{pmatrix} -2 \\ 3 \end{pmatrix}$$

and this tells us that the solutions for x_1 and x_2 are $x_1 = -2$ and $x_2 = 3$.

We now have a systematic approach to the solution of systems of linear equations; all we have to do is multiply the inverse of the coefficient matrix $\mathbf{A}$ by the column vector $\mathbf{B}$ of constant terms, and read off the elements of the resulting column vector. This applies not only to two linear equations in two variables, but in general to n linear equations in n variables; in each case, the solutions for the x's are given by the respective elements of the product matrix $\mathbf{A}^{-1}\cdot\mathbf{B}$. Of course, there remains the question of *how* to obtain the inverse of a matrix, and (as we shall see later) this is just about as difficult as the original problem of solving a system of linear equations. Nevertheless, the method we have introduced in this section provides us with a *systematic* way of solving systems of linear equations, and this is very important in this age of electronic computers. In the next section we shall study another matrix approach to the solution of a system of linear equations, which, at the same time, will serve to find the inverse of the coefficient matrix. Other methods of determining the inverse of a matrix are given in the books referred to at the end of this chapter.

9.5 ELEMENTARY ROW OPERATIONS

In this section we shall demonstrate how the *method of elimination* of Sections 7.2 can be *simplified* and *unified* by working only with the coefficients and constant terms written in matrix form. To illustrate, let us return to the example on page 195, where we used the method of elimination to solve the system of equations

$$\begin{aligned} 2x_1 + 3x_2 &= 5 \\ -5x_1 - 2x_2 &= 4 \end{aligned}$$

The coefficient matrix and the column vector of constant terms are, respectively,

$$\mathbf{A} = \begin{pmatrix} 2 & 3 \\ -5 & -2 \end{pmatrix} \quad \text{and} \quad \mathbf{B} = \begin{pmatrix} 5 \\ 4 \end{pmatrix}$$

and to simplify our notation we shall combine these two matrices into the one matrix

$$(\mathbf{A} \mid \mathbf{B}) = \left(\begin{array}{cc|c} 2 & 3 & 5 \\ -5 & -2 & 4 \end{array}\right)$$

where the vertical line serves to separate the elements of the coefficient matrix from the constant terms. This matrix is called the *augmented coefficient matrix.*

In the work which follows, we shall again solve the system

$$\begin{aligned} 2x_1 + 3x_2 &= 5 \\ -5x_1 - 2x_2 &= 4 \end{aligned}$$

by the method of elimination, but this time we shall indicate on the *left-hand side* what each step does to the system of equations, and on the *right-hand side* what it does to the matrix $(\mathbf{A} \mid \mathbf{B})$. Proceeding as on page 195, we shall eliminate x_2 from the first equation by multiplying the expressions on both sides of the first equation by 2, multiplying the expressions on both sides of the second equation by 3, and then adding the expressions on both sides of the second equation to those of the first. Symbolically, we thus get

$$\begin{aligned} 4x_1 + 6x_2 &= 10 \\ -15x_1 - 6x_2 &= 12 \end{aligned} \qquad \left(\begin{array}{cc|c} 4 & 6 & 10 \\ -15 & -6 & 12 \end{array}\right)$$

and

$$\begin{aligned} -11x_1 \qquad &= 22 \\ -15x_1 - 6x_2 &= 12 \end{aligned} \qquad \left(\begin{array}{cc|c} -11 & 0 & 22 \\ -15 & -6 & 12 \end{array}\right)$$

If we then divide the expressions on both sides of the first equation by -11, we get

$$\begin{aligned} x_1 \qquad &= -2 \\ -15x_1 - 6x_2 &= 12 \end{aligned} \qquad \left(\begin{array}{cc|c} 1 & 0 & -2 \\ -15 & -6 & 12 \end{array}\right)$$

and we can stop since we have found that $x_1 = -2$ (and we can determine the value of x_2 by substituting $x_1 = -2$ into the second equation, as we did on page 195). On page 195 we also solved for x_2 by returning to the original system of equations and eliminating x_1, but we did so only to give a further illustration of the mechanics involved in the method of elimination.

To save time and labor in problems of this kind, we can omit the work on the left-hand side altogether; instead, we simply work with the augmented coefficient matrix $(\mathbf{A} \mid \mathbf{B})$, manipulating the elements in its rows by

(1) *Multiplying each element of a row by the same number, not zero;*

(2) *adding (subtracting) each element of a row to (from) the corresponding element of another row;*

(3) *interchanging two rows.*

These operations are generally referred to as *elementary row operations*—we did not use the third one in our example, but it is sometimes needed to put an augmented coefficient matrix $(\mathbf{A} \mid \mathbf{B})$ into a desired form (see, for example, Exercise 8 on page 271).

When we solve a system of linear equations by this method, namely, by applying elementary row operations to the augmented coefficient matrix $(\mathbf{A} \mid \mathbf{B})$, we generally continue the process until the matrix is reduced to the form

$$\left(\begin{array}{cc|c} 1 & 0 & ? \\ 0 & 1 & ? \end{array}\right), \quad \left(\begin{array}{ccc|c} 1 & 0 & 0 & ? \\ 0 & 1 & 0 & ? \\ 0 & 0 & 1 & ? \end{array}\right), \quad \left(\begin{array}{cccc|c} 1 & 0 & 0 & 0 & ? \\ 0 & 1 & 0 & 0 & ? \\ 0 & 0 & 1 & 0 & ? \\ 0 & 0 & 0 & 1 & ? \end{array}\right), \quad \text{etc.,}$$

because the solutions for the x's are then given by the numbers taking the place of the question marks. In other words, *we continue the process until the coefficient matrix to the left of the vertical line has been converted into an identity matrix, and the solutions for the x's are then given by the elements of the column vector to the right of the vertical line.*

In actual practice, it is often possible to reduce the required detail by combining several of the elementary row operations into a single step. To illustrate, let us solve the following system of three linear equations in the variables x_1, x_2, and x_3:

$$\begin{aligned} x_1 - 2x_2 + x_3 &= 8 \\ 3x_1 + 5x_2 + 7x_3 &= 6 \\ 2x_1 - 3x_2 - 5x_3 &= 7 \end{aligned}$$

Starting with the matrix

$$\left(\begin{array}{ccc|c} 1 & -2 & 1 & 8 \\ 3 & 5 & 7 & 6 \\ 2 & -3 & -5 & 7 \end{array}\right)$$

let us first "eliminate" the 3 and the 2 in the *first column* by subtracting *three times* the elements of the first row from the corresponding elements of the second row, and then subtracting *twice* the elements of the first row from the corresponding elements of the third row. This gives

$$\left(\begin{array}{ccc|c} 1 & -2 & 1 & 8 \\ 0 & 11 & 4 & -18 \\ 2 & -3 & -5 & 7 \end{array}\right) \quad \text{and} \quad \left(\begin{array}{ccc|c} 1 & -2 & 1 & 8 \\ 0 & 11 & 4 & -18 \\ 0 & 1 & -7 & -9 \end{array}\right)$$

and if we divide the elements of the second row by 11, we get

$$\left(\begin{array}{ccc|c} 1 & -2 & 1 & 8 \\ 0 & 1 & 4/11 & -18/11 \\ 0 & 1 & -7 & -9 \end{array}\right)$$

Then, to "eliminate" the -2 and the lower 1 from the *second column*, we add *twice* the elements of the second row to the corresponding elements of the first row, and subtract the elements of the second row from the corresponding elements of the third row. We thus obtain

$$\left(\begin{array}{ccc|c} 1 & 0 & 19/11 & 52/11 \\ 0 & 1 & 4/11 & -18/11 \\ 0 & 1 & -7 & -9 \end{array}\right) \quad \text{and} \quad \left(\begin{array}{ccc|c} 1 & 0 & 19/11 & 52/11 \\ 0 & 1 & 4/11 & -18/11 \\ 0 & 0 & -81/11 & -81/11 \end{array}\right)$$

and if we divide the elements of the third row by $-81/11$, we get

$$\left(\begin{array}{ccc|c} 1 & 0 & 19/11 & 52/11 \\ 0 & 1 & 4/11 & -18/11 \\ 0 & 0 & 1 & 1 \end{array}\right)$$

Finally, to "eliminate the 19/11 and 4/11 in the *third column*, we subtract

19/11 times the elements of the third row from the corresponding elements of the first row, and 4/11 times the elements of the third row from the corresponding elements of the second row. This gives

$$\left(\begin{array}{ccc|c} 1 & 0 & 0 & 3 \\ 0 & 1 & 0 & -2 \\ 0 & 0 & 1 & 1 \end{array}\right)$$

and we can read off the solutions as $x_1 = 3$, $x_2 = -2$, and $x_3 = 1$.

In case the reader feels that what we have done here is like "shooting a bird with a cannon," let us hasten to add that the method is seldom, if ever, used to solve systems of linear equations in two or three variables. Its advantages will become apparent, though, in Chapter 10, where we shall have to work with systems of linear equations in many variables; furthermore, we shall demonstrate next that the method which we have illustrated can be used also to find the *inverse* of a matrix.

If we perform elementary row operations on a square matrix $\mathbf{A}$ until it is changed into the identity matrix $\mathbf{I}$ of the same order, the total effect is the same as if we had multiplied $\mathbf{A}$ by its inverse $\mathbf{A}^{-1}$. (In fact, the reader may recall from Exercise 10 on page 260 that what we now refer to as elementary row operations can be accomplished also by multiplying the matrix $\mathbf{A}$ on the left by appropriate matrices.) Thus, when we apply elementary row operations to the matrix $(\mathbf{A} \mid \mathbf{B})$ until $\mathbf{A}$ is changed to $\mathbf{I}$, the effect is the same as if we had multiplied by $\mathbf{A}^{-1}$, and we can write

$$\mathbf{A}^{-1}(\mathbf{A} \mid \mathbf{B}) = (\mathbf{A}^{-1}\cdot\mathbf{A} \mid \mathbf{A}^{-1}\cdot\mathbf{B}) = (\mathbf{I} \mid \mathbf{A}^{-1}\cdot\mathbf{B})$$

It is of interest to note that this agrees with the result obtained in Section 9.4—the solutions given by the elements of the column vector to the right of the vertical line are, in fact, the elements of $\mathbf{A}^{-1}\cdot\mathbf{B}$.

This analysis also suggests a way of calculating the inverse of a square matrix $\mathbf{A}$. Suppose that instead of $(\mathbf{A} \mid \mathbf{B})$ we start with the matrix $(\mathbf{A} \mid \mathbf{I})$, where $\mathbf{I}$ is the identity matrix of the same order as $\mathbf{A}$. For instance, when $\mathbf{A}$ is of order 2×2 or 3×3, we would start with

$$(\mathbf{A} \mid \mathbf{I}) = \left(\begin{array}{cc|cc} a_{11} & a_{12} & 1 & 0 \\ a_{21} & a_{22} & 0 & 1 \end{array}\right)$$

or

$$(\mathbf{A} \mid \mathbf{I}) = \left(\begin{array}{ccc|ccc} a_{11} & a_{12} & a_{13} & 1 & 0 & 0 \\ a_{21} & a_{22} & a_{23} & 0 & 1 & 0 \\ a_{31} & a_{32} & a_{33} & 0 & 0 & 1 \end{array}\right)$$

Then, if we perform elementary row operations until $\mathbf{A}$ is changed into $\mathbf{I}$, as we did in the example on page 267, the total effect is the same as if we had multiplied by $\mathbf{A}^{-1}$, and we can write

$$\mathbf{A}^{-1}(\mathbf{A} \mid \mathbf{I}) = (\mathbf{A}^{-1}\cdot\mathbf{A} \mid \mathbf{A}^{-1}\cdot\mathbf{I}) = (\mathbf{I} \mid \mathbf{A}^{-1})$$

It follows that if we perform elementary row operations on $(\mathbf{A} \mid \mathbf{I})$ until $\mathbf{A}$ is changed to $\mathbf{I}$, then the matrix which consists of the elements to the right of the vertical line is converted into the inverse matrix $\mathbf{A}^{-1}$.

To illustrate this technique, let us find the inverse of the coefficient matrix of the first example of this section, namely, the inverse of the matrix

$$\mathbf{A} = \begin{pmatrix} 2 & 3 \\ -5 & -2 \end{pmatrix}$$

Using elementary row operations to change

$$\left(\begin{array}{cc|cc} 2 & 3 & 1 & 0 \\ -5 & -2 & 0 & 1 \end{array}\right) \quad \text{into} \quad \left(\begin{array}{cc|cc} 1 & 0 & ? & ? \\ 0 & 1 & ? & ? \end{array}\right)$$

let us first "eliminate" the 3 by adding 3/2 of each element of the second row to the corresponding element of the first row. This gives

$$\left(\begin{array}{cc|cc} -11/2 & 0 & 1 & 3/2 \\ -5 & -2 & 0 & 1 \end{array}\right)$$

and, subtracting 10/11 of each element of the first row from the corresponding element of the second row to "eliminate" the -5, we get

$$\left(\begin{array}{cc|cc} -11/2 & 0 & 1 & 3/2 \\ 0 & -2 & -10/11 & -4/11 \end{array}\right)$$

Finally, if we divide each element of the first row by $-11/2$ and each element of the second row by -2, we obtain

$$\left(\begin{array}{cc|cc} 1 & 0 & -2/11 & -3/11 \\ 0 & 1 & 5/11 & 2/11 \end{array}\right)$$

and we have thus verified the result which we gave on page 263, namely, that the inverse of matrix $\mathbf{A}$ is

$$\mathbf{A}^{-1} = \begin{pmatrix} -2/11 & -3/11 \\ 5/11 & 2/11 \end{pmatrix}$$

When we use this method to find the inverse of the coefficient matrix of a system of linear equations (or, for that matter, the inverse of any square matrix), it can happen that we arrive at a row with nothing but 0's to the left of the vertical line. If this is the case, *the matrix does not have an inverse* (and *the system of equations does not have a unique solution*). The reason for this, and a more direct criterion for deciding whether or not any given square matrix has an inverse, will be discussed in Section 9.6 (see also Exercise 9 below).

EXERCISES

1. With reference to the two matrices $\mathbf{A}$ and $\mathbf{A}^{-1}$ given on page 263, verify that the product $\mathbf{A} \cdot \mathbf{A}^{-1}$ is also equal to $\mathbf{I}$.

2. Evaluate the product $\mathbf{A}^{-1}\cdot\mathbf{A}$ to verify that the inverse of

$$\mathbf{A} = \begin{pmatrix} 1 & 2 \\ -2 & 1 \end{pmatrix} \quad \text{is} \quad \mathbf{A}^{-1} = \begin{pmatrix} 1/5 & -2/5 \\ 2/5 & 1/5 \end{pmatrix}$$

and use this result to solve the following systems of linear equations by calculating the corresponding products $\mathbf{A}^{-1}\cdot\mathbf{B}$:

$$\text{(a)}\quad \begin{aligned} x_1 + 2x_2 &= 1 \\ -2x_1 + x_2 &= 8 \end{aligned} \qquad \text{(b)}\quad \begin{aligned} x_1 + 2x_2 &= 4 \\ -2x_1 + x_2 &= -18 \end{aligned} \qquad \text{(c)}\quad \begin{aligned} x_1 + 2x_2 &= 12 \\ -2x_1 + x_2 &= 1 \end{aligned}$$

Check each answer by substituting the values obtained for the x's into the original equations.

3. Verify that the inverse of

$$\mathbf{A} = \begin{pmatrix} 1 & -2 \\ 2 & -3 \end{pmatrix} \quad \text{is} \quad \mathbf{A}^{-1} = \begin{pmatrix} -3 & 2 \\ -2 & 1 \end{pmatrix}$$

namely, that $\mathbf{A}^{-1}\cdot\mathbf{A} = \mathbf{I}$, and use this result to solve the following systems of linear equations by evaluating the corresponding products $\mathbf{A}^{-1}\cdot\mathbf{B}$:

$$\text{(a)}\quad \begin{aligned} x_1 - 2x_2 &= 7 \\ 2x_1 - 3x_2 &= 12 \end{aligned} \qquad \text{(b)}\quad \begin{aligned} x_1 - 2x_2 &= -14 \\ 2x_1 - 3x_2 &= -23 \end{aligned} \qquad \text{(c)}\quad \begin{aligned} x_1 - 2x_2 &= -2 \\ 2x_1 - 3x_2 &= 1 \end{aligned}$$

Check each answer by substituting the values obtained for the x's into the original equations.

4. Evaluate the product $\mathbf{A}^{-1}\cdot\mathbf{A}$ to verify that the inverse of

$$\mathbf{A} = \begin{pmatrix} 2 & 1 & -1 \\ 3 & 2 & 5 \\ 1 & 1 & 5 \end{pmatrix} \quad \text{is} \quad \mathbf{A}^{-1} = \begin{pmatrix} -5 & 6 & -7 \\ 10 & -11 & 13 \\ -1 & 1 & -1 \end{pmatrix}$$

and use this result to solve the following systems of linear equations by calculating the corresponding products $\mathbf{A}^{-1}\cdot\mathbf{B}$:

$$\text{(a)}\quad \begin{aligned} 2x_1 + x_2 - x_3 &= 3 \\ 3x_1 + 2x_2 + 5x_3 &= 12 \\ x_1 + x_2 + 5x_3 &= 8 \end{aligned} \qquad \text{(b)}\quad \begin{aligned} 2x_1 + x_2 - x_3 &= -5 \\ 3x_1 + 2x_2 + 5x_3 &= -1 \\ x_1 + x_2 + 5x_3 &= 3 \end{aligned}$$

Check each answer by substituting the values obtained for the x's into the original equations.

5. Find the inverse of the matrix

$$\mathbf{A} = \begin{pmatrix} 1 & 3 \\ 2 & 7 \end{pmatrix}$$

and use it to solve the system of linear equations

$$\begin{aligned} x_1 + 3x_2 &= 1 \\ 2x_1 + 7x_2 &= 0 \end{aligned}$$

6. Find the inverse of the matrix

$$\mathbf{A} = \begin{pmatrix} 1 & 1 & -1 \\ 2 & 1 & 3 \\ 3 & 3 & 1 \end{pmatrix}$$

and use it to solve the system of linear equations

$$\begin{aligned} x_1 + x_2 - x_3 &= 0 \\ 2x_1 + x_2 + 3x_3 &= 9 \\ 3x_1 + 3x_2 + x_3 &= 6 \end{aligned}$$

7. Solve the following system of linear equations by the method illustrated on page 266, namely, by performing elementary row operations on the augmented coefficient matrix $(\mathbf{A}|\mathbf{B})$:

$$\begin{aligned} 2x_1 + x_2 &= 3 \\ 5x_1 + 3x_2 &= 7 \end{aligned}$$

8. Solve the following system of linear equations by the method illustrated on page 267, namely, by performing elementary row operations on the augmented coefficient matrix $(\mathbf{A}|\mathbf{B})$:

$$\begin{aligned} x_2 + 3x_3 &= 3 \\ x_1 + 2x_2 + x_3 &= 1 \\ x_1 - 2x_2 \qquad &= 11 \end{aligned}$$

(*Hint:* the solution of this problem can be simplified by first interchanging some of the rows of the augmented coefficient matrix.)

9. **THE EXISTENCE OF THE INVERSE OF A 2 × 2 MATRIX.** By definition, the 2×2 matrix

$$\mathbf{A} = \begin{pmatrix} a_{11} & a_{12} \\ a_{21} & a_{22} \end{pmatrix} \text{ has the inverse } \mathbf{A}^{-1} = \begin{pmatrix} r & s \\ t & u \end{pmatrix}$$

if there are numbers r, s, t, and u such that

$$\begin{pmatrix} r & s \\ t & u \end{pmatrix}\begin{pmatrix} a_{11} & a_{12} \\ a_{21} & a_{22} \end{pmatrix} = \begin{pmatrix} 1 & 0 \\ 0 & 1 \end{pmatrix}$$

(a) Writing in full what is meant by

$$\begin{pmatrix} r & s \\ t & u \end{pmatrix}\begin{pmatrix} a_{11} & a_{12} \\ a_{21} & a_{22} \end{pmatrix}$$

show that the above condition leads to *four* linear equations in r, s, t, and u—*two* linear equations in r and s, and *two* linear equations in t and u.

(b) Using the formulas for x_1 and x_2 on page 196 (or the method of elimination) to solve the two systems of equations of part (a), show that there are unique solutions for r, s, t, and u (and, hence, $\mathbf{A}$ has an inverse) provided $a_{11}a_{22} - a_{21}a_{12}$ is not equal to zero. Actually, we can say more than that; *if* $a_{11}a_{22} - a_{21}a_{12} = 0$ *the matrix* $\mathbf{A}$ *does not have an inverse, and if* $a_{11}a_{22} - a_{21}a_{12} \neq 0$ *the matrix* $\mathbf{A}$ *has a unique inverse* (which we could determine by solving the four equations of part (a) for r, s, t, and u).

(c) Use the criterion of part (b) to check whether the following matrices have an inverse:

$$\begin{pmatrix} 3 & -6 \\ 2 & 4 \end{pmatrix}, \begin{pmatrix} 3 & 6 \\ 2 & 4 \end{pmatrix}, \begin{pmatrix} 9 & 6 \\ 6 & 4 \end{pmatrix}, \begin{pmatrix} -9 & 6 \\ -6 & 4 \end{pmatrix}, \text{ and } \begin{pmatrix} 9 & 6 \\ -6 & 4 \end{pmatrix}.$$

9.6 THE DETERMINANT OF A MATRIX

As we saw in the preceding section, the problem of solving a system of linear equations is closely related to that of finding the inverse of a matrix. Indeed, from Exercise 9 on page 271 we learn that the condition for

$$\begin{aligned} a_{11}x_1 + a_{12}x_2 &= b_1 \\ a_{21}x_1 + a_{22}x_2 &= b_2 \end{aligned}$$

to have a *unique solution* and the condition for

$$\mathbf{A} = \begin{pmatrix} a_{11} & a_{12} \\ a_{21} & a_{22} \end{pmatrix}$$

to have an *inverse* are the same; *in either case, the quantity* $a_{11}a_{22} - a_{21}a_{12}$ *must not equal zero.* If $a_{11}a_{22} - a_{21}a_{12} = 0$, namely, if the matrix **A** does not have an inverse, we say that it is *singular.*

Since the quantity $a_{11}a_{22} - a_{21}a_{12}$ plays such an important role in problems involving 2×2 matrices, we denote it with a special symbol and give it a special name—we write it as

$$\begin{vmatrix} a_{11} & a_{12} \\ a_{21} & a_{22} \end{vmatrix} = a_{11}a_{22} - a_{21}a_{12}$$

and refer to it as the *determinant* of the 2×2 matrix **A**. For example, the determinants of the two matrices

$$\begin{pmatrix} 3 & -7 \\ -9 & 5 \end{pmatrix} \quad \text{and} \quad \begin{pmatrix} 2 & -6 \\ -4 & 12 \end{pmatrix}$$

are, respectively,

$$\begin{vmatrix} 3 & -7 \\ -9 & 5 \end{vmatrix} = 3 \cdot 5 - (-9)(-7) = -48$$

and

$$\begin{vmatrix} 2 & -6 \\ -4 & 12 \end{vmatrix} = 2 \cdot 12 - (-4)(-6) = 0$$

and we can conclude that *the first matrix has an inverse, whereas the second is singular.*

If we duplicated the work on page 196 for a system of three linear equations in three variables, namely, if we used the method of elimination to solve the system of linear equations

$$\begin{aligned} a_{11}x_1 + a_{12}x_2 + a_{13}x_3 &= b_1 \\ a_{21}x_1 + a_{22}x_2 + a_{23}x_3 &= b_2 \\ a_{31}x_1 + a_{23}x_2 + a_{33}x_3 &= b_3 \end{aligned}$$

we would get

$$x_1 = \frac{b_1a_{22}a_{33} + a_{12}a_{23}b_3 + a_{13}b_2a_{32} - b_3a_{22}a_{13} - a_{32}a_{23}b_1 - a_{33}b_2a_{12}}{a_{11}a_{22}a_{33} + a_{12}a_{23}a_{31} + a_{13}a_{21}a_{32} - a_{31}a_{22}a_{13} - a_{32}a_{23}a_{11} - a_{33}a_{21}a_{12}}$$

(provided the expression in the denominator is not zero), and corresponding expressions *with the same denominator* for x_2 and x_3. Thus, the system of equations has a *unique solution* (one value for each x) if and only if the expression in the denominator is not zero, and if we duplicated the argument of Exercise 9 on page 271 for the 3×3 matrix

$$\mathbf{A} = \begin{pmatrix} a_{11} & a_{12} & a_{13} \\ a_{21} & a_{22} & a_{23} \\ a_{31} & a_{32} & a_{33} \end{pmatrix}$$

we would find that the same condition tells us whether or not the matrix **A** has an inverse. Extending the notation and the terminology introduced on page 272 to 3×3 matrices, we write the quantity *which must not equal zero for the inverse of* **A** *to exist* as

$$\begin{vmatrix} a_{11} & a_{12} & a_{13} \\ a_{21} & a_{22} & a_{23} \\ a_{31} & a_{32} & a_{33} \end{vmatrix} = \begin{array}{l} a_{11}a_{22}a_{33} + a_{12}a_{23}a_{31} + a_{13}a_{21}a_{32} \\ - a_{31}a_{22}a_{13} - a_{32}a_{23}a_{11} - a_{33}a_{21}a_{12} \end{array}$$

and we refer to it as the *determinant* of the 3×3 matrix **A**.

Since the expression which defines the determinant of a 3×3 matrix is fairly complicated (or, at least, difficult to remember), it is helpful to use the following scheme: *we begin by repeating the first two columns of the determinant as in the following array*

$$\begin{vmatrix} a_{11} & a_{12} & a_{13} \\ a_{21} & a_{22} & a_{23} \\ a_{31} & a_{32} & a_{33} \end{vmatrix} \begin{matrix} a_{11} & a_{12} \\ a_{21} & a_{22} \\ a_{31} & a_{32} \end{matrix}$$

and then we multiply the three elements which lie on each of the diagonal lines. If the diagonal slopes downward (going from left to right) we add the corresponding product, and if the diagonal slopes upward we subtract it. Using this method to evaluate the determinant of the coefficient matrix of the system of linear equations on page 267, we get

$$\begin{vmatrix} 1 & -2 & 1 \\ 3 & 5 & 7 \\ 2 & -3 & 5 \end{vmatrix} \begin{matrix} 1 & 2 \\ 3 & 5 \\ 2 & 3 \end{matrix} = \begin{array}{l} 1\cdot 5(-5) + (-2)7\cdot 2 + 1\cdot 3(-3) \\ - 2\cdot 5\cdot 1 - (-3)7\cdot 1 - (-5)3(-2) \end{array}$$

$$= -81$$

Since this result is not zero, we conclude that the given matrix *has* an inverse (and that the system of equations has a unique solution).

It is of interest to note that there is a similar scheme for the evaluation of the determinant of a 2×2 matrix. Without even having to repeat any of the columns, we write

$$\begin{vmatrix} a_{11} & a_{12} \\ a_{21} & a_{22} \end{vmatrix} = a_{11}a_{22} - a_{21}a_{12}$$

and it can be seen that we have only to multiply the elements on the respective diagonals, and subtract or add depending on whether the arrow points up or down.

Although determinants serve many different purposes in various branches of mathematics, we have introduced them here for one reason only —to be able to decide whether any given matrix has an inverse. All we have to know, therefore, is whether a given determinant is zero, and as we shall see, this can often be resolved without actually having to evaluate the determinant. Instead, we make use of the fact that

> *If a row (or column) of a determinant contains nothing but zeros, then the determinant is equal to zero.*

For instance

$$\begin{vmatrix} 0 & 0 \\ 3 & 4 \end{vmatrix} = 0 \cdot 4 + 0 \cdot 3 = 0$$

and

$$\begin{vmatrix} 1 & 0 & 2 \\ 3 & 0 & 4 \\ 5 & 0 & 7 \end{vmatrix} = 1 \cdot 0 \cdot 7 + 0 \cdot 4 \cdot 5 + 2 \cdot 3 \cdot 0 - 5 \cdot 0 \cdot 2 - 0 \cdot 4 \cdot 1 - 7 \cdot 3 \cdot 0$$
$$= 0$$

More generally, we have only to observe that each of the products (which we add or subtract in the formulas for 2×2 and 3×3 determinants on pages 272 and 273) has among its factors *one element from each row and one element from each column.* (For instance, for a 3×3 determinant, $a_{12}a_{23}a_{31}$ has the factor a_{12} which is in the *first row* and the *second column,* a_{23} which is in the *second row* and the *third column,* and a_{31} which is in the *third row* and the *first column*; similarly, $a_{31}a_{22}a_{13}$ has the factor a_{31} which is in the *third row* and the *first column,* a_{22} which is in the *second row* and the *second column,* and a_{13} which is in the *first row* and the *third column.*) Thus, if the elements of one row (or column) are all zeros, each product has at least one factor *zero,* and their sum (the value of the determinant) is equal to *zero.**

In actual practice, we can hardly expect to find many determinants in which a row (or column) contains nothing but zeros, but there are certain rules according to which the elements of determinants can be manipulated, and *if a determinant equals zero, these manipulations (suitably applied) will lead to a determinant which has a row (or column) containing only zeros.*

---

* This also justifies the criterion on page 269, where we stated that the coefficient matrix does not have an inverse if we get a row containing nothing but zeros to the left of the vertical line.

These "manipulations" are very similar to the elementary row operations of Section 9.5—corresponding to the operations listed on page 266, we now have the following rules:

> **(1)** *if each element of a row (or column) is multiplied by the same number, the value of the determinant is multiplied by that number;*
>
> **(2)** *if each element of a row (or column) is added to (or subtracted from) the corresponding element of another row (or column), the value of the determinant remains unchanged;*
>
> **(3)** *if two rows (or columns) are interchanged, the value of the determinant is multiplied by* -1.

The first of these rules enables us to "factor" a number out of a row or a column of a determinant. For instance, if we multiply each element of the second row of the determinant

$$\begin{vmatrix} 2 & -6 \\ -4 & 12 \end{vmatrix}$$

by 1/2, the value of the determinant is multiplied by 1/2, and we can compensate for this by multiplying the determinant by 2, namely, by writing

$$\begin{vmatrix} 2 & -6 \\ -4 & 12 \end{vmatrix} = 2\begin{vmatrix} 2 & -6 \\ -2 & 6 \end{vmatrix}$$

If we then apply the second rule and add each element of the second row to the corresponding element of the first row, we get

$$2\begin{vmatrix} 2 & -6 \\ -2 & 6 \end{vmatrix} = 2\begin{vmatrix} 0 & 0 \\ -2 & 6 \end{vmatrix}$$

and since the first row contains nothing but zeros, we conclude that the value of the original determinant is zero.

To consider another example, suppose we have to solve the following system of linear equations:

$$\begin{aligned} x_1 - 2x_2 + 3x_3 &= 5 \\ 2x_1 + 5x_2 + 2x_3 &= 4 \\ 4x_1 + x_2 + 8x_3 &= 12 \end{aligned}$$

To see whether it is worthwhile to look for a unique solution (say, by the method of elimination of Chapter 7), let us check whether the determinant of the coefficient matrix, namely,

$$|\mathbf{A}| = \begin{vmatrix} 1 & -2 & 3 \\ 2 & 5 & 2 \\ 4 & 1 & 8 \end{vmatrix}$$

might equal zero. There is really no set rule which tells us how to go about this, but suppose, for the sake of argument, that we begin by subtracting the elements of the second row from the corresponding elements of the third row, getting

$$|\mathbf{A}| = \begin{vmatrix} 1 & -2 & 3 \\ 2 & 5 & 2 \\ 2 & -4 & 6 \end{vmatrix}$$

Then, if we divide each element of the third row by 2 (and compensate for it by multiplying the determinant by 2), we obtain

$$|\mathbf{A}| = 2\begin{vmatrix} 1 & -2 & 3 \\ 2 & 5 & 2 \\ 1 & -2 & 3 \end{vmatrix}$$

and it can be seen that if the elements of the first row are subtracted from the corresponding elements of the third row, we finally get

$$|\mathbf{A}| = 2\begin{vmatrix} 1 & -2 & 3 \\ 2 & 5 & 2 \\ 0 & 0 & 0 \end{vmatrix}$$

Thus, $|\mathbf{A}| = 0$ and we have found that the given system of equations does *not* have a unique solution; in fact, further investigation will show that the system is *inconsistent* (and there are no solutions).

As must be apparent from these two illustrations, the rule on page 274 can be modified by adding that

> *A determinant is zero also if two rows (or columns) are equal, or if the corresponding elements of two rows (or columns) are proportional.*

Thus, it can be seen that each of the determinants

$$\begin{vmatrix} 3 & -2 & 3 \\ 5 & 1 & 5 \\ 4 & -2 & 4 \end{vmatrix}, \quad \begin{vmatrix} 2 & -6 \\ 10 & -30 \end{vmatrix}, \quad \begin{vmatrix} 2 & 0 & -3 \\ 8 & 16 & -4 \\ 2 & 4 & -1 \end{vmatrix}$$

is equal to zero. In the first determinant the first and third columns are the same, in the second determinant each element of the second row is *five times* the corresponding element of the first row (and each element of the second column is *minus three times* the corresponding element of the first column), and in the third determinant each element of the second row is *four times* the corresponding element of the third row.

So far as determinants of 4×4, 5×5, . . . , matrices are concerned, let us merely point out that (as in the 2×2 case on page 272 and the 3×3 case on page 273) they are defined by the quantities which appear in the *denominators* of the symbolic solutions of corresponding systems of linear equations. They obey the same general rules as 2×2 and 3×3 determinants, and they correspond to matrices having an inverse if and only if they are not equal to zero. We shall not study determinants with more than 3 rows and 3 columns in this book, but detailed treatments may be found in most college algebra texts. Let us point out, though, that *the special schemes with the upward and downward diagonals work only for determinants of* 2×2 *and* 3×3 *matrices.*

EXERCISES

1. Evaluate the following determinants

(a) $\begin{vmatrix} 3 & -5 \\ -2 & 4 \end{vmatrix}$ (c) $\begin{vmatrix} 5 & 0 & -3 \\ -2 & 4 & 1 \\ 0 & 7 & 2 \end{vmatrix}$

(b) $\begin{vmatrix} -2 & 3 & 1 \\ 1 & 4 & 2 \\ 1 & -5 & 3 \end{vmatrix}$ (d) $\begin{vmatrix} -2 & 4 \\ 3 & 5 \end{vmatrix}$

2. To verify the three rules on page 275, evaluate the determinant

$$\begin{vmatrix} -3 & 5 & 2 \\ 4 & 1 & -1 \\ 2 & 6 & 1 \end{vmatrix}$$

and then recalculate its value after having, respectively,

(a) multiplied each element of the second row by 3;
(b) multiplied each element of the second column by 4;
(c) added each element of the first row to the corresponding element of the second row;
(d) subtracted each element of the third column from the corresponding element of the first column;
(e) interchanged the first two rows;
(f) interchanged the first and third columns.

3. Without using the formulas to evaluate the corresponding determinants, show that the following matrices are all singular:

(a) $\begin{pmatrix} 8 & 4 \\ -4 & -2 \end{pmatrix}$ (c) $\begin{pmatrix} -4 & 3 \\ 16 & -12 \end{pmatrix}$

(b) $\begin{pmatrix} 2 & -3 & 5 \\ 4 & 12 & 16 \\ 2 & 15 & 11 \end{pmatrix}$ (d) $\begin{pmatrix} 0 & -14 & 70 \\ 9 & 2 & -9 \\ 27 & 1 & -2 \end{pmatrix}$

4. CRAMER'S RULE. Determinants provide a convenient shorthand notation for writing the solutions of systems of linear equations. Verify that the symbolic solution of

$$a_{11}x_1 + a_{12}x_2 = b_1$$
$$a_{21}x_1 + a_{22}x_2 = b_2$$

given on page 196 can be written as

$$x_1 = \frac{\begin{vmatrix} b_1 & a_{12} \\ b_2 & a_{22} \end{vmatrix}}{\begin{vmatrix} a_{11} & a_{12} \\ a_{21} & a_{22} \end{vmatrix}} \quad \text{and} \quad x_2 = \frac{\begin{vmatrix} a_{11} & b_1 \\ a_{21} & b_2 \end{vmatrix}}{\begin{vmatrix} a_{11} & a_{12} \\ a_{21} & a_{22} \end{vmatrix}}$$

provided the coefficient matrix **A** is not singular. Observe that in the *numerator* of the solution for x_1 the constant terms b_1 and b_2 replace the first column of the coefficient matrix, and that in the solution for x_2 they replace the second column of the coefficient matrix. Use the above formulas to solve

(a) the system of equations of part (a) of Exercise 2 on page 270;
(b) the system of equations of part (c) of Exercise 3 on page 270;
(c) the systems of equations of parts (b) and (d) of Exercise 1 on page 201.

5. **CRAMER'S RULE, CONTINUED.** Verify that the symbolic solution of

$$a_{11}x_1 + a_{12}x_2 + a_{13}x_3 = b_1$$
$$a_{21}x_1 + a_{22}x_2 + a_{23}x_3 = b_2$$
$$a_{31}x_1 + a_{32}x_2 + a_{33}x_3 = b_3$$

for x_1 given on page 272 can be written as

$$x_1 = \frac{\begin{vmatrix} b_1 & a_{12} & a_{13} \\ b_2 & a_{22} & a_{23} \\ b_3 & a_{32} & a_{33} \end{vmatrix}}{\begin{vmatrix} a_{11} & a_{12} & a_{13} \\ a_{21} & a_{22} & a_{23} \\ a_{31} & a_{32} & a_{33} \end{vmatrix}}$$

provided the coefficient matrix **A** is not singular. Following *Cramer's Rule*, as this rule is called, write down corresponding solutions for x_2 and x_3 with the constant terms b_1, b_2, and b_3 replacing the second column of the coefficient matrix in the numerator of the solution for x_2, and the third column of the coefficient matrix in the numerator of the solution for x_3. Use this method to solve

(a) the system of equations on page 267, for which we already calculated the value of $|\mathbf{A}|$ on page 273;
(b) the system of equations of part (a) of Exercise 4 on page 270;
(c) the system of equations of Exercise 6 on page 270.

REFERENCES

Dwyer, P., *Linear Computations*. New York: John Wiley & Sons, Inc., 1951.

Searle, S. R., *Matrix Algebra for the Biological Sciences*. New York: John Wiley & Sons, Inc., 1966.

10

THE SIMPLEX METHOD

10.1 INTRODUCTION

In practical applications of linear programming it happens quite often that we run into situations involving ten or twenty variables and as many or more restrictions, or *constraints*, expressed in terms of linear inequalities. If this is the case, the geometrical approach of Section 8.2 cannot be used, and the method of inspecting all of the vertices of the region of feasible solutions becomes impractical. As we already pointed out on page 240, if a problem involves 6 variables which must be non-negative and satisfy 5 other linear inequalities, we have to investigate 462 potential vertices, each requiring the solution of a system of 6 linear equations in 6 variables. A good deal of this work can be avoided by employing the *Simplex method*, a special technique devised by G. B. Dantzig in 1947. This method is a highly efficient trial-and-error technique in which we begin with a feasible solution and check to see whether it maximizes (or minimizes) the *objective function* (namely, the linear expression which happens to be of interest). If not, which is usually the case, the Simplex method indicates the direction we must take in searching for a maximizing (or minimizing) solution, and if such a solution exists, it will eventually be reached. A very important feature of the Simplex method is that it utilizes to great advantage some of the matrix techniques of Chapter 9.

10.2 SLACK VARIABLES

To illustrate some of the main features of the Simplex method and the ideas on which it is based, let us refer again to the three examples of

Section 8.2, which dealt with the preparation of dietary animal foods, the construction of two kinds of wine racks, and the distribution of freezers from two warehouses to three cities. Writing the two variables of the dietary-animal-food example as x_1 and x_2 (instead of x and y), we find from page 224 that in this problem we must maximize the company's profit, namely,

$$3x_1 + 10x_2$$

where x_1 and x_2 (the amounts of animal foods A and B scheduled for production) must be non-negative and satisfy the two linear inequalities

$$2x_1 + 4x_2 \leqslant 80$$
$$x_1 + 5x_2 \leqslant 70$$

Now, the first step in the Simplex method is the conversion of linear inequalities into linear equations, and this is done by introducing so-called *slack variables.* Observe that if $2x_1 + 4x_2$ is actually *less than* 80, there exists a *positive* quantity x_3 such that

$$2x_1 + 4x_2 + x_3 = 80$$

If $2x_1 + 4x_2$ *equals* 80, then x_3 must be zero to satisfy the original inequality, and it follows that in either case $x_3 \geqslant 0$. Similarly, the second inequality can be replaced by

$$x_1 + 5x_2 + x_4 = 70$$

where x_4 is *positive* when $x_1 + 5x_2$ is *less than* 70, it is zero when $x_1 + 5x_2$ *equals* 70, and in either case $x_4 \geqslant 0$. The significance of these slack variables is easy to explain—*x_3 and x_4 tell us how many pounds of each food supplement are left over when the manager of the company schedules the production of x_1 dozen cans of animal food A and x_2 dozen cans of animal food B.*

Using these slack variables, we can now restate this linear programming problem as follows:

We must maximize

$$3x_1 + 10x_2$$

where x_1 and x_2, as well as the slack variables x_3 and x_4, must be non-negative and solutions of the system of linear equations

$$\begin{aligned} 2x_1 + 4x_2 + x_3 &= 80 \\ x_1 + 5x_2 + x_4 &= 70 \end{aligned}$$

Let us now give the same kind of treatment to the wine-rack example on page 228. In this problem we want to maximize the company's profit given by

$$2.40x_1 + 4.80x_2$$

where x_1 and x_2 must be non-negative and satisfy the linear inequalities

$$2.0x_1 + 2.0x_2 \leqslant 48$$
$$1.2x_1 + 2.4x_2 \leqslant 48$$
$$2.4x_1 + 0.8x_2 \leqslant 48$$

In order to convert these inequalities into equations, we introduce the three slack variables x_3, x_4, and x_5, which represent *the time (number of hours) each machine is idle when x_1 standard racks and x_2 de luxe racks are manufactured during the allotted time.* Adding x_3 to $2.0x_1 + 2.0x_2$, x_4 to $1.2x_1 + 2.4x_2$, and x_5 to $2.4x_1 + 0.8x_2$ to give 48 in each case, we can now restate the problem as follows:

We must maximize

$$2.40x_1 + 4.80x_2$$

where x_1 and x_2, as well as the slack variables x_3, x_4, and x_5, must be non-negative and solutions of the system of linear equations

$$\begin{aligned} 2.0x_1 + 2.0x_2 + x_3 \qquad\qquad &= 48 \\ 1.2x_1 + 2.4x_2 \qquad + x_4 \qquad &= 48 \\ 2.4x_1 + 0.8x_2 \qquad\qquad + x_5 &= 48 \end{aligned}$$

Finally, let us return to the example on page 226, which dealt with the delivery of 9 freezers from 2 warehouses to 3 cities. The quantity which we want to minimize in this problem is the cost of delivering the 9 freezers, namely,

$$x_1 + 3x_2 + 19.50$$

where x_1 and x_2 must be non-negative and satisfy four inequalities which can be written as

$$x_1 \leqslant 3$$
$$x_2 \leqslant 4,$$
$$x_1 + x_2 \leqslant 5$$
$$x_1 + x_2 \geqslant 3$$

What makes this example different from the other two is the fact that the inequalities do not all go the same way. In the last inequality, $x_1 + x_2$ is *greater than or equal to* 3, so that a non-negative slack variable will have to be *added on the right,* or *subtracted on the left.* If we introduce the four slack variables x_3, x_4, x_5, and x_6 such that

$$x_1 + x_3 = 3$$
$$x_2 + x_4 = 4$$
$$x_1 + x_2 + x_5 = 5$$
$$x_1 + x_2 - x_6 = 3$$

it can easily be seen from Figure 7.11 on page 217 that $x_3 = 3 - x_1$ is the number of freezers shipped from W_2 to C_1, $x_4 = 4 - x_2$ is the number of freezers shipped from W_2 to C_2, $x_5 = 5 - x_1 - x_2$ is the number of freezers shipped from W_1 to C_3, and $x_6 = x_1 + x_2 - 3$ is the number of freezers shipped from W_2 to C_3. We can thus restate this allocation problem as follows:

We must minimize

$$x_1 + 3x_2 + 19.5$$

where x_1 and x_2, as well as the slack variables x_3, x_4, x_5, and x_6, must be non-negative and solutions of the system of linear equations

$$\begin{aligned}
x_1 \quad + x_3 \quad\quad\quad\quad &= 3\\
x_2 \quad + x_4 \quad\quad\quad &= 4\\
x_1 + x_2 \quad\quad\quad + x_5 \quad &= 5\\
x_1 + x_2 \quad\quad\quad\quad - x_6 &= 3
\end{aligned}$$

This last example required a separate treatment only because *in the Simplex method all of the variables, including the slack variables, must be non-negative.* In fact, when there is an inequality such as $x_1 + x_2 \geqslant 3$ and the slack variable has to be introduced by writing $x_1 + x_2 - x_6 = 3$, the Simplex method requires a further modification which will be discussed on page 284.

10.3 BASIC FEASIBLE SOLUTIONS

What we did in the preceding section does not look like much of a simplification. In the first example we now have four variables instead of two, in the second example we now have five variables instead of two, and in the third example we now have six variables instead of two. This *does* make it seem as if the problems had become more complicated, but there are compensations. For instance, we can now use a theorem which tells us that many of the variables must be zero—specifically,

If we have to maximize (or minimize) a linear expression in k non-negative variables which must satisfy m linear inequali-

ties, and we introduce m non-negative slack variables to convert the inequalities into equations (as in the examples of the preceding section), then at least k of the k + m variables must be zero in the final solution.

Although the connection may not be immediately apparent, this is simply another way of saying that *the solution of a linear programming problem must correspond to a vertex of the region of feasible solutions.* [If one of the original variables is zero, this puts us on the boundary of the region of feasible solutions (for instance, the line $x_1 = 0$ or $x_2 = 0$ in the dietary-animal-food example); if one of the slack variables is zero, the inequality sign of one of the original inequalities is replaced by an equal sign and this also puts us on the boundary of the region of feasible solutions.]

If we knew *which two variables are zero* in the final solution of the dietary-animal-food example, we could substitute 0 for them in

$$\begin{aligned} 2x_1 + 4x_2 + x_3 \quad\quad &= 80 \\ x_1 + 5x_2 \quad\quad + x_4 &= 70 \end{aligned}$$

and this would leave us with the simple problem of having to solve the resulting system of two linear equations in the other two variables. Similarly, in the wine-rack example on page 281 we had $k = 2$ and $m = 3$, and if we knew *which two variables are zero* in the final solution, we could substitute 0 for them in

$$\begin{aligned} 2.0x_1 + 2.0x_2 + x_3 \quad\quad\quad\quad &= 48 \\ 1.2x_1 + 2.4x_2 \quad\quad + x_4 \quad\quad &= 48 \\ 2.4x_1 + 0.8x_2 \quad\quad\quad\quad + x_5 &= 48 \end{aligned}$$

and this would leave us with the relatively simple problem of having to solve the resulting system of three linear equations in the other three variables. *Thus, the key to the solution of any linear programming problem is to find k variables which equal zero in the final solution;* once this has been accomplished, the only thing that remains to be done is to solve a system of m linear equations in the other m variables.

In the Simplex method, we look for these k variables by beginning with a *basic feasible solution,* namely, a vertex of the region of feasible solutions, which corresponds to a given set of k variables equalling zero. We then check whether it solves the problem, and if not, we go on to another vertex by a method which we shall discuss in Section 10.4. Thus, the first step always consists of finding a basic feasible solution, and this is straightforward when the constant terms of the linear equations are *all positive*—we simply let the *original* k variables equal zero, so that *the slack variables will be equal to the constant terms.* For example, in the dietary-animal-food problem we had the equations

$$2x_1 + 4x_2 + x_3 \qquad = 80$$
$$x_1 + 5x_2 \qquad + x_4 = 70$$

and it can be seen that if we let $x_1 = 0$ and $x_2 = 0$, the solutions for the other two variables are $x_3 = 80$ and $x_4 = 70$. Similarly, in the wine-rack problem we had the equations

$$\begin{aligned} 2.0x_1 + 2.0x_2 + x_3 \qquad\qquad &= 48 \\ 1.2x_1 + 2.4x_2 \qquad + x_4 \qquad &= 48 \\ 2.4x_1 + 0.8x_2 \qquad\qquad + x_5 &= 48 \end{aligned}$$

and it can be seen that if we let $x_1 = 0$ and $x_2 = 0$, the solutions for the other three variables are $x_3 = 48$, $x_4 = 48$, and $x_5 = 48$.

If some of the constant terms are *negative*, this is not critical—all we have to do is to multiply the expressions on both sides of the *original* inequalities by -1. Thus, if a linear programming problem involves the inequality

$$3x_1 - 7x_2 \geqslant -4$$

we simply rewrite it as

$$-3x_1 + 7x_2 \leqslant 4$$

remembering, of course, that the sense of the inequality must be reversed.

Another complication arises when the system of linear inequalities includes one or more inequalities of the $\geqslant$ variety (and the corresponding constant terms are positive). For instance, if we take the allocation problem involving the 9 freezers, where we had the system of equations

$$\begin{aligned} x_1 \qquad + x_3 \qquad\qquad\qquad &= 3 \\ x_2 \qquad + x_4 \qquad\qquad &= 4 \\ x_1 + x_2 \qquad\qquad + x_5 \qquad &= 5 \\ x_1 + x_2 \qquad\qquad\qquad - x_6 &= 3 \end{aligned}$$

and let $x_1 = 0$ and $x_2 = 0$, we get $x_3 = 3$, $x_4 = 4$, $x_5 = 5$, and $x_6 = -3$, which is *not* a feasible solution because x_6 is *negative*. What we do in a situation like this is relatively simple—we introduce another variable by writing the equation which led to the negative solution for x_6 as

$$x_1 + x_2 - x_6 + x_7 = 3$$

If we then let $x_1 = 0$ and $x_2 = 0$, we get $x_3 = 3$, $x_4 = 4$, and $x_5 = 5$ from the first three equations, and $-x_6 + x_7 = 3$ from the fourth. Letting $x_6 = 0$ so that $x_7 = 3$ (which is not the only possibility since we could also have used $x_6 = 1$ and $x_7 = 4$, for example, or $x_6 = 2$ and $x_7 = 5$), we finally get the *basic feasible solution*

$$x_1 = 0,\ x_2 = 0,\ x_3 = 3,\ x_4 = 4,\ x_5 = 5,\ x_6 = 0, \text{ and } x_7 = 3$$

Physically speaking, this solution does not make sense since we cannot ship $x_1 + x_2 - 3 = -3$ freezers from warehouse W_2 to city C_3, but it *is* a basic feasible solution so far as the application of the Simplex method is concerned. The extra variable x_7, which we had to use in this last example, is referred to as an *artificial variable;* unlike the slack variables it does not have any "real" significance, and it was introduced for the sole purpose of getting the Simplex method started.

10.4 TRANSFORMATION OF FEASIBLE SOLUTIONS

As can easily be checked, none of the basic feasible solutions of the preceding section provided *final* solutions to the respective problems; in the dietary-animal-food problem the company's profit was

$$3x_1 + 10x_2 = 3(0) + 10(0) = 0$$

in the wine-rack example the total profit was

$$2.40x_1 + 4.80x_2 = 2.40(0) + 4.80(0) = 0$$

and in the allocation problem the solution was, physically speaking, impossible. In each case, we will thus have to look for other basic feasible solutions, namely, for other vertices of the region of feasible solutions. As in Section 8.3, we could do this by starting from scratch, looking for the points of intersection of other lines (planes, or hyper-planes, when there are originally more than two variables) which are part of the boundary of the region of feasible solutions. The disadvantage of this approach is that it can involve a tremendous amount of work (see discussion on page 240). In the Simplex method we proceed differently—*instead of considering all possible vertices, we proceed step-by-step from the initial basic feasible solution to other basic feasible solutions, changing in each step one of the zero variables to a non-zero variable* (*or, at least, to a variable which need not be zero*), *and vice versa, until the problem is solved.*

To illustrate this technique, let us refer again to the dietary-animal-food problem, where we had the system of equations

$$\begin{aligned} 2x_1 + 4x_2 + x_3 \qquad &= 80 \\ x_1 + 5x_2 \qquad + x_4 &= 70 \end{aligned}$$

and the initial basic feasible solution $x_1 = 0$, $x_2 = 0$, $x_3 = 80$, and $x_4 = 70$. Suppose, for the sake of argument, that we want to move from this vertex at which $x_1 = 0$ and $x_2 = 0$ to the one which corresponds to $x_1 = 0$ and $x_4 = 0$. (Of course, we could substitute $x_1 = 0$ and $x_4 = 0$ in the above equations and solve for x_2 and x_3, but this is precisely the kind of work we want to avoid in problems where we have to work with a great number of variables.)

In the Simplex method we go from the case where $x_1 = 0$ and $x_2 = 0$ to the case where $x_1 = 0$ and $x_4 = 0$ by performing *elementary row operations* (see page 266) on the augmented matrix $(\mathbf{A} \mid \mathbf{B})$ of coefficients and constant terms. For our example we have

$$\left(\begin{array}{cccc|c} 2 & 4 & 1 & 0 & 80 \\ 1 & 5 & 0 & 1 & 70 \end{array}\right)$$

and it should be observed that the third and fourth columns are like those of a 2×2 *identity matrix;* in fact, this is what made it possible to *read off* the solutions for x_3 and x_4 when x_1 and x_2 are equal to zero. To be able to *read off* the solutions for x_2 and x_3 when x_1 and x_4 are equal to zero, we shall thus have to move the $\begin{smallmatrix}0\\1\end{smallmatrix}$ column from the fourth column of the matrix to the second; in other words, we shall have to convert the augmented matrix to the form

$$\left(\begin{array}{cccc|c} ? & 0 & 1 & ? & ? \\ ? & 1 & 0 & ? & ? \end{array}\right)$$

where the question marks will have to be replaced with numbers by operating on the rows of the matrix $(\mathbf{A} \mid \mathbf{B})$. Observe that this will make the second and third columns of the matrix like those of a 2×2 identity matrix; their order is reversed, but this does not matter.

To change the second element of the first row to 0, we simply subtract *four fifths* of each element of the second row from the corresponding element of the first row, getting $2 - \frac{4}{5}(1) = \frac{6}{5}$, $4 - \frac{4}{5}(5) = 0$, $1 - \frac{4}{5}(0) = 1$, $0 - \frac{4}{5}(1) = -\frac{4}{5}$, and $80 - \frac{4}{5}(70) = 24$, and, hence,

$$\left(\begin{array}{cccc|c} \frac{6}{5} & 0 & 1 & -\frac{4}{5} & 24 \\ 1 & 5 & 0 & 1 & 70 \end{array}\right)$$

To change the second element of the second row to 1, we have only to divide each element of this row by 5, getting

$$\left(\begin{array}{cccc|c} \frac{6}{5} & 0 & 1 & -\frac{4}{5} & 24 \\ \frac{1}{5} & 1 & 0 & \frac{1}{5} & 14 \end{array}\right)$$

which corresponds to the system of equations

$$\begin{aligned} \frac{6}{5}x_1 \qquad + x_3 - \frac{4}{5}x_4 &= 24 \\ \frac{1}{5}x_1 + x_2 \qquad + \frac{1}{5}x_4 &= 14 \end{aligned}$$

Substituting $x_1 = 0$ and $x_4 = 0$ into these two equations, we can read off the solutions for the other two variables as $x_3 = 24$ and $x_2 = 14$, which are the new *constant terms.*

To give another example of a *transformation of (basic) feasible solutions,* as we referred to this process in the heading of this section, let us return to the wine-rack problem on page 281, for which we introduced the slack variables x_3, x_4, and x_5 to obtain the system of equations

$$\begin{aligned}
2.0x_1 + 2.0x_2 + x_3 \qquad\qquad &= 48 \\
1.2x_1 + 2.4x_2 \qquad + x_4 \qquad &= 48 \\
2.4x_1 + 0.8x_2 \qquad\qquad + x_5 &= 48
\end{aligned}$$

and the initial basic feasible solution $x_1 = 0$, $x_2 = 0$, $x_3 = 48$, $x_4 = 48$, and $x_5 = 48$. Suppose now that for reasons to be explained in Section 10.5, we want to go to the vertex which corresponds to $x_1 = 0$ and $x_4 = 0$. In matrix notation, this means that we must change the augmented matrix

$$\left(\begin{array}{ccccc|c} 2.0 & 2.0 & 1 & 0 & 0 & 48 \\ 1.2 & 2.4 & 0 & 1 & 0 & 48 \\ 2.4 & 0.8 & 0 & 0 & 1 & 48 \end{array}\right)$$

into the matrix

$$\left(\begin{array}{ccccc|c} ? & 0 & 1 & ? & 0 & ? \\ ? & 1 & 0 & ? & 0 & ? \\ ? & 0 & 0 & ? & 1 & ? \end{array}\right)$$

where the question marks will have to be replaced with numbers by performing suitable operations on the rows. Note that the second, third, and fifth columns of the new matrix are like those of a 3×3 identity matrix, though in a different order, which will make it possible to *read off* the solutions for x_2, x_3, and x_5 when x_1 and x_4 are zero; in fact, these solutions will be given by the new constant terms.

All we really have to do is move the $\begin{matrix}0\\1\\0\end{matrix}$ column from the fourth column of the matrix to the second. Thus, to change the second *element* of the *first* row to 0 while leaving the *third* and *fifth* elements of this row unchanged, we subtract *five sixths* $\left(\text{namely, } \dfrac{2.0}{2.4}\right)$ of each element of the second row from the corresponding element of the first row, getting $2.0 - \frac{5}{6}(1.2) = 1$, $2.0 - \frac{5}{6}(2.4) = 0$, $1 - \frac{5}{6}(0) = 1$, $0 - \frac{5}{6}(1) = -\frac{5}{6}$, $0 - \frac{5}{6}(0) = 0$, and $48 - \frac{5}{6}(48) = 8$, and, hence,

$$\left(\begin{array}{ccccc|c} 1 & 0 & 1 & -\frac{5}{6} & 0 & 8 \\ 1.2 & 2.4 & 0 & 1 & 0 & 48 \\ 2.4 & 0.8 & 0 & 0 & 1 & 48 \end{array}\right)$$

To change the *second* element of the *third* row to 0 while leaving the *third* and *fifth* elements of this row unchanged, we subtract *one third* $\left(\text{namely, } \frac{0.8}{2.4}\right)$ of each element of the second row from the corresponding element of the third row, getting $2.4 - \frac{1}{3}(1.2) = 2$, $0.8 - \frac{1}{3}(2.4) = 0$, $0 - \frac{1}{3}(0) = 0$, $0 - \frac{1}{3}(1) = -\frac{1}{3}$, $1 - \frac{1}{3}(0) = 1$, and $48 - \frac{1}{3}(48) = 32$, and, hence,

$$\left(\begin{array}{ccccc|c} 1 & 0 & 1 & -\frac{5}{6} & 0 & 8 \\ 1.2 & 2.4 & 0 & 1 & 0 & 48 \\ 2 & 0 & 0 & -\frac{1}{3} & 1 & 32 \end{array}\right)$$

Finally, to change the *second* element of the *second* row to 1, we divide each element of this row by 2.4, getting $\frac{1}{2}$, 1, 0, $\frac{5}{12}$, 0, and 20, and, hence,

$$\left(\begin{array}{ccccc|c} 1 & 0 & 1 & -\frac{5}{6} & 0 & 8 \\ \frac{1}{2} & 1 & 0 & \frac{5}{12} & 0 & 20 \\ 2 & 0 & 0 & -\frac{1}{3} & 1 & 32 \end{array}\right)$$

This augmented matrix corresponds to the system of equations

$$\begin{aligned} x_1 \qquad + x_3 - \frac{5}{6}x_4 \qquad &= 8 \\ \frac{1}{2}x_1 + x_2 \qquad + \frac{5}{12}x_4 \qquad &= 20 \\ 2x_1 \qquad\qquad - \frac{1}{3}x_4 + x_5 &= 32 \end{aligned}$$

and if we substitute $x_1 = 0$ and $x_4 = 0$, we can immediately *read off* the solutions for the other three variables as $x_3 = 8$, $x_2 = 20$, and $x_5 = 32$. This is the basic feasible solution which corresponds to $x_1 = 0$ and $x_4 = 0$.

So far we have discussed three important aspects of the Simplex method:

(1) *the introduction of slack variables to convert linear inequalities into linear equations;* (2) *the theorem on page 282, according to which at least k of the $k + m$ original and slack variables must be zero in the final solution; and* (3) *the matrix technique which enabled us to transform basic feasible solutions, namely, the method which enabled us to go from one set of k zero solutions to another.* On the other hand, we have not yet learned how to decide whether a given basic feasible solution actually maximizes (or minimizes) the objective function, how to determine which variable should be deleted from the set of zero solutions, and how to choose the variable which must take its place. All this will be discussed in Section 10.5.

EXERCISES

1. Restate each of the following linear programming problems in *standard form*, that is, with equations replacing the inequalities (after making their constant terms non-negative, if necessary). Also find the basic feasible solution in which the original variables are zero.*

   (a) Maximize $2x_1 + 7x_2$, where x_1 and x_2 are non-negative and must satisfy the inequalities

   $$x_1 + 2x_2 \leqslant 2$$
   $$x_1 - x_2 \leqslant 1$$

   (b) Maximize $3x_1 + 2x_2$, where the non-negative variables x_1 and x_2 must satisfy the inequalities

   $$4x_1 + x_2 \leqslant 200$$
   $$x_1 + x_2 \leqslant 80$$
   $$\frac{1}{3}x_1 + x_2 \leqslant 60$$

   (c) Minimize $-2x_1 + x_2$, where x_1 and x_2 are non-negative and must satisfy the inequalities

   $$3x_1 + 10x_2 \leqslant 30$$
   $$5x_1 + 2x_2 \leqslant 10$$
   $$x_1 - x_2 \geqslant -3$$

   (d) Maximize $3x_1 - 2x_2 + 5x_3$, where the non-negative variables x_1, x_2, and x_3, must satisfy the inequalities

   $$6x_1 + 2x_2 + 3x_3 \leqslant 6$$
   $$-2x_2 + x_3 \leqslant 3$$
   $$5x_1 - x_3 \geqslant -2$$

---

* When there is an artificial variable and, hence, the choice of the basic feasible solution is not unique, choose the one in which the corresponding slack variable is zero.

(e) Minimize $3x_1 - 2x_2$, where the variables x_1 and x_2 are non-negative and must satisfy the inequalities

$$\begin{aligned} x_1 + 4x_2 &\leqslant 40 \\ 2x_1 - x_2 &\leqslant 20 \\ x_1 - 2x_2 &\leqslant -10 \end{aligned}$$

(f) Maximize $2x_1 + 3x_2 - x_3$, where the non-negative variables x_1, x_2, and x_3, must satisfy the inequalities

$$\begin{aligned} 20x_1 + 12x_2 + 15x_3 &\leqslant 60 \\ 20x_1 + 12x_2 + 15x_3 &\geqslant 30 \\ x_1 + x_2 - 2x_3 &\leqslant 0 \end{aligned}$$

(g) Minimize $2x_1 + 1.5x_2$, where x_1 and x_2 must be non-negative and satisfy the inequalities

$$\begin{aligned} x_1 + x_2 &\geqslant 1 \\ x_1 + 3x_2 &\geqslant 3 \end{aligned}$$

2. Restate the linear programming problem of part (a) of Exercise 2 on page 232 in standard form (see Exercise 1), and determine the basic feasible solution in which the original variables are all equal to zero.

3. Restate the linear programming problem of part (a) of Exercise 3 on page 232 in standard form (see Exercise 1), and find the basic feasible solution in which the original variables are all equal to zero.

4. Restate the linear programming problem of Exercise 4 on page 232 in standard form (see Exercise 1), and determine the basic feasible solution in which the original variables are all equal to zero.

5. Restate the linear programming problem of Exercise 11 on page 233 in standard form (see Exercise 1), and find the basic feasible solution in which the original variables are all equal to zero.

6. Modify the following augmented matrix (of a system of two linear equations in four variables) so that one can read off the solutions for x_2 and x_3 when x_1 and x_4 are equal to zero:

$$\left(\begin{array}{cccc|c} 1 & 3 & 1 & 0 & 6 \\ 2 & 6 & 0 & 1 & 6 \end{array}\right)$$

What is the corresponding system of equations, and its solution when x_1 and x_4 are equal to zero? (*Hint:* move the $\begin{matrix} 0 \\ 1 \end{matrix}$ column from the fourth column of the matrix to the second.)

7. Modify the following augmented matrix (of a system of two linear equations in five variables) so that one can read off the solutions for x_1 and x_4 when x_2, x_3, and x_5 are equal to zero:

$$\left(\begin{array}{ccccc|c} 4 & 2 & 3 & 1 & 0 & 12 \\ 8 & 2 & -4 & 0 & 1 & -16 \end{array}\right)$$

What are these solutions? Having obtained this result, modify the augmented matrix further so that one can read off the solutions for x_1 and x_2 when x_3, x_4, and x_5 are equal to zero. What are these solutions?

8. Further modify the augmented matrix on page 288, so that one can read off the basic feasible solution which corresponds to $x_3 = 0$ and $x_4 = 0$.

9. Modify the following augmented matrix (of a system of three linear equations in five variables), so that one can read off the solutions for x_2, x_4, and x_5 when x_1 and x_3 are equal to zero:

$$\left(\begin{array}{rrrrr|r} 2 & -1 & 1 & 0 & 0 & 2 \\ 1 & 1 & 0 & 1 & 0 & 3 \\ -1 & 1 & 0 & 0 & 1 & -2 \end{array}\right)$$

What are these solutions?

10. Modify the augmented matrix of the system of equations of part (a) of Exercise 1 so that one can read off the basic feasible solution in which x_2 and x_4 are equal to zero, and then continue to the basic feasible solution in which x_3 and x_4 are equal to zero. What are the corresponding basic feasible solutions?

11. Modify the augmented matrix of the system of equations of part (d) of Exercise 1 so that one can read off the basic feasible solution in which x_1, x_3, and x_4 are equal to zero.

12. ARTIFICIAL VARIABLES AND APPROXIMATIONS. Artificial variables are also used in problems which involve approximations. For instance, if there had been *approximately* 80 pounds of the first supplement available in the dietary-animal-food problem which we have been using as an illustration, it is possible for $2x_1 + 4x_2$ to exceed 80 by a small amount. We take care of this by replacing the first of the two equations on page 280 with

$$2x_1 + 4x_2 + x_3 - x_5 = 80$$

where the two variables x_3 and x_5 must both be non-negative. How would we have to modify the system of equations on page 281 (the one pertaining to the wine-rack problem) if only approximately 48 hours were available on Machines I and II?

10.5 THE SIMPLEX METHOD

To demonstrate how we decide whether a given basic feasible solution maximizes the objective function, let us consider the following linear programming problem in three variables in symbolic form:* *we must maximize the objective function given by*

$$z = c_1x_1 + c_2x_2 + c_3x_3$$

---

* The modification that is required for linear programming problems in which we must *minimize* the objective function will be discussed on page 302.

where the non-negative variables x_1, x_2, and x_3 have to satisfy the linear inequalities

$$a_{11}x_1 + a_{12}x_2 + a_{13}x_3 \leqslant b_1$$
$$a_{21}x_1 + a_{22}x_2 + a_{23}x_3 \leqslant b_2$$
$$a_{31}x_1 + a_{32}x_2 + a_{33}x_3 \leqslant b_3$$

and the constant terms, the b's, are all non-negative. To restate this problem in standard form (see Exercise 1 on page 289), we introduce the non-negative slack variables x_4, x_5, and x_6, so that the three inequalities can be replaced with the linear equations

$$\begin{aligned} a_{11}x_1 + a_{12}x_2 + a_{13}x_3 + x_4 \qquad\qquad &= b_1 \\ a_{21}x_1 + a_{22}x_2 + a_{23}x_3 \qquad + x_5 \qquad &= b_2 \\ a_{31}x_1 + a_{32}x_2 + a_{33}x_3 \qquad\qquad + x_6 &= b_3 \end{aligned}$$

Finally, to treat all of the variables on an *equal basis,* we modify the objective function by writing its values as

$$z = c_1x_1 + c_2x_2 + c_3x_3 + c_4x_4 + c_5x_5 + c_6x_6$$

where c_4, c_5, and c_6 will have to be zero to keep the problem unchanged. *The fact that these c's must be zero will be ignored for the moment, so that our argument will apply regardless of which three variables are the original variables and which three variables are the slack variables.*

Proceeding as in Section 10.4, let us begin with the basic feasible solution $x_1 = 0$, $x_2 = 0$, $x_3 = 0$, $x_4 = b_1$, $x_5 = b_2$, and $x_6 = b_3$, where the last three values were obtained by substituting $x_1 = 0$, $x_2 = 0$, and $x_3 = 0$ into the three equations and reading off the values of x_4, x_5, and x_6. Writing the corresponding value of the objective function as z_0, we get

$$\begin{aligned} z_0 &= c_1 \cdot 0 + c_2 \cdot 0 + c_3 \cdot 0 + c_4 \cdot b_1 + c_5 \cdot b_2 + c_6 \cdot b_3 \\ &= c_4b_1 + c_5b_2 + c_6b_3 \end{aligned}$$

and we shall now have to investigate *whether this is the best we can do.* To answer this question, suppose we try to find out whether it might be profitable to remove x_1 from the set of zero solutions and replace it with x_4, x_5, or x_6. Since x_2 and x_3 are still equal to zero (and we do not know whether the third zero variable is x_4, x_5, or x_6), we can now write the above system of equations as

$$\begin{aligned} a_{11}x_1 + x_4 \qquad\qquad &= b_1 \\ a_{21}x_1 \qquad + x_5 \qquad &= b_2 \\ a_{31}x_1 \qquad\qquad + x_6 &= b_3 \end{aligned}$$

where the first equation can also be written as $x_4 = b_1 - a_{11}x_1$, the second equation can be written as $x_5 = b_2 - a_{21}x_1$, and the third equation can be written as $x_6 = b_3 - a_{31}x_1$. Since x_2 and x_3 are still equal to zero, the value of the objective function is now given by

$$z = c_1x_1 + c_2 \cdot 0 + c_3 \cdot 0 + c_4x_4 + c_5x_5 + c_6x_6$$

and if we substitute into this formula the above expressions for x_4, x_5, and x_6, we get

$$z = c_1x_1 + c_4(b_1 - a_{11}x_1) + c_5(b_2 - a_{21}x_1) + c_6(b_3 - a_{31}x_1)$$

Multiplying out, collecting all terms involving x_1, and factoring out x_1, we can write this value of the objective function as

$$z = c_4b_1 + c_5b_2 + c_6b_3 + x_1[c_1 - (a_{11}c_4 + a_{21}c_5 + a_{31}c_6)]$$

and since $c_4b_1 + c_5b_2 + c_6b_3$ is the *initial value* of the objective function which we denoted z_0, we finally get

$$z = z_0 + x_1[c_1 - (a_{11}c_4 + a_{21}c_5 + a_{31}c_6)]$$

Since x_1 cannot be negative, the value of the objective function will thus *increase* (that is, it will be greater than z_0) when the quantity *in brackets* is positive.

If we applied the same argument to the variables x_2 and x_3, we would find that the deletion of x_2 from the set of zero solutions would change the value of the objective function to

$$z = z_0 + x_2[c_2 - (a_{12}c_4 + a_{22}c_5 + a_{32}c_6)]$$

and that the deletion of x_3 from the set of zero solutions would change the value of the objective function to

$$z = z_0 + x_3[c_3 - (a_{13}c_4 + a_{23}c_5 + a_{33}c_6)]$$

In either case, the value of the objective function will *increase* (that is, it will be greater than z_0) when the quantity in brackets is positive. In view of the importance of these quantities (in brackets), we refer to them as *indicators* and write them as Δ_1, Δ_2, and Δ_3, where Δ is the Greek letter *delta*, and each subscript is the same as that of the corresponding variable which we removed from the set of zero solutions.

We have thus found an answer to the question raised at the beginning of this section:

> *A given basic solution is not optimal (that is, the value of the objective function can be increased) if at least one of the indicators is positive. Otherwise, the solution maximizes the objective function, although it may not be unique when one or more of the indicators is zero.**

---

* We should caution the reader that some authors define the indicators as $-\Delta$ instead of Δ, so that this rule will be rephrased accordingly in their books.

To facilitate the calculation of the Δ's, we use the following kind of scheme, which is called a *Simplex tableau:*

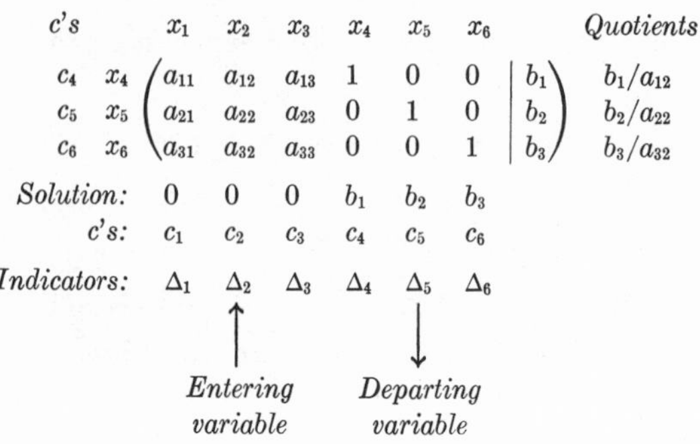

This whole arrangement is centered around the augmented matrix of the system of equations on page 292. On top of each column of the coefficient matrix we indicate the variable to which it belongs, and to the left of each row we indicate which variable can be read off the corresponding equation, namely, which variable equals the corresponding constant term (in the given basic feasible solution). Further to the left we give the coefficients of these x's in the formula for the objective function.

The first line below the augmented matrix contains the basic feasible solution to which the tableau pertains (namely, the corresponding solution for each x), and the second line contains the corresponding c's, namely, the corresponding coefficients of the x's in the formula for the objective function. Finally, the third line below the augmented matrix contains the indicators, *which are obtained by subtracting from the corresponding c (in the second line below the augmented matrix) the sum of the products obtained by multiplying each element of the corresponding column of the augmented matrix by the corresponding c on the extreme left.* As can easily be verified, this will lead to the expressions for Δ_1, Δ_2, and Δ_3 which we gave on page 293; also, Δ_4, Δ_5, and Δ_6 will be zero *and this is always the case with variables which do not belong to the set of zero solutions.* (Obviously, we cannot improve the objective function by deleting a variable from the set of zero solutions which does not belong to it.)

The indicators also tell us which variable should be deleted from the set of zero solutions. Since this variable *enters* the set of (more important) variables whose solution need not be zero, it is officially called the *entering variable.* The rule which we follow in selecting the entering variable is very simple—*we choose the one whose indicator is largest.* Although this will not guarantee that the corresponding improvement of the objective function is a maximum, *we are assured, at least, that we are going in the right direction.** It is customary to indicate the entering variable by means of an arrow pointing upward, as in the tableau on page 294, where we assumed that the entering variable is x_2.

After we have determined the entering variable, the next, and *final*, step is to choose the *departing variable*, namely, the variable which must take the place of the entering variable among the zero solutions. If we assume that the entering variable is x_2 in our example, then x_1 and x_3 are still equal to zero, and we can write the system of equations on page 292 as

$$\begin{aligned} a_{12}x_2 + x_4 \qquad\qquad &= b_1 \\ a_{22}x_2 \qquad + x_5 \qquad &= b_2 \\ a_{32}x_2 \qquad\qquad + x_6 &= b_3 \end{aligned}$$

Since we shall now have to determine whether it is x_4, x_5, or x_6 which becomes one of the zero variables, let us see what happens in each case. If $x_4 = 0$, the first of the above equations yields

$$a_{12}x_2 = b_1 \qquad \text{and, hence,} \qquad x_2 = b_1/a_{12}$$

if $x_5 = 0$, the second of the above equations yields

$$a_{22}x_2 = b_2 \qquad \text{and, hence,} \qquad x_2 = b_2/a_{22}$$

and if $x_6 = 0$, the third of the above equations yields

$$a_{32}x_2 = b_3 \qquad \text{and, hence,} \qquad x_2 = b_3/a_{32}$$

Note that these are the quotients which we wrote in the right-hand column of the Simplex tableau on page 294.

If any of these quotients are negative, the corresponding cases can immediately be ruled out for they would not lead to feasible solutions; otherwise, we might be tempted to choose the case where x_2 is a maximum (see footnote below), but as we shall see, this would also lead to trouble. Suppose, then, that we let $x_4 = 0$, so that $x_2 = b_1/a_{12}$. If we substitute this value of x_2 into the second and third equations given above we obtain

$$\begin{aligned} a_{22}(b_1/a_{12}) + x_5 &= b_2 \\ a_{32}(b_1/a_{12}) + x_6 &= b_3 \end{aligned}$$

and if we solve these equations for x_5 and x_6, we get

$$x_5 = b_2 - a_{22}(b_1/a_{12}) \qquad \text{and} \qquad x_6 = b_3 - a_{32}(b_1/a_{12})$$

---

* For instance, if the entering variable is x_2, we find from page 293 that the corresponding increase in the value of the objective function is given by

$$z - z_0 = x_2[c_2 - (a_{12}c_4 + a_{22}c_5 + a_{32}c_6)] = x_2\Delta_2$$

and it follows that the improvement of the objective function depends on the *new* value of x_2 as well as the indicator Δ_2.

These solutions for x_5 and x_6 are feasible only if they are *non-negative*, namely, if

$$b_2 - a_{22}(b_1/a_{12}) \geqslant 0 \qquad \text{and} \qquad b_3 - a_{32}(b_1/a_{12}) \geqslant 0$$

and it can easily be shown by the methods of Section 7.3 that we can also write these inequalities as

$$b_1/a_{12} \leqslant b_2/a_{22} \qquad \text{and} \qquad b_1/a_{12} \leqslant b_3/a_{32}$$

Since b_1/a_{12}, b_2/a_{22}, and b_3/a_{32} are the three quotients appearing in the right-hand column of the Simplex tableau on page 294, we can thus say that x_4 can be the departing variable only *if the quotient b_1/a_{12} is the smallest of the quotients in the right-hand column of the Simplex tableau (after all negative values have been ruled out)*.

Since this kind of argument holds in general, we always begin our search for the *departing variable* by calculating the appropriate quotients for the right-hand column of the Simplex tableau—*they are obtained by dividing the costant terms, the b's, by the corresponding coefficients of the entering variable.* (Had the entering variable been x_1 in our example, the three quotients would have been b_1/a_{11}, b_2/a_{21}, and b_3/a_{31}, and had the entering variable been x_3, the three quotients would have been b_1/a_{13}, b_2/a_{23}, and b_3/a_{33}.) Then we use the following rule:

> *The departing variable corresponds to the row for which the quotient in the right-hand column is as small as possible, yet non-negative.**

To complete the picture, we draw an arrow pointing downward below the column which corresponds to the departing variable, as we did in the tableau on page 294, where we assumed that the departing variable is x_5.

To illustrate all these steps, let us refer again to the dietary-animal-food example, for which we have already performed a good deal of the required work. Modifying the objective function as indicated on page 292, we shall thus have to maximize

$$3x_1 + 10x_2 + 0 \cdot x_3 + 0 \cdot x_4$$

where x_1, x_2, x_3, and x_4 must be non-negative and solutions of the system of equations

$$\begin{aligned} 2x_1 + 4x_2 + x_3 \phantom{{}+x_4} &= 80 \\ x_1 + 5x_2 \phantom{{}+x_3} + x_4 &= 70 \end{aligned}$$

(The fact that c_3 and c_4 must both equal zero in the objective function is easily explained; after all, the amount of each food supplement that is left over does not contribute to the company's profit.)

* Special problems arise when the smallest of these non-negative quotients is *zero* or *not unique;* such situations are referred to as *degeneracies,* and they are discussed briefly in Exercise 15 on page 304.

Using the same basic feasible solution as on page 284, namely, $x_1 = 0$, $x_2 = 0$, $x_3 = 80$, and $x_4 = 70$, we obtain the following *initial Simplex tableau:*

c's		x_1	x_2	x_3	x_4		*Quotients*
0	x_3	2	4	1	0	80	$80/4 = 20$
0	x_4	1	5	0	1	70	$70/5 = 14$
Solution:		0	0	80	70		
c's:		3	10	0	0		
Indicators:		3	10	0	0		
			↑ *Entering variable*		↓ *Departing variable*		

The indicators were calculated as

$$\begin{aligned}
\Delta_1 &= 3 - (2\cdot 0 + 1\cdot 0) = 3 \\
\Delta_2 &= 10 - (4\cdot 0 + 5\cdot 0) = 10 \\
\Delta_3 &= 0 - (1\cdot 0 + 0\cdot 0) = 0 \\
\Delta_4 &= 0 - (0\cdot 0 + 1\cdot 0) = 0
\end{aligned}$$

and since several of the Δ's are positive, we conclude that the given basic feasible solution is *not optimal,* that is, it does not maximize the objective function. Since Δ_2 is the largest of these indicators, we find that the *entering variable* is x_2, and since 14 is positive and the smaller of the two quotients on the right-hand side of the tableau, we find that the *departing variable* is x_4. (These quotients were obtained by dividing the constant terms, 80 and 70, by the respective elements of the second column of the matrix, namely, by 4 and by 5.)

All this means that we must go from the basic feasible solution in which $x_1 = 0$ and $x_2 = 0$ to the basic feasible solution in which $x_1 = 0$ and $x_4 = 0$, a job which was done already on page 286. As we showed on that page, the corresponding solutions for x_2 and x_3 are $x_2 = 14$ and $x_3 = 24$, and, copying the resulting augmented matrix from page 286, we obtain the following *second Simplex tableau:*

c's		x_1	x_2	x_3	x_4		*Quotients*
0	x_3	$\frac{6}{5}$	0	1	$-\frac{4}{5}$	24	$24 \div \frac{6}{5} = 20$
10	x_2	$\frac{1}{5}$	1	0	$\frac{1}{5}$	14	$14 \div \frac{1}{5} = 70$
Solution:		0	14	24	0		
c's:		3	10	0	0		
Indicators:		1	0	0	-2		
		↑ *Entering variable*		↓ *Departing variable*			

where the Δ's were calculated as

$$\begin{aligned}
\Delta_1 &= 3 - \left(\frac{6}{5}\cdot 0 + \frac{1}{5}\cdot 10\right) &&= 1\\
\Delta_2 &= 10 - (0\cdot 0 + 1\cdot 10) &&= 0\\
\Delta_3 &= 0 - (1\cdot 0 + 0\cdot 10) &&= 0\\
\Delta_4 &= 0 - \left(-\frac{4}{5}\cdot 0 + \frac{1}{5}\cdot 10\right) &&= -2
\end{aligned}$$

Since Δ_1 is positive, we conclude that the solution is *not optimal;* in fact, since Δ_1 is the only positive indicator, x_1 will have to be the *entering variable* for the next step. The quotients that are required for the determination of the departing variable are again shown on the right, and since 20 is the smaller of the two, we find that the departing variable must be x_3. This means that we shall now have to go from the basic feasible solution in which the zero variables are x_1 and x_4 to the basic feasible solution in which the zero variables are x_3 and x_4.

Proceeding as in Section 10.4, we shall thus have to change the augmented matrix

$$\left(\begin{array}{cccc|c} \frac{6}{5} & 0 & 1 & -\frac{4}{5} & 24 \\ \frac{1}{5} & 1 & 0 & \frac{1}{5} & 14 \end{array}\right)$$

to the form

$$\left(\begin{array}{cccc|c} 1 & 0 & ? & ? & ? \\ 0 & 1 & ? & ? & ? \end{array}\right)$$

where the question marks will have to be replaced with numbers by performing suitable operations on the rows. This will make the first two columns of the augmented matrix like those of a 2×2 identity matrix, and we will be able to read off the solutions for x_1 and x_2 when x_3 and x_4 are equal to zero.

To change the first element of the second row to 0, we subtract *one sixth* of each element of the first row from the corresponding element of the second row, getting $\frac{1}{5} - \frac{1}{6}\left(\frac{6}{5}\right) = 0$, $1 - \frac{1}{6}(0) = 1$, $0 - \frac{1}{6}(1) = -\frac{1}{6}$, $\frac{1}{5} - \frac{1}{6}\left(-\frac{4}{5}\right) = \frac{1}{3}$, and $14 - \frac{1}{6}(24) = 10$. Then, to change the first element of the first row to 1, we multiply each element of this row by 5/6, so that the new augmented matrix becomes

$$\left(\begin{array}{cccc|c} 1 & 0 & \frac{5}{6} & -\frac{2}{3} & 20 \\ 0 & 1 & -\frac{1}{6} & \frac{1}{3} & 10 \end{array}\right)$$

As can be seen by inspection, the corresponding basic feasible solution is $x_1 = 20, x_2 = 10, x_3 = 0$, and $x_4 = 0$, and the *third Simplex tableau* becomes

$$\begin{array}{rr} c\text{'s} & \\ 3 & x_1 \\ 10 & x_2 \end{array} \begin{array}{c} \begin{array}{cccc} x_1 & x_2 & x_3 & x_4 \end{array} \\ \left(\begin{array}{cccc|c} 1 & 0 & \frac{5}{6} & -\frac{2}{3} & 20 \\ 0 & 1 & -\frac{1}{6} & \frac{1}{3} & 10 \end{array}\right) \end{array}$$

$$\begin{array}{rcccc} \textit{Solution:} & 20 & 10 & 0 & 0 \\ c\textit{'s:} & 3 & 10 & 0 & 0 \\ \textit{Indicators:} & 0 & 0 & -\frac{5}{6} & -\frac{4}{3} \end{array}$$

where the Δ's were calculated as

$$\Delta_1 = 3 - (1\cdot 3 + 0\cdot 10) = 0$$

$$\Delta_2 = 10 - (0\cdot 3 + 1\cdot 10) = 0$$

$$\Delta_3 = 0 - \left(\frac{5}{6}\cdot 3 - \frac{1}{6}\cdot 10\right) = -\frac{5}{6}$$

$$\Delta_4 = 0 - \left(-\frac{2}{3}\cdot 3 + \frac{1}{3}\cdot 10\right) = -\frac{4}{3}$$

Since none of these Δ's is positive, we conclude that the solution is *optimal,* namely, that the company's profit will be a maximum if they produce (and sell) $x_1 = 20$ dozen cans of animal food A and $x_2 = 10$ dozen cans of animal food B.

Having obtained this result, we shall also want to know whether the solution is *unique,* and to this end we have to inspect the Δ's which correspond to the zero solutions. Since the zero variables in this final tableau are x_3 and x_4, and since $\Delta_3 = -\frac{5}{6}$ and $\Delta_4 = -\frac{4}{3}$ are both *negative,* we conclude that our solution is, in fact, unique. Of course, this agrees with the results obtained in Sections 8.2 and 8.3.

To paraphrase an expression which we used on page 268, solving the dietary-animal-food problem by the Simplex method may have seemed like "kicking a pebble with a bulldozer"; it was certainly much easier to solve the problem geometrically as in Section 8.2, or by the inspection of all vertices of the region of feasible solutions as in Section 8.3. As there is no advantage to using the Simplex method when the whole situation can be pictured geometrically, let us illustrate it further with the *four-variable problem* of Section 8.3. Restating the gasoline-mixing problem on page 237 so that it is ready for the Simplex technique, *we find that we shall have to maximize*

$$24{,}000x_1 + 30{,}000x_2 + 48{,}000x_3 + 36{,}000x_4 + 0\cdot x_5 + 0\cdot x_6$$

*where all of these non-negative variables must be solutions of the system of linear equations**

$$\begin{aligned} x_1 + x_2 + x_3 + x_4 + x_5 \qquad &= 10 \\ 2x_1 + x_2 + 4x_3 + x_4 \qquad + x_6 &= 20 \end{aligned}$$

Since $k = 4$ and $m = 2$ in this example, we find that (according to the theorem on page 282) at least 4 of the 6 variables must be zero in the final solution; in fact, we shall begin with the basic feasible solution in which $x_1 = 0$, $x_2 = 0$, $x_3 = 0$, and $x_4 = 0$, and, hence, $x_5 = 10$ and $x_6 = 20$. Thus, the *first Simplex tableau* becomes

c's		x_1	x_2	x_3	x_4	x_5	x_6		*Quotients*
0	x_5	1	1	1	1	1	0	10	$10 \div 1 = 10$
0	x_6	2	1	4	1	0	1	20	$20 \div 4 = 5$
Solution:		0	0	0	0	10	20		
c's:		24,000	30,000	48,000	36,000	0	0		
Indicators:		24,000	30,000	48,000	36,000	0	0		
				↑ *Entering variable*			↓ *Departing variable*		

Since some of the Δ's are positive, we conclude that the given basic feasible solution does not maximize the objective function, and since $\Delta_3 = 48{,}000$ is the largest of the Δ's, we find that the *entering variable* is x_3. Calculating the corresponding quotients shown on the right-hand side, we find that the smaller of the two is 5, and, hence, that the *departing variable* is x_6. This means that x_6 will have to take the place of x_3 among the zero solutions, or, in other words, that we shall have to move the $\begin{smallmatrix} 0 \\ 1 \end{smallmatrix}$ column from the sixth column of the augmented matrix to the third.

To change the third element of the first row to 0, we subtract *one fourth* of each element of the second row from the corresponding element of the first row, and to change the third element of the second row to 1, we then divide each element of the second row by 4. This changes the augmented matrix to

$$\left(\begin{array}{cccccc|c} \frac{1}{2} & \frac{3}{4} & 0 & \frac{3}{4} & 1 & -\frac{1}{4} & 5 \\ \frac{1}{2} & \frac{1}{4} & 1 & \frac{1}{4} & 0 & \frac{1}{4} & 5 \end{array}\right)$$

---

* The coefficients of x_5 and x_6 in the objective function are *zero*, because x_5 (that part of the plant capacity which is not utilized) and x_6 (the amount of anti-knock ingredient which is left over) do *not* contribute to the profit which the refinery makes on the sale of the gasoline.

which corresponds to the system of equations

$$\frac{1}{2}x_1 + \frac{3}{4}x_2 \qquad + \frac{3}{4}x_4 + x_5 - \frac{1}{4}x_6 = 5$$

$$\frac{1}{2}x_1 + \frac{1}{4}x_2 + x_3 + \frac{1}{4}x_4 \qquad + \frac{1}{4}x_6 = 5$$

and it can be seen by inspection that the new basic feasible solution in which x_1, x_2, x_4, and x_6 are zero, is $x_1 = 0$, $x_2 = 0$, $x_3 = 5$, $x_4 = 0$, $x_5 = 5$, and $x_6 = 0$. Thus, the *second Simplex tableau* becomes

c's		x_1	x_2	x_3	x_4	x_5	x_6		*Quotients*
0	x_5	$\frac{1}{2}$	$\frac{3}{4}$	0	$\frac{3}{4}$	1	$-\frac{1}{4}$	5	$5 \div \frac{3}{4} = \frac{20}{3}$
48,000	x_3	$\frac{1}{2}$	$\frac{1}{4}$	1	$\frac{1}{4}$	0	$\frac{1}{4}$	5	$5 \div \frac{1}{4} = 20$
Solution:		0	0	5	0	5	0		
c's:		24,000	30,000	48,000	36,000	0	0		
Indicators:		0	18,000	0	24,000	0	−12,000		
					↑ *Entering variable*	↓ *Departing variable*			

(Note that we labeled the first row x_5 and the second row x_3, since these are the variables whose values we can read off the corresponding equations after substituting zero for x_1, x_2, x_4, and x_6.)

Since Δ_2 and Δ_4 are positive, the solution is still *not optimal;* in fact, since Δ_4 is the larger of the two, x_4 must be the *entering variable* for the next step. Calculating the quotients given on the right-hand side, we find that they are both positive, that the first is smaller than the second, and, hence, that the *departing variable* must be x_5. This means that x_5 will have to take the place of x_4 among the zero variables, or, in other words, that we will have to move the $\begin{smallmatrix}1\\0\end{smallmatrix}$ column from the fifth column of the augmented matrix to the fourth. To accomplish this, we first subtract 1/3 of each element of the first row from the corresponding element of the second row, and then we divide each element of the first row by 3/4. This changes the augmented matrix to

$$\left(\begin{array}{cccccc|c} \frac{2}{3} & 1 & 0 & 1 & \frac{4}{3} & -\frac{1}{3} & \frac{20}{3} \\ \frac{1}{3} & 0 & 1 & 0 & -\frac{1}{3} & \frac{1}{3} & \frac{10}{3} \end{array}\right)$$

which corresponds to the system of equations

$$\frac{2}{3}x_1 + x_2 \qquad + x_4 + \frac{4}{3}x_5 - \frac{1}{3}x_6 = \frac{20}{3}$$

$$\frac{1}{3}x_1 \qquad + x_3 \qquad - \frac{1}{3}x_5 + \frac{1}{3}x_6 = \frac{10}{3}$$

and it can be seen by inspection that the new basic feasible solution in which x_1, x_2, x_5, and x_6 are zero, is $x_1 = 0$, $x_2 = 0$, $x_3 = 10/3$, $x_4 = 20/3$, $x_5 = 0$, and $x_6 = 0$. Thus, the *third Simplex tableau* becomes

c's		x_1	x_2	x_3	x_4	x_5	x_6	
36,000	x_4	$\frac{2}{3}$	1	0	1	$\frac{4}{3}$	$-\frac{1}{3}$	$\frac{20}{3}$
48,000	x_3	$\frac{1}{3}$	0	1	0	$-\frac{1}{3}$	$\frac{1}{3}$	$\frac{10}{3}$
Solution:		0	0	$\frac{10}{3}$	$\frac{20}{3}$	0	0	
c's:		24,000	30,000	48,000	36,000	0	0	
Indicators:		−16,000	−6,000	0	0	−32,000	−4,000	

where the two rows are now labeled x_4 and x_3, since these are the two variables which equal the corresponding constant terms. Since none of the Δ's is positive and all of the Δ's corresponding to zero variables are negative, we conclude that the solution is not only *optimal*, but also *unique*. This agrees with the result obtained on page 240: the refinery's profit will be a maximum on the sales of 10/3 million gallons of Gasoline C and 20/3 million gallons of Gasoline D.

A complete discussion of the Simplex method with all its facets and ramifications would require considerably more space than we can devote to it in this book. In both of our examples things worked out very well, without complications, but we already pointed out that certain modifications are required when the constant terms of the original inequalities are not all positive, and when the inequalities do not all go the same way. These situations, and other complications, are treated further in some of the exercises which follow. Another problem which we have not yet discussed is *what to do when the objective function has to be minimized.* The modification which is required in that case is very simple—*we replace each term of the objective function with its negative, and then treat the problem as a maximization problem.* Thus, in the allocation problem on page 282 we would maximize $-x_1 - 3x_2 - 19.5$ (or simply $-x_1 - 3x_2$, since there is nothing anyone can do about the -19.5) instead of minimizing $x_1 + 3x_2 + 19.5$. Other *special problems* that arise in connection with the Simplex method are treated in the books referred to at the end of this chapter.

EXERCISES

1. The following is the *first Simplex tableau* for part (a) of Exercise 1 on page 289:

$$
\begin{array}{cc|cccc|c|l}
c\text{'s} & & x_1 & x_2 & x_3 & x_4 & & \textit{Quotients} \\
0 & x_3 & 1 & 2 & 1 & 0 & 2 & \\
0 & x_4 & 1 & -1 & 0 & 1 & 1 & \\
\multicolumn{2}{r|}{\textit{Solutions:}} & 0 & 0 & 2 & 1 & & \\
\multicolumn{2}{r|}{c\text{'s:}} & 2 & 7 & 0 & 0 & & \\
\multicolumn{2}{r|}{\textit{Indicators:}} & & & & & &
\end{array}
$$

Complete this tableau by calculating the indicators, determining the entering variable, calculating the corresponding quotients, and determining the departing variable.

2. Using the results of Exercise 1, complete the Simplex solution of part (a) of Exercise 1 on page 289.

3. The following is the *second Simplex tableau* for part (b) of Exercise 1 on page 289:

$$
\begin{array}{cc|ccccc|c|l}
c\text{'s} & & x_1 & x_2 & x_3 & x_4 & x_5 & & \textit{Quotients} \\
3 & x_1 & 1 & \frac{1}{4} & \frac{1}{4} & 0 & 0 & 50 & \\
0 & x_4 & 0 & \frac{3}{4} & -\frac{1}{4} & 1 & 0 & 30 & \\
0 & x_5 & 0 & \frac{11}{12} & -\frac{1}{12} & 0 & 1 & 43\frac{1}{3} & \\
\multicolumn{2}{r|}{\textit{Solution:}} & 50 & 0 & 0 & 30 & 43\frac{1}{3} & & \\
\multicolumn{2}{r|}{c\text{'s:}} & 3 & 2 & 0 & 0 & 0 & & \\
\multicolumn{2}{r|}{\textit{Indicators:}} & & & & & & &
\end{array}
$$

Complete this tableau by calculating the indicators, determining the entering variable, calculating the corresponding quotients, and determining the departing variable.

4. Using the results of Exercise 3, complete the solution of part (b) of Exercise 1 on page 289.

5. The following is the *first Simplex tableau* for part (c) of Exercise 1 on page 289:

$$
\begin{array}{cc|ccccc|c|l}
c\text{'s} & & x_1 & x_2 & x_3 & x_4 & x_5 & & \textit{Quotients} \\
0 & x_3 & 3 & 10 & 1 & 0 & 0 & 30 & \\
0 & x_4 & 5 & 2 & 0 & 1 & 0 & 10 & \\
0 & x_5 & -1 & 1 & 0 & 0 & 1 & 3 & \\
\multicolumn{2}{r|}{\textit{Solution:}} & 0 & 0 & 30 & 10 & 3 & & \\
\multicolumn{2}{r|}{c\text{'s:}} & 2 & -1 & 0 & 0 & 0 & & \\
\multicolumn{2}{r|}{\textit{Indicators:}} & & & & & & &
\end{array}
$$

Complete this tableau by calculating the indicators, determining the entering variable, calculating the corresponding quotients, and determining the departing variable.

6. Using the results of Exercise 5, complete the solution of part (c) of Exercise 1 on page 289.

7. Use the Simplex method to solve Exercise 1 on page 232.

8. Use the Simplex method to solve Exercise 6 on page 232.

9. Use the Simplex method to solve part (a) of Exercise 10 on page 233.

10. Use the Simplex method to solve Exercise 11 on page 233.

11. Use the Simplex method to solve Exercise 11 on page 242.

12. Use the Simplex method to solve Exercise 12 on page 242.

13. Referring to the work on page 288 and the results of Exercise 8 on page 291, solve the wine-rack example on page 281 by the Simplex method.

14. ARTIFICIAL VARIABLES. To make sure that an artificial variable will *not* appear in the final solution of a linear programming problem, we assign it a *very large negative coefficient* in the objective function of a maximization problem, and a *very large positive coefficient* in a minimization problem. Follow this suggestion to solve part (e) of Exercise 1 on page 290 by the Simplex method. (*Hint:* maximize $-3x_1 + 2x_2 - 20x_6$, where x_6 is the artificial variable.)

15. DEGENERACIES. Degeneracies, or special situations, arise in the Simplex method when several variables become zero in a single step. This can happen when the smallest non-negative quotient (calculated to determine the departing variable) is the *same* for several rows, or when it is equal to *zero.* An example of this is the allocation problem on page 282, where the first Simplex tableau becomes

c's		x_1	x_2	x_3	x_4	x_5	x_6	x_7		*Quotients*
0	x_3	1	0	1	0	0	0	0	3	
0	x_4	0	1	0	1	0	0	0	4	
0	x_5	1	1	0	0	1	0	0	5	
−10	x_7	1	1	0	0	0	−1	1	3	
Solution:		0	0	3	4	5	0	3		
c's:		−1	−3	0	0	0	0	−10		
Indicators:										

if we take care of the artificial variable by writing the value of the objective function which is to be *maximized* as $-x_1 - 3x_2 - 10x_7$ (see also reference to this problem on page 284).

(a) Complete this tableau and show that the departing variable can be either x_3 or x_7.

(b) Show that if we use the departing variable x_3 and construct the next Simplex tableau, we find that we have arrived at the correct solution $x_1 = 3$ and $x_2 = 0$ (see page 228), but that the Simplex method tells us to continue.

(c) Show that if we use the departing variable x_7 in part (a) and construct the next Simplex tableau, we also arrive at the correct solution $x_1 = 3$ and $x_2 = 0$.

There are special techniques for handling degeneracies like this, and they are discussed in detail in the three books referred to below.

REFERENCES

Bennion, E. G., *Elementary Mathematics of Linear Programming and Game Theory*. East Lansing, Mich.: Michigan State University Press, 1960.

Garvin, W. W., *Introduction to Linear Programming*. New York: McGraw-Hill Book Co., Inc., 1960.

Gass, S. I., *Linear Programming: Methods and Applications*. New York: McGraw-Hill Book Co., Inc., 1958.

11

SEQUENCES AND LIMITS

11.1 INTRODUCTION

The purpose of this chapter is to introduce two basic concepts which are needed for the study of calculus in Chapters 12, 13, and 14—*the limit of a sequence and the limit of a function.* As a prerequisite, we shall devote Section 11.2 to various kinds of *progressions,* with which most readers are probably familiar from elementary algebra.

11.2 PROGRESSIONS

When we studied *simple interest* in Chapter 4, we saw that if P dollars are borrowed at the simple interest rate i, the amount owed at the end of the first year is $P + (P \cdot i)$, the amount owed at the end of the second year is $P + 2(P \cdot i)$, the amount owed at the end of the third year is $P + 3(P \cdot i)$, the amount owed at the end of the fourth year is $P + 4(P \cdot i)$, and so forth. What is characteristic about these amounts is that each one is obtained from the preceding amount by adding $P \cdot i$, which makes them an *arithmetic progression.* In general, if we begin with the number a and repeatedly add the same number d (called the *common difference*), then the numbers $a, a + d, a + 2d, a + 3d, a + 4d, \ldots,$ are said to constitute an *arithmetic progression.*

In contrast, if we look at the *compound interest* formula on page 139, we find that if P dollars are borrowed at the interest rate i compounded annually, the amount owed at the end of the first year is $P(1 + i)$, the amount owed at the end of the second year is $P(1 + i)^2$, the amount owed at the end of the third year is $P(1 + i)^3$, the amount owed at the end of the fourth year is $P(1 + i)^4$, and so forth. What is characteristic about these amounts is that each one is obtained from the preceding amount by multiplying by $(1 + i)$, which makes them a *geometric progression*. In general, if we begin with the number a and repeatedly multiply by the same number r (called the *common ratio*), then the numbers $a, ar, ar^2, ar^3, ar^4, \ldots$, are said to constitute a *geometric progression.*

Although the term "progression" is used mostly in connection with arithmetic progressions and geometric progressions, it applies to *any succession of numbers which follow a specific pattern.* The reader will surely remember problems like the following, in which he is given the first few terms of a succession of numbers, and then asked to find the next term or the next few terms:

$$1, 3, 5, \ldots$$

$$1, 4, 9, 16, \ldots$$

$$2, 6, 12, 20, 30, 42, \ldots$$

Each of these sets of numbers constitutes a progression provided the numbers follow a specific pattern, and the problem is to discover the pattern so that the succession of numbers can be continued. So far as the first two examples are concerned, the answers seem "obvious:" in the first case we are evidently dealing with the positive odd integers and the next few terms of the progression are 7, 9, 11, and 13; in the second example the numbers can be written as 1^2, 2^2, 3^2, and 4^2, so that the next few numbers can evidently be written as $5^2 = 25$, $6^2 = 36$, $7^2 = 49$, and $8^2 = 64$. So far as the third example is concerned, the pattern is not quite so "obvious," but it is easily discerned once we write the first six terms as $1 \cdot 2$, $2 \cdot 3$, $3 \cdot 4$, $4 \cdot 5$, $5 \cdot 6$, and $6 \cdot 7$—following this pattern, we find that the next two terms are $7 \cdot 8 = 56$ and $8 \cdot 9 = 72$.

A careful reader may have observed that we repeatedly wrote "obvious" in quotes. To be truthful, the answers are not obvious at all, and there is no reason why in the first example the numbers 1, 3, and 5 could not be followed by 20 and 61, or by any numbers that happen to suit our fancy. It is true, of course, that

$$1, 3, 5, 7, 9, 11, 13, \ldots$$

presents a *very simple* pattern which follows a *very simple* rule, but a good mathematician can easily construct other rules which lead to

$$1, 3, 5, 20, 61, \ldots$$

$$1, 3, 5, -5, -75, \ldots$$

or to any numbers he may wish to choose (see page 309 and also Exercise 2 on page 313).

The point we have been trying to make is that expressions such as "and so forth," "etc.," and the mathematical ". . ." can be very deceptive. *To find the next term of a progression, or for that matter any term of a progression, we must know the rule, or pattern, by which the progression is defined.* Generally, this is done by giving a formula for the kth term, which we denote t_k; given such a formula, we have only to substitute $k = 5$, for example, to get the fifth term t_5, we have only to substitute $k = 8$ to get the eighth term t_8, and so on.*

The formula for the kth term of an arithmetic progression is easy to find. Writing the first few terms as a, $a + d$, $a + 2d$, $a + 3d$, $a + 4d$, $a + 5d, \ldots$, it can be seen that the coefficient of d is always *one less* than the number of the term, so that in general

$$t_k = a + (k - 1)d$$

for any positive integer k. Thus, if the first term of an arithmetic progression is $a = 17$ and the common difference is $d = 3$, then the 6th, 10th, and 19th terms are, respectively,

$$t_6 = 17 + (6 - 1)3 = 32$$

$$t_{10} = 17 + (10 - 1)3 = 44$$

and

$$t_{19} = 17 + (19 - 1)3 = 71$$

So far as the simple interest problem on page 306 is concerned, the formula for the kth term, namely, the amount owed after $k - 1$ years, is given by

$$t_k = P + (k - 1)(P \cdot i)$$

which is equivalent to the formula on page 95 with $k - 1$ substituted for n. (In case the reader is confused by this difference in notation, let us point out that we now start counting with the year in which the money is borrowed, whereas on page 95 we started one year later.)

The formula for the kth term of a geometric progression is also easy to find. Writing the first few terms as a, ar, ar^2, ar^3, ar^4, $ar^5, \ldots$, it can be

---

* Although it is generally desirable to give a formula for the kth term, there are progressions for which this cannot be done. Consider, for example, the progression which is formed by the successive digits in the decimal expansion of $\sqrt{2} = 1.4142135 \ldots$; there is no "formula" for the kth term of the progression

$$1, 4, 1, 4, 2, 1, 3, 5, \ldots$$

since $\sqrt{2}$ is an irrational number whose decimal representation neither terminates nor repeats (see discussion on page 46). Nevertheless, if we had the time and the patience (or suitable electronic equipment) we could determine, say, $t_{1,000}$ or even $t_{1,000,000}$.

seen that the exponent of r is always *one less* than the number of the corresponding term, so that in general

$$t_k = a \cdot r^{k-1}$$

for any positive integer k. Thus, if the first term of a geometric progression is $a = 128$ and the common ratio is $r = -\frac{1}{2}$, then the 5th, 11th, and 14th terms are, respectively,

$$t_5 = 128\left(-\frac{1}{2}\right)^{5-1} = 8$$

$$t_{11} = 128\left(-\frac{1}{2}\right)^{11-1} = \frac{1}{8}$$

$$t_{14} = 128\left(-\frac{1}{2}\right)^{14-1} = -\frac{1}{64}$$

So far as compound interest is concerned, the formula for the kth term, namely, the amount owed after $k - 1$ years, can now be written as

$$t_k = P(1 + i)^{k-1}$$

which is equivalent to the formula on page 139 with $k - 1$ substituted for n. If we substitute $k = 1$, we get the amount originally borrowed, namely, $t_1 = P(1 + i)^{1-1} = P(1 + i)^0 = P \cdot 1 = P$.

Returning for a moment to the three progressions on page 307, we might now add that the formulas for the kth terms were meant to be $t_k = 2k - 1$, $t_k = k^2$, and $t_k = k(k + 1)$, and this is the "obvious" way in which they were actually interpreted. Nevertheless, the formula for the kth term of the first progression could have been

$$t_k = (2k - 1) + \frac{13}{6}(k - 1)(k - 2)(k - 3)$$

since $\frac{13}{6}(k - 1)(k - 2)(k - 3)$ equals zero for $k = 1$, $k = 2$, and $k = 3$. Thus, we would have obtained the same results as before for t_1, t_2, and t_3, but for the next two terms we would have gotten

$$t_4 = (2 \cdot 4 - 1) + \frac{13}{6} \cdot 3 \cdot 2 \cdot 1 = 20$$

and

$$t_5 = (2 \cdot 5 - 1) + \frac{13}{6} \cdot 4 \cdot 3 \cdot 2 = 61$$

instead of 7 and 9. [The following is another example which illustrates the danger of trying to *guess* the next term of a progression without knowing the formula, or rule, for t_k: the author once spent hours trying to determine the number which follows 42, 50, 59, 66, 72, 79, 86, 96, 102, and 110, only to be told that these are subway stops in New York City, and that the next stop is 116th Street (or Columbia University).]

In many problems involving progressions we are interested also in the sums of several terms. So far as business applications are concerned, this is true, particularly, in connection with geometric progressions, and to give an example, suppose that Mr. Brown, planning for his retirement, regularly deposits $1,000 in a savings account on the first day of each year. He started this program on January 1, 1960, when he was 50 years old, and he intends to make the last payment on January 1, 1974, just before he becomes 65. Assuming that his bank will continue to pay 4 percent compounded quarterly, he wants to know what his balance will be on the day he makes the final deposit. Using a formula like that on page 139, he finds that on January 1, 1974, the value of the first $1,000 deposit will have become

$$1000\left(1+\frac{.04}{4}\right)^{14\cdot 4} = 1000(1.01)^{56}$$

the value of the second payment will have become

$$1000\left(1+\frac{.04}{4}\right)^{13\cdot 4} = 1000(1.01)^{52}$$

the value of the third payment will have become

$$1000\left(1+\frac{.04}{4}\right)^{12\cdot 4} = 1000(1.01)^{48}$$

while that of the thirteenth and fourteenth payments will have become $1000(1.01)^8$ and $1000(1.01)^4$; of course, on January 1, 1974, the value of the final payment will simply be $1,000. Thus, the January 1, 1974, balance of Mr. Brown's account will be

$$1000(1.01)^{56} + 1000(1.01)^{52} + 1000(1.01)^{48} + \dots$$
$$\dots + 1000(1.01)^{8} + 1000(1.01)^{4} + 1000$$

and we could evaluate this sum by looking up the various powers of 1.01 in Table I. This would not be very difficult, but it can be simplified by making use of the fact that the numbers we have to add are the first fifteen terms of a geometric progression whose first term is $a = 1000(1.01)^{56}$ and whose common ratio is $r = (1.01)^{-4}$.

What we need, therefore, is a formula for the sum, S_n, of the first n terms of a geometric progression with the first term a and the common ratio r, namely, a short-cut formula for determining the value of

$$S_n = a + ar + ar^2 + ar^3 + \dots + ar^{n-2} + ar^{n-1}$$

If we multiply the expressions on both sides of this equation by r, we get

$$\begin{aligned} r \cdot S_n &= r(a + ar + ar^2 + ar^3 + \ldots + ar^{n-2} + ar^{n-1}) \\ &= ar + ar^2 + ar^3 + ar^4 + \ldots + ar^{n-1} + ar^n \end{aligned}$$

and if we then subtract "equals from equals," namely, the expressions on both sides of the equation for $r \cdot S_n$ from those of the equation for S_n, we get

$$\begin{aligned} S_n - r \cdot S_n = &\ (a + ar + ar^2 + ar^3 + \ldots + ar^{n-2} + ar^{n-1}) \\ &- (ar + ar^2 + ar^3 + ar^4 + \ldots + ar^{n-1} + ar^n) \end{aligned}$$

Since each term except a and ar^n is *added as well as subtracted* on the right-hand side of this last equation, we are left with

$$S_n - r \cdot S_n = a - ar^n$$

which can also be written as

$$S_n(1 - r) = a(1 - r^n)$$

Finally, dividing by $1 - r$ we get

$$S_n = \frac{a(1 - r^n)}{1 - r}$$

which is the desired *formula for the sum of the first n terms of a geometric progression* provided that r is not equal to 1. (If r equals 1, the terms of the progression are all equal to a, the formula for S_n cannot be used, but the sum is simply equal to $n \cdot a$.)

Returning now to our numerical example, we have only to substitute $n = 15$, $a = 1000(1.01)^{56}$ and $r = (1.01)^{-4}$, to write the January 1, 1974, balance of the savings account as

$$\begin{aligned} S_{15} &= 1000(1.01)^{56} \cdot \frac{1 - [(1.01)^{-4}]^{15}}{1 - (1.01)^{-4}} \\ &= 1000(1.01)^{56} \cdot \frac{1 - (1.01)^{-60}}{1 - (1.01)^{-4}} \end{aligned}$$

Looking up the necessary powers of 1.01 in Tables I and II, we find that $(1.01)^{56} = 1.745810$, $(1.01)^{-60} = 0.550450$, and $(1.01)^{-4} = 0.960980$, so that

$$\begin{aligned} S_{15} &= 1000(1.745810) \cdot \frac{1 - 0.550450}{1 - 0.960980} \\ &= \$20{,}113.50 \end{aligned}$$

These calculations would have been even easier (see Exercise 9 on page 315) if we had inverted the order of the terms of the geometric progression so that $a = 1000$ and $r = (1.01)^4$.

This last example is a typical *annuity problem*, namely, a problem in which equal payments are made regularly at equal intervals of time. Actually, our problem was a bit more difficult than the most straightforward kind of annuity problem (see Exercise 11 on page 315) because the conversion period did not coincide with the interval between successive payments.

To consider another example in which the formula for the sum of n terms of a geometric progression can be used to advantage, suppose that someone wants to provide for his child's higher education by purchasing what is called a *deferred annuity certain* on the child's 10th birthday; specifically, he wants to provide for payments of \$5,000 to be made on the child's 17th, 18th, 19th, 20th, and 21st birthdays. *The problem is to determine the amount A which the parent will have to pay.* Incidentally, we referred to this kind of annuity as *deferred* because the payments do not start right away, and as *certain* because they are not contingent upon anyone's being dead or alive; if the child dies before his 21st birthday, all remaining payments presumably go to his heirs.*

To simplify the calculations, let us suppose that the money is invested at 5 percent compounded annually, so that on the child's 10th birthday the *present values* (see discussion of *compound discount* on page 141) of the five payments are, respectively, $5{,}000(1.05)^{-7}$, $5{,}000(1.05)^{-8}$, $5{,}000(1.05)^{-9}$, $5{,}000(1.05)^{-10}$, and $5{,}000(1.05)^{-11}$. Thus, the total amount the parent will have to invest on the child's 10th birthday is given by the sum

$$A = 5{,}000(1.05)^{-11} + 5{,}000(1.05)^{-10} + 5{,}000(1.05)^{-9} + 5{,}000(1.05)^{-8} + 5{,}000(1.05)^{-7}$$

where we inverted the order of the five terms to simplify subsequent calculations.

To evaluate this sum, we have only to observe that the five terms constitute a geometric progression with the first term $a = 5{,}000(1.05)^{-11}$ and the common ratio $r = 1.05$. If we substitute these values together with $n = 5$ into the formula for S_n on page 311, we get

$$A = 5{,}000(1.05)^{-11} \cdot \frac{1 - (1.05)^5}{1 - 1.05}$$

and if we then look up the values of $(1.05)^5$ and $(1.05)^{-11}$ in Tables I and II, we obtain

$$\begin{aligned} A &= 5{,}000(0.584679) \cdot \frac{1 - 1.276282}{1 - 1.05} \\ &= \$16{,}159 \end{aligned}$$

* In actual practice, most annuities written by life insurance companies, trust companies, or banks *are* contingent upon the recipient's being alive, but this introduces complications into the calculations which we cannot handle at this time. It involves probabilities of survival, say, the probability that a man who starts getting monthly annuity (pension) payments at age 65 will still be getting them (that is, he will still be alive) ten, fifteen, or twenty years later. Simple problems of this kind will be discussed briefly in Chapter 16.

rounded to the nearest dollar. This will provide the desired funds for the child's higher education.

The formula for the sum of the terms of a geometric progression provides considerable simplifications in problems involving the yield rate of bonds, sinking funds for the replacement of buildings and machinery, the depletion of oil wells, questions concerning capitalized cost, and, of course, annuities, as was shown in our two numerical examples. For most of these problems there are *special formulas* and *special tables* which can be found in books on the mathematics of finance. These formulas and these tables are, of course, of great value to anyone specializing, say, in cost accounting or in actuarial science, but it is important to remember that all one really needs in these problems is the simple little formula for the sum of the first n terms of a geometric progression. Incidentally, we did not discuss the formula for the sum of the first n terms of an *arithmetic progression*, as it is difficult to find non-trivial applications of this formula in problems of business and economics. Nevertheless, the formula is given in Exercise 7 on page 314.

EXERCISES

1. Find a *simple* rule or formula which characterizes each of the following progressions and write down the next three terms:

(a) 0, 1, 3, 4, 6, 7, 9, . . . ;
(b) 384, −192, 96, −48, 24, . . . ;
(c) 2, 4, −8, −16, 32, 64, −128, . . . ;
(d) 1, 1/3, 1/5, 1/7, 1/9, . . . ;
(e) 5, 15/2, 10, 25/2, 15, 35/2, . . . ;
(f) 1, 3, 6, 10, 15, 21, 28, ...

2. On page 307 we suggested the possibility that the next two terms of the progression 1, 3, 5, . . . , might conceivably be −5 and −75. Verify that this would actually be the case if the formula for the kth term were given by

$$t_k = 6\cdot 2^k - 3^k - 4(1 + k)$$

3. Write the first four terms of the following progressions whose kth terms are:

(a) $t_k = 1/k$; (c) $t_k = \dfrac{(-1)^k}{k^2}$;

(b) $t_k = \dfrac{k}{k+1}$; (d) $t_k = k(k+1)(k+2)$.

4. Write the first five terms of the *arithmetic progressions* for which

(a) $a = 4$ and $d = 5$; (c) $a = 4$ and $t_4 = 19$;
(b) $t_3 = 9$ and $d = 2$; (d) $t_2 = 7$ and $t_5 = -2$.

5. Mr. Jones has been offered a teaching job which pays a starting salary of $4,400 a year and a guaranteed annual raise of $300. How much will he earn during the 12th year?

6. Mr. Smith opened a savings account for his son by depositing \$50 on the day he was born, and on each subsequent birthday he deposited \$15 more than the year before. How much did he deposit on his son's 15th birthday?

7. **SUM OF THE TERMS OF AN ARITHMETIC PROGRESSION.** Using the same notation as in the text and letting l denote the nth term, we can write the sum of the first n terms of an arithmetic progression (with the first term a and the constant difference d) as

$$S_n = a + (a + d) + (a + 2d) + \ldots + (l - 2d) + (l - d) + l$$

Note that the common difference d is *subtracted* (rather than added), when we go backwards starting with the nth term. In fact, if we completely invert the order of the terms, we can write the sum of the first n terms as

$$S_n = l + (l - d) + (l - 2d) + \ldots + (a + 2d) + (a + d) + a$$

and if we *add* these two expressions for S_n, we get

$$\begin{aligned} 2 \cdot S_n = {} & a + (a + d) + (a + 2d) + \ldots + (l - 2d) + (l - d) + l \\ & + l + (l - d) + (l - 2d) + \ldots + (a + 2d) + (a + d) + a \end{aligned}$$

Now, if we *pairwise* add the terms which we have written one beneath the other, the d's will cancel out, and we will always get $a + l$, so that

$$\begin{aligned} 2 \cdot S_n &= (a + l) + (a + l) + \ldots + (a + l) + (a + l) \\ &= n(a + l) \end{aligned}$$

and we finally get

$$S_n = \frac{n(a + l)}{2}$$

(a) Making use of the fact that l is the nth term of the arithmetic progression, show that the formula for the sum of the first n terms can also be written as

$$S_n = \frac{n[2a + (n - 1)d]}{2}$$

(b) Referring to Exercise 5, find Mr. Jones' total earnings for the first 12 years he will be at this job.

(c) Referring to Exercise 6, what is Mr. Smith's total deposit (not counting interest) after he has just made the deposit on his son's 15th birthday?

(d) A national press service ranks football teams by asking 35 prominent coaches to list whichever teams they consider to be first, second, third, . . . , and tenth. To combine these ratings, the press service awards 10 points for a first-place vote, 9 points for a second-place vote, 8 points for a third-place vote, . . . , and 1 point for a tenth-place vote. What is the total number of points awarded to all of the teams?

(e) A department store's sales totaled \$1,240,000 in 1968 and \$727,000 in 1959. If the store's sales increased by the same amount each year, what is this amount and what were their overall combined sales for the years 1959 through 1968?

(f) Show that the sum of the first k positive integers, namely, $1 + 2 + 3 + \ldots + k$ equals $\frac{k(k+1)}{2}$.

8. Write the first five terms of the *geometric progressions* for which

(a) $a = 2$ and $r = 6$;
(c) $t_3 = 12$ and $r = 2$;
(b) $a = 81$ and $r = -2/3$;
(d) $t_5 = 243$ and $t_2 = -9$.

9. Verify the balance of $20,113.50 which we gave on page 311, by inverting the order of the terms of the geometric progression [so that $a = 1{,}000$ and $r = (1.01)^4$].

10. Suppose that Mr. Jones of Exercise 5 had the option of taking an annual raise of 4 percent (of his preceding year's salary) instead of the fixed annual raise of $300. Which option would be more profitable so far as his total earnings for the first 12 years are concerned?

11. SIMPLE ANNUITIES. An annuity is said to be *simple*, if the interval between successive payments coincides with the conversion period at which interest is being paid.

(a) Show that if the size of each payment is R dollars and the interest rate per conversion period is i, then the *amount* (total value) of all the payments at the time of the nth payment is given by

$$S = R \cdot \frac{(1+i)^n - 1}{i}$$

(The factor by which we multiply R in this formula is usually denoted $s_{\overline{n}|i}$, and its values may be looked up in most handbooks of mathematical tables.)

(b) If someone invests $50 at the end of each month at 6 percent compounded monthly, what is the balance of his account at the end of two years?

(c) If someone invests $200 at the end of every three months at 4 percent compounded quarterly, what is the balance of his account at the end of 10 years?

(d) If we deposit $80 in a savings account at the end of every six months and the bank pays 4 percent compounded semi-annually, what will be our balance at the end of five years?

12. THE PRESENT VALUE OF A SIMPLE ANNUITY. The *present value* of a simple n-payment annuity is the total (discounted) value of all payments at the beginning of the first period, namely, one conversion period before the first payment is being made.

(a) Show that if the size of each payment is R dollars and the interest rate per conversion period is i, then the present value of an n-payment simple annuity is given by

$$A = R \cdot \frac{1 - (1 + i)^{-n}}{i}$$

(The factor by which we multiply R in this formula is usually denoted $a_{\overline{n}|i}$, and its values may be looked up in most handbooks of mathematical tables.)

(b) Find the present value of an annuity paying \$2,000 at the end of each year for 5 years, if the interest rate is 5 percent compounded annually.

(c) Find the present value of an annuity paying \$120 at the end of each month for 4 years, if the interest rate is 6 percent compounded monthly.

13. With reference to the *double-declining-balance* method of depreciation of Exercise 13 on page 143, show that the amounts by which the property is depreciated in successive years constitute a geometric progression. What is its common ratio and what is its first term?

14. What equal monthly payments would someone have to make, if he has three years to repay \$3,000 which he borrowed from a bank at 6 percent compounded monthly. Compare this result with the answer to Exercise 1 on page 101.

15. SINKING FUNDS. A *sinking fund* is a fund which is accumulated for the express purpose of paying an obligation at a future date.

(a) A truck costs \$3,200, and it has a scrap value of \$600 at the end of 5 years. What equal amounts will have to be paid into a sinking fund at the end of each year to provide for the replacement of the truck, if the fund earns 5 percent compounded annually?

(b) The manager of a company wishes to accumulate a sinking fund to provide for the replacement of a \$10,000 machine (with no scrap value) at the end of 9 years. What equal deposits should he make at the end of each six months in a fund which earns 4 percent compounded semiannually?

16. DEPLETION. Mr. Green has spent \$300,000 for an oil well which is expected to produce an income of \$50,000 a year for 12 years. Since this asset will be depleted after 12 years, Mr. Green deposits a certain part of each year's \$50,000 income into a sinking fund (paying 5 percent compounded annually), so that this fund will total \$300,000 after 12 years, and, hence, make up for the depletion of the well.

(a) What equal amounts will he have to deposit in the sinking fund at the end of each year?

(b) What percentage of his original investment is the portion of the annual income that does *not* go into the sinking fund?

11.3 INFINITE SEQUENCES

In this section we shall study *infinite sequences*, namely, progressions which have infinitely many terms. When we say that they have "infinitely many terms," we mean that they have *as many terms as there are natural numbers;* in fact, the natural numbers, themselves, constitute the infinite sequence

$$1, 2, 3, 4, 5, 6, 7, 8, \ldots$$

whose kth term is given by the formula $t_k = k$. Other examples of infinite sequences are

$$1, 1/2, 1/3, 1/4, 1/5, 1/6, 1/7, \ldots$$
$$3/2, 5/3, 7/4, 9/5, 11/6, 13/7, \ldots$$
$$3, -3/2, 3/4, -3/8, 3/16, -3/32, \ldots$$
$$-1, +1, -1, +1, -1, +1, -1, +1, \ldots$$

whose kth terms are, respectively, $t_k = 1/k$, $t_k = \dfrac{2k+1}{k+1}$, $t_k = 3(-1/2)^{k-1}$, and $t_k = (-1)^k$, as can easily be verified by substituting $k = 1, 2, 3, 4, 5, \ldots$, into the respective formulas.

In the study of infinite sequences, we are usually interested mostly in *what happens in the long run,* namely, what happens to the kth term, t_k, when k becomes very large. To illustrate, let us take another look at the five infinite sequences given above. So far as the first one is concerned, namely, 1, 2, 3, 4, 5, 6, 7, 8, . . . , it is apparent that the terms get larger and larger, and we say that they *increase beyond any bound.* (No matter what number we might pick for k, a million, a billion, etc., the terms of the sequence will eventually get larger.)

For the second infinite sequence, 1, 1/2, 1/3, 1/4, 1/5, 1/6, 1/7, . . . , the situation is quite different; the terms get smaller and smaller, but at the same time they come closer and closer to 0. In the language of mathematics, we say that *this infinite sequence has the limit 0,* and we indicate this by writing

$$\lim_{k \to \infty} 1/k = 0$$

where "lim" stands for *limit* and "$k \to \infty$" stands for *k approaches infinity,* or in other words, *k increases beyond any bound.*

In the third infinite sequence shown above the kth term is given by $t_k = \dfrac{2k+1}{k+1}$, and Figure 11.1 shows what happens in the long run to 3/2,

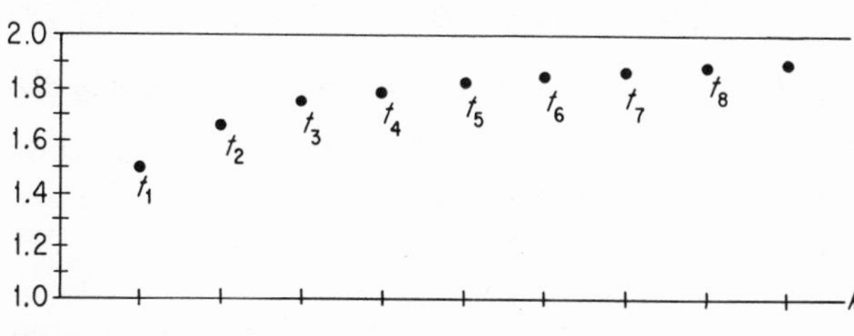

FIG. 11.1

5/3, 7/4, 9/5, 11/6, 13/7, . . . ; the numbers get larger and larger, but at the same time they come closer and closer to 2. Thus, we say that this infinite sequence has the *limit* 2, and we write

$$\lim_{k\to\infty} \frac{2k+1}{k+1} = 2$$

So far as the fourth infinite sequence on page 317 is concerned, the formula for the kth term is $t_k = 3(-1/2)^{k-1}$, which means that its terms constitute a *geometric progression,* and what happens in the long run to 3, $-3/2$, 3/4, $-3/8$, 3/16, $-3/32$, . . . , is pictured in Figure 11.2. The terms

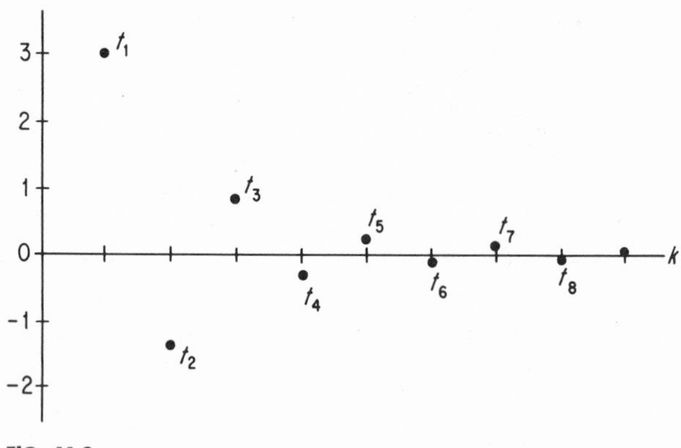

FIG. 11.2

are alternately positive and negative, but at the same time they come closer and closer to 0. As in the second example, we say that the *limit* of the infinite sequence is 0, and we write

$$\lim_{k\to\infty} 3(-1/2)^{k-1} = 0$$

This is true, incidentally, for any infinite sequence whose terms constitute a geometric progression with r, the common ratio, *numerically* less than 1.

Intuitively speaking, the concept of the *limit of an infinite sequence* is not difficult to grasp, but it is an entirely different matter to define it in a rigorous way. Suppose, for example, that somebody doubts our claim that the terms of the infinite sequence 3/2, 5/3, 7/4, 9/5, 11/6, 13/7, . . . , whose kth term is $t_k = \dfrac{2k+1}{k+1}$, will actually *get close and stay close* to the number 2. Surely, his doubt should be dispelled if we could show to him that *if he picks an arbitrary positive number which may be as small as he wants, we will always be able to find a number K such that t_K and all subsequent terms of the sequence will differ from 2 by less than the number he picked.* If he picks 0.000001, for example, we shall have to produce a number K

such that the difference between 2 and t_K (as well as the difference between 2 and every subsequent term) is less than 0.000001, and it will be left to the reader to demonstrate in Exercise 2 on page 327 that the answer is $K = 1{,}000{,}000$. What is important about this argument is the fact that we could also have found such a number K if our friend had picked 0.0000000000000000001 instead of 0.000001, or any number even smaller than that.

Using precisely this kind of argument, let us now give the following definition of the *limit of an infinite sequence:*

> *The infinite sequence* $t_1, t_2, t_3, t_4, \ldots,$ *has the limit* L *if and only if for every positive number* ϵ *(epsilon), however small, there exists a positive integer* K *such that* $|L - t_k| < \epsilon$ *for every* $k \geq K$.

As we explained on page 209, $|L - t_k|$ is the *absolute value* of the difference between L and t_k, namely, the *magnitude* of the difference (disregarding its sign).

Although we now have a formal definition of the limit of an infinite sequence, it really does not help much in trying to *find the limit of an infinite sequence,* or in trying to decide *whether the limit of an infinite sequence actually exists.* In most practical situations we rely on an inspection of the formula for t_k, or we draw diagrams like those of Figures 11.1 and 11.2. Suppose, for example, that we want to find the limit of the infinite sequence 1/2, 4/15, 11/34, 22/59, 37/90, . . . , whose kth term is given by the formula

$$t_k = \frac{2k^2 - 3k + 2}{3k^2 + 4k - 5}$$

As it is always easier to work with $1/k$, $1/k^2$, $1/k^3$, $1/k^4$, . . . , which all *approach 0* when $k \to \infty$, we divide the numerator and the denominator of the expression for t_k by k^2, getting

$$t_k = \frac{2 - 3\left(\frac{1}{k}\right) + 2\left(\frac{1}{k^2}\right)}{3 + 4\left(\frac{1}{k}\right) - 5\left(\frac{1}{k^2}\right)}$$

Hence, we conclude that t_k has the limit

$$\frac{2 - 3(0) + 2(0)}{3 + 4(0) - 5(0)} = \frac{2}{3}$$

as $k \to \infty$.

An infinite sequence which has a limit is said to *converge,* or *be convergent,* while an infinite series which does not have a limit is said to *diverge,* or *be divergent.* We can thus say that the first of the infinite sequences on page 317 diverges, while the next three converge, respectively, to the limits 0, 2, and 0. The fifth, and last, infinite sequence on that page, namely,

$$-1, +1, -1, +1, -1, +1, -1, +1, \ldots$$

is also *divergent* even though its terms do not increase beyond any bound What happens in this case is different—the terms alternate between -1 and $+1$, without staying close to either of these two numbers. Another example of this kind of divergence is given by the infinite sequence

$$1/2, 3/4, 1/4, 7/8, 1/8, 15/16, 1/16, 31/32, \ldots$$

where the even-numbered terms approach 1, the odd-numbered terms approach 0, but the sequence *as a whole* does not have a limit.

Limits of infinite sequences play a very important role in mathematics. They are used to *define* special irrational numbers, and even functions, as we shall see in Section 11.4. The irrational number $e = 2.71828\ldots$, for example, which we mentioned in Exercise 9 on page 142 (in connection with the *continuous conversion* of interest) and on page 148, is the limit of the infinite sequence

$$(1+1)^1, \left(1+\frac{1}{2}\right)^2, \left(1+\frac{1}{3}\right)^3, \left(1+\frac{1}{4}\right)^4, \left(1+\frac{1}{5}\right)^5, \ldots$$

whose kth term is given by $t_k = \left(1+\frac{1}{k}\right)^k$. (As the reader was asked to show in Exercise 9 on page 164, the 100th term of this infinite sequence is approximately 2.7.)

11.4 INFINITE SERIES

In Section 11.2 we let S_n denote the sum of the first n terms of arithmetic or geometric progressions. Applying this symbol more generally, we shall now let S_n denote the sum of the first n terms of any progression $t_1, t_2, t_3, t_4, t_5, \ldots$, so that

$$\begin{aligned} S_1 &= t_1 \\ S_2 &= t_1 + t_2 \\ S_3 &= t_1 + t_2 + t_3 \\ S_4 &= t_1 + t_2 + t_3 + t_4 \\ S_5 &= t_1 + t_2 + t_3 + t_4 + t_5 \\ &\ldots\ldots\ldots\ldots \end{aligned}$$

Evidently, these S's also constitute an infinite sequence, a sequence whose kth term is given by

$$S_k = t_1 + t_2 + t_3 + \ldots + t_k$$

and if this sequence *converges*, namely, if $\lim_{k \to \infty} S_k$ exists, we refer to it as the *value* of the *infinite series*

$$t_1 + t_2 + t_3 + t_4 + t_5 + t_6 + t_7 + t_8 + \ldots$$

Informally, we might refer to an expression like this as an "infinite sum," or as a "sum of infinitely many terms," but this kind of language could easily be misunderstood. *All we are talking about is a limit, and this limit would not be reached even if we kept adding term after term for millions upon millions of years.*

To give an example of an infinite series, let us refer again to the geometric progression $a, ar, ar^2, ar^3, ar^4, \ldots$, whose first term is a and whose common ratio is r. Using the formula for the first n terms (with 1, 2, 3, and k substituted for n), we get

$$S_1 = a$$

$$S_2 = a + ar = \frac{a(1 - r^2)}{1 - r}$$

$$S_3 = a + ar + ar^2 = \frac{a(1 - r^3)}{1 - r}$$

$$\ldots\ldots\ldots\ldots\ldots\ldots\ldots\ldots$$

and in general

$$S_k = a + ar + ar^2 + \ldots + ar^{k-1} = \frac{a(1 - r^k)}{1 - r}$$

This kind of sequence is often referred to as a *geometric series,* and it should be observed that there *is* a distinction between the terms "geometric progression" and "geometric series;" whereas 1, 2, 4, 8, and 16 constitute a geometric *progression* of five terms, the corresponding geometric *series* consists of the numbers 1, $1 + 2 = 3$, $1 + 2 + 4 = 7$, $1 + 2 + 4 + 8 = 15$, and $1 + 2 + 4 + 8 + 16 = 31$, and there is no longer a common ratio between successive terms.

As we already pointed out on page 318, geometric progressions converge to 0 when r is *numerically* less than 1; in that case r^k approaches 0 when $k \to \infty$, and we get

$$\lim_{k \to \infty} S_k = \lim_{k \to \infty} \frac{a(1 - r^k)}{1 - r} = \frac{a}{1 - r}$$

for the *value of the infinite series*

$$a + ar + ar^2 + ar^3 + ar^4 + ar^5 + ar^6 + \ldots$$

For instance, the infinite series

$$1/2 + 1/4 + 1/8 + 1/16 + 1/32 + 1/64 + \ldots$$

has the value

$$\frac{a}{1-r} = \frac{1/2}{1-1/2} = 1$$

and the infinite series

$$2 - 4/3 + 8/9 - 16/27 + 32/81 - 64/243 + \ldots$$

has the value

$$\frac{a}{1-r} = \frac{2}{1-(-2/3)} = \frac{6}{5}$$

Geometrically, we can picture the first of these two examples as in Figure 11.3. First we go half the distance from 0 to 1, then we go half of

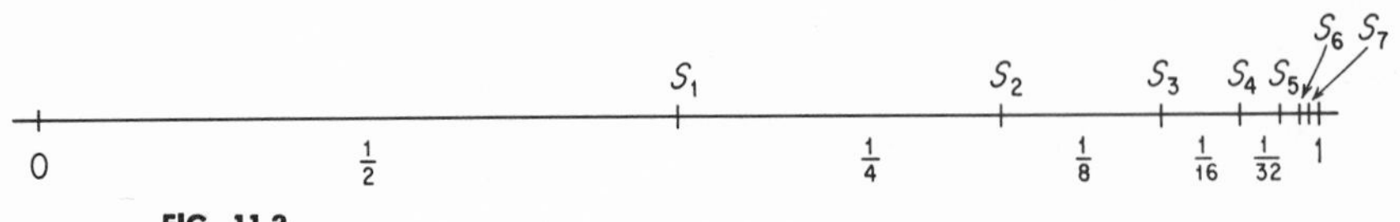

FIG. 11.3

the remaining distance, then again half of the remaining distance, and so on, and so on. No matter how many steps we might take, we would never reach 1, but on the other hand *the sum of the distances has the limit 1.*

To consider a practical application, suppose that somebody wants to establish a fund (earning 5 percent compounded annually) for the maintenance of his family crypt. The maintenance cost is \$100 a year with the first payment due immediately, and what we would like to know is how much money will have to be paid into the fund to take care of the *perpetual* maintenance of the family crypt. Since the payment due a year from now has a *present value* of $100(1.05)^{-1}$, the payment that is due two years from now has a *present value* of $100(1.05)^{-2}$, the payment that is due three years from now has a *present value* of $100(1.05)^{-3}$, and so on, the total amount required now is

$$100 + 100(1.05)^{-1} + 100(1.05)^{-2} + 100(1.05)^{-3} + \ldots$$

Since the individual terms constitute a geometric progression with $a = 100$ and $r = (1.05)^{-1}$, we find that the *value of this infinite series* is given by

$$\frac{a}{1-r} = \frac{100}{1-(1.05)^{-1}} = \frac{100}{\dfrac{1.05-1}{1.05}} = \$2{,}100$$

Thus, an initial investment of \$2,100 will take care of the perpetual maintenance of the family crypt; in fact, this kind of annuity is called a *perpetuity*. (Note that after the first \$100 is paid out immediately, this leaves \$2,000, which (at 5 percent compounded annually) earns just enough to pay the \$100 due at the end of the first year. This argument holds year after year, and, looking at the problem in this way, we could actually have solved it without any reference to infinite series, limits, or geometric progressions.

Although the infinite series which we have studied so far all had *values* (that is, the corresponding infinite sequences $S_1, S_2, S_3, S_4, S_5, \ldots$, were all *convergent*), it is easy to give examples where this is not the case. For instance, the infinite series

$$1 + 2 + 3 + 4 + 5 + 6 + 7 + 8 + \ldots$$
$$2 + 6 + 18 + 54 + 162 + 486 + \ldots$$
$$1 - 5 + 25 - 125 + 625 - 3125 + \ldots$$

do not have values, and neither does the infinite series

$$1 - 1 + 1 - 1 + 1 - 1 + 1 - 1 + \ldots$$

Generally speaking, questions about the *convergence* of infinite series (namely, questions about the existence of their *values*) are often difficult to decide. In view of the fact that the terms keep getting smaller and smaller, it may come as a surprise to the reader that the infinite series

$$1 + 1/2 + 1/3 + 1/4 + 1/5 + 1/6 + \ldots$$

called the *harmonic series*, does not converge—by adding a sufficient number of terms of this series, we will actually be able to exceed any bound (see Exercise 14 on page 329).

What we have learned here about limits and infinite series would have come in very handy back in Chapter 2; in fact, when we referred to *non-terminating decimals* on page 46, we were really talking about infinite series. So far as *repeating decimals* are concerned, two of the examples on page 46 were

$$\frac{14}{33} = 0.4242424242424242424242424242\ldots$$

and

$$\frac{1}{3} = 0.3333333333333333333333333333\ldots$$

and it should be noted that in each case the decimal expansion represents an infinite series whose terms constitute a geometric progression. In the first case we have

$$\frac{42}{100} + \frac{42}{10000} + \frac{42}{1000000} + \frac{42}{100000000} + \cdots$$

namely, an infinite series whose terms constitute a geometric progression with the first term $a = 42/100$ and the common ratio $r = 1/100$. Hence, the formula on page 321 yields

$$\frac{a}{1-r} = \frac{42/100}{1-1/100} = \frac{42/100}{99/100} = \frac{14}{33}$$

and this is the fraction with which we originally began on page 45 when we obtained $\frac{14}{33} = 0.4242424242...$ by long division. Similarly, $0.33333333...$ can be written as

$$\frac{3}{10} + \frac{3}{100} + \frac{3}{1000} + \frac{3}{10000} + \frac{3}{100000} + \cdots$$

where the terms constitute a geometric progression with the first term $a = 3/10$ and the common ratio $r = 1/10$. Its value is

$$\frac{a}{1-r} = \frac{3/10}{1-1/10} = \frac{3/10}{9/10} = \frac{1}{3}$$

and this is the fraction for which we suggested on page 46 that we would obtain $0.3333333333...$ by long division.

Generalizing from these two examples, it can easily be seen that *any repeating decimal is really an infinite series whose terms constitute a geometric progression* (and we might add that this is true also for repeating binary fractions and for repeating fractions written to any other base, see Exercise 5 on page 328.) Making use of this fact, it is easy to find the fraction which corresponds to any repeating decimal, say, to $0.2525252525252525...$ Writing this repeating decimal as

$$\frac{25}{100} + \frac{25}{10000} + \frac{25}{1000000} + \frac{25}{100000000} + \cdots$$

where the terms constitute a geometric progression with the first term $a = 25/100$ and the common ratio $r = 1/100$, we get

$$0.2525252525252525252525... = \frac{a}{1-r} = \frac{25/100}{1-1/100} = \frac{25}{99}$$

An alternate way of solving this kind of problem will be explained in Exercise 4 on page 327.

When it comes to *irrational numbers*, namely, non-terminating decimals which do not repeat (see page 46), we are still talking about infinite series, but the situation is more complicated—the terms of the series will not constitute geometric progressions. For instance, when we write $\sqrt{2} = 1.41424...$, we are really saying that $\sqrt{2}$ is the value of the infinite series

$$1 + \frac{4}{10} + \frac{1}{100} + \frac{4}{1000} + \frac{2}{10000} + \frac{4}{100000} + \cdots$$

and when we write $\pi = 3.14159\ldots$, we are really saying that π is the value of the infinite series

$$3 + \frac{1}{10} + \frac{4}{100} + \frac{1}{1000} + \frac{5}{10000} + \frac{9}{100000} + \cdots$$

Evidently, the terms of these series do not constitute geometric progression; in fact, there are no simple formulas for their kth terms.

To complete our discussion of real numbers which we began in Section 2.3, we can now say that *the real numbers include the rational numbers (or fractions) and all convergent infinite series whose terms are rational numbers.* Actually, that is what we meant on page 40 when we said that any irrational number can be approximated to any desired degree of accuracy by means of rational numbers—clearly, to get as close as we want to the value of a convergent infinite series we have only to add a sufficient number of terms.

Perhaps the most important use of infinite series is in the *definition* of functions, and, hence, in calculating the values of these functions to any desired degree of accuracy by adding a sufficient number of terms. To give an example, let us consider the *exponential function* introduced on page 148, whose equation is $y = e^x$. The values of this function can be calculated by making use of the fact that

$$e^x = 1 + x + \frac{x^2}{2} + \frac{x^3}{2\cdot 3} + \frac{x^4}{2\cdot 3\cdot 4} + \frac{x^5}{2\cdot 3\cdot 4\cdot 5} + \cdots$$

where the kth term of this infinite series is

$$t_k = \frac{x^{k-1}}{(k-1)!}$$

and where $(k-1)!$, which reads "$k - 1$ *factorial,*" represents the product $(k-1)(k-2)\cdot\ldots\cdot 3\cdot 2\cdot 1$; this is a short-hand notation which we shall discuss further in Chapter 15.

To illustrate the use of this series for e^x, let us first calculate the value of the irrational number e, itself. Substituting $x = 1$ into the first five terms of this series, we get

$$1 + 1 + 1/2 + 1/6 + 1/24 = 2.7083$$

and if we use one more term we get

$$1 + 1 + 1/2 + 1/6 + 1/24 + 1/120 = 2.7167$$

Both of these results are *very close* to $2.71828\ldots$, the value of e given originally on page 142, and it is of interest to note that both of our approximations are much closer than the one given by the sixth term of the sequence on page 320, namely, $\left(1 + \frac{1}{6}\right)^6 = 2.52$.

To give another illustration, let us use the first five terms of the series for e^x to calculate $e^{0.5}$ as well as $e^{-0.5}$, and compare the results with 1.649 and 0.607, the corresponding values given in Table III. Substituting $x = 0.5$ into the first five terms, we get

$$1 + 0.5 + \frac{(0.5)^2}{2} + \frac{(0.5)^3}{6} + \frac{(0.5)^4}{24} = 1.648$$

and substituting $x = -0.5$ we get

$$1 + (-0.5) + \frac{(-0.5)^2}{2} + \frac{(-0.5)^3}{6} + \frac{(-0.5)^4}{24} = 0.607$$

Needless to say, the results are extremely close.

Two other functions which can be defined to a great advantage in terms of infinite series are the *sine* and *cosine functions* which we studied in Chapter 6; their series are

$$\sin x = x - \frac{x^3}{3!} + \frac{x^5}{5!} - \frac{x^7}{7!} + \frac{x^9}{9!} - \dots$$

$$\cos x = 1 - \frac{x^2}{2!} + \frac{x^4}{4!} - \frac{x^6}{6!} + \frac{x^8}{8!} - \dots$$

and it is easy to discern the general patterns without actually having to write down the formulas for the kth terms. (As we explained on page 325, $2! = 2$, $3! = 3\cdot 2$, $4! = 4\cdot 3\cdot 2$, $5! = 5\cdot 4\cdot 3\cdot 2$, $6! = 6\cdot 5\cdot 4\cdot 3\cdot 2$, and so on.) These series converge for all real values of x, and it is important to realize that we can thus *define* these trigonometric functions without any reference to angles, triangles, or other geometrical configurations. Before we use these series to verify some of the entries of Table VI, let us point out, though, that x must be in *radians* (see page 169); we could use *degrees*, but the series would then have to be modified accordingly.

To begin with, let us use the first three terms of the series for $\sin x$ to determine $\sin 40°$. Substituting $x = 40\cdot\frac{\pi}{180} = 0.698$ (since one degree equals $\pi/180$ radians), we get

$$0.698 - \frac{(0.698)^3}{6} + \frac{(0.698)^5}{120} = 0.6427$$

and this is almost identical with the tabular value of 0.6428. Similarly, using the first three terms of the series for $\cos x$ to determine $\cos 13°$, we substitute $x = 13\cdot\frac{\pi}{180} = 0.227$, getting

$$1 - \frac{(0.227)^2}{2} + \frac{(0.227)^4}{24} = 0.9743$$

where the tabular value is 0.9744.

The examples which we have given here served to illustrate how the first few terms of infinite series can be used to calculate (approximate) the values of various functions. The theory on which this is based (as well as further examples of infinite series and their applications) will be given in Section 12.7.

EXERCISES

1. Given the following kth terms of infinite sequences, discuss their convergence or divergence, and determine their limit if it exists:

(a) $t_k = \dfrac{k-3}{k}$; (e) $t_k = \dfrac{k^2+1}{k+2}$;

(b) $t_k = (-2)^k$; (f) $t_k = 1 + \left(\dfrac{1}{5}\right)^k$;

(c) $t_k = \dfrac{1}{2k-1}$; (g) $t_k = \dfrac{7k^3 - 2k + 1}{5k^3 + 4k^2}$;

(d) $t_k = 1/k^3$; (h) $t_k = \dfrac{k^2 - 5k + 3}{3k^3 + k^2 - 1}$.

2. On page 318 we claimed that $t_k = \dfrac{2k+1}{k+1}$ is the kth term of an infinite sequence which has the limit 2.

(a) Find a simple expression for the difference $2 - t_k$;
(b) Using the result of part (a), solve the inequality

$$2 - t_k < 0.000001$$

for k, and thus verify the claim that from the millionth term on the difference between 2 and t_k is less than 0.000001.

3. Write each of the following repeating decimals as an infinite series whose terms constitute a geometric progression, and find its value, that is, the corresponding *simple* (or *common*) fraction:

(a) 0.555555555555 . . . ; (d) 3.04444444444444 . . . ;
(b) 1.353535353535 . . . ; (e) 0.153153153153153 . . . ;
(c) 0.003737373737 . . . ; (f) 0.285714285714285714 . . .

[*Hint:* write part (b) as $1 + 0.353535\ldots$ and part (d) as $3 + 0.044444\ldots$]

4. The following is a very simple "trick" for finding the simple, or common, fraction which corresponds to a repeating decimal. Using the illustration on page 323 as an example, let us write the given repeating decimal as

$$x = 0.424242424242424242\ldots$$

If we then multiply the expressions on both sides of this equation by 100, we obtain

$$100x = 42.424242424242424242\ldots$$

and, *subtracting equals from equals*, we get

$$99x = 42 \qquad \text{and, hence,} \qquad x = \frac{42}{99} = \frac{14}{33}$$

Since the digits repeated in pairs we multiplied by 100, but if they had repeated in cycles or 3 or 4 we would have multiplied by 1,000 or 10,000, and if the same digit had repeated again and again we would have multiplied by 10. Use this method to rework the six parts of Exercise 3.

5. Write each of the following *repeating binary fractions* as an infinite series whose terms constitute a geometric progression, and find its value, that is, the corresponding simple decimal fraction:

(a) 0.1010101010101010 . . . ;
(b) 0.110110110110110110 . . . ;
(c) 0.1111111111111111 . . . ;
(d) 0.1100110011001100 . . .

(*Hint:* make use of the fact that in the binary system 0.1 = 1/2, 0.01 = 1/4, 0.001 = 1/8, 0.0001 = 1/16, and so on.)

6. PERPETUITIES. A *perpetuity* is an annuity whose payments begin on a given date and continue forever.

(a) If money is worth 5 percent compounded annually, what is the present value of a perpetuity which pays $1,000 at the end of each year? (*Hint:* use the formula for the value of an infinite series whose terms constitute a geometric progression.)
(b) What would be the present value of the annuity of part (a) if payments were to stop after the 40th year? Compare the results.
(c) What would be the present value of the perpetuity of part (a) if it paid $2,000 at the end of every two years instead of $1,000 at the end of every year?

7. CAPITALIZED COST. The *capitalized cost* of an asset is its original cost plus the present value of all future replacements which are assumed to continue forever.

(a) A store must replace $20,000 worth of fixtures (with no scrap value) every 10 years at the same cost. Find the capitalized cost if the money for the replacements is invested at 4 percent compounded annually.
(b) A machine costing $8,000 has to be replaced every 6 years at which time it has a scrap value of $500. Find the capitalized cost if the money for the replacements is invested at 4 percent compounded quarterly.
(c) The wall-to-wall carpeting of an office, costing $3,000, must be replaced every 8 years. Find the capitalized cost if the money for replacements is invested at 3 percent compounded semi-annually.

8. Using the first five terms of the infinite series for e^x on page 325, approximate the value of

(a) e^2; (c) e^{-1}; (e) $e^{-1.5}$;

(b) $e^{0.1}$; (d) $e^{1/3}$; (f) e^{-5}.

Compare the results with the corresponding entries in Table III.

9. In Exercise 9 on page 142 we stated that if money is invested at 6 percent compounded continuously, the effective rate is $e^{.06} - 1 = 0.0618$. Verify this result using the first four terms of the series for e^x on page 325.

10. Use the first two terms of the infinite series for $\sin x$ on page 326 (with x rounded to three decimals) to find the value of

(a) $\sin 20°$;

(b) $\sin -\pi/12$;

(c) $\sqrt{2}$, making use of the fact that $\sin 45° = \sqrt{2}/2$.

11. Use the first three terms of the infinite series for $\cos x$ on page 326 (with x rounded to three decimals) to find the value of

(a) $\cos 63°$;

(b) $\cos -50°$;

(c) $\sqrt{3}$, making use of the fact that $\cos \pi/6 = \sqrt{3}/2$.

12. Prove that if the first term of an infinite series is 1/2, the next two terms are 1/4, the next four terms are 1/8, the next eight terms are 1/16, the next sixteen terms are 1/32, . . . , the series is *divergent.*

13. TEST FOR CONVERGENCE. There are various methods of testing whether an infinite series is convergent; according to the *comparison test,* an infinite series converges if each of its terms is numerically less than or equal to the corresponding term of a convergent series of positive terms. Use the fact that the geometric series

$$1 + \frac{1}{2} + \frac{1}{4} + \frac{1}{8} + \frac{1}{16} + \cdots$$

converges (to the limit 2) to demonstrate that the infinite series

$$1 + \frac{1}{2!} + \frac{1}{3!} + \frac{1}{4!} + \frac{1}{5!} + \cdots$$

is convergent. (The significance of the factorials 2!, 3!, 4!, . . . , is explained on page 326.)

14. TEST FOR DIVERGENCE. There are various methods of testing whether an infinite series is divergent; according to the *comparison test,* an infinite series of positive terms diverges if each of its terms is greater than or equal to the corresponding term of an infinite series of positive terms which is known to diverge. Use this method and the result of Exercise 12 to prove the *divergence* of the *harmonic series*

$$1 + \frac{1}{2} + \frac{1}{3} + \frac{1}{4} + \frac{1}{5} + \frac{1}{6} + \frac{1}{7} + \frac{1}{8} + \cdots$$

11.5 THE LIMIT OF A FUNCTION

Although there seems to be the widely-held belief that calculus is meant only for students of advanced mathematics, the basic ideas of calculus are really quite easy to understand. In fact, everything is based on two concepts—the *limit of an infinite sequence*, which we have already discussed, and the *limit of a function* (or, better, *the limit of the values of a function*). This second concept is easy to illustrate and easy to explain informally, but it is difficult to define in a rigorous way.

To consider an example, let us take the quadratic function given by $y = 3x^2 + 1$, and let us investigate what happens to the values of y when x approaches 2 by taking on the sequence of values

$$1, 4/3, 6/4, 8/5, 10/6, 12/7, \ldots$$

whose kth term is $t_k = \dfrac{2k}{k+1}$. Substituting these values of x into the equation of the quadratic function, namely, $y = 3x^2 + 1$, we find that the corresponding values of y constitute the sequence

$$3(1)^2 + 1 = 4$$
$$3(4/3)^2 + 1 = 19/3$$
$$3(6/4)^2 + 1 = 31/4$$
$$3(8/5)^2 + 1 = 217/25$$
$$3(10/6)^2 + 1 = 28/3$$
$$3(12/7)^2 + 1 = 481/49$$
$$\cdots\cdots\cdots\cdots$$

whose kth term is $3\left(\dfrac{2k}{k+1}\right)^2 + 1$. Writing this expression for the kth term as $3\left(\dfrac{2}{1+1/k}\right)^2 + 1$ and making use of the fact that $1/k$ approaches 0 as $k \to \infty$, we find that the sequence of y's has the limit $3(2/1)^2 + 1 = 13$.

Geometrically, this can be pictured as in Figure 11.4, where we have drawn the graph of $y = 3x^2 + 1$ and on it a sequence of points P_1, P_2, P_3, P_4, . . . , whose x-coordinates are 1, 4/3, 6/4, 8/5, 10/6, 12/7, . . . , namely, the values of the sequence whose kth term is $\dfrac{2k}{k+1}$. This sequence of points approaches the point Q whose x-coordinate is 2, and without even looking at the y-coordinates of the points P_1, P_2, P_3, P_4, . . . , it is obvious that they must approach the y-coordinate of Q, namely, $3(2)^2 + 1 = 13$.

Although we have demonstrated only that y approaches 13 when x

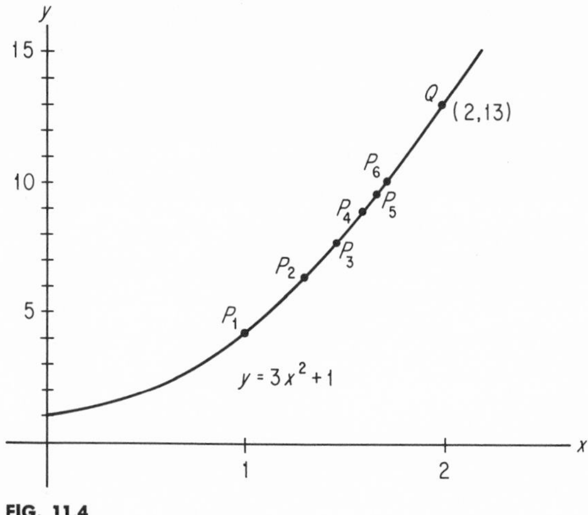

FIG. 11.4

approaches 2 via the special sequence whose kth term is $\frac{2k}{k+1}$, it should be apparent that *we would get the same result for any other sequence of x's having the limit* 2, and this is what we mean when we say that *the given function has the limit* 13 *when x approaches* 2. Symbolically, we write this as $\lim_{x\to 2}(3x^2+1) = 13$ or as $\lim_{x\to 2} y = 13$, which reads as "the limit of y when x approaches 2."

Had we used sequences of x's having the limits 1, 3, or 10 in our example, instead of 2, it must be clear that similar arguments would have led to $\lim_{x\to 1} y = 3(1)^2 + 1 = 4$, $\lim_{x\to 3} y = 3(3)^2 + 1 = 28$, and $\lim_{x\to 10} y = 3(10)^2 + 1 = 301$. Each of these values was obtained by substituting the limit approached by x into the equation of the given function, namely, $y = 3x^2 + 1$, and this method is often used (in fact, it is used whenever possible) to determine the limit of a function.

Unfortunately, it does not always work, as is illustrated by the following example: consider the function which is given by

$$f(x) = \frac{x^2 - 9}{x - 3}$$

for all real values of x except $x = 3$. If we tried to substitute $x = 3$ to determine $\lim_{x\to 3} f(x)$, we would get 0/0 which is *undefined*, but if we substituted $x = 3/2, 6/3, 9/4, 12/5, 15/6, 18/7, \ldots$ (namely, the values of the sequence which has the kth term $\frac{3k}{k+1}$ and the limit 3), we would find that the corresponding y's are 9/2, 15/3, 21/4, 27/5, 33/6, 39/7, . . . (namely, the values of the sequence which has the kth term

$$\frac{\left(\frac{3k}{k+1}\right)^2 - 9}{\frac{3k}{k+1} - 3} = \frac{6k+3}{k+1}$$

and the limit 6.) Thus, $\lim_{x \to 3} f(x) = 6$ even though $f(3)$, the value of the function at $x = 3$ is *undefined.* To take care of situations like this, we agree to a very simple convention—we interpret $x \to a$ as "x approaches a *without ever getting there.*" So far as our example is concerned, we can also write

$$f(x) = \frac{x^2 - 9}{x - 3} = \frac{(x-3)(x+3)}{x-3} = x + 3$$

so long as x does not equal 3, and so far as $\lim_{x \to 3} f(x)$ is concerned, we can substitute $x = 3$, getting $\lim_{x \to 3} f(x) = 3 + 3 = 6$. This agrees, of course, with the answer which we obtained before.

Examples of functions for which $\lim_{x \to a} y$ *does not exist* for some value of a are easiest to present geometrically. Consider, for example, the function whose graph is shown in Figure 11.5—if we take a sequence of x's

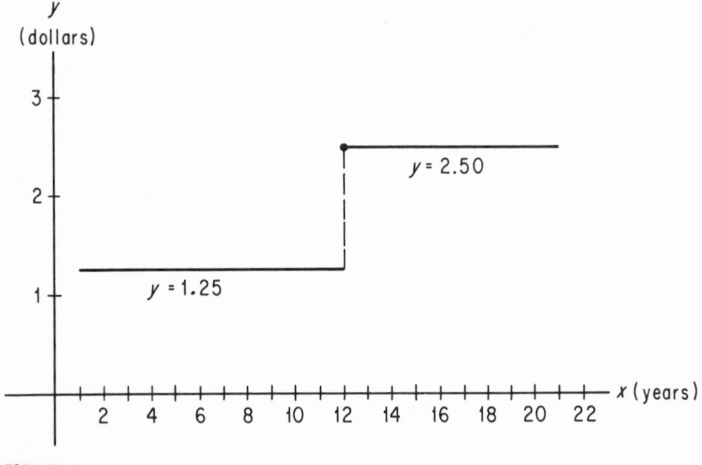

FIG. 11.5

approaching 12 from the left the y's will all equal 1.25, if we take a sequence of x's approaching 12 from the right the y's will all equal 2.50, and if we take a sequence of x's alternating between values less than 12 and values greater than 12, the y's will alternate between 1.25 and 2.50 (without approaching a limit). In this kind of situation $\lim_{x \to 12} f(x)$ *does not exist,* and the example is by no means far-fetched: $f(x)$ might be the price of admission at a county fair, with everyone under 12 admitted at half price. Another example of a function for which $\lim_{x \to a} y$ does not exist for some value (or values) of x is shown in Figure 11.6; in this case the values of the function

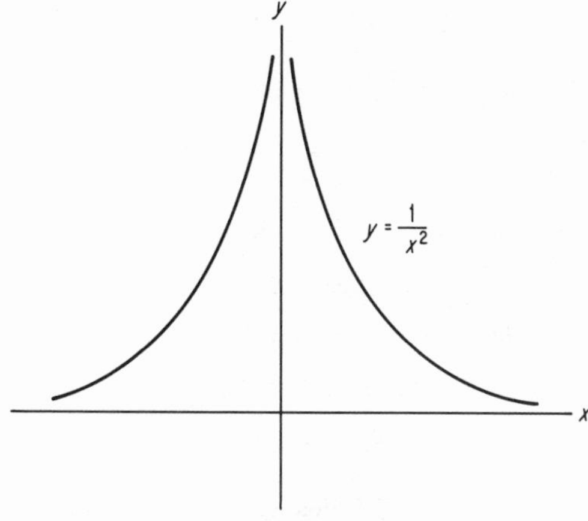

FIG. 11.6

increase beyond any bound when x approaches 0, and $\lim_{x \to 0} 1/x^2$ does not exist.

The difficulties which we experienced in the last three examples are closely tied to the idea of *continuity.* In the example on page 331 the function was not defined for $x = 3$ and its graph is *discontinuous* because there is a gap (a point missing) at $x = 3$. So far as Figure 11.5 and 11.6 are concerned, the functions are both *discontinuous*—evidently, neither graph can be drawn in a *continuous stroke,* that is, without lifting the pen or the pencil off the paper. In all these examples we have used the terms "continuous" and "discontinuous" rather intuitively, but they suggest the following definition:

> *A function with the values $f(x)$ is continuous at $x = a$ if and only if $f(a)$ is defined and* $\lim_{x \to a} f(x) = f(a)$.

Furthermore, we say that a function is *continuous in an interval,* if it is continuous at each point of the interval. Thus, the function of Figure 11.6, the one given by $y = 1/x^2$, is continuous in the interval from 1 to 2 or the interval from 5 to 10, but not in the interval from 0 to 1 or the interval from -3 to 2.

In case the reader is disturbed by the difficulty of some of the definitions of this chapter, let us point out that he should be able to get along in the remainder of this book interpreting such things as the limit of a sequence, the limit of a function, and continuity in the more intuitive sense, which we used to motivate the formal definitions.

EXERCISES

1. Given $y = 3x + 4$, find (a) $\lim_{x\to 0} y$; (b) $\lim_{x\to -1} y$; (c) $\lim_{x\to 4} y$; (d) $\lim_{x\to -3} y$. (*Hint:* try to picture the graph of the function, and, thus, judge whether these limits can be obtained by substitution.)

2. Given $f(x) = x^2 - 2x + 5$, find (a) $\lim_{x\to 1} f(x)$; (b) $\lim_{x\to 0} f(x)$; (c) $\lim_{x\to 3} f(x)$; and (d) $\lim_{x\to -2} f(x)$. (*Hint:* Try to picture the graph of the function, and, thus, judge whether these limits can be obtained by substitution.)

3. If $g(x) = \dfrac{x^4}{x^2} + 1$ for all real values of x for which x^4/x^2 is defined, find the value of x for which the function is undefined and also find its limit at that point.

4. The function given by $f(x) = \dfrac{3(x^2 - 4)}{5x(x + 2)}$ is defined for all real values of x except $x = 0$ and $x = -2$.

   (a) Does $\lim_{x\to 0} f(x)$ exist, and if so what is its value?

   (b) Does $\lim_{x\to -2} f(x)$ exist, and if so what is its value?

5. If $f(x) = x$ for all values of x greater than or equal to 1 and $f(x) = 2 - x$ for all values of x less than 1, does $\lim_{x\to 1} f(x)$ exist, and if so what is its value?

6. Evaluate each of the following limits, if possible, and explain your answers:

   (a) $\lim_{x\to 0} 3/x^3$;

   (b) $\lim_{x\to 1} \dfrac{x^2 + 2x - 3}{x^2 + x - 2}$;

   (c) $\lim_{x\to -2} \dfrac{x + 2}{x + 5}$;

   (d) $\lim_{x\to \infty} \dfrac{3x + 2}{5x + 8}$.

   [*Hint:* in part (b) factor the numerator as well as the denominator, and in part (d) divide the numerator and denominator by x.]

7. A function with the values $f(x)$ is *discontinuous* at $x = a$ if (1) $f(a)$ does not exist, (2) $\lim_{x\to a} f(x)$ does not exist, or (3) $\lim_{x\to a} f(x)$ does not equal $f(a)$. Which of these reasons for discontinuity applies to each of the following examples:

   (a) $f(x) = 1$ for $x > 0$ and $f(x) = -1$ for $x \leqslant 0$, at $x = 0$;

   (b) $f(x) = \dfrac{x^2 - 1}{x - 1}$, for $x \neq 1$, at $x = 1$;

(c) $f(x) = \dfrac{x^2 + x}{x}$ for $x > 0, f(0) = 1/2$, and $f(x) = 1 - x$ for $x < 0$, at $x = 0$;

(d) $f(x) = 1$ for $x > 2$ and $f(x) = 1$ for $x < 2$, at $x = 2$;

(e) $f(x) = 1$ for $x < 3$ and $f(x) = 2$ for $x \geqslant 3$, at $x = 3$;

(f) $f(x) = 2$ for $x \neq 1, f(1) = 1$, at $x = 1$.

8. The current postage rate for airmail letters is 10 cents per ounce (and each fractional part of an ounce) up to 7 ounces; from then on it is 80 cents up to one pound. Plot a graph showing the airmail postage of a letter weighing anywhere up to one pound. At what points is this graph discontinuous?

9. THEOREMS ABOUT LIMITS. In the evaluation of limits we often make use of the following "intuitively obvious" theorems, in which $f(x)$ and $g(x)$ are the values of two functions and k is a constant:*

(1) $\lim_{x \to a} k = k$

(2) $\lim_{x \to a} k \cdot f(x) = k\left[\lim_{x \to a} f(x)\right]$

(3) $\lim_{x \to a} [f(x) + g(x)] = \lim_{x \to a} f(x) + \lim_{x \to a} g(x)$

(4) $\lim_{x \to a} f(x) \cdot g(x) = \left[\lim_{x \to a} f(x)\right]\left[\lim_{x \to a} g(x)\right]$

(5) $\lim_{x \to a} \dfrac{f(x)}{g(x)} = \dfrac{\lim_{x \to a} f(x)}{\lim_{x \to a} g(x)}$

provided that all these limits exist and in (5) $\lim_{x \to a} g(x)$ does not equal zero.

(a) State each of these theorems in words.
(b) Which of these theorems did we use tacitly in Exercise 1 when we obtained the limit by substitution? Explain your answer.
(c) Which of these theorems did we use tacitly in Exercise 2 when we obtained the limit by substitution? Explain your answer.
(d) Which of these theorems was used tacitly in part (c) of Exercise 6 when we obtained the limit by substitution? Explain your answer.
(e) Find the limit of the function of Exercise 4 as $x \to 3$ and justify each step by means of one of the above theorems.
(f) Evaluate

$$\lim_{x \to 2} \frac{5x^2(x - 7)}{x + 3}$$

justifying each step by means of one of the above theorems.

---

* Formal proofs of these theorems require a more rigorous definition of the limit of a function than we gave in this section.

12

DIFFERENTIAL CALCULUS

12.1 INTRODUCTION

Calculus deals with two special kinds of limits, called *derivatives* and *integrals*, which have numerous applications in all branches of science. The processes of finding these limits are called *differentiation* and *integration*, and we thus speak of *differential* and *integral calculus*. In the original draft of this book we devoted one chapter to each of these subjects, but since the first one got too long, we separated theory and applications; this is unfortunate in a way, but seemed necessary. Thus, Chapter 12 is devoted to the basic ideas and to the mechanics of differentiation, while Chapter 13 is devoted mostly to applications. Chapter 14, dealing with integration, is devoted to theory as well as applications, although some very important applications (to problems of probability) are deferred until Chapter 16.

12.2 RATES OF CHANGE

Few things are more important in business and economics than the study of *changes:* changes in a company's sales, changes in the value of the dollar, changes in the gross national product, changes in the values of stocks, changes in hourly wages, changes in interest rates, and so on. Equally important, though, are the *rates* at which these changes are taking place. After all, if we were told that a company's sales increased by $2,000,000, the significance of this information would depend largely on whether this change took place over one year, two years, or perhaps even ten. Similarly, if we are told that the Consumer Price Index has gone down by 0.3 points, this does not mean very much until we find out whether this change took place over a week, a month, or a year.

So far, we have limited our study of *rates of change* to phenomena represented by linear functions, and we have done this for the very simple reason that they are the only functions whose values change at a *constant rate.* As we saw in Section 4.2, this constant rate of change is given by the slope, b, of the line $y = a + bx$; in fact, b represents the change in y which corresponds to an *increase of one unit* in x.

When it comes to other kinds of functions, we not only run into difficulties trying to measure rates of change, but we find that the related concept of the *slope* (direction, or steepness) of a curve is not even defined. To illustrate this, let us suppose that the supply for certain small bearings is given by the equation

$$f(x) = 2{,}000x + 5{,}000x^2$$

where x is the price per bearing in cents. Now, if we look at the graph of this function in Figure 12.1, we find that (going from left to right) the

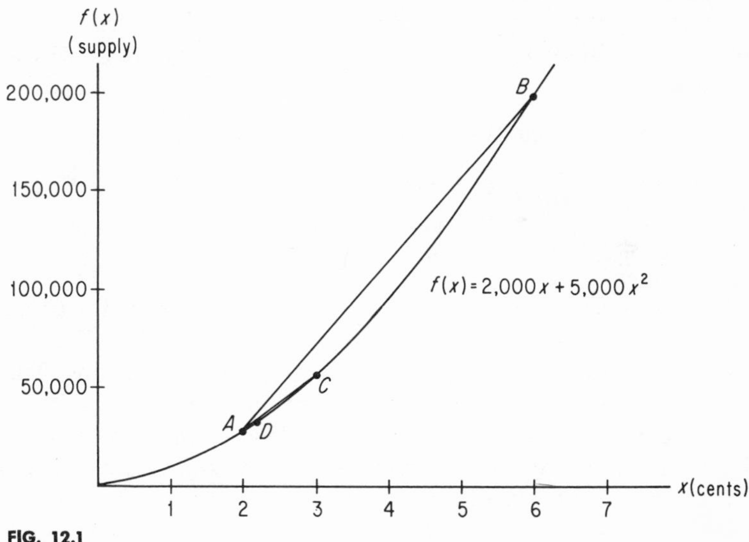

FIG. 12.1

values of the function increase, and that they do so at a *faster and faster rate;* at least, the curve gets steeper and steeper, and this suggests an increasing rate of change.

To investigate this more closely, let us see what happens when the price of the bearings is increased from 2 cents to 6 cents a piece. Making the necessary substitutions, we find that for $x = 2$ the supply is given by

$$f(2) = 2{,}000(2) + 5{,}000(2)^2 = 24{,}000$$

and that for $x = 6$ it is given by

$$f(6) = 2{,}000(6) + 5{,}000(6)^2 = 192{,}000$$

Hence, the supply increases by $192{,}000 - 24{,}000 = 168{,}000$ bearings when x changes from 2 cents to 6 cents, and we could say that *on the average* the supply of the bearings increased by $\frac{168{,}000}{4} = 42{,}000$ bearings for each one-cent increase in x. In other words, the average rate of change for this interval is 42,000, and, geometrically speaking,

$$\frac{192{,}000 - 24{,}000}{6 - 2} = 42{,}000$$

is the *slope* of the line segment joining points A and B of Figure 12.1.

As is evident from this diagram, the slope of the line segment AB does not really reflect what we might refer to as the slope, direction, or steepness of the curve at point A, or at point B, and it does not tell us that the curve is actually *steeper* (and the rate of change is *greater*) at B than it is at A. If, for the sake of argument, we are interested primarily in what happens in the vicinity of point A, it might be better to see what happens when x changes by a smaller amount, say, when it changes from 2 to 3. Since we already know that $f(2) = 24{,}000$, we have only to calculate $f(3)$, for which we get

$$f(3) = 2{,}000(3) + 5{,}000(3)^2 = 51{,}000$$

Thus, the *average rate of change* for the interval from $x = 2$ to $x = 3$ is

$$\frac{f(3) - f(2)}{3 - 2} = \frac{51{,}000 - 24{,}000}{3 - 2} = 27{,}000$$

and, geometrically speaking, this is the *slope* of the line segment AC of Figure 12.1. This is less than the average rate which we obtained for the interval from $x = 2$ to $x = 6$, but it is apparent that the line segment AC is still "steeper" than the curve appears to be at point A.

To get even closer, let us find the slope of the line segment AD of Figure 12.1, namely, the *average rate* at which the values of the function change on the very small interval from $x = 2$ to $x = 2.1$. Since

$$f(2.1) = 2{,}000(2.1) + 5{,}000(2.1)^2 = 26{,}250$$

and we have already shown that $f(2) = 24{,}000$, we get

$$\frac{f(2.1) - f(2)}{2.1 - 2} = \frac{26{,}250 - 24{,}000}{0.1} = 22{,}500$$

and this pretty well tells the story of what happens in the vicinity of point A. The slope of line segment AD is 22,500 and this is just about indicative of the direction, steepness, or slope of the curve at point A. Also, 22,500 is pretty nearly the *average rate* at which the values of the function increase in the vicinity of point A, namely, in the vicinity of $x = 2$. Of course, we could approximate this situation even more closely by considering the interval from $x = 2$ to $x = 2.01$, or the interval from $x = 2$ to $x = 2.001$, but we shall leave it to the reader to show in Exercise 1 on page 345 that the corresponding average rates of change are, respectively, 22,050 and 22,005.

The purpose of this discussion has been to lead to the "ultimate" step of letting the second point on the curve approach point A as a limit. If we let the x-coordinate of the second point on the curve be $2 + \Delta x$, where Δx (*delta* x) is presumably very small, then the *slope* of the line segment which joins point A and this nearby point is given by

$$\frac{f(2 + \Delta x) - f(2)}{(2 + \Delta x) - 2} = \frac{f(2 + \Delta x) - f(2)}{\Delta x}$$

and we can evaluate this quantity by making use of the fact that the equation of the given function is $f(x) = 2{,}000x + 5{,}000x^2$. Substituting $2 + \Delta x$ for x, we get

$$\begin{aligned} f(2 + \Delta x) &= 2{,}000(2 + \Delta x) + 5{,}000(2 + \Delta x)^2 \\ &= 4{,}000 + 2{,}000(\Delta x) + 5{,}000[4 + 4(\Delta x) + (\Delta x)^2] \\ &= 24{,}000 + 22{,}000(\Delta x) + 5{,}000(\Delta x)^2 \end{aligned}$$

and since we already know that $f(2) = 24{,}000$, we get

$$\begin{aligned} \frac{f(2 + \Delta x) - f(2)}{\Delta x} &= \frac{24{,}000 + 22{,}000(\Delta x) + 5{,}000(\Delta x)^2 - 24{,}000}{\Delta x} \\ &= 22{,}000 + 5{,}000(\Delta x) \end{aligned}$$

Finally, letting $\Delta x \to 0$ (namely, letting the second point on the curve approach point A), we find that

$$\lim_{\Delta x \to 0} \frac{f(2 + \Delta x) - f(2)}{\Delta x} = 22{,}000$$

and this defines the (*instantaneous*) *rate at which the values of this function change when* $x = 2$; *at the same time, it also defines what we mean by the slope of the given curve at the point A of Figure* 12.1.

If we use the same line of reasoning in connection with any arbitrary function, we can now give a general definition of what we mean by an *instantaneous rate of change* and *the slope of a curve at a given point*. Writing the values of such a function as $y = f(x)$, we first determine the *average rate* at which the values of the function change between x and $x + \Delta x$, namely, the slope of the line segment PQ of Figure 12.2. This gives

$$b = \frac{f(x + \Delta x) - f(x)}{(x + \Delta x) - x} = \frac{f(x + \Delta x) - f(x)}{\Delta x}$$

and if we take the limit of this quantity as $\Delta x \to 0$, we get

$$\lim_{\Delta x \to 0} \frac{f(x + \Delta x) - f(x)}{\Delta x}$$

which defines the *instantaneous rate* (also called the *marginal rate*) *at which the values of the function change at any given value of x;* at the same time, it also defines the *slope* of the curve at the corresponding point P of Figure 12.2.

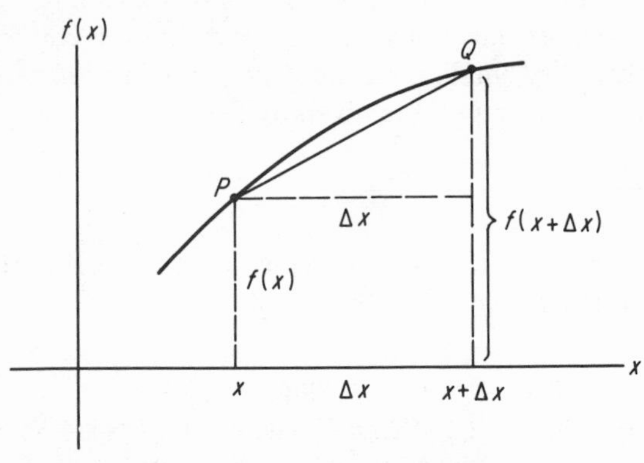

FIG. 12.2

If we apply this technique to the function with which we began our numerical example, namely, $f(x) = 2{,}000x + 5{,}000x^2$, without restricting ourselves to $x = 2$, we get

$$\begin{aligned} f(x + \Delta x) &= 2{,}000(x + \Delta x) + 5{,}000(x + \Delta x)^2 \\ &= 2{,}000x + 2{,}000(\Delta x) + 5{,}000[x^2 + 2x(\Delta x) + (\Delta x)^2] \\ &= 2{,}000x + 2{,}000(\Delta x) + 5{,}000x^2 + 10{,}000x(\Delta x) \\ &\qquad + 5{,}000(\Delta x)^2 \\ f(x + \Delta x) - f(x) &= 2{,}000(\Delta x) + 10{,}000x(\Delta x) + 5{,}000(\Delta x)^2 \\ \frac{f(x + \Delta x) - f(x)}{\Delta x} &= 2{,}000 + 10{,}000x + 5{,}000(\Delta x) \end{aligned}$$

and, hence,

$$\lim_{\Delta x \to 0} \frac{f(x + \Delta x) - f(x)}{\Delta x} = 2{,}000 + 10{,}000x$$

This enables us to calculate the *instantaneous* (or *marginal*) *rate* at which $f(x)$, the supply of the bearings, is increasing for any price x. For $x = 1$, for example, the values of the function are increasing at an instantaneous rate of 12,000 (bearings); for $x = 2$ the instantaneous rate is 22,000; for $x = 5$ the instantaneous rate is 52,000; and for $x = 10$ it is 102,000. Of course, the value we got here for $x = 2$ agrees with the result obtained on page 339.

12.3 THE DERIVATIVE

The special kind of limit which we discussed in the preceding section is called a *derivative*, and the process of finding it is called *differentiation*. Due to their use in many different areas, derivatives have been (and still are) denoted by many different symbols. If the values of a function are given by $y = f(x)$, the corresponding values of the derivative can be written as

$$f'(x),\ \frac{dy}{dx},\ f',\ y',\ D_xy,\ D_xf(x),\ \frac{d}{dx}f(x)$$

and, although this is mainly a matter of personal taste, we shall use mostly the first two. The $f'(x)$ notation has the advantage that it makes it clear that *the derivative of a function is, itself, a function;* furthermore, it makes it easy to write the value of the derivative at $x = a$, for instance, as $f'(a)$. For example, in our numerical illustration the values of the function were given by

$$f(x) = 2{,}000x + 5{,}000x^2$$

those of the derivative were given by

$$f'(x) = 2{,}000 + 10{,}000x$$

and for $x = 1$, 2, 5, and 10, we could thus have written $f'(1) = 12{,}000$, $f'(2) = 22{,}000$, $f'(5) = 52{,}000$, and $f'(10) = 102{,}000$.

The $\frac{dy}{dx}$ notation has the advantage that it states explicitly that we are dealing with the *derivative of y with respect to x*. In other words, this derivative measures the rate of change of y when there is a change in x, and it is important to make this explicit when a problem involves more than two variables; as we shall see in Sections 12.5 and 13.4, there are situations in which we have to deal with $\frac{dy}{dx}$ as well as $\frac{dy}{dq}$ (and perhaps also with $\frac{dy}{dt}$ or $\frac{dy}{dz}, \ldots$) in one and the same problem. The symbol $\frac{dy}{dx}$ has the *serious disadvantage* of looking like a fraction, which it is *not;* the whole expression stands for the special limit which is called a derivative.

Sections 12.4 through 12.6 will be devoted mainly to the mechanics of differentiation—first we shall discuss some general rules which facilitate the problem of finding derivatives, then we shall present some special methods of differentiation, and finally we shall discuss the derivatives of the special functions which we introduced in Chapters 5 and 6. After that we shall see what happens when we differentiate a function which is, itself, a derivative, and as we have pointed out earlier, Chapter 13 will be devoted mostly to applications.

Since many beginners seem to have some purely technical difficulties with the basic mechanics of differentiation, it will help to approach the problem systematically as in the following *four* steps, where the first three steps consist of setting up the *slope* (or *difference quotient*)

$$\frac{f(x + \Delta x) - f(x)}{(x + \Delta x) - x} = \frac{f(x + \Delta x) - f(x)}{\Delta x}$$

and the fourth step consists of taking the limit of this quantity as $\Delta x \to 0$:

1. *Find $f(x + \Delta x)$ by substituting $x + \Delta x$ into the expression, or formula, for the values of the function.*

2. *Subtract $f(x)$ from $f(x + \Delta x)$ and simplify, if possible.*

3. *Divide the difference obtained in the second step by Δx.*

4. *Find the limit of the expression (slope, or difference quotient) obtained in the third step as $\Delta x \to 0$; very often this can be done by simply substituting 0 for Δx.*

To illustrate these four steps (which are sometimes referred to as the *delta process*), let us differentiate the function given by

$$f(x) = \frac{5}{x}$$

whose graph is shown in Figure 12.3. (As we indicated in Exercise 15 on page 125, this kind of function is called a *hyperbola*, and it is sometimes used to describe the relationship between price and demand.) Proceeding as indicated above, we get

1. $f(x + \Delta x) = \dfrac{5}{x + \Delta x}$

2. $$f(x + \Delta x) - f(x) = \frac{5}{x + \Delta x} - \frac{5}{x} = \frac{5x - 5(x + \Delta x)}{x(x + \Delta x)} = \frac{-5(\Delta x)}{x(x + \Delta x)}$$

3. $\dfrac{f(x + \Delta x) - f(x)}{\Delta x} = \dfrac{-5}{x(x + \Delta x)}$

4. $\dfrac{dy}{dx} = \lim\limits_{\Delta x \to 0} \dfrac{f(x + \Delta x) - f(x)}{\Delta x} = \dfrac{-5}{x^2}$

(In the second step we simplified the difference by getting a *common denominator*, and had we not done this we would have run into considerable difficulties.)

To illustrate the significance of this result, we chose several points on the graph of Figure 12.3 and drew the *tangent lines*, whose slopes are given

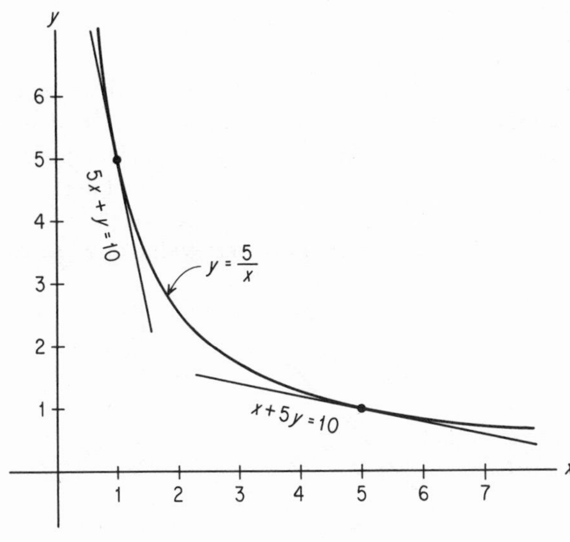

FIG. 12.3

by the corresponding derivatives, and, hence, are indicative of the direction, or steepness, of the curve at these points. For $x = 1$, for example, we get $y = \dfrac{5}{1} = 5$ for the value of the function, $\dfrac{dy}{dx} = \dfrac{-5}{1^2} = -5$ for the value of the derivative, so that the equation of the tangent line is

$$\frac{y - 5}{x - 1} = -5$$

according to the point-slope formula on page 98. As can easily be verified, this equation can also be written as $5x + y = 10$. Similarly, for $x = 5$ we get $y = \dfrac{5}{5} = 1$ and $\dfrac{dy}{dx} = \dfrac{-5}{5^2}$, so that the equation of the tangent line can be written as

$$\frac{y - 1}{x - 5} = -1/5 \qquad \text{or as} \qquad x + 5y = 10$$

Like tangents to circles, the tangent lines of Figure 12.3 *touch the curve without intersecting it;* this is typical of most tangent lines, but need not be the case, as is illustrated in Exercise 5 on page 345. All we can say really is that *the slope of the tangent line (namely, the value of the derivative) is indicative of the direction, or steepness, of a curve at a given point.* In general, if the values of a function are given by $y = f(x)$ and its derivative at $x = a$ is denoted $f'(a)$, then the equation of the tangent line at $x = a$ is given by

$$\frac{f(x) - f(a)}{x - a} = f'(a)$$

To conclude this introduction to the concept of a derivative, let us add that there *are* functions whose derivatives *do not exist;* or at least, their derivatives may not exist for all values of x within their domain. For one thing, a function has to be *continuous* before it can be differentiated, but even if it is continuous it may not have a derivative at some point (or points) as is illustrated in Figure 12.4. For every value of x less than 1 the

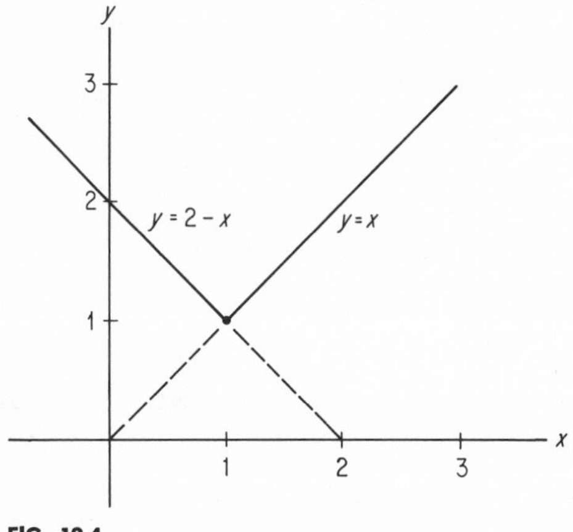

FIG. 12.4

curve has a slope of -1, for every value of x greater than 1 the curve has the slope $+1$, but at $x = 1$, itself, the limit $\lim_{\Delta x \to 0} \frac{f(x + \Delta x) - f(x)}{\Delta x}$ does not exist (and the direction of the curve is undefined). [In Exercise 9 on page 346 the reader will be asked to *prove* this by letting Δx assume the values $-1/2$, $1/4$, $-1/8$, $1/16$, $-1/32$, $1/64$, $-1/128$, . . . , which follow a very obvious pattern approaching 0, and determining the corresponding values of $\frac{f(1 + \Delta x) - 1}{\Delta x}$.]

EXERCISES

1. Referring to the illustration on page 337, show that
   (a) the average rate at which the values of the function increase on the interval from $x = 2$ to $x = 2.01$ is 22,050;
   (b) the average rate at which the values of the function increase on the interval from $x = 2$ to $x = 2.001$ is 22,005.

2. The concept of an instantaneous rate of change is most easily explained with an example from physics, where an object is dropped out of a window which is, say, 144 feet above the ground. It will hit the ground 3 seconds after it was released, and we can say that its average speed was $\frac{144}{3} = 48$ feet per second, but this would hardly be descriptive of the fact that it fell slowly at first and then kept going faster and faster. Using the well-known law of falling bodies, according to which the total distance dropped in the first t seconds is given by $f(t) = 16t^2$, find
   (a) the average speed of the object from $t = 1$ to $t = 2$;
   (b) the average speed of the object from $t = 1$ to $t = 1.1$;
   (c) the average speed of the object from $t = 1$ to $t = 1.01$;
   (d) the average speed of the object from $t = 1$ to $t = 1 + \Delta t$;
   (e) the limit of the average speed of part (d) as $\Delta t \to 0$, which defines the *instantaneous speed* of the falling object after 1 second, and which is the value of the derivative of the given function at $t = 1$.

   Also follow the four steps on page 342 to show that the derivative of the function is given by $f'(t) = 32t$, and use this result to find the instantaneous speed of the falling body
   (f) 1/2 second after it was released;
   (g) 2 seconds after it was released;
   (h) the instant it hits the ground (namely, after 3 seconds).

3. Use the four steps outlined on page 342 to find the derivatives of the functions given by the following equations:

   (a) $f(x) = 3$; (d) $f(x) = x^2$; (g) $f(x) = \frac{1}{5x^2}$;
   (b) $y = 2x - 5$; (e) $f(x) = 7x^2 - 3$;
   (c) $f(t) = t + 3$; (f) $f(x) = x^3$; (h) $f(x) = \sqrt{x}$.

   [*Hint:* in part (f) make use of the fact that $(a + b)^3 = a^3 + 3a^2b + 3ab^2 + b^3$, in part (g) get a common denominator in step (2) before dividing by Δx, and in part (h) multiply and divide by $\sqrt{x+\Delta x} + \sqrt{x}$ as part of step (2).]

4. Find the equation of the tangent line to the curve of part (d) of Exercise 3 at $x = 2$, and draw the graph of the function as well as the tangent line.

5. Find the equation of the tangent line to the curve of part (f) of Exercise 3 at $x = 0$, and draw the graph of the function as well as the tangent line.

6. Find the equations of the tangent lines to the curve of part (g) of Exercise 3 at $x = -1$ and $x = 1$, and draw the graph of the function as well as the two tangent lines.

7. On page 111 we expressed the demand for a certain detergent by means of the equation

$$D = 520 - 45p + p^2$$

where p is the price per box (in cents) and D is the weekly demand (in thousands of boxes). What is the instantaneous (or *marginal*) rate of change of the demand for the detergent when the price per box is 21 cents?

8. On page 129 we expressed the supply for a certain small ceramic insulator by means of the equation

$$S = 2p + 4p^2$$

where p is the price per insulator in cents and the supply is in units of 100 insulators. What is the instantaneous (or marginal) rate at which the supply for the insulators is changing when the price is 5 cents? What is the *average* rate of change when the price is increased from 5 cents to 5.5 cents, and why are the two answers different? Draw a graph, if necessary.

9. With reference to Figure 12.4, calculate the value of $\frac{f(1 + \Delta x) - 1}{\Delta x}$ for $\Delta x = -1/2, 1/4, -1/8, 1/16, -1/32, 1/64, -1/128, 1/256, \ldots$, and discuss what happens *in the long run* to the values of these difference quotients (or slopes).

12.4 SPECIAL RULES OF DIFFERENTIATION

The four steps outlined on page 342 are used only when absolutely necessary, and, hence, fairly seldom—in actual practice, the derivatives of most functions can be written down directly by following a few relatively simple rules. Some of these rules will be given below, while others will be discussed in later sections of this chapter. To simplify our work, it will be assumed throughout that $f(x)$, $g(x)$, and $h(x)$ are the values of *differentiable functions*, namely, functions whose derivatives exist.

The first rule we shall consider asserts that if the values of a function are *all equal*, the derivative of the function is 0 for all values of x. Formally,

If $f(x) = k$, where k is a constant, then $f'(x) = 0$

and it would hardly seem necessary to require a proof that the derivative of a constant is zero. After all, $y = k$ is the equation of a *horizontal line*, whose slope (and, hence, the derivative for all values of x) is zero. Incidentally, the reader was asked to prove this rule for $k = 3$ in part (*a*) of Exercise 3 on page 345.

The next rule pertains to functions given by equations of the form

$f(x) = x^n$, where n is a *positive integer*. Later on, we shall extend the rule to the case where n can also be a negative integer or even a fraction, but for the time being let us merely show that

If $f(x) = x^n$, where n is a positive integer, then $f'(x) = n \cdot x^{n-1}$

In words, to differentiate x^n we reduce the exponent by 1 and multiply by n.

To prove this result, we have to make use of the *binomial theorem*, with which the reader may be familiar from elementary algebra (and which we shall prove formally on page 445.) The binomial theorem applies to the expansion of $(a + b)^n$, where n is a positive integer, and for some of the first few values of n we get

$$(a + b)^2 = a^2 + 2ab + b^2$$
$$(a + b)^3 = a^3 + 3a^2b + 3ab^2 + b^3$$
$$(a + b)^4 = a^4 + 4a^3b + 6a^2b^2 + 4ab^3 + b^4$$

In general, the expansion can be written as

$$(a + b)^n = a^n + \frac{n}{1} a^{n-1}b + \frac{n(n-1)}{1 \cdot 2} a^{n-2}b^2 + \frac{n(n-1)(n-2)}{1 \cdot 2 \cdot 3} a^{n-3}b^3 + \ldots + b^n$$

where there are $n + 1$ terms, the first term is a^n, the last term is b^n, and we go from each term to the next by subtracting 1 from the exponent of a, adding 1 to the exponent of b, multiplying by the next largest integer in the denominator of the coefficient, and multiplying by the next smallest integer in the numerator of the coefficient. (For instance, to go from the third term to the fourth, we decrease the exponent of a from $n - 2$ to $n - 3$, increase the exponent of b from 2 to 3, multiply the denominator of the coefficient by 3, and the numerator by $n - 2$.)

Substituting x for a and Δx for b in the binomial expansion of $(a + b)^n$, we can take care of the first step on page 342 by writing

$$f(x + \Delta x) = (x + \Delta x)^n$$
$$= x^n + n \cdot x^{n-1}(\Delta x) + \frac{n(n-1)}{1 \cdot 2} \cdot x^{n-2}(\Delta x)^2 + \frac{n(n-1)(n-2)}{1 \cdot 2 \cdot 3} \cdot x^{n-3}(\Delta x)^3 + \ldots + (\Delta x)^n$$

Then, for the next two steps we get

$$f(x + \Delta x) - f(x) = n \cdot x^{n-1}(\Delta x) + \frac{n(n-1)}{1 \cdot 2} \cdot x^{n-2}(\Delta x)^2 + \frac{n(n-1)(n-2)}{1 \cdot 2 \cdot 3} \cdot x^{n-3}(\Delta x)^3 + \ldots + (\Delta x)^n$$

and

$$\frac{f(x + \Delta x) - f(x)}{\Delta x} = n \cdot x^{n-1} + \frac{n(n-1)}{1 \cdot 2} \cdot x^{n-2}(\Delta x)$$
$$+ \frac{n(n-1)(n-2)}{1 \cdot 2 \cdot 3} \cdot x^{n-3}(\Delta x)^2 + \ldots + (\Delta x)^{n-1}$$

and when we finally take the limit as $\Delta x \to 0$, we obtain

$$\lim_{\Delta x \to 0} \frac{f(x + \Delta x) - f(x)}{\Delta x} = n \cdot x^{n-1}$$

This completes the proof, and if we are asked to differentiate $f(x) = x^7$, for example, or $g(x) = x^5$, we can immediately write down the respective answers as $f'(x) = 7x^6$ and $g'(x) = 5x^4$.

The third rule which we shall consider in this section asserts that if the values of a function are all multiplied by a constant, then the values of the derivative are multiplied by the same constant. Formally,

If $f(x) = k \cdot g(x)$, where k is a constant, then $f'(x) = k \cdot g'(x)$

To prove this rule we have only to follow the four steps on page 342, according to which we get

$$f(x + \Delta x) = k \cdot g(x + \Delta x)$$
$$f(x + \Delta x) - f(x) = k \cdot g(x + \Delta x) - k \cdot g(x)$$
$$= k[g(x + \Delta x) - g(x)]$$
$$\frac{f(x + \Delta x) - f(x)}{\Delta x} = \frac{k[g(x + \Delta x) - g(x)]}{\Delta x}$$
$$= k\left[\frac{g(x + \Delta x) - g(x)}{\Delta x}\right]$$

and finally,

$$\lim_{\Delta x \to 0} \frac{f(x + \Delta x) - f(x)}{\Delta x} = \lim_{\Delta x \to 0} k\left[\frac{g(x + \Delta x) - g(x)}{\Delta x}\right]$$
$$= k \cdot \left[\lim_{\Delta x \to 0} \frac{g(x + \Delta x) - g(x)}{\Delta x}\right]$$
$$= k \cdot g'(x)$$

Note that when we "factored out" k in the last step we made use of the second limit theorem of Exercise 9 on page 335.

To illustrate this result, let us differentiate $y = 12x^5$. All we have to do is multiply 12 by the derivative of x^5, namely, by $5x^4$, and we get

$$\frac{dy}{dx} = 12 \cdot 5x^4 = 60x^4$$

Similarly, if $f(x) = \frac{1}{2}x^4$, then $f'(x) = \frac{1}{2}\cdot 4x^3 = 2x^3$; and if $f(x) = 17x$, then $f'(x) = 17(1\cdot x^0) = 17\cdot 1 = 17$.

The fourth rule pertains to functions whose values are sums or differences of several terms. We shall state it and prove it for *sums of two terms*, but then we shall demonstrate how it can easily be generalized to sums and differences involving more than two terms. Formally,

If $f(x) = g(x) + h(x)$, then $f'(x) = g'(x) + h'(x)$

which means, in fact, that we can differentiate "term by term." To prove this rule we shall again follow the four steps on page 342, according to which we now have

$$\begin{aligned} f(x + \Delta x) &= g(x + \Delta x) + h(x + \Delta x) \\ f(x + \Delta x) - f(x) &= [g(x + \Delta x) + h(x + \Delta x)] - [g(x) + h(x)] \\ &= [g(x + \Delta x) - g(x)] + [h(x + \Delta x) - h(x)] \\ \frac{f(x + \Delta x) - f(x)}{\Delta x} &= \frac{[g(x + \Delta x) - g(x)] + [h(x + \Delta x) - h(x)]}{\Delta x} \\ &= \frac{g(x + \Delta x) - g(x)}{\Delta x} + \frac{h(x + \Delta x) - h(x)}{\Delta x} \end{aligned}$$

and, finally,

$$\begin{aligned} \lim_{\Delta x \to 0} \frac{f(x + \Delta x) - f(x)}{\Delta x} &= \lim_{\Delta x \to 0} \left[\frac{g(x + \Delta x) - g(x)}{\Delta x} + \frac{h(x + \Delta x) - h(x)}{\Delta x}\right] \\ &= \lim_{\Delta x \to 0} \frac{g(x + \Delta x) - g(x)}{\Delta x} + \lim_{\Delta x \to 0} \frac{h(x + \Delta x) - h(x)}{\Delta x} \\ &= g'(x) + h'(x) \end{aligned}$$

where we made use of the third limit theorem of Exercise 9 on page 335, according to which *the limit of a sum equals the sum of the limits*.

Applying this rule, we can immediately write down the derivative of $f(x) = 3x^2 + 5x^4$ as

$$f'(x) = 3\cdot 2x^1 + 5\cdot 4x^3 = 6x + 20x^3$$

Also, if we had to differentiate $y = 2x^5 - 3x^7$ we could write this equation as $y = 2x^5 + (-3x^7)$, so that we get

$$\frac{dy}{dx} = 2\cdot 5x^4 + (-3)7x^6 = 10x^4 - 21x^6$$

but we could have obtained this result *directly*, differentiating "term by term" and writing

$$\frac{dy}{dx} = 2\cdot 5x^4 - 3\cdot 7x^6 = 10x^4 - 21x^6$$

When there are more than two terms, as for example in $y = 3x^2 + 5x^3 + 3x^4$, we could write the equation as $y = (3x^2 + 5x^3) + 3x^4$ and apply the rule *twice*, but this would not differ from differentiating "term by term," so that we might just as well write directly

$$\frac{dy}{dx} = 3\cdot 2x^1 + 5\cdot 3x^2 + 3\cdot 4x^3 = 6x + 15x^2 + 12x^3$$

There are two more rules of differentiation which we shall take up in this section—the *product rule* and the *quotient rule.* The first of these applies to functions whose values are products of two factors, and formally it states that

$$\textit{If } f(x) = g(x)\cdot h(x), \textit{ then } f'(x) = g(x)\cdot h'(x) + h(x)\cdot g'(x)$$

This tells us that the derivative of $g(x)\cdot h(x)$ is given by $g(x)$ *times the derivative of* $h(x)$ *plus* $h(x)$ *times the derivative of* $g(x)$. To prove this rule we shall again follow the four steps on page 342, employing the *trick* of adding and subtracting the quantity $g(x + \Delta x)\cdot h(x)$ in the second step. Thus, we get

$$\begin{aligned}
f(x + \Delta x) &= g(x + \Delta x)\cdot h(x + \Delta x) \\
f(x + \Delta x) - f(x) &= g(x + \Delta x)\cdot h(x + \Delta x) - g(x)\cdot h(x) \\
&= g(x + \Delta x)\cdot h(x + \Delta x) - g(x + \Delta x)\cdot h(x) \\
&\qquad + g(x + \Delta x)\cdot h(x) - g(x)\cdot h(x) \\
&= g(x + \Delta x)[h(x + \Delta x) - h(x)] \\
&\qquad + h(x)[g(x + \Delta x) - g(x)] \\
\frac{f(x + \Delta x) - f(x)}{\Delta x} &= g(x + \Delta x)\cdot\frac{h(x + \Delta x) - h(x)}{\Delta x} \\
&\qquad + h(x)\cdot\frac{g(x + \Delta x) - g(x)}{\Delta x}
\end{aligned}$$

and, finally,

$$\begin{aligned}
\lim_{\Delta x\to 0}\frac{f(x + \Delta x) - f(x)}{\Delta x} &= \lim_{\Delta x\to 0}\left[g(x + \Delta x)\cdot\frac{h(x + \Delta x) - h(x)}{\Delta x}\right. \\
&\qquad \left. + h(x)\cdot\frac{g(x + \Delta x) - g(x)}{\Delta x}\right] \\
&= g(x)\left[\lim_{\Delta x\to 0}\frac{h(x + \Delta x) - h(x)}{\Delta x}\right] \\
&\qquad + h(x)\left[\lim_{\Delta x\to 0}\frac{g(x + \Delta x) - g(x)}{\Delta x}\right] \\
&= g(x)\cdot h'(x) + h(x)\cdot g'(x)
\end{aligned}$$

where we made use of the second, third, and fourth limit theorems of

Exercise 9 on page 335, as well as the fact that $\lim_{\Delta x \to 0} g(x + \Delta x) = g(x)$.

To illustrate this rule, let us differentiate $y = (x^2 - 1)(3x + 4)$ without first multiplying out the product term by term. Since the derivative of $x^2 - 1$ is $2x$ and the derivative of $3x + 4$ is 3, we get

$$\begin{aligned}\frac{dy}{dx} &= (x^2 - 1)\cdot 3 + (3x + 4)\cdot 2x \\ &= 3x^2 - 3 + 6x^2 + 8x \\ &= 9x^2 + 8x - 3\end{aligned}$$

and it will be left to the reader to verify in Exercise 3 on page 358 that the result would have been the same if we had first multiplied $x^2 - 1$ by $3x + 4$ and then differentiated term by term.

The sixth, and final, rule of this section is the *quotient rule*, which applies to functions whose values are the ratios of two expressions involving x. Formally, it states that

$$\textit{If } f(x) = \frac{g(x)}{h(x)}, \textit{ then } f'(x) = \frac{h(x)\cdot g'(x) - g(x)\cdot h'(x)}{h(x)^2}$$

which tells us to "multiply the denominator by the derivative of the numerator, subtract the product of the numerator and the derivative of the denominator, and then divide by the square of the denominator." The proof of this rule is again a straightforward application of the four steps on page 342, and it will be left as an exercise [see Exercise 14 on page 359, where we shall suggest that the reader use a trick similar to the one used in step (2) of the proof of the product rule.]

An important application of the quotient rule is its use in demonstrating that the formula for differentiating x^n holds also for *negative integral exponents*, say, when $f(x) = x^{-3}$ or $f(x) = x^{-1}$. Thus, we shall want to show that

If $f(x) = x^{-n}$, where n is a positive integer,
then $f'(x) = -n\cdot x^{-n-1}$

To this end, let us write the equation of the function as

$$f(x) = \frac{1}{x^n}$$

where the numerator is $g(x) = 1$, the denominator is $h(x) = x^n$, and n is a positive integer. Thus, $g'(x) = 0$ according to the rule on page 346, $h'(x) = n\cdot x^{n-1}$ according to the rule on page 347, and substitution into the formula for the quotient rule yields

$$f'(x) = \frac{x^n\cdot 0 - 1(n\cdot x^{n-1})}{(x^n)^2} = \frac{-n\cdot x^{n-1}}{x^{2n}}$$

$$= -n \cdot x^{(n-1)-2n}$$

$$= -n \cdot x^{-n-1}$$

Hence, if $f(x) = x^{-3}$ then $f'(x) = -3x^{-4}$, if $f(x) = 5x^{-4}$ then $f'(x) = 5(-4 \cdot x^{-5}) = -20x^{-5}$, and if $f(x) = \frac{1}{x} = x^{-1}$ then $f'(x) = -x^{-2} = \frac{-1}{x^2}$.

The reader may have observed that we took certain linguistic liberties in the examples of this section. Instead of saying that we differentiate $y = (x^2 - 1)(3x + 4)$, we should really have said that we *differentiate the function* given by this particular equation, and instead of referring to $f'(x) = -3x^{-4}$ as the derivative of $f(x) = x^{-3}$, we should really have referred to $f'(x)$ as the value of the derivative of the given function at x. However, it is customary to take these liberties in order to simplify our language, and there is no danger in doing this, so long as we always remember that there *is* a difference between the values of a function and the function itself. Keeping this in mind, we shall thus continue to refer to $f'(x) = 60x^4$ as the derivative of $f(x) = 12x^5$, we shall continue to say that the derivative of $5x^{-4}$ is $-20x^{-5}$, and we shall continue to say that we differentiate $f(x) = 3x^2 + 5x^4$ and get $f'(x) = 6x + 20x^3$.

12.5 SOME METHODS OF DIFFERENTIATION

In this section we shall present three special methods of differentiation which often provide great simplifications when the rules of the preceding section cannot easily be applied. To introduce the first of these techniques, suppose we are asked to differentiate

$$y = (1 + 7x^3)^{25}$$

Of course, we could expand $(1 + 7x^3)^{25}$ by means of the *binomial theorem* (see page 347) and then differentiate term by term, but it would hardly seem necessary to have to point out that this would involve a considerable amount of work. Instead, let us treat the given function as a *composite function* (see Exercise 19 on page 83), namely, as a "function of a function," by denoting the expression in parentheses with the letter q. Thus, we have

$$y = q^{25} \qquad \text{and} \qquad q = 1 + 7x^3$$

and the rules of the preceding section yield

$$\frac{dy}{dq} = 25q^{24} \qquad \text{and} \qquad \frac{dq}{dx} = 21x^2$$

This does not yet give us $\frac{dy}{dx}$, but we can obtain this derivative in one more step by applying the so-called *chain rule of differentiation**

$$\frac{dy}{dx} = \frac{dy}{dq} \cdot \frac{dq}{dx}$$

Before we apply this rule, let us make it very clear that the formula does *not* pertain to fractions and that we are *not cancelling* the quantity dq; each of the symbols $\frac{dy}{dx}$, $\frac{dy}{dq}$, and $\frac{dq}{dx}$ represents a separate derivative, and the chain rule simply states that *the first is given by the product of the other two.* Returning now to our example, we get

$$\begin{aligned} \frac{dy}{dx} &= (25q^{24})(21x^2) \\ &= 25(1 + 7x^3)^{24} \cdot 21x^2 \\ &= 525x^2(1 + 7x^3)^{24} \end{aligned}$$

and it turned out to be very easy to solve a problem which at first looked rather forbidding.

In actual practice, the chain rule is used so often that it becomes almost automatic to write down the result without the intermediate steps, that is, without actually denoting the new variable by the letter q (or some other symbol). For instance, using this kind of *mental substitution,* we can immediately write the derivative of

$$f(x) = 24(2 + 5x + 3x^2)^7$$

as

$$f'(x) = 24 \cdot 7(2 + 5x + 3x^2)^6(5 + 6x)$$

where $5 + 6x$ is the derivative of $2 + 5x + 3x^2$. Hence, the result is

$$f'(x) = 168(5 + 6x)(2 + 5x + 3x^2)^6$$

Also, if we apply the chain rule separately to each term, we can immediately write the derivative of

$$y = 2(1 + 5x)^3 + 12(2 - 7x^2)^5$$

as

$$\frac{dy}{dx} = 2 \cdot 3(1 + 5x)^2 \cdot 5 + 12 \cdot 5(2 - 7x^2)^4(-14x)$$

where 5 is the derivative of $1 + 5x$ and $-14x$ is the derivative of $2 - 7x^2$. Hence, the result is

$$\frac{dy}{dx} = 30(1 + 5x)^2 - 840x(2 - 7x^2)^4$$

* A proof of this rule can be found in almost any college textbook on calculus.

In some instances the "chain" of the chain rule consists of several "links." To differentiate

$$y = 4[1 + (5 + x^4)^3]^6$$

for example, we could substitute q for $1 + (5 + x^4)^3$ and r for $(5 + x^4)$, so that we can write

$$y = 4q^6, \qquad q = 1 + r^3, \qquad \text{and} \qquad r = 5 + x^4$$

and, hence,

$$\frac{dy}{dq} = 24q^5, \qquad \frac{dq}{dr} = 3r^2, \qquad \text{and} \qquad \frac{dr}{dx} = 4x^3$$

Now, the formula for the *chain rule* becomes*

$$\frac{dy}{dx} = \frac{dy}{dq} \cdot \frac{dq}{dr} \cdot \frac{dr}{dx}$$

so that the answer to our problem is given by

$$\begin{aligned} \frac{dy}{dx} &= 24q^5 \cdot 3r^2 \cdot 4x^3 \\ &= 24[1 + (5 + x^4)^3]^5 \cdot 3(5 + x^4)^2 \cdot 4x^3 \\ &= 288x^3(5 + x^4)^2[1 + (5 + x^4)^3]^5 \end{aligned}$$

With some experience, even this kind of "messy" problem can be done *mentally*, that is, without actually introducing the letters q and r.

The second special method of differentiation which we shall present in this section is based on the fact that it is sometimes easier to differentiate the *inverse of a function* (see page 65) than the function, itself. In that case we make use of the fact that *the derivative of y with respect to x is the reciprocal of the derivative of x with respect to y*, namely, that†

$$\frac{dy}{dx} = \frac{1}{\frac{dx}{dy}}$$

To avoid the temptation of confusing these derivatives with fractions, we could write this formula as

$$f'(x) = \frac{1}{g'(y)}$$

---

* Actually, we could say that in this case the "ordinary" chain rule is simply used twice; all we have to do is write

$$\frac{dy}{dx} = \frac{dy}{dq} \cdot \frac{dq}{dx} = \frac{dy}{dq}\left(\frac{dq}{dr} \cdot \frac{dr}{dx}\right)$$

† A proof of this rule can be found in almost any college textbook on calculus.

where $x = g(y)$ is the *inverse* of $y = f(x)$, namely, the same equation solved for x instead of y, but we would then have to be careful to remember that in $f'(x)$ the *prime* denotes differentiation with respect to x, while in $g'(y)$ the *prime* denotes differentiation with respect to y.

To illustrate this special technique, suppose we are asked to differentiate $y = \sqrt{x}$, where the domain of the function is $x > 0$. To solve for x, we have only to square the expressions on both sides of the equation, getting

$$x = y^2 \qquad \text{and, hence,} \qquad \frac{dx}{dy} = 2y$$

Thus

$$\frac{dy}{dx} = \frac{1}{\dfrac{dx}{dy}} = \frac{1}{2y} = \frac{1}{2\sqrt{x}}$$

and the problem is solved. A very important application of this technique will be given in Section 12.6, where we shall make use of the fact that a logarithmic function is the inverse of the exponential function (having the same base).

We first used the term "implicit" in Section 4.2 in connection with the linear equation $cx + dy + e = 0$, which we referred to as *implicit* because it is solved for neither y nor x. More generally, we refer to any function as *implicit* if it is given by an equation such as

$$x^2 + y^3 = 5x + 4y, \quad x \cdot e^y = x^2 + \cos y, \quad \text{or} \quad 5xy = x^3 - y^2$$

namely, by an equation which is *not* of the form $y = f(x)$ or $x = g(y)$. To differentiate functions like these (with respect to x or with respect to y) it is sometimes possible to solve first for y in terms of x or x in terms of y, but it is generally much easier to use what is called *implicit differentiation.*

Actually, all this amounts to is *differentiating term by term and using the chain rule where necessary.* To illustrate this technique, it will be convenient to use the seventh of the symbols for derivatives which we gave on page 341; instead of $f'(x)$ we shall write $\frac{d}{dx}f(x)$, and, using the chain rule, we shall write the derivative of $g(y)$ with respect to x as

$$\frac{d}{dx}g(y) = \frac{d}{dy}g(y) \cdot \frac{dy}{dx} = g'(y) \cdot \frac{dy}{dx}$$

where it must be understood, of course, that the *prime* in $g'(y)$ denotes differentiation with respect to y. *This is the key to the whole situation.*

To illustrate this kind of differentiation, let us refer to the first of the above equations, namely,

$$x^2 + y^3 = 5x + 4y$$

and try to find $\frac{dy}{dx}\cdot$ Showing more detail than is really necessary, we differentiate each term with respect to x, getting

$$\frac{d}{dx}(x^2) + \frac{d}{dx}(y^3) = \frac{d}{dx}(5x) + \frac{d}{dx}(4y)$$

$$2x + \frac{d}{dy}(y^3)\cdot\frac{dy}{dx} = 5 + \frac{d}{dy}(4y)\cdot\frac{dy}{dx}$$

$$2x + 3y^2\cdot\frac{dy}{dx} = 5 + 4\cdot\frac{dy}{dx}$$

and all that remains to be done is to solve this equation for $\frac{dy}{dx}\cdot$ Collecting all terms involving $\frac{dy}{dx}$ on the left-hand side of the equation and all the other terms on the right-hand side, we get

$$3y^2\cdot\frac{dy}{dx} - 4\cdot\frac{dy}{dx} = 5 - 2x$$

$$(3y^2 - 4)\frac{dy}{dx} = 5 - 2x$$

and, finally,

$$\frac{dy}{dx} = \frac{5 - 2x}{3y^2 - 4}$$

It is typical of problems of this kind that the answer will be in terms of both x and y, but this seldom poses any difficulties in further work or applications.

To give another example of implicit differentiation, let us find $\frac{dy}{dx}$ for the function which is given by the third of the equations on page 355, namely,

$$5xy = x^3 - y^2$$

We *could* solve this equation for y by means of the quadratic formula of Section 4.6, but this would involve quite a bit more work. To differentiate implicitly, we shall have to use the product rule on page 350 on the left-hand side, getting

$$\frac{d}{dx}(5xy) = \frac{d}{dx}(x^3) - \frac{d}{dx}(y^2)$$

$$5x\cdot\frac{d}{dx}(y) + y\cdot\frac{d}{dx}5(x) = \frac{d}{dx}(x^3) - \frac{d}{dy}(y^2)\cdot\frac{dy}{dx}$$

$$5x\cdot\frac{dy}{dx} + 5y = 3x^2 - 2y\cdot\frac{dy}{dx}$$

Collecting terms, we then get

$$5x \cdot \frac{dy}{dx} + 2y \cdot \frac{dy}{dx} = 3x^2 - 5y$$

$$(5x + 2y) \cdot \frac{dy}{dx} = 3x^2 - 5y$$

and, finally,

$$\frac{dy}{dx} = \frac{3x^2 - 5y}{5x + 2y}$$

Let us now use implicit differentiation to demonstrate that the rule for differentiating x^n holds also when n is a *positive fraction*, say, when $y = x^{r/s}$, where r and s are positive integers and the domain of the function is $x > 0$. If we raise the expressions on both sides of the equation $y = x^{r/s}$ to the power s, we get

$$y^s = (x^{r/s})^s = x^r$$

and implicit differentiation yields

$$s \cdot y^{s-1} \cdot \frac{dy}{dx} = r \cdot x^{r-1}$$

or

$$\frac{dy}{dx} = \frac{r \cdot x^{r-1}}{s \cdot y^{s-1}}$$

Now, if we substitute $x^{r/s}$ for y in the denominator, we get

$$\frac{dy}{dx} = \frac{r \cdot x^{r-1}}{s(x^{r/s})^{s-1}}$$

and it will be left to the reader (in Exercise 16 on page 359) to apply the laws of exponents of Section 5.2 to show that the result can be written as

$$\frac{dy}{dx} = \frac{r}{s} \cdot x^{\frac{r}{s}-1}$$

For instance, if $f(x) = x^{4/3}$ then $f'(x) = \frac{4}{3}x^{1/3}$, if $y = x^{12/5}$ then $\frac{dy}{dx} = \frac{12}{5}x^{7/5}$, and, as in the rule on page 347, *we always multiply by the exponent and reduce it by 1*. In Exercise 17 on page 359 the reader will be asked to show that this rule holds also when the exponent of x is a *negative fraction*.

EXERCISES

1. Find $f'(x)$ for each part by using the rules of Section 12.4, and also evaluate $f'(0)$ and $f'(2)$ where these derivatives exist:

   (a) $f(x) = 25$; (b) $f(x) = x^{10}$;

(c) $f(x) = 3x$;

(d) $f(x) = -4x^2$;

(e) $f(x) = x^2 + 3$;

(f) $f(x) = x + 5x^2 - 7x^4$;

(g) $f(x) = x^3(x^2 - 1)$;

(h) $f(x) = (1 + x^5)(1 + x^4)$;

(i) $f(x) = \dfrac{x+3}{x-2}$;

(j) $f(x) = \dfrac{3x - x^4}{2x^2 + 5}$;

(k) $f(x) = x^{-30}$;

(l) $f(x) = 3 + \dfrac{1}{x^4}$.

2. Using the rules of Section 12.4, verify the value obtained on page 340 for the derivative of $y = 2{,}000x + 5{,}000x^2$.

3. On page 351 we illustrated the product rule by differentiating $y = (x^2 - 1)(3x + 4)$. Verify the result by first multiplying out and then differentiating term by term.

4. Given $u(x) = 3x + 2$ and $v(x) = x^2 + 1$, find

(a) $u'(x)$ and $v'(x)$;

(b) $\dfrac{d}{dx}[u(x) + v(x)]$;

(c) $\dfrac{d}{dx}[u(x) \cdot v(x)]$;

(d) $\dfrac{d}{dx}\left[\dfrac{u(x)}{v(x)}\right]$.

5. In Exercise 1 on page 130 we gave the total receipts for x television sets by means of the equation

$$R = 120x\left(1 - \frac{x}{10000}\right)$$

Find the instantaneous (marginal) rate at which these receipts are changing when $x = 200$.

6. A company's total sales revenue is given by the equation $f(x) = 2x + x^2$, where x is the number of years the company has been in business and $f(x)$ is in millions of dollars.

(a) At what rate is the company's total sales revenue growing after 3 years?

(b) Find the equation of the tangent line at $x = 3$ and use it to predict the company's total sales revenue for the fifth year *if the growth rate were to remain constant after the third year*. How does this compare with the corresponding value obtained by substituting $x = 5$ into the original formula?

7. A department store's profit is given by $P = 240{,}000 + 3{,}200x - 40x^2$, where x is their daily expenditure on advertising. Without actually calculating any values of this function or plotting its graph, judge whether it would be profitable for them to increase their advertising budget if their current advertising expenditures are (a) \$30 per day, and (b) \$50 per day.

8. Use the chain rule to differentiate

(a) $y = (2 + x^4)^6$;

(b) $f(x) = (3 + 2x + 6x^2)^5$;

(c) $y = 3\left(2x + \dfrac{1}{x}\right)^4$;

(d) $y = 2(3 + 5x - 4x^2)^{-3}$;

(e) $g(x) = [1 + (4 - x^3)^5]^2$.

9. Given $y = 2 + 3x + 2x^2$, find $\dfrac{dx}{dy}$ and the value of this derivative at $x = 1$. (Read carefully!)

10. The relationship between the price for a product (in cents) and the demand (in thousands of units) is given by

$$p = \sqrt{20 - 3D - D^2}$$

Find $\dfrac{dD}{dp}$ at $p = 4$, namely, the marginal rate at which the demand is changing when the price of the product is 4 cents.

11. Given $y^2 = x^3 + 6x + 5$, find $\dfrac{dy}{dx}$ and the value of this derivative at $x = 2$.

12. Given $3x^2y^3 = 5y + 3x - 2$, find $\dfrac{dy}{dx}$.

13. In Exercise 7 on page 115 the reader was asked to show that someone who wants to be twice as close to the beach as to his office (see Figure 4.23) should live somewhere on the hyperbola whose equation is

$$3y^2 + 12y - x^2 = 36$$

If he buys a house at the point (12, 6) and his street is actually tangent to the hyperbola at this point, find

(a) the equation of the street (which is presumed to be a straight line);
(b) how far he would have to travel along this street to get to the beach (assuming that all units are in miles).

14. Prove the *quotient rule* by following the four steps on page 342, and, after getting a common denominator in step (2), adding and subtracting $g(x)\cdot h(x)$ in the numerator, so that the numerator becomes

$$g(x + \Delta x)\cdot h(x) - g(x)\cdot h(x + \Delta x)$$
$$= h(x)[g(x + \Delta x) - g(x)] - g(x)[h(x + \Delta x) - h(x)]$$

15. Give an alternate proof of the *quotient rule* on page 351 by writing $\dfrac{g(x)}{h(x)}$ as $g(x)\cdot\dfrac{1}{h(x)} = g(x)[h(x)]^{-1}$ and then using the product rule and chain differentiation.

16. Verify the simplification of the exponent of x in the final step of the proof on page 357.

17. Use the result on page 357 and the quotient rule to show that the rule for differentiating x^n holds also when n is a *negative fraction*, say, when $y = x^{-r/s}$, where r and s are positive integers.

18. Use the rule proved in Exercise 17 to differentiate

(a) $f(x) = x^{-1/2}$;
(b) $f(x) = 4x^{-2/3}$;
(c) $y = \dfrac{3}{x^2\sqrt{x}}$;
(d) $y = (2 + 3x - 5x^2)^{-3/2}$.

19. The demand for a product (in hundreds of cartons) is related to its price (in cents) by means of the equation

$$D = \frac{500}{\sqrt{p}}$$

Use the rule of Exercise 17 to find the instantaneous (marginal) rate at which the demand is decreasing when the price is 25 cents per carton.

12.6 THE DERIVATIVES OF SPECIAL FUNCTIONS

In this section we shall learn how to differentiate the special functions which we introduced in Chapters 5 and 6. First of all, let us show that the derivative of the *exponential function* given by $f(x) = e^x$ is the function, itself; namely, that

If $f(x) = e^x$, *then* $f'(x) = e^x$

Following the four steps outlined on page 342, we get

$$\begin{aligned} f(x + \Delta x) &= e^{x+\Delta x} \\ f(x + \Delta x) - f(x) &= e^{x+\Delta x} - e^x \\ &= e^x(e^{\Delta x} - 1) \\ \frac{f(x + \Delta x) - f(x)}{\Delta x} &= \frac{e^x(e^{\Delta x} - 1)}{\Delta x} \\ &= e^x\left[\frac{e^{\Delta x} - 1}{\Delta x}\right] \end{aligned}$$

and we are stymied for a moment, for if we tried to substitute $\Delta x = 0$ into $\frac{e^{\Delta x} - 1}{\Delta x}$ we would get $\frac{0}{0}$, which is *undefined*. To evaluate the limit of $\frac{e^{\Delta x} - 1}{\Delta x}$ as $\Delta x \to 0$, let us make use of the *infinite series* for e^x which we gave without proof on page 325; substituting Δx for x, we can write

$$e^{\Delta x} = 1 + (\Delta x) + \frac{(\Delta x)^2}{2} + \frac{(\Delta x)^3}{2 \cdot 3} + \frac{(\Delta x)^4}{2 \cdot 3 \cdot 4} + \dots$$

and if we subtract 1 from both sides of this equation and divide by Δx, we get

$$\frac{e^{\Delta x} - 1}{\Delta x} = 1 + \frac{(\Delta x)}{2} + \frac{(\Delta x)^2}{2 \cdot 3} + \frac{(\Delta x)^3}{2 \cdot 3 \cdot 4} + \dots$$

Hence,

$$\lim_{\Delta x \to 0} \frac{e^{\Delta x} - 1}{\Delta x} = 1$$

and it follows that

$$\lim_{\Delta x \to 0} e^x \left[\frac{e^{\Delta x} - 1}{\Delta x}\right] = e^x \left[\lim_{\Delta x \to 0} \frac{e^{\Delta x} - 1}{\Delta x}\right] = e^x \cdot 1 = e^x$$

which completes the proof.

The formula for the derivative of e^x can easily be generalized by applying the chain rule of differentiation. For instance, if $f(x) = a \cdot e^{bx}$ we can immediately write

$$f'(x) = a \cdot e^{bx} \cdot \frac{d}{dx}(bx) = a \cdot e^{bx} \cdot b = ab \cdot e^{bx}$$

and if we apply this formula to the demand function of Figure 5.5 on page 147, the one which was given by the equation

$$D = 1{,}280e^{-0.0725p}$$

we get

$$\frac{dD}{dp} = 1{,}280(-0.0725)e^{-0.0725p} = -92.8e^{-0.0725p}$$

Thus, at $p = 20$, for example, we find that the demand changes at a rate of $-92.8e^{-0.0725(20)} = -92.8e^{-1.45}$ or approximately -22 (packages of the cake mix) when there is a unit change in p. The fact that the rate is *negative* implies that the values of the function are *decreasing* (as is apparent also from Figure 5.5), and it should be pointed out, perhaps, that the result which we have obtained does *not* represent the decrease in demand when the price is increased from 20 cents to 21 cents (which would be closer to 20.5 than 22). No, our result is an instantaneous (or marginal) rate of change, and it represents the slope of the exponential curve of Figure 5.5 at the point where $p = 20$.

Most of the *growth curves* studied in business and economics involve variations of the exponential function. We already met the *modified exponential function* on page 148, where a function of this kind was used to describe how the demand for a new meat tenderizer changes with time. Another important growth curve which has roughly the shape of an elongated letter S (see Figure 12.5) is the *logistic curve,* an example of which is given by

$$y = \frac{20{,}000}{1 + 50e^{-0.5x}}$$

where y is the expected (or predicted) enrollment at a relatively new university and x is the number of years that have elapsed since the enrollment of the first freshman class. Note that if we substitute $x = 0$, we find that the original enrollment was slightly below 400; it is also apparent

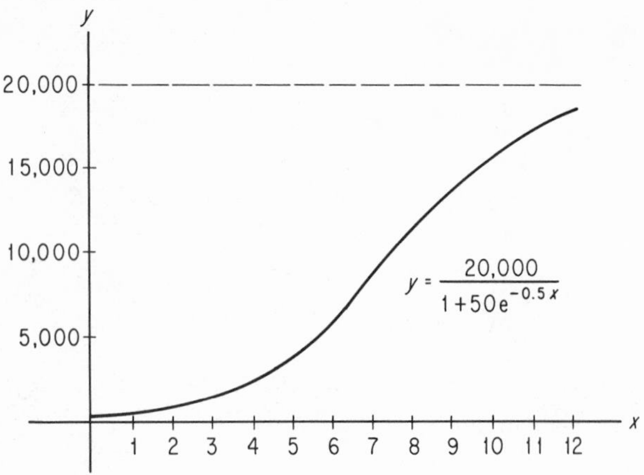

FIG. 12.5

from the equation that the enrollment will eventually *approach* (but never exceed) 20,000 students. Suppose now that we would like to know the *annual rate* at which the school can be expected to grow 3 years after the enrollment of the first freshman class. To find $\frac{dy}{dx}$ at $x = 3$, which is the quantity we are trying to determine, let us first write the equation as

$$y = 20{,}000(1 + 50e^{-0.5x})^{-1}$$

Then, repeatedly applying the chain rule, we get

$$\begin{aligned}\frac{dy}{dx} &= 20{,}000(-1)(1 + 50e^{-0.5x})^{-2}\cdot\frac{d}{dx}(1 + 50e^{-0.5x})\\ &= -20{,}000(1 + 50e^{-0.5x})^{-2}\cdot 50e^{-0.5x}\cdot\frac{d}{dx}(-0.5x)\\ &= -20{,}000(1 + 50e^{-0.5x})^{-2}\cdot 50e^{-0.5x}(-0.5)\\ &= \frac{500{,}000e^{-0.5x}}{(1 + 50e^{-0.5x})^2}\end{aligned}$$

and if we substitute $x = 3$ this becomes

$$\begin{aligned}\frac{dy}{dx} &= \frac{500{,}000e^{-1.5}}{(1 + 50e^{-1.5})^2}\\ &= \frac{500{,}000(0.223)}{[1 + 50(0.223)]^2}\\ &= 755\end{aligned}$$

where $e^{-1.5} = 0.223$ was obtained from Table III. Thus, after 3 years the university's enrollment is growing at an annual rate of 755 students.

In the beginning of Section 5.3 we gave the *general form* of the equation of an exponential function as $y = a \cdot b^x$, where b is referred to as its *base.* To differentiate an exponential function with the base b, we simply make use of the formula on page 162, according to which we can write

$$y = a \cdot e^{x(\ln b)} \qquad \text{instead of} \qquad y = a \cdot b^x$$

where $\ln b$ is the *natural logarithm* of b, namely, its logarithm to the base e. Applying the chain rule, we thus get

$$\begin{aligned}\frac{dy}{dx} &= a \cdot e^{x(\ln b)} \cdot \frac{d}{dx} x(\ln b) \\ &= a \cdot e^{x(\ln b)} \cdot (\ln b) \\ &= a \cdot b^x (\ln b)\end{aligned}$$

where we finally substituted $a \cdot b^x$ back in for $a \cdot e^{x(\ln b)}$. To state this result formally,

If $y = a \cdot b^x$, *then* $\dfrac{dy}{dx} = a(\ln b) \cdot b^x$

Thus, if $y = 3 \cdot 2^x$ then $\dfrac{dy}{dx} = 3(\ln 2) \cdot 2^x = 2.079 \cdot 2^x$ since $\ln 2$ is approximately 0.693.

Since many students (and even some experienced mathematicians) tend to forget the formula for converting from the base b to the base e and also the formula for the derivative of $a \cdot b^x$, we shall give another way of differentiating $a \cdot b^x$ in Exercise 8 on page 368.

Having introduced logarithmic functions as the *inverses* of exponential functions with the same base, we will be able to differentiate $y = \ln x$ (and also $y = \log_b x$) by the second method of Section 12.5. Writing $y = \ln x$ as $x = e^y$, we have

$$\frac{dx}{dy} = e^y$$

and since $\dfrac{dy}{dx}$ is the *reciprocal* of $\dfrac{dx}{dy}$ according to the rule on page 354, it follows that

$$\frac{dy}{dx} = \frac{1}{\dfrac{dx}{dy}} = \frac{1}{e^y}$$

Since $e^y = x$, we have thus shown that

If $y = \ln x$, *then* $\dfrac{dy}{dx} = \dfrac{1}{x}$

To differentiate $y = \log_b x$ we could rewrite this equation as $x = b^y$, differentiate with respect to y, and then make use of the fact that $\frac{dy}{dx} = \frac{1}{\frac{dx}{dy}}$; another possibility is to use the formula of Exercise 15 on page 165 to convert the logarithm to the base b to a natural logarithm (to the base e) and then make use of the fact that the derivative of $\ln x$ is $1/x$. Easiest, perhaps, is the method in which we take the natural logarithm of the expressions on both sides of $x = b^y$, getting

$$\ln x = \ln b^y \qquad \text{and, hence,} \qquad \ln x = y(\ln b)$$

according to the rule on page 154. If we then differentiate *implicitly* with respect to x, we get

$$\frac{d}{dx}(\ln x) = (\ln b)\cdot\frac{d}{dx}y$$

$$\frac{1}{x} = (\ln b)\cdot\frac{dy}{dx}$$

and all that remains to be done is divide by $\ln b$. We have thus shown that

If $y = \log_b x$, *then* $\frac{dy}{dx} = \frac{1}{x(\ln b)}$

For example, if $y = \log_{10} x$, then $\frac{dy}{dx} = \frac{1}{x(\ln 10)}$ where $\ln 10$ is approximately equal to 2.3.

When we used the infinite series for $e^{\Delta x}$ in the proof on page 360, it may have occurred to the reader that it might be possible to obtain the derivative of e^x directly by differentiating

$$y = e^x = 1 + x + \frac{x^2}{2} + \frac{x^3}{2\cdot 3} + \frac{x^4}{2\cdot 3\cdot 4} + \frac{x^5}{2\cdot 3\cdot 4\cdot 5} + \cdots$$

term by term. This would give

$$\frac{dy}{dx} = 0 + 1 + \frac{2x}{2} + \frac{3x^2}{2\cdot 3} + \frac{4x^3}{2\cdot 3\cdot 4} + \frac{5x^4}{2\cdot 3\cdot 4\cdot 5} + \cdots$$

$$= 1 + x + \frac{x^2}{2} + \frac{x^3}{2\cdot 3} + \frac{x^4}{2\cdot 3\cdot 4} + \cdots$$

which can readily be identified as the infinite series for e^x.

This method of differentiation can be used in connection with many other functions, although we will have to watch out for the possibility that the resulting infinite series may not converge for all of the same values of x as the original series. Another problem is that when we differentiate an infinite series term by term, the result is also an infinite series, and it takes a good deal of luck or experience, preferably both, to be able to identify the function which this infinite series represents. To give an example where we happen to be lucky in this respect, let us use this method to show that

If $f(x) = \sin x$, then $f'(x) = \cos x$

Referring to the infinite series on page 326, we have

$$f(x) = \sin x = x - \frac{x^3}{3!} + \frac{x^5}{5!} - \frac{x^7}{7!} + \frac{x^9}{9!} - \cdots$$

so that term by term differentiation yields

$$f'(x) = 1 - \frac{3x^2}{3!} + \frac{5x^4}{5!} - \frac{7x^6}{7!} + \frac{9x^8}{9!} - \cdots$$

Since $3/3! = 1/2!$, $5/5! = 1/4!$, $7/7! = 1/6!$, $9/9! = 1/8!, \ldots$, as can easily be verified by writing the factorials in full (see page 325), it follows that

$$f'(x) = 1 - \frac{x^2}{2!} + \frac{x^4}{4!} - \frac{x^6}{6!} + \frac{x^8}{8!} - \cdots$$

and this infinite series is easily recognizable as the one for $\cos x$ on page 326. Using the same technique, the reader will be asked to show that

If $f(x) = \cos x$, then $f'(x) = -\sin x$

in Exercise 14 on page 370.

12.7 HIGHER DERIVATIVES

We have repeatedly emphasized the point that the derivative of a function is also a function, and there is no reason, therefore, why we cannot *differentiate a derivative*. For instance, the derivative of $f(x) = x^4$ is $f'(x) = 4x^3$, and if we differentiate again we obtain a function whose values are $4(3x^2) = 12x^2$. It is customary to refer to this function as the *second derivative*, and if the values of the original function and its derivative are denoted $f(x)$ and $f'(x)$, those of the second derivative are denoted $f''(x)$. With reference to the preceding example, we can thus write $f(x) = x^4$, $f'(x) = 4x^3$, and $f''(x) = 12x^2$.

If we use the $\frac{dy}{dx}$ notation, it is customary to write the second derivative as $\frac{d^2y}{dx^2}$, and for $y = e^{3x^2}$, for example, we get

$$\frac{dy}{dx} = e^{3x^2} \cdot \frac{d}{dx}(3x^2) = 6x \cdot e^{3x^2}$$

by "mental substitution," and then

$$\begin{aligned}\frac{d^2y}{dx^2} &= 6x\cdot\frac{d}{dx}(e^{3x^2}) + e^{3x^2}\cdot\frac{d}{dx}(6x)\\ &= 6x(6x\cdot e^{3x^2}) + 6\cdot e^{3x^2}\\ &= (36x^2+6)e^{3x^2}\end{aligned}$$

by use of the product rule and further "mental substitution."

If we continue this process and differentiate again, namely, if we differentiate the second derivative, we obtain the *third derivative,* which we denote $f'''(x)$ or $\frac{d^3y}{dx^3}$. Continuing in this way, we can also define a *fourth derivative,* a *fifth derivative,* a *sixth derivative,* and so forth. For instance, in the first example of this section we had $f(x) = x^4$, $f'(x) = 4x^3$, $f''(x) = 12x^2$, and we can now add that $f'''(x) = 24x$, $f^{(\mathrm{IV})}(x) = 24$, and that from then on all higher derivatives are zero.

Higher derivatives play many important roles in advanced mathematics. They are used, for example, in determining infinite series like the ones which we gave without proof in Section 11.4. The method by which such series are obtained is actually quite simple — all we have to do is substitute into the formula

$$f(x) = f(0) + f'(0)x + \frac{f''(0)}{2!}x^2 + \frac{f'''(0)}{3!}x^3 + \ldots$$

where $f(0)$ is the value of the given function at $x = 0$, $f'(0)$ is the value of its first derivative at $x = 0$, $f''(0)$ is the value of its second derivative at $x = 0$, $f'''(0)$ is the value of its third derivative at $x = 0$, and so on. (The *factorials,* 2!, 3!, 4!, . . . , are as defined on page 326.) This kind of series is called a *Maclaurin's series,* and we should add that it represents the corresponding function only for those values of x for which it is convergent.

To illustrate the use of the *Maclaurin's formula,* let us apply it to find an infinite series for $f(x) = (1+x)^p$, where p can be any positive or negative integer or fraction. Writing the values of the function and its first few derivatives on the left and the corresponding values at $x = 0$ on the right, we get

$$\begin{aligned}f(x) &= (1+x)^p & f(0) &= 1\\ f'(x) &= p(1+x)^{p-1} & f'(0) &= p\\ f''(x) &= p(p-1)(1+x)^{p-2} & f''(0) &= p(p-1)\\ f'''(x) &= p(p-1)(p-2)(1+x)^{p-3} & f'''(0) &= p(p-1)(p-2)\\ &\cdots\cdots & &\cdots\cdots\end{aligned}$$

and substitution into the formula yields

$$(1+x)^p = 1 + px + \frac{p(p-1)}{2!}x^2 + \frac{p(p-1)(p-2)}{3!}x^3 + \ldots$$

It is of interest to note that the infinite series we have obtained here is actually a generalization of the *binomial expansion* of $(a + b)^n$ with $a = 1$ and $b = x$. The rule for going from one term to the next is *exactly* as on page 347, although there will no longer be a last term unless p happens to be a positive integer. The infinite series converges, incidentally, for any value of x between -1 and 1, as is shown in most calculus texts.

Having obtained this infinite series for $(1 + x)^p$, let us now illustrate its use by determining $\sqrt{1.3}$ and $\sqrt[3]{975}$. Since the first of these two quantities can be written as $(1 + 0.3)^{1/2}$, substitution of $x = 0.3$ and $p = \frac{1}{2}$ into the formula for $(1 + x)^p$ yields

$$\begin{aligned}\sqrt{1.3} &= 1 + \frac{1}{2}(0.3) + \frac{\frac{1}{2}\left(-\frac{1}{2}\right)}{2}(0.3)^2 + \frac{\frac{1}{2}\left(-\frac{1}{2}\right)\left(-\frac{3}{2}\right)}{6}(0.3)^3 + \dots \\ &= 1 + 0.15 - 0.01125 + 0.0016875 + \dots \\ &= 1.1404 \text{ (rounded to four decimals)}\end{aligned}$$

and this is extremely close to the corresponding value given in Table V. To evaluate the second quantity, let us first write 975 as 1,000(0.975), so that

$$\sqrt[3]{975} = \sqrt[3]{1{,}000(0.975)} = 10\cdot\sqrt[3]{0.975} = 10(1 - 0.025)^{1/3}$$

This enables us to substitute $x = -0.025$ and $p = \frac{1}{3}$ into the formula for the Maclaurin's series for $(1 + x)^p$, and we get

$$\begin{aligned}\sqrt[3]{975} &= 10\left[1 + \frac{1}{3}(-0.025) + \frac{\frac{1}{3}\left(-\frac{2}{3}\right)}{2}(-0.025)^2 + \dots\right] \\ &= 10[1 - 0.00833 - 0.000069 + \dots] \\ &= 9.916 \text{(rounded to three decimals)}\end{aligned}$$

EXERCISES

1. Differentiate each of the following:

(a) e^{4x};	(f) $(1 + 3e^x)^2$;
(b) e^{-12x};	(g) $\dfrac{2 - 3e^x}{1 + 2e^x}$;
(c) 4^{3x};	(h) $(1 + 2x^3)e^{-x}$;
(d) e^{x^2};	(i) $x^2\cdot 3^{4x}$;
(e) $x\cdot e^x$;	(j) $\dfrac{1 + 5^x}{1 - 5^x}$.

2. On page 149 we expressed the demand for a new meat tenderizer (in thousands of packages) by means of the equation

$$y = 100 - 94e^{-x}$$

where x is the number of years the product has been on the market. At which annual rate is the demand growing after 2 years? Compare this with the actual change in the demand between $x = 2$ and $x = 3$, and explain why there is a difference between the two results.

3. In Exercise 8 on page 151 we used the equation

$$y = e^{-0.00012x}$$

to determine y, the proportion of tires (made by a certain manufacturer) that are still usable after having been driven for x miles. Find the values of $\frac{dy}{dx}$ at $x = 5{,}000$ and $x = 25{,}000$, and explain the significance of these results.

4. If D is the demand for a product (in thousands of units), the total sales revenue in thousands of dollars is given by

$$R = 500D \cdot e^{-0.2D}$$

Find the derivative of R with respect to D at $D = 3$ and $D = 6$, and explain the significance of these results.

5. With reference to Exercise 4 calculate the quantity $\dfrac{\frac{dR}{dD}}{R} \cdot 100$ for $D = 3$ and $D = 6$. What do these results *mean*?

6. Find the derivatives of the functions given by

(a) $y = \ln 4x$;

(b) $y = \ln x^2$;

(c) $f(x) = 2x - 3(\ln x)$;

(d) $y = x^2(\ln x)$;

(e) $f(x) = \dfrac{\ln x}{x^3}$;

(f) $y = (\ln x)^5$;

(g) $f(x) = (3 + x^2)(\log_{10} x)$;

(h) $y = \dfrac{x}{\log_{10} x}$.

7. The relationship between the weekly demand for a radio in a certain market area and its price (in dollars) is given by

$$D = \ln (p + 100)$$

Find the derivative of D with respect to p at $p = 20$ and $p = 50$. What is the significance of these two derivatives?

8. LOGARITHMIC DIFFERENTIATION. In some problems it is easier to differentiate $\ln y$ than y, and then find the derivative of y with respect to x by making use of the fact that $\frac{d}{dx}(\ln y) = \frac{1}{y} \cdot \frac{dy}{dx}$. This is referred to as *logarithmic dif-*

ferentiation, and to illustrate it, let us find the derivative of

$$y = \frac{(1-x)^3}{(2+x)^5}$$

We first write this equation as

$$\begin{aligned}\ln y &= \ln \frac{(1-x)^3}{(2+x)^5}\\ &= \ln (1-x)^3 - \ln (2+x)^5\\ &= 3\cdot\ln (1-x) - 5\cdot\ln (2+x)\end{aligned}$$

and if we then differentiate with respect to x, we get

$$\frac{1}{y}\cdot\frac{dy}{dx} = \frac{-3}{1-x} - \frac{5}{2+x}$$

and, hence,

$$\frac{dy}{dx} = y\left[\frac{-3}{1-x} - \frac{5}{2+x}\right] = \frac{(1-x)^3}{(2+x)^5}\left[\frac{-3}{1-x} - \frac{5}{2+x}\right]$$

Use this method to differentiate

(a) $y = \dfrac{(1+x)(3-x)}{(4-x)(1-x)}$; (c) $y = a\cdot b^x$;

(b) $y = \dfrac{x^2+3x-1}{(x+4)(x+3)}$; (d) $y = e^{e^x}$.

9. Verify the result obtained on page 364 for the derivative of $\log_b x$ by

(a) writing the equation $y = \log_b x$ as $x = b^y$, differentiating with respect to y using the formula on page 363, and then making use of the fact that $\dfrac{dy}{dx}$ is the reciprocal of $\dfrac{dx}{dy}$.

(b) changing the base of the logarithm from b to e by means of the formula on page 165, and then making use of the fact that the derivative of $\ln x$ is $1/x$.

10. Find the first four derivatives of the function given by

$$f(x) = x^4 - 3x^3 + x^2 + 5$$

11. Find the first two derivatives of each of the following:

(a) $f(x) = x^3 - 3x^2 + 5$;

(b) $y = 3x^4 - 4x^3$;

(c) $y = x^4 - 8x^2 + 3$.

12. Find the first five derivatives of $\ln(1+x)$, their values at $x = 0$, and substitute these results into the formula on page 366 to show that the *Maclaurin's series* for $\ln(1+x)$ is

$$\ln(1+x) = x - \frac{1}{2}x^2 + \frac{1}{3}x^3 - \frac{1}{4}x^4 + \frac{1}{5}x^5 - \ldots$$

Also use the first four terms of this series to find the values of (a) $\ln 1.1$, (b) $\ln 1.5$, and (c) $\ln 0.8$.

13. Use the first three terms of the *Maclaurin's series* for $(1 + x)^p$ on page 366 to evaluate

(a) $\sqrt{1.5}$; (c) $\sqrt{5}$;

(b) $\sqrt[3]{0.6}$; (d) $\sqrt[3]{9}$.

$\Bigg[$*Hint:* in part (c) make use of the fact that $5 = 4\cdot\frac{5}{4} = 4(1 + 0.25)$, and in part (d) make use of the fact that $9 = 8\cdot\frac{9}{8} = 8\left(1 + \frac{1}{8}\right)$.$\Bigg]$

14. Differentiate the Maclaurin's series for $\cos x$ on page 326 term by term, to show that if $f(x) = \cos x$, then $f'(x) = -\sin x$.

15. When we showed on page 360 that the derivative of e^x is e^x, we actually made use of the Maclaurin's series for e^x. *Assuming that this rule for differentiating e^x had been obtained by other means,* use the formula on page 366 to show that the Maclaurin's series for e^x is

$$e^x = 1 + x + \frac{x^2}{2} + \frac{x^3}{2\cdot 3} + \frac{x^4}{2\cdot 3\cdot 4} + \frac{x^5}{2\cdot 3\cdot 4\cdot 5} + \cdots$$

13

DIFFERENTIAL CALCULUS: APPLICATIONS

13.1 INTRODUCTION

Most applications of differential calculus to business and economics arise in *optimization problems,* namely, in problems in which we want to find the best way of performing a certain operation. The theory of the preceding chapter is thus used to find the conditions which will maximize a company's profit, which will minimize the cost of production, which will maximize the efficiency of a process, which will hold losses to a minimum, which will maximize the yield of investments, and so on. An entirely different kind of application of differential calculus will be discussed briefly in Section 13.3.

13.2 MAXIMA AND MINIMA

In each of the problems which we shall study in this section there will be one *independent variable* (whose values can presumably be controlled) and one *dependent variable* (whose values we hope to maximize or minimize). To make this possible, it will always be assumed that the two variables are related by means of a known function, and, hence, our problem reduces to that of *maximizing or minimizing* the values of this function. (Situations in which there are several independent variables will be treated separately in Section 13.4.)

Looking at problems of this kind geometrically, we shall say that a point on the graph of $y = f(x)$ is a *relative maximum* if it is higher than any nearby point, and that it is a *relative minimum* if it is lower than any nearby point. Thus, in Figure 13.1 there is a relative maximum at point P,

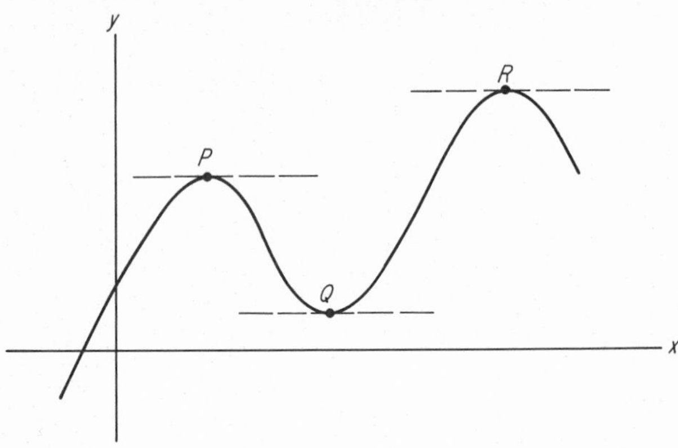

FIG. 13.1

a relative minimum at point Q, and another relative maximum at point R. It is apparent from this graph that a relative maximum need not be the *highest* point on a curve and that a relative minimum need not be the *lowest*—although there is a relative maximum at point P of Figure 13.1 (which is higher than any *nearby* point), the function assumes greater values further to the right, and although there is a relative minimum at point Q, the function assumes smaller values further to the left. It should also be noted that as we have drawn the graph of Figure 13.1, the curve has a *horizontal slope* (and, hence, the function has a *zero derivative*) at points P, Q, and R. Although it is generally true that a zero derivative implies that there is a relative maximum or a relative minimum, and vice versa, there are exceptions—the graph of Figure 12.4 on page 344 has a relative minimum at $x = 1$, where the derivative of the function does not exist, and the graph of $y = x^3$ (which the reader was asked to plot in Exercise 5 on page 345) has neither a relative maximum nor a relative minimum at $x = 0$, where its slope is horizontal and the derivative of the function is zero. Another example of this kind is shown in Figure 13.2, where the function has a zero derivative and its graph a horizontal slope at point N, without there being a relative maximum or a relative minimum.

If a function is differentiable however, *a relative maximum or minimum can exist only when the slope of its graph is horizontal*, and we therefore begin all optimization problems (to which calculus applies) by looking for the values of the independent variable at which the derivative of the function is zero. Then we must check whether there is a relative maximum or a relative minimum for each of these values, or whether we are faced

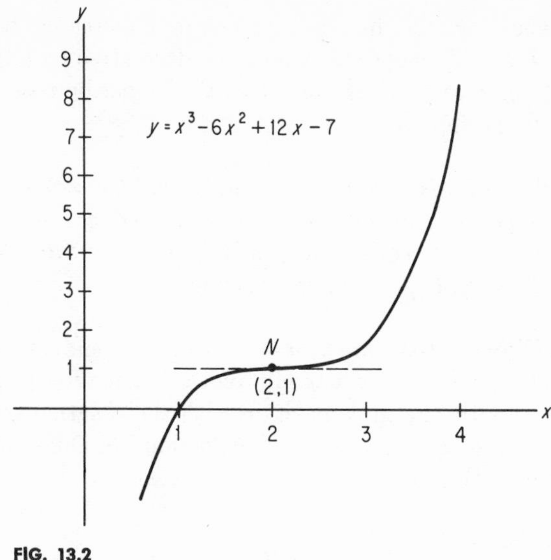

FIG. 13.2

with a situation like that shown in Figure 13.2. This could be done geometrically by plotting a few nearby points (the points corresponding to $x = 1$ and $x = 3$, for instance, in Figure 13.2), but there exists a systematic way which is generally much easier. To explain how it works, let us inspect the two diagrams of Figure 13.3. In the first diagram there is a

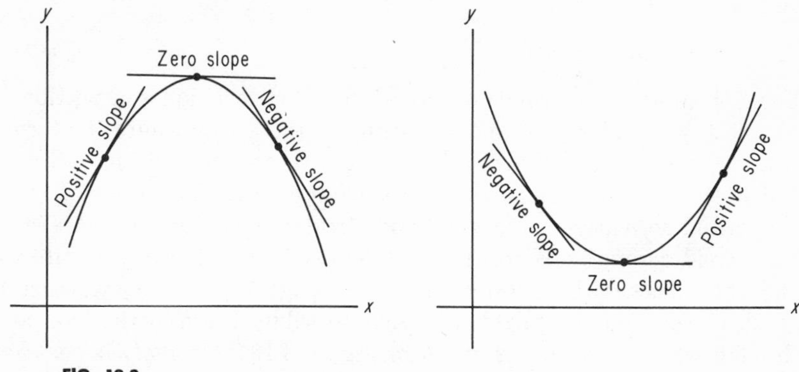

FIG. 13.3

relative maximum, and if we move *from left to right* it can be seen that the slope (and, hence, the derivative of the function) is at first positive, but it decreases, becomes zero, and then negative. This means that the derivative is *decreasing*, namely, that its rate of change, the *second derivative*, must be *negative*. Similarly, in the second diagram there is a relative minimum, and if we move *from left to right* it can be seen that the slope (and, hence, the derivative of the function) is at first negative, but it increases, becomes zero, and then positive. This means that now the derivative is *increasing*, namely, that its rate of change, the *second derivative*, must be *positive*. We thus have the following criterion:

> *If the first derivative is zero at a given point and the second derivative is negative, there must be a relative maximum; if the first derivative is zero at a given point and the second derivative is positive, there must be a relative minimum.*

If the first and second derivatives are *both zero* at a given point, we simply resort to the method suggested first, namely, plot a few nearby points.

Let us illustrate this theory in connection with the function given by $y = x^3 - 9x^2 + 24x$, whose graph we studied in Section 3.3. Differentiating twice with respect to x, we get

$$\frac{dy}{dx} = 3x^2 - 18x + 24$$

and

$$\frac{d^2y}{dx^2} = 6x - 18$$

and to find the values of x at which the first derivative is zero, we shall have to solve the quadratic equation $3x^2 - 18x + 24 = 0$, which simplifies to

$$x^2 - 6x + 8 = 0$$

Using the quadratic formula or any of the other techniques of Section 4.6, we get $x = 2$ and $x = 4$, and, substituting these values into the formula obtained for the second derivative, we get, respectively, $6(2) - 18 = -6$ and $6(4) - 18 = 6$. Thus, there is a *relative maximum* at $x = 2$ (where the second derivative is negative) and a *relative minimum* at $x = 4$ (where the second derivative is positive). These results are shown in Figure 13.4, and they answer the question asked on page 77, namely, whether the graph of the function might not oscillate wildly between the five points through which we drew its graph in Figure 3.10. *Our analysis has shown that the curve cannot have any "turning points" (that is, relative maxima or minima) other than those at* $x = 2$ *and* $x = 4$.

To give another illustration of this technique, let us analyze the function of Figure 13.2, whose equation was $y = x^3 - 6x^2 + 12x - 7$. Differentiating twice with respect to x, we get

$$\frac{dy}{dx} = 3x^2 - 12x + 12$$

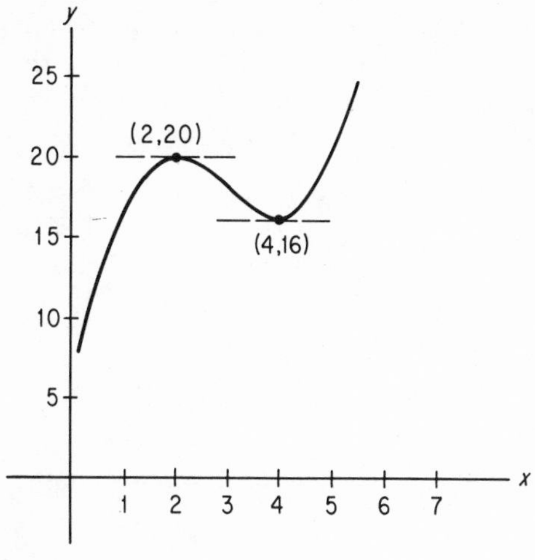

FIG. 13.4

and

$$\frac{d^2y}{dx^2} = 6x - 12$$

and to find the values at which the first derivative is zero, we shall thus have to solve the quadratic equation $3x^2 - 12x + 12 = 0$, which simplifies to

$$x^2 - 4x + 4 = 0$$

The only solution of this equation is $x = 2$, and if we substitute this value of x into $6x - 12$, the expression we obtained for the second derivative, we get $6(2) - 12 = 0$. Since the second derivative is thus also zero at $x = 2$, we continue by investigating the values of the function at two nearby points, say, at $x = 1.9$ and $x = 2.1$, for which we get

$$f(1.9) = (1.9)^3 - 6(1.9)^2 + 12(1.9) - 7 = 0.999$$

and

$$f(2.1) = (2.1)^3 - 6(2.1)^2 + 12(2.1) - 7 = 1.001$$

Since one of these values is less than $f(2) = 1$ while the other is greater than 1, we conclude that there is *neither a relative maximum nor a relative minimum* at $x = 2$ (as is apparent, of course, from Figure 13.2). Actually, a function *could* have a relative maximum or minimum at a point where its first two derivatives are both zero; this is illustrated in the two parts of Exercise 6 on page 380.

As our first "real" application, let us consider a retailer's problem of pricing an electric alarm clock which costs him \$4.00. Somehow he knows that if he charges x dollars per clock he will be able to sell $480 - 40x$

clocks, and his problem is to determine *how much he should charge per clock so as to maximize his total profit.* Since his total profit is given by the product of the number of clocks he will sell, $480 - 40x$, and his profit per clock, $x - 4$, the quantity he will have to maximize is given by

$$y = (480 - 40x)(x - 4)$$

Differentiating twice, first by the product rule, we get

$$\frac{dy}{dx} = (480 - 40x)\cdot 1 + (x - 4)\cdot(-40) = 640 - 80x$$

and

$$\frac{d^2y}{dx^2} = -80$$

so that there is the possibility for a relative maximum or minimum when

$$640 - 80x = 0$$

namely, at $x = 8$. Since the second derivative is *negative* for that value of x (or, for that matter, for any value of x), we conclude that the function has a *relative maximum* at $x = 8$; in other words, *the retailer's profit will be a maximum if he charges* \$8.00 *for each of the clocks.* In fact, this maximum profit will be \$640, as can easily be verified by substituting $x = 8$ into the original equation.

As our second application let us consider an *inventory problem,* in which it is required to determine how often a certain item (say, a frozen food) should be ordered, and how large an order should be placed each time, so as to *minimize* the total cost of maintaining inventory (namely, the cost of placing the orders *plus* the cost of keeping the item in stock). To simplify matters, it will be assumed that there is a known monthly demand for R packages of the frozen food and that the customers are buying it at a constant rate, so that the inventory at any given time is given by the

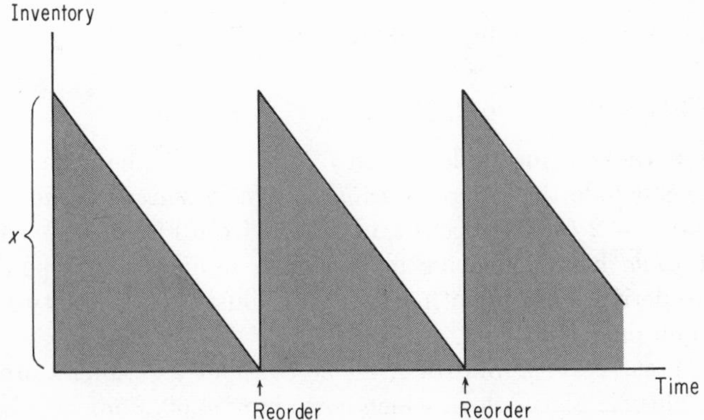

FIG. 13.5

graph of Figure 13.5. This also assumes that the time required to replenish the stock is negligible, and that no shortage in the item will ever be allowed. Now, if each order is of size x (packages), then $\frac{R}{x}$ orders will have to be placed each month to meet the total demand (of R packages), and if K is the cost of placing an order (regardless of its size), the *total monthly cost of placing orders* is $K\left(\frac{R}{x}\right) = \frac{K \cdot R}{x}$. Since the size of the inventory is assumed to change from x to 0 at a constant rate (see Figure 13.5), the average inventory size is $x/2$, and if the cost of carrying a package in inventory for a month is I, then the *total inventory carrying cost* for a month is $I\left(\frac{x}{2}\right) = \frac{I}{2}x$. Thus, the *total cost of maintaining inventory for a month* is given by

$$f(x) = \frac{K \cdot R}{x} + \frac{I}{2} \cdot x$$

where K, R, and I are assumed to be known constants. In order to find the minimum value of this function, we differentiate twice, getting

$$f'(x) = -KR \cdot x^{-2} + \frac{I}{2}$$

and

$$f''(x) = 2KR \cdot x^{-3}$$

where we made use of the fact that $\frac{1}{x}$ can be written as x^{-1} and, hence, its derivative equals $-x^{-2}$, and that the derivative of x^{-2} is $-2x^{-3}$. Putting the first derivative equal to zero, we get

$$-KRx^{-2} + \frac{I}{2} = 0$$

and, solving for x, we obtain

$$\frac{I}{2} = \frac{KR}{x^2}, \qquad x^2 = \frac{2KR}{I} \qquad \text{and, hence,} \qquad x = \pm\sqrt{\frac{2KR}{I}}$$

Since x, the size of each order, cannot be negative, it follows that the only possible solution is

$$x = \sqrt{\frac{2KR}{I}}$$

Note that the corresponding cost of maintaining inventory is a *minimum* since K, I, and R are positive constants, so that $2KR \cdot x^{-3}$, the second derivative, is *positive* for $x = \sqrt{\frac{2KR}{I}}$.

To give a numerical illustration of this result, suppose that there is a monthly demand for 4,000 packages of the frozen food, that the cost of placing an order is \$5.00, and that the cost of maintaining a package in inventory for a month is 25 cents. Substituting these values into the formula for x, we get

$$x = \sqrt{\frac{2(5)(4{,}000)}{0.25}} = 400$$

(see Exercise 8 on page 164), which means that the 4,000 packages needed each month should be ordered 400 at a time (and, hence, $\frac{4{,}000}{400} = 10$ times a month, or just about once every 3 days).

To consider one more example, suppose that the relationship between the demand for a product (say, a new kind of battery) and its price (in cents) is given by the equation

$$D = 25{,}000e^{-0.05p}$$

and that we want to find the value of p for which the *total sales revenue* will be greatest. Since the total sales revenue is given by the product of p (price) and D (demand), the function whose values we shall want to maximize is given by

$$f(p) = 25{,}000p \cdot e^{-0.05p}$$

Differentiating with respect to p, we get

$$\begin{aligned} f'(p) &= 25{,}000p(-0.05)e^{-0.05p} + 25{,}000e^{-0.05p} \\ &= 25{,}000e^{-0.05p}(-0.05p + 1) \end{aligned}$$

which can equal zero only when

$$-0.05p + 1 = 0$$

namely, when $0.05p = 1$, and, hence, $p = 20$. It will be left to the reader to verify in Exercise 21 on page 382 that the second derivative is *negative* at $p = 20$, so that the total sales revenue will be a *maximum* when the price per battery is 20 cents.

Before we turn to other applications of differential calculus, let us caution the reader against the indiscriminate application of the method which we have just discussed. As we already saw from the graph of Figure 12.4, there are situations where the derivative at a maximum or minimum point of a curve does not exist. Also, we must always be careful to check *whether the answers we get fall within the domain for which the function is defined, or for which it has meaningful applications.* To illustrate this point, let us refer back to the example on page 111, where we had the demand curve

$$D = 520 - 45p + p^2$$

with p being the price of a box of detergent in cents and D the weekly demand in thousands of boxes. Differentiating twice with respect to p, we get

$$\frac{dD}{dp} = -45 + 2p \qquad \text{and} \qquad \frac{d^2D}{dp^2} = 2$$

and we might be tempted to conclude that the demand is a minimum when $-45 + 2p = 0$, namely, when the detergent sells at two boxes for 45 cents. This is *nonsense* for the simple reason that the given function provides a suitable model only for a limited set of values of p—as we already indicated on page 112, the demand will surely not increase again (that is, the curve will not turn up again) when the price is increased beyond $p = 22.5$ cents. If we limit the domain of the function, say, to the interval from $p = 10$ to $p = 20$, it is apparent from Figure 13.6 that the demand is a minimum at

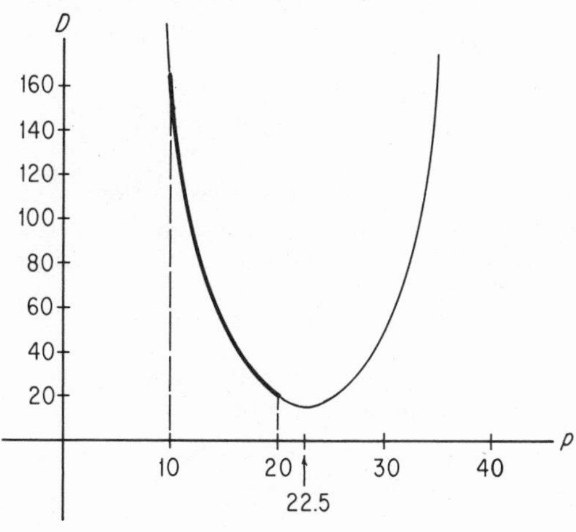

FIG. 13.6

$p = 20$ cents. Situations like this are by no means rare, and we must always be on the alert for problems in which desired maxima or minima occur at the endpoints of the interval (or intervals) for which the independent variable is defined.

EXERCISES

1. For what value of x is $y = 3 - 4x + 2x^2$ a minimum?
2. Find the coordinates of the highest point on the graph of $y = 4x - x^2$.
3. Use the results of part (a) of Exercise 11 on page 369 to find the relative maxima and minima of $y = x^3 - 3x^2 + 5$ and plot the graph of this function.

4. Use the results of part (c) of Exercise 11 on page 369 to investigate the points at which the first derivative of the given function is zero, and plot its graph.

5. Investigate the relative maxima and minima of the function of Exercise 10 on page 369.

6. Investigate the relative maxima and minima of

   (a) $y = -x^4$; (b) $y = 2(x - 1)^4 + 1$.

7. **INFLECTION POINTS.** If the second derivative of a function is *zero* at a point, but the first derivative remains non-negative (as in Figure 13.2) or non-positive, we say that there is an *inflection point.*

   (a) Verify that the graph of the function of part (b) of Exercise 11 on page 369 has an inflection point at $x = 0$;
   (b) Show that $y = -x^5$ has an inflection point at $x = 0$ by demonstrating that the first two derivatives are zero at that point and that the first derivative *does not change its sign.*
   (c) Show that if

$$f(x) = k \cdot e^{-\frac{1}{2}x^2}$$

   for all real values of x and $k > 0$, this function has a maximum at $x = 0$ and inflection points at $x = -1$ and $x = 1$. This function plays a very important role in statistics, where its graph is referred to as a *normal curve.*

8. With reference to Exercise 4 on page 114, how many passengers would maximize the travel agency's profit on the Rose Bowl trip?

9. With reference to Exercise 5 on page 114, how much should the retailer charge for the toy cars so as to maximize his total profit?

10. With reference to Exercise 3 on page 130, how many thousands of Christmas tree ornaments should the manufacturer produce so as to maximize

    (a) the total sales revenue;
    (b) his total profit.

11. A company which leases fleets of cars to large corporations discounts the total bill by 2 percent for each car in excess of 12. For how many cars would the leasing firm's receipts be a maximum? [*Hint:* if they charged k dollars per car and there were no discount, the bill for $12 + x$ cars would amount to $k(12 + x)$ dollars.]

12. The management of a company making optical equipment has found that the demand for certain lenses is given by

$$D = 85e^{-0.01p}$$

    where p is the price per lens in dollars. How many lenses should they make so as to maximize their total sales revenue?

13. The manufacturer of a new alloy knows that at p dollars a ton he can sell $240 - p$ tons and that the manufacture will cost him $\frac{12,000}{240 - p} + 30$ dollars per ton. How much should he charge and how many tons should he manufacture so as to maximize his total profit?

14. A manufacturer of cardboard boxes wants to make open boxes out of pieces of cardboard 30 inches long and 30 inches wide by cutting squares out of the corners (see Figure 13.7) and folding up the sides.

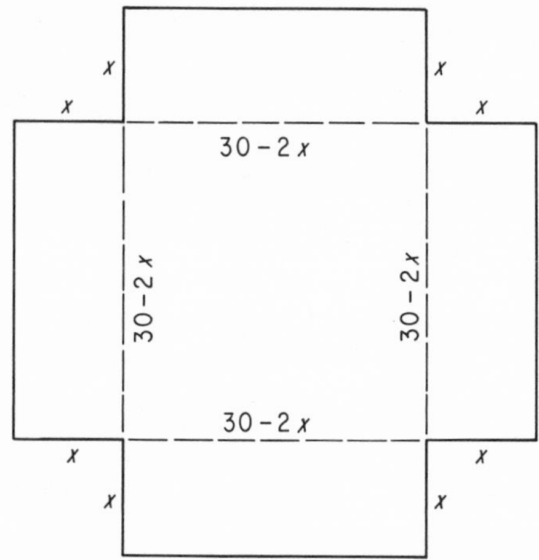

FIG. 13.7

(a) Show that if x is the side of these squares, then the volume of the boxes is given by

$$V = 4x^3 - 120x^2 + 900x$$

(b) What size squares should be cut out of the corners of the pieces of cardboard so as to maximize the volume of these open boxes?

15. A rectangular warehouse with a floor space of 6,000 square feet is to be built in a county where zoning regulations require a 20 foot utility easement in the front and in the back, and a 12 foot utility easement on each side. What are the dimensions of the smallest rectangular piece of land on which this warehouse can be built? $\left(\textit{Hint:}\text{ let the two sides of the warehouse be } x \text{ and } \frac{6,000}{x}.\right)$

16. Importers claim that if the government charges a tax of t cents on an ounce of a certain kind of perfume imported from an Asian country, they will be able to sell $45,000 - 300t$ ounces of the perfume. Assuming that this claim is correct, what tax should the government charge so as to maximize its total tax revenue on this perfume?

17. A real estate investor feels that in n years he will be able to sell an apartment house for $250,000 + 20,000n$ dollars. If the interest rate paid by banks is 5 percent compounded annually, the *present value* of the sales price of the apartment house n years hence is

$$P = (250{,}000 + 20{,}000n)(1.05)^{-n}$$

(where we simply discounted the sales price for n years at 5 percent.) For how many years should the investor hold on to the apartment house so as to maximize this present value, and, hence, his profit on the transaction? (Use $\ln 1.05 = 0.04879$.)

18. The manager of a dude ranch figures that with z horses in his stable the weekly profit from their rental will be $96\sqrt{z} - 8z$ dollars. How many horses should he keep so as to maximize his profit?

19. A certain study showed that a person with x years of formal education can expect lifetime earnings of $500{,}000 - 240{,}000e^{-x/6}$ dollars, and that a year of formal education costs on the average \$2,000. How many years of formal education will thus maximize a person's net lifetime earnings (namely, his earnings minus the expense of his formal education)?

20. A television executive claims that if a soap manufacturer will spend an extra x thousand dollars on television commercials, his total profit will be increased by $24x^2e^{-0.4x}$ thousand dollars. By how much should the soap manufacturer increase his advertising budget so as to maximize his profit, and what will be the corresponding increase in his profit?

21. With reference to the example on page 378, show that the second derivative is *negative* at $p = 20$.

13.3 TIME RATES, PERCENTAGE CHANGES, AND RELATED RATES

Many of the rates of change with which we are concerned in the study of economics, or in the operation of a business, are *time rates*; they indicate how rapidly changes are taking place in such things as the gross national product, the prices of stocks, farm employment in the United States, the mining of various minerals, foreign trade, the prices of assorted commodities, and so on. If the values of a quantity are given by $y = f(t)$, where t denotes time, its *time rate* is simply the derivative $\frac{dy}{dt}$, namely, its instantaneous rate of change with respect to time. To give an example, suppose that a corporation's annual earnings are given by the equation

$$y = 20 + 3t + \frac{1}{5}t^2$$

where y is in millions of dollars and t is in years (*coded* so that $t = 0$ corresponds to 1965, $t = 1$ corresponds to 1966, $t = 2$ corresponds to 1967, and so forth). Now, if we differentiate with respect to t, we get

$$\frac{dy}{dt} = 3 + \frac{1}{5}(2t) = 3 + \frac{2}{5}t$$

and it can be seen that (unlike the insurance example on page 98) the growth rate is *not constant*. In 1966, for instance, the corporation's earnings grew at an annual rate of $3 + \frac{2}{5}(1) = 3.4$ million dollars, and in 1970 its earnings should grow at an annual rate of $3 + \frac{2}{5}(5) = 5$ million dollars.

These figures are difficult to interpret unless we also know something about the actual size of the corporation's earnings. After all, the 1966 growth rate of 3.4 million dollars would have been *tremendous* if the corporation's 1965 earnings had totaled 2 million dollars, but it would have been *pretty sad* if the corporation's 1965 earnings had totaled 500 million dollars. Thus, we need a measure which compares a time rate (or a growth rate) with the size of the quantity in which the change is actually taking place, namely, a measure which compares $\frac{dy}{dt}$ with y. To this end, we introduce the *relative time rate*

$$\frac{\frac{dy}{dt}}{y} = \frac{1}{y}\cdot\frac{dy}{dt}$$

which, multiplied by 100, gives the *percentage rate of change of the variable y*. Returning now to the above example where we had $y = 20 + 3t + \frac{1}{5}t^2$ and $\frac{dy}{dt} = 3 + \frac{2}{5}t$, we thus find that in 1966 the corporation's earnings were growing at an annual rate of

$$\frac{1}{y}\cdot\frac{dy}{dt} = \frac{1}{20 + 3(1) + \frac{1}{5}(1)^2}\cdot(3.4) = 0.147 \text{ (or 14.7 percent)}$$

and that in 1970 the corporation's earnings should be growing at an annual rate of

$$\frac{1}{y}\cdot\frac{dy}{dt} = \frac{1}{20 + 3(5) + \frac{1}{5}(5)^2}\cdot 5 = 0.125 \text{ (or 12.5 percent)}$$

It is of interest to note that whereas the 1970 growth rate (or time rate) is greater than that for 1966, the relative growth rate is less.

When we speak of *related rates*, we are referring to situations involving several variables, say, two variables x and y, and we are concerned with the relationship between the two *time rates* $\frac{dx}{dt}$ and $\frac{dy}{dt}$, or that between the two *relative time rates* $\frac{1}{x}\cdot\frac{dx}{dt}$ and $\frac{1}{y}\cdot\frac{dy}{dt}$. The way in which we study the first kind of relationship is very straightforward—we simply use the *chain rule* of Section 12.5 and write

$$\frac{dy}{dt} = \frac{dy}{dx}\cdot\frac{dx}{dt}$$

The way in which we handle the relationship between two relative time rates is explained in Exercise 10 on page 387.

To illustrate how we study the relationship between two time rates, suppose that y denotes the size of the labor force which an industry requires to manufacture x units (of a certain product), and that the correspondence between x and y is given by the equation

$$y = \frac{1}{2}\sqrt{x}$$

What we would like to know is *the rate at which the labor force should be increased,* if at present there is a demand for 40,000 units of the product (and an adequate labor force to manufacture it), but the demand is increasing at the constant rate of 10,000 units per year. Differentiating $y = \frac{1}{2}\sqrt{x} = \frac{1}{2}\cdot x^{1/2}$ with respect to x, we get

$$\frac{dy}{dx} = \frac{1}{2}\cdot\frac{1}{2}\cdot x^{-1/2} = \frac{1}{4\sqrt{x}}$$

and, hence, by the chain rule

$$\frac{dy}{dt} = \frac{1}{4\sqrt{x}}\cdot\frac{dx}{dt}$$

Now, if we substitute $x = 40{,}000$ and $\frac{dx}{dt} = 10{,}000$, we obtain

$$\begin{aligned}\frac{dy}{dt} &= \frac{1}{4\sqrt{40{,}000}}\cdot 10{,}000\\ &= \frac{10{,}000}{800}\\ &= 12.5 \text{ workers per year}\end{aligned}$$

and it follows that they should add just about *one new worker per month.* Of course, this rate will vary with x, and when the production has reached 360,000 units,

$$\frac{dy}{dt} = \frac{1}{4\sqrt{360{,}000}} \cdot 10{,}000$$

$$= \frac{10{,}000}{2{,}400}$$

$$= 4.17 \text{ workers per year}$$

and they will have to add just about *one new worker every three months.*

EXERCISES

1. In Exercise 10 on page 151 we claimed that a manufacturer's profit from the sales of a novelty toy is given by

$$y = 8{,}000 + 30{,}000e^{-0.4t}$$

where y is in dollars and t is the number of years the toy has been on the market.

(a) At what rate and at what percentage rate is the manufacturer's profit changing after the product has been on the market for two years?
(b) At what rate and at what percentage rate will the manufacturer's profit be changing after the product will have been on the market for ten years?

2. In Exercise 6 on page 114 we expressed the annual consumption of beer in the United States by means of the equation

$$y = 95.6 + 1.84x + 0.12x^2$$

where y is in millions of barrels and x is in years (*coded* so that $x = 0$ corresponds to 1960, $x = 1$ corresponds to 1961, $x = 2$ corresponds to 1962, and so on).

(a) At what annual rate was the beer consumption in the United States growing in 1960 and 1965, and at what annual rate will it be growing in 1970 and 1975?
(b) At what percentage rate was the annual beer consumption in the United States growing in 1960 and 1965, and at what percentage rate will it be growing in 1970 and 1975?

3. A new company's gross earnings are given by

$$y = 24{,}000e^{0.2t}$$

where y is in dollars and t is the number of years the company has been in business.

(a) At what rate will the company's gross earnings be growing after it has been in business for eight years?
(b) At what percentage rate will the company's gross earnings be growing after it has been in business for eight years?

4. The price of tomatoes in a certain market area is given by

$$p = 2 + \frac{60}{30 - S}$$

where S is the daily supply in thousands of crates and p is the price in dollars per crate. At what rate will the price be changing if the current daily supply is 10,000 crates, but it is decreasing at a rate of 200 crates per day?

5. In Exercise 15 on page 125 we expressed the demand for a detergent by means of the equation

$$D = \frac{1{,}000}{p} - 30$$

where D is in thousands of boxes and p is the price per box in cents. If the price is going up at a rate of a cent per box a week, what is the corresponding rate of change in the demand (in boxes per week) if

(a) the current price is 20 cents per box;
(b) the current price is 25 cents per box?

6. A company keeps its emergency water supply in a storage tank having the shape of a sphere with a radius of 20 feet. If the tank is less than half full, the amount of water in the tank, in cubic feet, is given by

$$A = \frac{\pi}{3} \cdot h^2(60 - h)$$

where h is the height of the water in feet (see Figure 13.8). If, during an emergency, water is being drawn from the tank at a rate of 200 cubic feet per hour, at what rate (in inches per hour) will the water level be going down the instant the height of the water in the tank is 8 feet? (Approximate π as 3.14.)

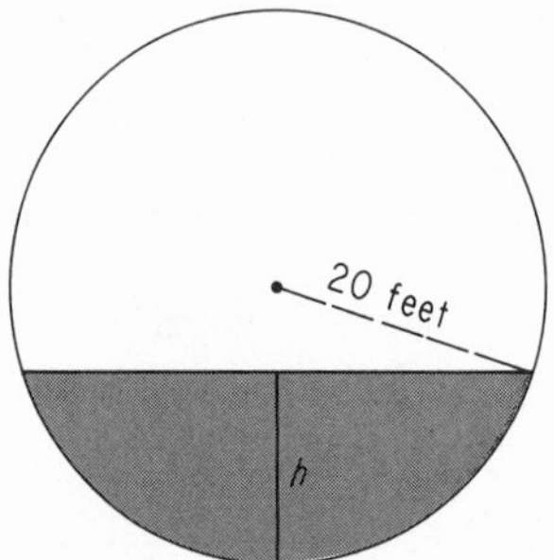

FIG. 13.8

7. The annual profit of a land development company is given by

$$P = 0.06C - 0.005C^2$$

where C is its capitalization, and P as well as C are in millions of dollars. If the company's capitalization is increasing at a rate of half a million dollars a year, what is the rate of change of the company's profit (in dollars per year) if its capitalization is

(a) \$2,000,000; (c) \$6,000,000;
(b) \$4,000,000; (d) \$8,000,000.

Also find the corresponding *percentage rates* $\frac{1}{P}\cdot\frac{dP}{dt}\cdot 100$ at which the company's profit is changing.

8. A ship is sailing straight out to sea at 20 miles per hour from a pier at point A of Figure 13.9. How fast is the ship moving away from a lighthouse 12 miles down the coast when it is 5 miles out at sea?

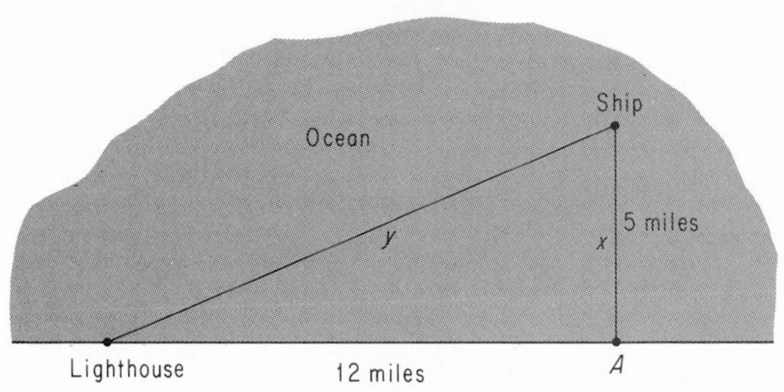

FIG. 13.9

9. With reference to Exercise 4 on page 368, find the *rate* as well as the *percentage rate* at which the total sales revenue is changing when there is a demand for 3,000 units but the demand is decreasing at a rate of 100 units a month. (*Hint:* the percentage rate of change is given by $\frac{1}{R}\cdot\frac{dR}{dt}\cdot 100.$)

10. ELASTICITY OF DEMAND. When we are dealing with two or more variables, we are also interested at times in comparing their relative rates of change (as defined on page 383). For instance, if p is the price of a product and D is its demand, the relative rates of change of these two variables are $\frac{1}{p}\cdot\frac{dp}{dt}$ and $\frac{1}{D}\cdot\frac{dD}{dt}$, and the *ratio* of the second to the first can be written as

$$\frac{\frac{1}{D}\cdot\frac{dD}{dt}}{\frac{1}{p}\cdot\frac{dp}{dt}} = \frac{p}{D}\cdot\frac{dD}{dt}\cdot\frac{dt}{dp} = \frac{p}{d}\cdot\frac{dD}{dp}$$

(where we made use of the fact that $\frac{dt}{dp}$ is the reciprocal of $\frac{dp}{dt}$, and the chain rule of Section 12.5). The resulting quantity

$$\eta = \frac{p}{D}\cdot\frac{dD}{dp}$$

is generally called the *elasticity of demand*, it is denoted by the Greek letter

η (*eta*), and it gives the approximate *percentage change in demand which corresponds to an increase of one percent in the price.* For instance, if $p = 20$ in the example on page 111, where the demand for a detergent was given by

$$D = 520 - 45p + p^2$$

we find that $D = 520 - 45(20) + (20)^2 = 70$, $\dfrac{dD}{dp} = -45 + 2p = -45 + 2(20) = -5$, and, hence, that

$$\eta = \frac{p}{D}\cdot\frac{dD}{dp} = \frac{20}{70}\cdot(-5) = -1.45$$

This means that an increase of 1 percent in the price will lead to an *approximate* decrease of 1.45 percent in the demand. Thus, if the retailers plan a 5 percent *increase* in the price, they should expect a *decrease* of $5(1.45) = 7.25$ percent in the demand.

(a) In Exercise 4 on page 131 we expressed the demand for a certain product by means of the equation

$$D = 120 - p^2$$

where p is the price in dollars per carton and the demand is in thousands of cartons. Find the elasticity of demand when the price per carton is \$3.00 and show that a 6 percent increase in the price should produce about a one percent decrease in demand.

(b) On page 129 we expressed the demand for a ceramic insulator by means of the equation $D = 231 - 18p$, where p is the price per insulator in cents. Find the elasticity of demand when $p = 5$, and determine what percentage increase in the price would lead to a decrease of about 4.5 percent in the demand.

(c) Given $D = 100e^{-p}$, find the elasticity of demand at $p = 5$, and use the result to find the approximate change in demand which will correspond to a *decrease* of 2 percent in p.

(d) Show that if $D = a\cdot p^b$, where a and b are constants, the elasticity of demand is equal to b.

(e) Use the result of Exercise 10 on page 359 to show that when

$$p = \sqrt{20 - 3D - D^2}$$

the elasticity of demand at $p = 4$ is equal to -6.4. What does this tell us about a contemplated two percent increase in the price?

13.4 PARTIAL DIFFERENTIATION

In Section 3.4 we barely touched upon functions of *several independent variables*, but it is important to appreciate the fact that in reality, namely, in most "real" applications, situations involving several independent variables are much more common than those in which there is only one.

Retail prices, for example, depend on salaries paid to salesmen, store rental, advertising, wholesale prices, . . . ; dividends paid by corporations depend on their earnings per share, their overall financial condition, their policy concerning research and development, taxes, . . . ; and interest rates, to mention one more example, depend on the demand for mortgage money, the availability of cash, government regulations, and numerous other factors.

When we deal with more than one independent variable, everything becomes (mathematically speaking) much more complicated, and this applies particularly to rates of change. When several independent variables are all changing at the same time, it can be very difficult to determine how these changes *interact* (that is, how they affect each other), and it can be a very hard job, indeed, to determine how the rate of change of a dependent variable is related to those of all of the independent variables.

So far as the work of this book is concerned, we shall consider only situations in which there are two independent variables x and y, and a dependent variable whose values are given by $z = f(x, y)$. In particular, we shall study only *partial derivatives,* namely, derivatives in which *all but one of the independent variables are treated as constants.* For instance, if we are given the equation

$$z = 2x^2 + 4xy - y^2 + 5x - 3y$$

we are said to be differentiating z *partially* with respect to x, if we treat y as a constant and otherwise proceed as in ordinary differentiation. Writing this partial derivative as $\frac{\partial z}{\partial x}$ (where ∂ is the lower case Greek letter *delta*), we thus get

$$\frac{\partial z}{\partial x} = 4x + 4y + 5$$

where $4x$ is the derivative of $2x^2$, $4y$ is the derivative of $4xy$ since $4y$ is treated as a constant, 5 is the derivative of $5x$, while the derivatives of y^2 and $3y$ are *zero*. Similarly, $\frac{\partial z}{\partial y}$ denotes the partial derivative of z with respect to y, and it is obtained by treating x as a constant and otherwise proceeding as in ordinary differentiation. We thus get

$$\frac{\partial z}{\partial y} = 4x - 2y - 3$$

where $4x$ is the derivative of $4xy$, $-2y$ is the derivative of $-y^2$, -3 is the derivative of $-3y$, while the derivatives of $2x^2$ and $5x$ are *zero*.

Returning to the example on page 84, where we expressed the relationship between z (the cost of a certain product in dollars), x (the cost of raw materials in dollars per pound), and y (the cost of labor in dollars per hour), by means of the equation

$$z = 130 + 12x + 27y$$

we can now write

$$\frac{\partial z}{\partial x} = 12 \quad \text{and} \quad \frac{\partial z}{\partial y} = 27$$

This means that *when the cost of labor is held fixed, an increase of* \$1.00 *per pound in the cost of raw materials causes an increase of* \$12.00 *in the cost of the product*, and that *when the cost of raw materials is held fixed, an increase of* \$1.00 *in the hourly cost of labor brings about an increase of* \$27.00 *in the cost of the product.*

If we differentiate $\frac{\partial z}{\partial x}$ partially *with respect to* x (that is, if we differentiate $\frac{\partial z}{\partial x}$ with respect to x treating y as a constant), we get the *second partial derivative* $\frac{\partial^2 z}{\partial x^2}$, and if we differentiate $\frac{\partial z}{\partial x}$ partially *with respect to* y (that is, if we differentiate $\frac{\partial z}{\partial x}$ with respect to y treating x as a constant), we get the *second partial derivative* $\frac{\partial^2 z}{\partial y\, \partial x}$. The other two *second partial derivatives* $\frac{\partial^2 z}{\partial y^2}$ and $\frac{\partial^2 z}{\partial x\, \partial y}$ are defined in the same way, and it is of interest to note that $\frac{\partial^2 z}{\partial y\, \partial x}$ and $\frac{\partial^2 z}{\partial x\, \partial y}$ are *always equal.* This can be illustrated here by referring to the example on page 389 where we had $\frac{\partial z}{\partial x} = 4x + 4y + 5$ and $\frac{\partial z}{\partial y} = 4x - 2y - 3$; we now get

$$\frac{\partial^2 z}{\partial x^2} = 4, \quad \frac{\partial^2 z}{\partial y^2} = -2, \quad \frac{\partial^2 z}{\partial y\, \partial x} = 4, \quad \text{and} \quad \frac{\partial^2 z}{\partial x\, \partial y} = 4$$

We have introduced these higher partial derivatives primarily because they are needed, as in Section 13.2, to decide whether a function has a relative maximum, a relative minimum, or neither, for given values of the independent variables x and y. A *necessary condition* for a relative maximum or a relative minimum is that *the first partial derivatives* $\frac{\partial z}{\partial x}$ *and* $\frac{\partial z}{\partial y}$ *are both equal to zero,* but this is not enough—*there is a relative maximum if*

$$\frac{\partial^2 z}{\partial x^2} < 0, \quad \frac{\partial^2 z}{\partial y^2} < 0, \quad \text{and} \quad \frac{\partial^2 z}{\partial x^2} \cdot \frac{\partial^2 z}{\partial y^2} - \left(\frac{\partial^2 z}{\partial x\, \partial y}\right)^2 > 0$$

and there is a relative minimum if

$$\frac{\partial^2 z}{\partial x^2} > 0, \quad \frac{\partial^2 z}{\partial y^2} > 0, \quad \text{and} \quad \frac{\partial^2 z}{\partial x^2} \cdot \frac{\partial^2 z}{\partial y^2} - \left(\frac{\partial^2 z}{\partial x\, \partial y}\right)^2 > 0$$

To illustrate this theory, which is proved in most advanced calculus texts, let us investigate the function given by

$$z = x^2 + y^2 - 6x - 4y + 18$$

Performing the necessary partial differentiations, we get

$$\frac{\partial z}{\partial x} = 2x - 6, \quad \frac{\partial z}{\partial y} = 2y - 4, \quad \frac{\partial^2 z}{\partial x^2} = 2, \quad \frac{\partial^2 z}{\partial y^2} = 2, \quad \frac{\partial^2 z}{\partial x\, \partial y} = 0$$

and it follows that $\frac{\partial z}{\partial x}$ and $\frac{\partial z}{\partial y}$ are zero when $2x - 6 = 0$ and $2y - 4 = 0$, namely, when $x = 3$ and $y = 2$. Since $\frac{\partial^2 z}{\partial x^2}$ and $\frac{\partial^2 z}{\partial y^2}$ are *positive* (regardless of the values of x and y), there *is* the possibility of a relative minimum, and since

$$\frac{\partial^2 z}{\partial x^2} \cdot \frac{\partial^2 z}{\partial y^2} - \left(\frac{\partial^2 z}{\partial x\, \partial y}\right)^2 = 4 > 0$$

we conclude that the function *has* a relative minimum at $x = 3$ and $y = 2$. In fact, this minimum value of the function is

$$z = 3^2 + 2^2 - 6(3) - 4(2) + 18 = 5$$

To consider a practical application, suppose that a manufacturer who makes shirts out of two kinds of material knows from past experience that if he makes x dozen shirts out of the first kind of material and y dozen shirts out of the second kind of material, they will sell for $80 - 3x$ and $60 - 2y$ dollars per dozen, respectively. How many dozens of each kind should he schedule for production *so as to maximize his profit*, knowing that the cost of manufacturing x dozen shirts out of the first kind of material and y dozen shirts out of the second kind of material is $12x + 8y + 4xy$ dollars?

Since his total sales revenue is given by $x(80 - 3x) + y(60 - 2y)$, where $x(80 - x)$ is the amount of money received for the shirts made out of the first kind of material and $y(60 - 2y)$ is the amount of money received for the shirts made out of the second kind of material, his profit is

$$\begin{aligned} z &= x(80 - 3x) + y(60 - 2y) - (12x + 8y + 4xy) \\ &= 80x - 3x^2 + 60y - 2y^2 - 12x - 8y - 4xy \end{aligned}$$

Now, if we differentiate partially with respect to x and y, we get

$$\frac{\partial z}{\partial x} = 80 - 6x - 12 - 4y$$

and

$$\frac{\partial z}{\partial y} = 60 - 4y - 8 - 4x$$

and the values of these two partial derivatives are zero when $80 - 6x - 12 - 4y = 0$ and $60 - 4y - 8 - 4x = 0$, namely, when

$$6x + 4y = 68$$

$$4x + 4y = 52$$

Subtracting "equals from equals," we get $2x = 16$ and, hence, $x = 8$, and if we then substitute this value of x into the second equation, we get $4(8) + 4y = 52$, $4y = 20$, and $y = 5$.

To check whether $x = 8$ and $y = 5$ will actually maximize the manufacturer's profit, we shall have to investigate the second partial derivatives, which are

$$\frac{\partial^2 z}{\partial x^2} = -6, \qquad \frac{\partial^2 z}{\partial y^2} = -4, \qquad \text{and} \qquad \frac{\partial^2 z}{\partial x\,\partial y} = -4$$

Since the first two are *negative* and

$$\frac{\partial^2 z}{\partial x^2}\cdot\frac{\partial^2 z}{\partial y^2} - \left(\frac{\partial^2 z}{\partial x\,\partial y}\right)^2 = (-6)(-4) - (-4)^2 = 8 > 0$$

it follows that the manufacturer's profit will indeed be a *maximum* if he schedules the production of 8 dozen shirts made out of the first kind of material and 5 dozen shirts made out of the second kind of material. In fact, this maximum profit will be

$$\begin{aligned} z &= 80(8) - 3(8)^2 + 60(5) - 2(5)^2 - 12(8) - 8(5) - 4(8)(5) \\ &= \$402.00 \end{aligned}$$

Another important use of partial differentiation is in the theory which underlies what is called *curve fitting by the method of least squares*. To illustrate this technique, suppose that a publisher's sales totaled 7 million dollars in 1966, 8 million dollars in 1967, and 15 million dollars in 1968; the problem is to fit a *trend line* to these data and perhaps, use it to predict future sales. The given data are shown in Figure 13.10, where we have *coded* the years so that $x = 1$ corresponds to 1966, $x = 2$ corresponds to 1967, and $x = 3$ corresponds to 1968.

Since the three points do not lie on a straight line, all we can ask for is a line which somehow provides the *best fit* to the given data, namely, a line which *best describes* the overall growth pattern of the company's sales. The criterion which is most widely used for this purpose (namely, that of providing the best possible fit) is the criterion of *least squares*—it requires that *the sum of the squares of the vertical deviations (distances) from the points to the line be a minimum*. In other words, with reference to Figure 13.10, we shall have to find the line for which the sum of the squares of line segments AD, BE, and CF is a minimum. The reason why we are asked to minimize the sum of the *squares* of the deviations instead of the sum of the deviations, themselves, is that some of the deviations will be positive, some will be

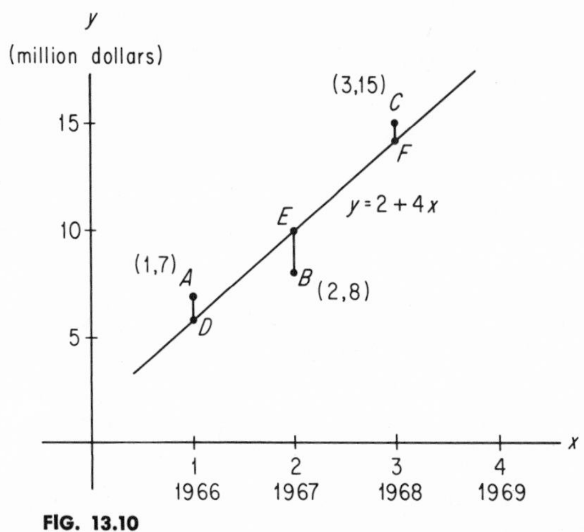

FIG. 13.10

negative, so that their sum could be zero even though the line provides a very poor fit; this is illustrated in Exercise 12 on page 397.

If we write the equation of the line as $y = a + bx$, our problem is to determine the values of a and b for which the least squares criterion will be attained. To this end, we shall have to express the length of the line segments AD, BE, and CF in terms of a and b, and then find the values of a and b which will minimize the sum of their squares. Now, for $x = 1$ the company's sales were $y = 7$ (million dollars), the corresponding value on the line is $a + b(1) = a + b$, so that the vertical distance AD of Figure 13.10 is

$$7 - (a + b) = 7 - a - b$$

Similarly, for $x = 2$ and $x = 3$ the company's sales were $y = 8$ and $y = 15$, giving us corresponding values on the line of $a + b(2) = a + 2b$ and $a + b(3) = a + 3b$, so that the vertical distances BE and CF of Figure 13.10 are, respectively,

$$8 - (a + 2b) = 8 - a - 2b \quad \text{and} \quad 15 - (a + 3b) = 15 - a - 3b$$

Thus, the quantity we shall have to minimize is the sum of squares

$$Q = (7 - a - b)^2 + (8 - a - 2b)^2 + (15 - a - 3b)^2$$

which depends on the two unknown quantities a and b—for each pair of values of a and b we will get a *different line* and generally also a different value of Q.

To find the minimum value of Q, we shall put the two partial derivatives $\frac{\partial Q}{\partial a}$ and $\frac{\partial Q}{\partial b}$ equal to zero, and then solve the resulting equations for a and b. We thus get

$$\frac{\partial Q}{\partial a} = 2(7 - a - b)(-1) + 2(8 - a - 2b)(-1) + 2(15 - a - 3b)(-1)$$
$$= 6a + 12b - 60$$
$$\frac{\partial Q}{\partial b} = 2(7 - a - b)(-1) + 2(8 - a - 2b)(-2) + 2(15 - a - 3b)(-3)$$
$$= 12a + 28b - 136$$

and, hence, the system of linear equations $6a + 12b - 60 = 0$ and $12a + 28b - 136 = 0$, which can also be written as

$$6a + 12b = 60$$
$$12a + 28b = 136$$

As can easily be verified, the solution of this system of linear equations is $a = 2$ and $b = 4$, so that the equation of the *least squares line* is

$$y = 2 + 4x$$

If we wanted to use this equation to predict the publisher's sales, say, for 1972, we would only have to substitute $x = 7$, getting $y = 2 + 4(7) = 30$ million dollars. Incidentally, we did not check whether our solution for a and b actually constitutes a minimum; it will be left to the reader to take care of this in Exercise 13 on page 397.

In actual practice, we never go through all these steps when we fit a straight line to observed data. The problem of finding the values of a and b in the *least squares line* $y = a + bx$ can be solved *symbolically*, and in Exercise 15 on page 397 the reader will be asked to show that (as in our numerical example) this leads to two linear equations which are easily solved for a and b.

EXERCISES

1. In a certain city, the daily demand for beef (in pounds) is given by the equation

$$z = 3{,}800 - 27x + 33y$$

where x is the average retail price of beef (in cents per pound) and y is the average retail price of pork (in cents per pound). Calculate the two partial derivatives $\frac{\partial z}{\partial x}$ and $\frac{\partial z}{\partial y}$ and explain precisely what they mean.

2. A banker figures the size of a 20-year mortgage he is willing to give on a one-family house by means of the formula

$$z = 2x_1 + 0.02(x_2)^2$$

where x_1 is the size of the downpayment, x_2 is the applicant's monthly salary, and all figures are in dollars. Calculate the two partial derivatives $\frac{\partial z}{\partial x_1}$ and $\frac{\partial z}{\partial x_2}$ and explain precisely what they mean.

3. Calculate $\frac{\partial z}{\partial x}$, $\frac{\partial z}{\partial y}$, $\frac{\partial^2 z}{\partial x^2}$, and $\frac{\partial^2 z}{\partial y^2}$ for each of the following:

(a) $z = x^2 + 3xy - y^2$; (d) $z = 3x^2 + 2y - x \cdot e^y$;

(b) $z = x^3 + x^2y^2 - 3y^3$; (e) $z = \ln x + 3x^2y$;

(c) $z = 3x + 2y - \frac{x}{y}$; (f) $z = x(\ln y) + y(\ln x)$.

4. Verify for each part of Exercise 3 that $\frac{\partial^2 z}{\partial y \partial x} = \frac{\partial^2 z}{\partial x \partial y}$.

5. If $z = 100 - x^2 - y^2 - 14x + 8y$, find the values of x and y for which z is a maximum. What is this maximum value of z?

6. Check each of the following for the possible existence of a relative maximum or a relative minimum:

(a) $z = 2x^2 - 2xy + y^2 - 16x + 10y + 12$;

(b) $z = x^2 - 3xy - 2y^2 - 5x + y$;

(c) $z = e^{-(x^2+y^2)}$.

7. A construction company pays untrained workers \$1.50 an hour and trained workers \$2.50 an hour. Knowing that the cost of a certain job (in dollars) will be

$$z = 2{,}000 + 27x^3 - 72xy + 8y^2$$

if they use x untrained workers and y trained workers, how many workers of each kind should they use so as to *minimize their cost*?

8. A pharmaceutical firm can make $20 - \frac{50}{x} - \frac{24}{y}$ pounds of an antibiotic out of x pounds of ingredient A and y pounds of ingredient B, where ingredient A costs \$3.00 a pound, ingredient B costs \$4.00 a pound, and the antibiotic sells for \$24.00 a pound.

(a) Subtracting the cost of the ingredients, $3x + 4y$, from the total sales revenue, $24\left(20 - \frac{50}{x} - \frac{24}{y}\right)$, express the pharmaceutical firm's profit, z, in terms of x and y.

(b) Using the result of part (a), determine how many pounds of each ingredient they should use so as to *maximize their profit*. What is this maximum profit.

9. The total profit of a restaurant was found to depend mostly on the amount of money spent on advertising and the quality of the preparation of the food (measured in terms of the salaries paid to the chefs). In fact, the manager of the restaurant found that if he pays his chefs x dollars per hour and spends y dollars a week on advertising, the restaurant's weekly profit (in dollars) will be

$$z = 412x + 806y - x^2 - y^2 - xy$$

What hourly wages should the manager pay his chefs and how much should he spend on advertising, so as to *maximize the restaurant's profit*?

10. A company makes two kinds of detergents which are competitive, so that if D_1 and D_2 are the respective demands when the prices the company gets for them are p_1 and p_2, then

$$D_1 = 5 - 2p_1 + p_2$$

and

$$D_2 = 1 + 5p_1 - 3p_2$$

where the demands are in millions of boxes and the prices are in cents per box.

(a) Solve this system of equations for p_1 and p_2 (in terms of D_1 and D_2), and use the result to show that the total sales revenue on D_1 million boxes of the first detergent and D_2 million boxes of the second detergent will be

$$D_1(16 - 3D_1 - D_2) + D_2(27 - 5D_1 - 2D_2)$$

million cents.

(b) If it costs the company 4 cents to produce a box of the first kind of detergent and 17 cents to produce a box of the second kind of detergent, show that the company's profit is *not* a maximum when $D_1 = 1$ and $D_2 = 1$.

11. In the inventory problem on page 377 we balanced the *inventory carrying cost* against the *cost of placing orders*. An interesting variation of this problem arises when we allow for the possibility of running out of stock, and consider also the *cost (penalty) of late delivery* to customers. Suppose, for instance, that a regional distributor gets orders for R color television sets per day, C is the cost of holding a set in inventory for one day, D is the penalty per day for not delivering a set on time, and K is the cost of placing and executing an order (regardless of its size). Now, if an order for x sets is placed (and immediately filled) every y days, it can be shown that the *average daily cost of maintaining inventory* is given by

$$z = \frac{Cx^2 + D(Ry - x)^2}{2Ry} + \frac{K}{y}$$

(a) Find $\frac{\partial z}{\partial x}$, equate this partial derivative to zero, and show that the resulting equation, solved for x, becomes

$$x = \frac{RDy}{C + D}$$

(b) Find $\frac{\partial z}{\partial y}$, equate this partial derivative to zero, and, substituting for x the expression obtained in part (a), show that the solution for y is

$$y = \sqrt{\frac{2K(C + D)}{CDR}}$$

(c) Substituting this solution for y into the expression obtained for x in part (a), show that the corresponding solution for x is

$$x = \sqrt{\frac{2DKR}{C(C + D)}}$$

(d) *How often* and *how many* sets should the distributor order from the factory if $R = 16$, $K = \$6.00$, $C = \$0.25$, and $D = \$0.75$?

12. With reference to the example on page 393, show that the sum of the vertical deviations from the three points to the line $y = 18 - 4x$ is equal to *zero*; in fact, show that they are -7, -2, and 9. Plot this line on a diagram showing also the three given points, and judge the "goodness" of the fit.

13. With reference to the least-squares example on page 394, find all of the second derivatives and verify that the *sum of squares* Q is, indeed, a minimum for the given values of a and b.

14. Rework the least-squares example in the text coding the three years $-1, 0, 1$, instead of 1, 2, and 3. Does this change simplify the calculations?

15. THE METHOD OF LEAST SQUARES. To find the equation of the line which best fits a given set of points (x_1, y_1), (x_2, y_2), (x_3, y_3), . . . , and (x_n, y_n) by the method of least squares, we minimize the *sum of the squares of the vertical deviations* from the points to the line, as is illustrated in Figure 13.11. If the equation of the line is $y = a + bx$, the vertical deviations from the points to the line are given by the differences

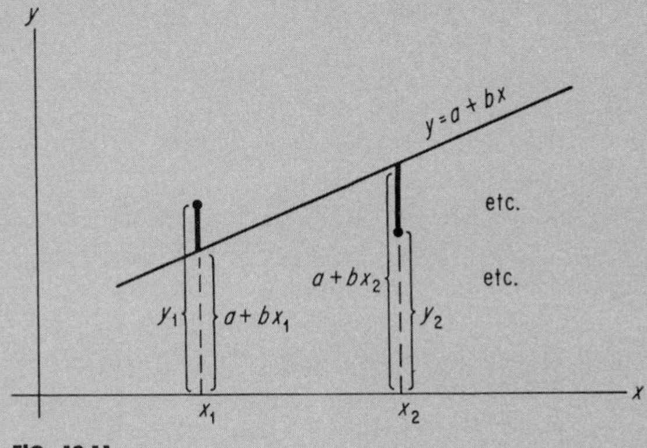

FIG. 13.11

$$y_1 - (a + bx_1) = y_1 - a - bx_1$$
$$y_2 - (a + bx_2) = y_2 - a - bx_2$$
$$y_3 - (a + bx_3) = y_3 - a - bx_3$$
$$\cdots\cdots\cdots\cdots\cdots\cdots$$
$$y_n - (a + bx_n) = y_n - a - bx_n$$

as can be seen from Figure 13.11; thus, the quantity which has to be minimized is given by

$$Q = (y_1 - a - bx_1)^2 + (y_2 - a - bx_2)^2 + (y_3 - a - bx_3)^2 + \ldots + (y_n - a - bx_n)^2$$

Equating the partial derivatives $\frac{\partial Q}{\partial a}$ and $\frac{\partial Q}{\partial b}$ to zero, show that the resulting equations can be written in the form

$$\sum y = a \cdot n + b(\sum x)$$

and

$$\sum xy = a(\sum x) + b(\sum x^2)$$

where n is the number of points, $\sum x$ is the sum of their x-coordinates, $\sum x^2$ is the sum of the squares of their x-coordinates, $\sum y$ is the sum of their y-coordinates, and $\sum xy$ is the sum of the products obtained by multiplying the x- and y-coordinates of each point. [The Greek letter $\sum$ (*sigma*) stands for "sum."] The above equations which provide the solutions for a and b are generally referred to as the *normal equations*.

16. **THE METHOD OF LEAST SQUARES, CONTINUED.** Find $\sum x$, $\sum x^2$, $\sum y$ and $\sum xy$ for the example on page 393 where n equalled 3, and show that the normal equations obtained by substituting all these values are the same as the two equations on page 394. (Other applications may be found in Exercises 11 and 12 on page 203.)

14

INTEGRAL CALCULUS

14.1 INTRODUCTION

In the introduction to Chapter 12 we stated that calculus deals with two special kinds of limits called *derivatives* and *integrals*. Then we proceeded to introduce the derivative as a *limit of a function* which represents the slope, steepness, or direction, of a curve at a point. In contrast, an integral is a *limit of a sequence*, but it also has an important geometrical interpretation —as we shall see in Section 14.2, *integrals represent areas under curves.*

Integrals do not have as many *direct* applications as derivatives to problems of business and economics. *Indirectly*, though, they play a very important role in the definition of *probability*, and, hence, they are of basic importance in statistics and in the many areas of management science which involve elements of uncertainty. This relationship between integrals and probability will be discussed later in the chapter on probability (in Section 16.6, to be exact).

14.2 THE AREA UNDER A CURVE

Whenever we are dealing with *continuously changing variables*, we must be extremely careful not to misinterpret their significance. Suppose, for example, that the demand for a new kind of high-intensity reading lamp is given by the equation

$$f(x) = 120 + 144x^2$$

where x is the number of years that have lapsed since the lamp was first put on the market. Now, if we substitute $x = 1$ into this equation, we get

$$f(1) = 120 + 144(1)^2 = 264$$

and we might say that there is a demand for 264 lamps a year after they have been introduced. This would be correct, but only if the demand is interpreted as an *annual rate*. They will not sell 264 of these lamps in a fraction of a second or even on the day that the product has been on the market for exactly one year—*no, but they would sell* 264 *of the lamps during the second year provided the demand remained constant at the level at which it was at the end of the first year.*

Of course, this is not going to happen. According to the given equation the demand will *not* remain constant: after a year and a half it will have become

$$f(1.5) = 120 + 144(1.5)^2 = 444$$

and after two years it will have become

$$f(2) = 120 + 144(2)^2 = 696$$

This raises a very interesting question—*how many of the lamps will they actually sell during the second year that the product is on the market?*

If we were satisfied with a rough estimate of their second-year sales, we could say that since the demand is increasing from an annual rate of 264 at $x = 1$ to an annual rate of 696 at $x = 2$, they will sell anywhere from 264 to 696 of the lamps. If we wanted to narrow this down a bit, we could say that they will sell *at least* $\frac{1}{2}(264) = 132$ lamps during the first half of the second year, *at least* $\frac{1}{2}(444) = 222$ lamps during the second half, and, hence, *at least* $132 + 222 = 354$ lamps during the second year. This situation is pic-

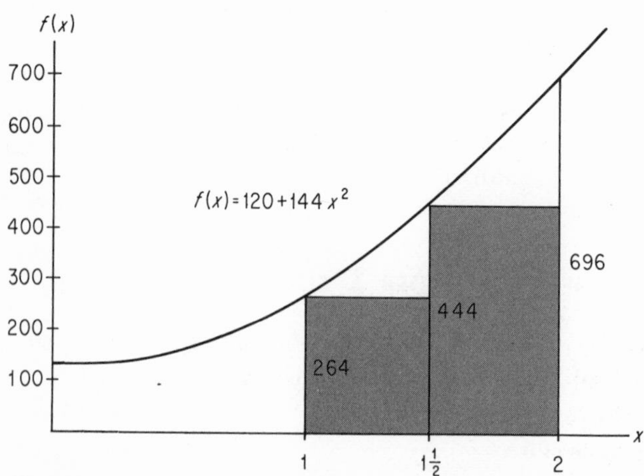

FIG. 14.1

tured in Figure 14.1, where we have drawn the graph of $f(x) = 120 + 144x^2$ and also the two rectangles whose *areas* represent the respective half-year sales [assuming that the demand remains at the constant annual rate of $f(1) = 264$ during the first half of the year and at the constant annual rate of $f(1.5) = 444$ during the second half of the year.] Note that the first rectangle has a height of $f(1) = 264$, a base of 1/2, and, hence, an area of $\frac{1}{2}(264) = 132$, while the second rectangle has a height of $f(1.5) = 444$, a base of 1/2, and, hence, an area of $\frac{1}{2}(444) = 222$.

To get an approximation of the second-year sales which is even better, let us suppose that the demand remains constant throughout each month *at the level at which it is at the beginning of the month*, and (as a matter of convenience) let us suppose, furthermore, that each month is 1/12 of a year. In the *first month* of the second year they would thus sell $\frac{1}{12}\cdot f(1) = \frac{1}{12}(264)$ $= 22$ lamps, in the *second month* they would sell $\frac{1}{12}\cdot f\left(1\frac{1}{12}\right) = \frac{1}{12}(289)$ $= 24\frac{1}{12}$ lamps, in the *third month* they would sell $\frac{1}{12}\cdot f\left(1\frac{2}{12}\right) = \frac{1}{12}(316)$ $= 26\frac{4}{12}$ lamps, . . . , and in the *twelfth month* they would sell $\frac{1}{12}\cdot f\left(1\frac{11}{12}\right)$ $= \frac{1}{12}(649) = 54\frac{1}{12}$ lamps. Leaving it to the reader to find the corresponding figures for the other eight months (see Exercise 6 on page 409), we thus find that their second-year sales will total

$$22 + 24\frac{1}{12} + 26\frac{4}{12} + \ldots + 54\frac{1}{12} = 438\frac{2}{12}$$

If we picture this approximation of the second-year sales as in Figure 14.2, we find that the total of $438\frac{2}{12}$ is actually *the sum of the areas of the twelve shaded rectangles*. The height of the first rectangle is $f(1) = 264$, its base is 1/12, and, hence, its *area* is $\frac{1}{12}(264) = 22$; the height of the second rectangle is $f\left(1\frac{1}{12}\right) = 289$, its base is 1/12, and, hence, its *area* is $\frac{1}{12}(289)$ $= 24\frac{1}{12}$; . . . ; and the height of the twelfth rectangle is $f\left(1\frac{11}{12}\right) = 649$, its base is 1/12, and, hence, its *area* is $\frac{1}{12}(649) = 54\frac{1}{12}$.

There is no reason why this kind of approximation cannot be improved, say, by holding the demand constant for each day (at the level at which it is at the beginning of the day). The result would then be given by the sum of the areas of 365 rectangles like those of Figure 14.3, which is approxi-

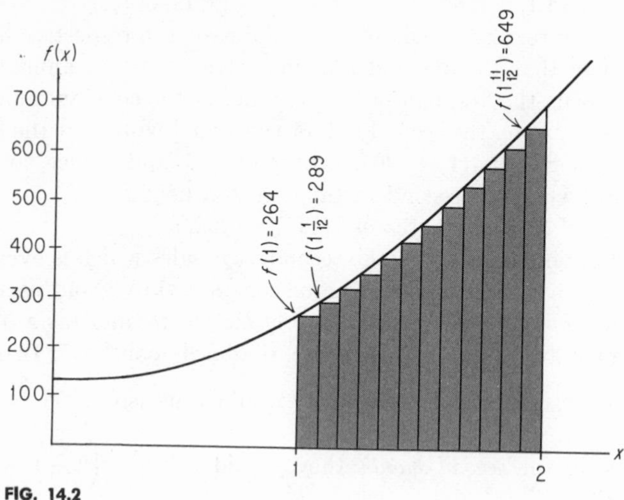

FIG. 14.2

mately 455.41, as we shall see on page 405. This value may be perfectly adequate to predict the total second-year sales, but more important by far is the idea which our method suggests—*if we choose smaller and smaller intervals over which the demand is assumed to be constant, then the total second-year sales will approach the corresponding area under the curve, namely, the shaded area of Figure 14.4.*

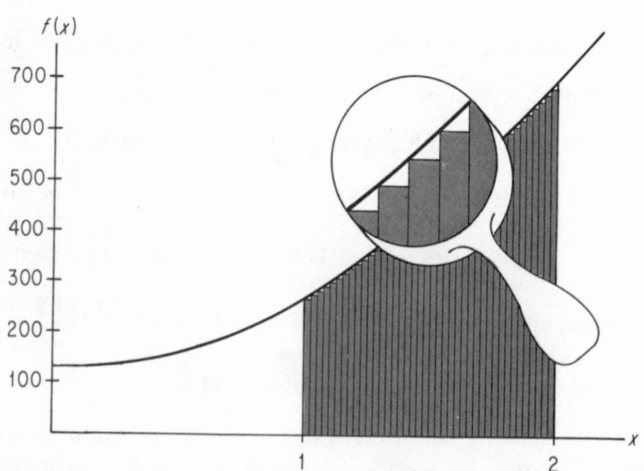

FIG. 14.3

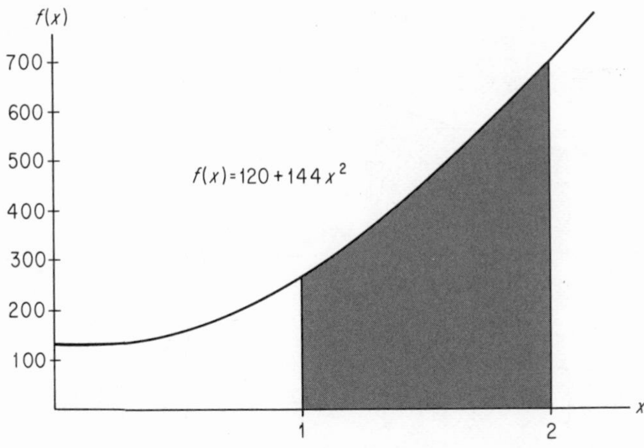

FIG. 14.4

This sounds very reasonable, but let us point out that so far as elementary geometry is concerned, such an area is *not even defined*; all we talk about in elementary geometry are the areas of regions made up of rectangles, triangles, circles, or parts of circles. However, if we follow the suggestion of the preceding paragraph, we can now *define* an area like that of Figure 14.4 as *the limit which is approached by the sum of the areas of appropriate rectangles (like those of Figures 14.1, 14.2, and 14.3) when the number of rectangles increases beyond any bound, and, at the same time, the base of each rectangle gets smaller and smaller, namely, when the base of each rectangle approaches zero as a limit.*

To evaluate this limit for our numerical example, let us divide the interval from $x = 1$ to $x = 2$ into n equal parts, where n is an arbitrary positive integer. The base of each rectangle will then be $1/n$, as is indicated in Figure 14.5, and the heights of the n rectangles are, respectively,

$$f(1) = 120 + 144(1)^2$$

$$f\left(1 + \frac{1}{n}\right) = 120 + 144\left(1 + \frac{1}{n}\right)^2$$

$$f\left(1 + \frac{2}{n}\right) = 120 + 144\left(1 + \frac{2}{n}\right)^2$$

. . . .

$$f\left(1 + \frac{n-1}{n}\right) = 120 + 144\left(1 + \frac{n-1}{n}\right)^2$$

The sum of the areas of the n rectangles of Figure 14.5, which we shall denote S_n, is thus given by

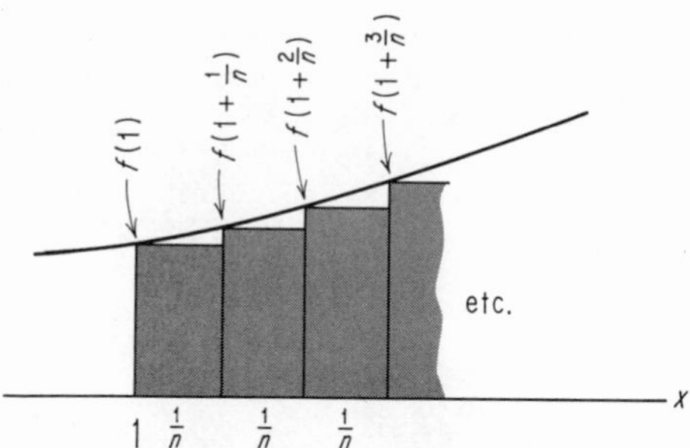

FIG. 14.5

$$S_n = \frac{1}{n}\left[120 + 144(1)^2\right] + \frac{1}{n}\left[120 + 144\left(1 + \frac{1}{n}\right)^2\right]$$
$$+ \frac{1}{n}\left[120 + 144\left(1 + \frac{2}{n}\right)^2\right] + \ldots + \frac{1}{n}\left[120 + 144\left(1 + \frac{n-1}{n}\right)^2\right]$$

and (after collecting terms and performing other simplifications which we shall omit) it can be written as

$$S_n = 264 + \frac{288}{n^2}[1 + 2 + \ldots + (n - 1)]$$
$$+ \frac{144}{n^3}[1^2 + 2^2 + \ldots + (n - 1)^2]$$

To simplify this further, we shall have to use the formula for the *sum of the first k positive integers* which the reader was asked to prove in part (*f*) of Exercise 7 on page 315, namely,

$$1 + 2 + 3 + \ldots + k = \frac{k(k + 1)}{2}$$

and also the formula for the *sum of their squares*

$$1^2 + 2^2 + 3^2 + \ldots + k^2 = \frac{k(k + 1)(2k + 1)}{6}$$

which is proved in most college algebra texts by what is called *mathematical induction;* we shall not prove it here, but the reader can easily check for himself that the formula holds, say, for $k = 1, 2, 3, 4$, and 5.

When $k = n - 1$, the two formulas become

$$1 + 2 + 3 + \ldots + (n - 1) = \frac{(n - 1)n}{2}$$

and

$$1^2 + 2^2 + 3^2 + \ldots + (n - 1)^2 = \frac{(n - 1)n(2n - 1)}{6}$$

so that the expression which we obtained for the sum of the n rectangles of Figure 14.5 can now be written as

$$S_n = 264 + \frac{288}{n^2}\left[\frac{(n-1)n}{2}\right] + \frac{144}{n^3}\left[\frac{(n-1)n(2n-1)}{6}\right]$$

and further simplifications (which the reader will be asked to perform in Exercise 5 on page 409) lead to the final result

$$S_n = 456 - \frac{216}{n} + \frac{24}{n^2}$$

Had we treated this general case first, we could have saved ourselves a good deal of work on page 401. Substituting $n = 12$ into the formula obtained for S_n, we get

$$456 - \frac{216}{12} + \frac{24}{12^2} = 456 - 18 + \frac{2}{12} = 438\frac{2}{12}$$

without having to go to the trouble of calculating the area of each rectangle. Incidentally, it was with the use of this formula that we obtained 455.41 (rounded to two decimals) for the case where $n = 365$, namely, for the case where the demand was held constant each day.

Finally, to complete the solution of our problem, we shall have to perform one more step—we shall have to find the *limit* of the sum of the areas of the n rectangles when their base, $1/n$, approaches zero. We shall write this as $n \to \infty$, where ∞ is the symbol for *infinity*; $n \to \infty$ reads "n goes to infinity," and it means that n increases beyond any bound. Since $216/n$ and $24/n^2$ both approach zero when $n \to \infty$, we get

$$\lim_{n\to\infty} \left(456 - \frac{216}{n} + \frac{24}{n^2}\right) = 456$$

and this figure represents the *actual second-year sales of the given kind of lamp*. Geometrically speaking, it *is* the area of the shaded region of Figure 14.4, namely, the area of the region bounded by the x-axis, the graph of $f(x) = 120 + 144x^2$, and the two vertical lines $x = 1$ and $x = 2$.

14.3 THE DEFINITE INTEGRAL

The argument which we used in the preceding section is not limited to the particular example where the demand for a product increases continuously with time in accordance with the formula $f(x) = 120 + 144x^2$. Areas under curves arise in many applications (relating to all sorts of situations), and it is for this reason that the kind of limit which we determined in the preceding section, namely, the limit of the sum of the areas of *more and more rectangles which become narrower and narrower,* has a special symbol and also a special name. It is denoted

$$\int_a^b f(x)\,dx$$

and it is referred to as the *definite integral (of the given function) from a to b.* For any continuous function with the values $f(x)$, it *defines* the area of the region bounded by the x-axis, the graph of $y = f(x)$, and the two vertical lines $x = a$ and $x = b$, as in Figure 14.6. (Actually, definite integrals can also be defined for some functions which have discontinuities, but we shall not be concerned with this here.)

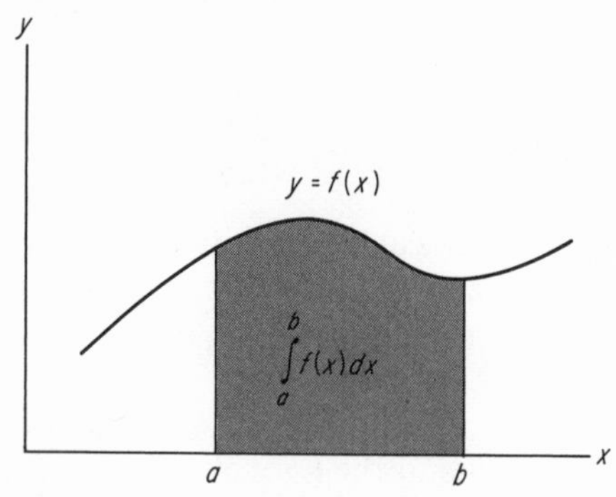

FIG. 14.6

The symbol $\int$ is called the *integral sign,* and it is really an elongated S, standing for "sum." The function whose values $f(x)$ are the heights of the rectangles is called the *integrand,* and a and b are called the *limits of integration*; they tell us "from where to where" the area goes. The dx serves to indicate that we divide the interval from a to b along the *x-axis* into n equal parts, which we might denote Δx in accordance with the notation of Section 12.2, and then take the limit as $\Delta x \to 0$. It must be understood, however, and it cannot be too strongly emphasized, that the symbol $\int_a^b f(x)dx$ *as a whole* represents the limit which we refer to as a definite integral; individually, $\int$ and dx do not really have any significance.

Using this notation, we can now write the second-year sales which we derived in the preceding section as

$$\int_1^2 (120 + 144x^2)\,dx$$

and it must be apparent that the evaluation of a definite integral like this can be very involved, to say the least. Even though $f(x) = 120 + 144x^2$ represents a very simple kind of function, a considerable amount of work was needed to find a general expression for the sum of the areas of the n rectangles, simplify it (that is, put it into a manageable form), and then take the limit as $n \to \infty$. Fortunately, there exists a theorem, called the *fundamental theorem of integral calculus,* which makes it possible to avoid most of this work. This theorem will be introduced in Section 14.4, and until then we shall let the reader struggle with the exercises that follow.

EXERCISES

1. Suppose that in the example of Section 14.2 the growth of the demand for the lamps had been linear, so that $f(x) = 120 + 144x$, where the significance of x and $f(x)$ are the same as before.

   (a) Subdividing the interval from $x = 1$ to $x = 2$ into n equal intervals (as in Figure 14.7 for $n = 13$), show that the *sum* of the areas of the n rectangles (which approximates the second-year sales) can be written as

   $$264 + \frac{144}{n^2}[1 + 2 + 3 + \ldots + (n - 1)]$$

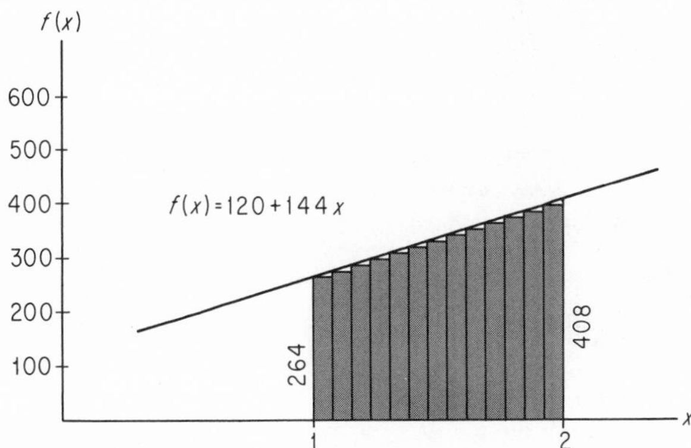

FIG. 14.7

   (b) Use the formula for the sum of the first k positive integers on page 404 to show that the sum of the areas of the n rectangles can be written as $336 - \frac{72}{n}$

   (c) Find the actual second-year sales by taking the limit of the expression obtained in part (b) as $n \to \infty$.

   (d) The result of part (c) gives the area of the region bounded by the x-axis, the line $f(x) = 120 + 144x$, and the two vertical lines $x = 1$ and $x = 2$. Since this is a *trapezoid,* verify the result of part (c) by making use of the formula according to which the area of a trapezoid is *half* the product of the *sum of the two parallel sides* and the *altitude*, namely, the perpendicular distance between the two parallel sides.

2. To find the area of the region bounded by the x-axis, the graph of $f(x) = x^2$, and the vertical line $x = 1$, we divide the interval from 0 to 1 into n equal parts and then form rectangles as in either of the two diagrams of Figure 14.8.

(a) Show that if we form the rectangles as in the *first diagram*, the sum of the areas of the n rectangles is

$$\frac{1}{3} - \frac{1}{2n} + \frac{1}{6n^2}$$

and if we form the rectangles as in the *second diagram*, the sum of the areas of the n rectangles is

$$\frac{1}{3} + \frac{1}{2n} + \frac{1}{6n^2}$$

(*Hint:* make use of the formula for the sum of the squares of the first k positive integers on page 404.)

(b) Explain why the *actual* area under this parabola from $x = 0$ to $x = 1$ must always lie *between* the two expressions obtained in part (a), and why it must, be equal to 1/3.

3. Making use of the formula $1^3 + 2^3 + 3^3 + \ldots + k^3 = \dfrac{k^2(k+1)^2}{4}$, find the area bounded by the x-axis, the graph of $y = -x^3$, and the vertical line $x = 1$. Note that the heights of the rectangles, being given by the values of the function, will be *negative*, and, hence, the final answer will be *negative*. What general rule can we derive from this? [*Hint:* form the rectangles as in the second diagram of Figure 14.8, so that the height of the first rectangle will be $-\left(\frac{1}{n}\right)^3$, that of the second rectangle will be $-\left(\frac{2}{n}\right)^3$, and so on.]

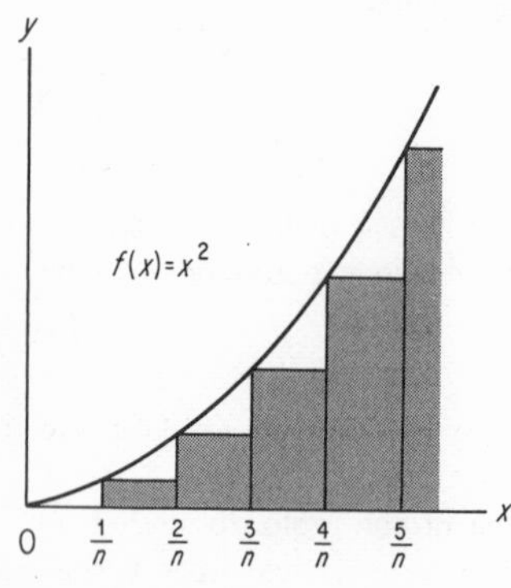

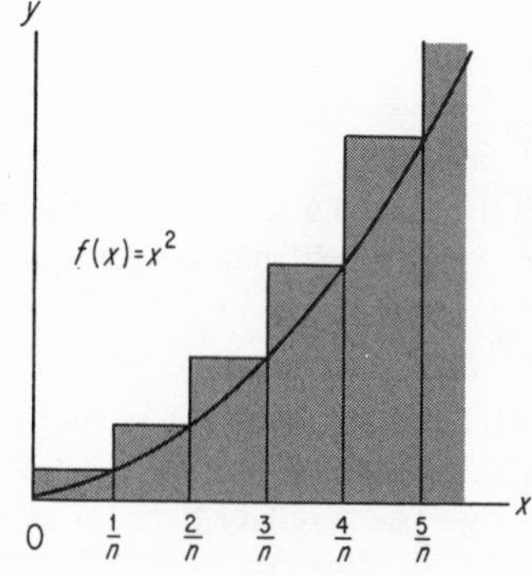

FIG. 14.8

4. Draw the regions whose areas are given by the following definite integrals:

(a) $\int_1^3 (1 + 3x)\,dx$; (e) $\int_2^5 \frac{1}{x}\,dx$;

(b) $\int_{-1}^1 (4 - x)\,dx$; (f) $\int_1^3 e^x\,dx$;

(c) $\int_2^4 (1 + x^2)\,dx$; (g) $\int_0^2 (2x - x^2)\,dx$;

(d) $\int_1^3 (x^2 - 4x + 3)\,dx$; (h) $\int_2^3 (1 - e^{-x})\,dx$.

5. Show in detail the simplifications which we omitted on page 405 in the last step of the derivation of the formula for S_n.

6. Complete the calculations of the example on page 401, namely, find the figures for the other eight months to verify that the total for the year is $438\frac{2}{12}$.

14.4 THE FUNDAMENTAL THEOREM

After we defined derivatives in the beginning of Chapter 12, we showed that there are many special formulas and many special methods which enable us to differentiate *without having to go through the whole detailed process of evaluating the necessary limits by means of the four steps outlined on page* 342. Even greater simplifications are possible in the evaluation of definite integrals—by using a special theorem, called the *fundamental theorem of integral calculus*, we can find the values of most definite integrals *without having to go through the cumbersome process of determining the limit of the sum of the areas of rectangles (as we did in the preceding sections)*. The proof of this theorem is difficult, but to express it *in words*, the value of the definite integral

$$\int_a^b f(x)\,dx$$

can be obtained by finding a function *whose derivative equals the integrand* $f(x)$, and then subtracting the value of this function at $x = a$ from its value at $x = b$. More formally

If $f(x)$ is the derivative of $F(x)$, and both of these functions are continuous on the interval from a to b, then

$$\int_a^b f(x)\,dx = F(b) - F(a)$$

and we find that the whole problem of evaluating a definite integral reduces to that of finding a function (or functions) whose derivative is of a given form. This process is referred to as *anti-differentiation,* and it is amazing, to say the least, that the two basic limits of calculus, derivatives and integrals, are related in this way. Note that we used the corresponding *capital letter* to denote the anti-derivative of the given function. This is common practice, and we might, similarly, write the anti-derivative of $g(x)$ as $G(x)$, the anti-derivative of $q(x)$ as $Q(x)$, and so forth.

It is difficult to illustrate the fundamental theorem without having learned how to anti-differentiate, but let us use it anyhow to re-evaluate the second-year sales of the lamps with which we were concerned throughout Section 14.2. Making use of the fact that $f(x) = 120 + 144x^2$ is the derivative of $F(x) = 120x + 48x^3$, for example, which is easily verified since

$$F'(x) = 120 + 48\cdot 3x^2 = 120 + 144x^2$$

we can now write

$$\int_1^2 (120 + 144x^2)\, dx = F(2) - F(1)$$

where $F(2) = 120(2) + 48(2)^3 = 624$ and $F(1) = 120(1) + 48(1)^3 = 168$. Hence, the second-year sales of the given kind of lamp (namely, the area of the shaded region of Figure 14.1) equal

$$\int_1^2 (120 + 144x^2)\, dx = 624 - 168 = 456$$

and this agrees with the result obtained in Section 14.2 *after a great deal of work.*

14.5 ANTI-DIFFERENTIATION

Although the terms "anti-derivative" and "anti-differentiation" are widely used, it is more common to refer to the anti-derivative of a function as its *indefinite integral,* and to refer to the process of anti-differentiation simply as *integration.* Thus, if $F'(x) = f(x)$, we refer to $F(x)$ as the *indefinite integral* of $f(x)$ and we write it as

$$F(x) = \int f(x)\, dx$$

As on page 406, the symbols $\int$ and dx, individually, do not have any significance; the whole expression $\int f(x)\, dx$ represents the function (or, perhaps, functions) whose derivative is $f(x)$.

So far as the above example is concerned, we could have written the information about the anti-derivative of $120 + 144x^2$ as

$$\int (120 + 144x^2)\, dx = 120x + 48x^3$$

and it may have occurred to the reader that $F(x) = 120x + 48x^3$ is *not* the only function whose derivative is $120 + 144x^2$; other possibilities are $F(x) = 120x + 48x^3 + 3$, $F(x) = 120x + 48x^3 - 17$, and, in general, any function of the form $F(x) = 120x + 48x^3 + C$, where C is an arbitrary constant. This simply expresses the fact that *the derivative of a constant is zero,* and if we turn this argument around, we can now say that *the anti-derivative of zero is a constant.*

In general, if $F(x)$ is an *anti-derivative* of $f(x)$, then so is $F(x) + C$, and to allow for the existence of this constant we always write

$$\int f(x)\,dx = F(x) + C \qquad \text{instead of} \qquad \int f(x)\,dx = F(x)$$

where C is called the *constant of integration.* How the value of this constant is determined in any given example, is illustrated on page 413.

In Chapter 12 we proved that the derivative of x^n is $n \cdot x^{n-1}$, where n can be any positive or negative integer or fraction. Thus, the derivative of x^{n+1} is $(n + 1)x^n$, the derivative of $\frac{1}{n+1} \cdot x^{n+1}$ is $\frac{1}{n+1} \cdot (n + 1)x^n = x^n$, and, hence, the *anti-derivative* of x^n is $\frac{1}{n+1} \cdot x^{n+1}$, and we can write

$$\int x^n dx = \frac{1}{n+1} \cdot x^{n+1} + C$$

for any rational number n except -1; what happens when $n = -1$ is explained on page 414. This result is very easy to remember: *to integrate a power of x we increase the exponent by 1 and divide by the new exponent.* To give a few examples,

$$\int x^5\,dx = \frac{1}{6} \cdot x^6 + C$$

$$\int \frac{1}{x^3}\,dx = \int x^{-3}\,dx = \frac{1}{-2} \cdot x^{-2} + C = -\frac{1}{2x^2} + C$$

and

$$\int \sqrt{x}\,dx = \int x^{1/2}\,dx = \frac{1}{3/2} \cdot x^{3/2} + C = \frac{2}{3} \cdot x\sqrt{x} + C$$

Also, for $n = 0$ the integrand becomes $x^0 = 1$, and we get

$$\int 1\,dx = \int x^0\,dx = \frac{1}{1} \cdot x^1 + C = x + C$$

which simply expresses the fact that since the derivative of x is 1, the *anti-derivative* of 1 is x (plus a constant of integration); to confuse matters, we sometimes write $\int 1\,dx$ simply as $\int dx$.

So far we have discussed rules of integration which are analogous to the first two rules of differentiation of Section 12.4. Analogous to the third and fourth rules of that section we have

$$\int k \cdot f(x)\, dx = k \cdot \int f(x)\, dx$$

where k is a constant, and

$$\int [f(x) \pm g(x)]\, dx = \int f(x)\, dx \pm \int g(x)\, dx$$

where the signs are either *both plus or both minus*. Thus, we can "factor a constant out of an integral," and we can integrate "term by term." Note also that if we combine the first of these two rules with the last of the preceding examples, we get

$$\int k\, dx = k \cdot \int 1\, dx = kx + C$$

which simply says that the integral of any constant k is kx (plus a constant of integration).

To illustrate all these rules, let us integrate (namely, find the *anti-derivative* of) $12x^5 - \frac{5}{x^2} + 3$. Leaving it to the reader to find the rule which justifies each step, we get

$$\begin{aligned}
\int \left(12x^5 - \frac{5}{x^2} + 3\right) dx &= \int (12x^5 - 5x^{-2} + 3)\, dx \\
&= \int 12x^5\, dx - \int 5x^{-2}\, dx + \int 3\, dx \\
&= 12 \cdot \int x^5\, dx - 5 \cdot \int x^{-2}\, dx + \int 3\, dx \\
&= 12 \cdot \frac{1}{6} \cdot x^6 - 5 \cdot \frac{1}{-1} \cdot x^{-1} + 3x + C \\
&= 2x^6 + \frac{5}{x} + 3x + C
\end{aligned}$$

There is also a method of integration which is analogous to the *product rule*, the fifth rule of Section 12.4; this method, called *integration by parts*, will be discussed in Exercise 8 on page 420.

To give an applied example which is solved by anti-differentiation, let us suppose that the *marginal productivity* of an industrial operation (say, the production of electric furnaces) is given by

$$f(x) = \frac{60}{x^2} + 10$$

where x is the capitalization in millions of dollars. [In case the reader is not familiar with the term "marginal productivity," it is the *rate* at which production increases (or decreases) when there is a unit increase in capitalization; in other words, it is the *derivative of production with respect to capitalization.*] Suppose, furthermore, that when the capitalization is \$5,000,000 they can produce 62 of these furnaces per week, and they want to know *how many they will be able to produce if their capitalization is increased to* \$10,000,000. To express production in terms of capitalization, we shall have to *anti-differentiate* the marginal productivity, namely, $\frac{60}{x^2} + 10$; thus, we get

$$F(x) = \int \left(\frac{60}{x^2} + 10\right) dx = \int (60x^{-2} + 10)\, dx$$

$$= 60 \cdot \frac{1}{-1} \cdot x^{-1} + 10x + C$$

$$= -\frac{60}{x} + 10x + C$$

The next step is to evaluate the constant of integration C, and to this end we make use of the fact that for $x = 5$ (million dollars) the production is $F(5) = 62$. Substituting these values into the equation $F(x) = -\frac{60}{x} + 10x + C$, we get

$$62 = -\frac{60}{5} + 10 \cdot 5 + C = -12 + 50 + C$$

and, solving for C, this becomes $C = 62 + 12 - 50 = 24$. Thus, the equation which expresses production in terms of capitalization is

$$F(x) = -\frac{60}{x} + 10x + 24$$

and it follows that for $x = 10$ (namely, when their capitalization is \$10,000,000) they will be able to produce

$$F(10) = -\frac{60}{10} + 10 \cdot 10 + 24 = 118$$

of the electric furnaces.

So far as the special functions of Section 12.6 are concerned, let us merely list the following integration formulas, which can all be verified by simply differentiating the results and observing that these derivatives equal the respective integrands:

$$\int e^x\, dx = e^x + C$$

$$\int b^x\, dx = \frac{b^x}{\ln b} + C$$

$$\int \frac{1}{x}\, dx = \ln x + C$$

Note that the third of these integration formulas demonstrates why we had to exclude $n = -1$ when we gave the general rule for integrating x^n. (For those readers who did *not* omit the material on trigonometric functions, the integrals of sin x and cos x are given in Exercise 9 on page 421.) The following examples illustrate the use of these formulas:

$$\int 7e^x\,dx = 7e^x + C$$

$$\int 10^x\,dx = \frac{10^x}{\ln 10} + C = 0.434\cdot 10^x + C$$

and

$$\int \frac{5}{x}\,dx = 5\cdot \ln x + C$$

and if we wanted to use the first of these results to evaluate the area of the shaded region of Figure 14.9, we would get

$$\begin{aligned}\int_2^4 7e^x\,dx &= (7e^4 + C) - (7e^2 + C)\\ &= 7e^4 - 7e^2\\ &= 7(54.60) - 7(7.389)\\ &= 330.48\end{aligned}$$

where the values of e^4 and e^2 were obtained from Table III. Note that *when we evaluate a definite integral the constant of integration cancels, so that it may just as well be left out.*

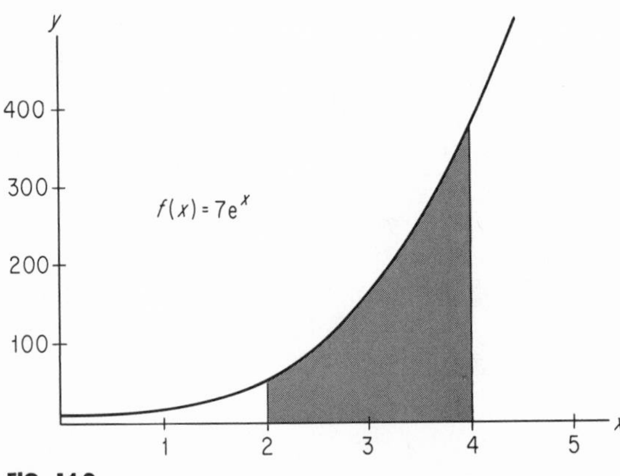

FIG. 14.9

In Section 12.5 we studied three special methods of differentiation; so far as integration is concerned, there are numerous special techniques, but we shall treat only the one which is the counterpart of the *chain rule* of differentiation, namely, *integration by substitution.* To illustrate how this goes, let us work with the integral

$$\int 5(1 + x^3)^4 \cdot 3x^2\,dx$$

whose integrand "happens to be" the derivative of $(1 + x^3)^5$, as can easily be verified by means of the chain rule of Section 12.5. Now, if we let

$$q = 1 + x^3$$

it follows that $\frac{dq}{dx} = 3x^2$, and the integral can be written as

$$\int 5q^4 \cdot \frac{dq}{dx}\,dx \qquad \text{or as} \qquad \int 5q^4\,dq$$

if we substitute dq for $\frac{dq}{dx}\,dx$. *This last step, the substitution of dq for $\frac{dq}{dx}\,dx$, is the key to the whole method, for now the integrand is entirely in terms of the new variable q, and, hopefully, the integration can be performed by means of known techniques.* So far as our example is concerned, we get

$$\int 5(1 + x^3)^4 \cdot 3x^2\,dx = \int 5q^4\,dq = 5 \cdot \frac{1}{5} \cdot q^5 + C = q^5 + C$$

and in terms of the original variable, x,

$$\int 5(1 + x^3)^4 \cdot 3x^2\,dx = (1 + x^3)^5 + C$$

It is important to note that the substitution $q = 1 + x^3$ happened to work in this example because the derivative of $1 + x^3$ (namely, $3x^2$) was also a factor of the integrand; had we been given the integral

$$\int 5(1 + x^3)^4 \cdot 3x\,dx$$

an experienced eye would have recognized immediately that *the substitution $q = 1 + x^3$ will not work.* On the other hand, it would have worked for the integral

$$\int (1 + x^3)^4 \cdot x^2\,dx$$

which we could have written as

$$\frac{1}{3}\int (1 + x^3)^4 \cdot 3x^2\,dx$$

using the trick explained in the footnote to the next example.

The following are two further illustrations of *integration by substitution;* first, let us determine

$$\int (a + bx)^n\,dx$$

where a, b, and n are constants, and n is not equal to -1. Now, if we let

$$q = a + bx$$

it follows that $\frac{dq}{dx} = b$, but instead of substituting dq for $\frac{dq}{dx}\,dx$, namely, dq for $b\,dx$, as in the preceding example, it will be more convenient to substitute $\frac{1}{b}\,dq$ for dx.* Thus, we get

$$\begin{aligned}\int (a + bx)^n\,dx &= \int q^n \cdot \frac{1}{b}\,dq \\ &= \frac{1}{b} \cdot \int q^n\,dq \\ &= \frac{1}{b} \cdot \frac{1}{n+1} \cdot q^{n+1} + C\end{aligned}$$

and in terms of the original variable, x,

$$\int (a + bx)^n\,dx = \frac{1}{b(n+1)} \cdot (a + bx)^{n+1} + C$$

For instance,

$$\int (4 + 3x)^5\,dx = \frac{1}{3 \cdot 6} \cdot (4 + 3x)^6 + C = \frac{(4 + 3x)^6}{18} + C$$

$$\begin{aligned}\int (1 - 2x)^{-4}\,dx &= \frac{1}{(-2)(-3)} \cdot (1 - 2x)^{-3} + C \\ &= \frac{1}{6(1 - 2x)^3} + C\end{aligned}$$

and with some experience this kind of integration can be performed by "mental substitution," that is, without having to go through any details. (In Exercise 6 on page 419 the reader will be asked to derive a corresponding integration formula for the case where $n = -1$.)

Finally, let us use the method of integration by substitution to integrate $x \cdot e^{x^2}$, namely, to determine

$$\int x \cdot e^{x^2}\,dx$$

---

* Alternately, we could have written the integral as $\frac{1}{b} \int (a + bx)^n \cdot b\,dx$ and then substituted dq for $b\,dx$; in this way we would have taken care of the "missing constant b" by multiplying by $\frac{b}{b} = 1$ and taking the numerator inside the integral (which is permissible by virtue of the rule on page 412).

If we let

$$q = x^2$$

it follows that $\frac{dq}{dx} = 2x$, but instead of substituting dq for $\frac{dq}{dx}\,dx$, namely dq for $2x\,dx$, as in the first example, it will be more convenient to substitute $\frac{1}{2}\,dq$ for $x\,dx$. Thus, we get

$$\int x \cdot e^{x^2}\,dx = \int e^q \cdot \frac{1}{2}\,dq = \frac{1}{2}\int e^q\,dq = \frac{1}{2}e^q + C$$

and in terms of the original variable, x,

$$\int x \cdot e^{x^2}\,dx = \frac{1}{2} \cdot e^{x^2} + C$$

When will integration by substitution work? The only answer we can give to this question is that we must always be on the lookout for a quantity q whose derivative is also part of (that is, a factor of) the integrand. An experienced eye will immediately detect that the method will work for

$$\int x^4(1 + x^5)^8\,dx, \quad \int e^{2x}(1 - 3e^{2x})^4\,dx, \quad \text{and} \quad \int x^8 e^{x^9}\,dx$$

and that the corresponding substitutions are $q = 1 + x^5$, $q = 1 - 3e^{2x}$, and $q = x^9$.

Incidentally, it may have occurred to the reader that when we substituted dq for $\frac{dq}{dx}\,dx$, we could have saved a good deal of work by treating $\frac{dq}{dx}$ as a *fraction*—in our first example we had $\frac{dq}{dx} = b$, which would have given $dq = b\,dx$, and, hence, $\frac{1}{b}\,dq = dx$; in our second example we had $\frac{dq}{dx} = 2x$, which would have given $dq = 2x\,dx$, and, hence, $\frac{1}{2}\,dq = x\,dx$. *This is true—it works—but, generally speaking, it is a dangerous practice to treat derivatives as if they were fractions.*

To give another applied example which is solved by anti-differentiation, suppose that the time a mechanic requires to assemble a certain piece of machinery decreases at a *rate* of $-112e^{-0.5t}$ *minutes per month*, where t is the number of months he has been on the job. Suppose also that he can assemble the piece of machinery in 9.5 minutes after he has been on the job for 10 months, and that it is desired to know how long it will take him after he has been on the job for 15 months. If we let $F(t)$ denote the time it will take the mechanic to assemble the piece of machinery after he has been on the job for t months, we can write

$$F(t) = \int -112e^{-0.5t}\,dt$$

To perform this integration we let $q = -0.5t$, so that $\frac{dq}{dt} = -0.5$ and we can substitute $\frac{1}{-0.5}\,dq$ for dt (see also Exercise 5 on page 419). Thus, we get

$$\begin{aligned} F(t) &= \int -112e^q \cdot \frac{1}{-0.5}\,dq \\ &= 224 \int e^q\,dq \\ &= 224 \cdot e^q + C \\ &= 224 \cdot e^{-0.5t} + C \end{aligned}$$

The next step is to evaluate the constant of integration C, and to this end we make use of the fact that $F(10) = 9.5$. Substituting $t = 10$ and $F(10) = 9.5$, we get

$$9.5 = 224 \cdot e^{-0.5(10)} + C = 224 \cdot e^{-5} + C$$

and, upon solving for C, we obtain

$$C = 9.5 - 224 \cdot e^{-5} = 9.5 - 224(0.0067) = 8$$

where the value of e^{-5} came from Table III. Thus, the equation which expresses the time it takes the mechanic to assemble the piece of machinery in terms of the number of months he has been on the job is

$$F(t) = 224 \cdot e^{-0.5t} + 8$$

and it follows that after he has been on the job for 15 months he will be able to assemble the piece of machinery in

$$\begin{aligned} F(15) &= 224 \cdot e^{-0.5(15)} + 8 \\ &= 224 \cdot e^{-7.5} + 8 \\ &= 224(0.00055) + 8 \\ &= 8.12 \text{ minutes.} \end{aligned}$$

EXERCISES

1. Evaluate the following integrals:

(a) $\int x^3\,dx$;

(b) $\int \frac{1}{x^4}\,dx$;

(c) $\int 12\,dx$;

(d) $\int \frac{1}{\sqrt{x}}\,dx$;

(e) $\int x^{3/4}\,dx$;

(f) $\int \frac{2}{x\sqrt{x}}\,dx$;

(g) $\int 1/x^2\,dx$;

(h) $\int x^{2/5}\,dx$.

2. Evaluate the following integrals:

(a) $\int (1 + 3x)\,dx$; (d) $\int (2 - 4x + 5x^2 - 4x^3)\,dx$;

(b) $\int (2x + 5x^4)\,dx$; (e) $\int (7 - 3x^2 + 6x^5)\,dx$;

(c) $\int (3\sqrt{x} - 2/\sqrt{x})\,dx$; (f) $\int (5x^{1/4} - 3x^{1/2})\,dx$.

3. Evaluate the following integrals:

(a) $\int (3x - 5e^x)\,dx$; (d) $\int (1 - e^x)\,dx$;

(b) $\int \left(x + 1 + \frac{1}{x}\right) dx$; (e) $\int 3 \cdot 2^x\,dx$;

(c) $\int 5^x\,dx$; (f) $\int 15/x\,dx$.

4. Use the formula obtained on page 416 for $\int (a + bx)^n\,dx$ to evaluate the following integrals:

(a) $\int (2 + 3x)^4\,dx$; (c) $\int (3 - 2x)^{-5}\,dx$;

(b) $\int \sqrt{1 - x}\,dx$; (d) $\int \frac{1}{\sqrt{2 + 5x}}\,dx$.

5. Making the substitution $q = ax$, show that

$$\int e^{ax}\,dx = \frac{1}{a} \cdot e^{ax} + C$$

and use this formula to evaluate the following integrals:

(a) $\int e^{-x}\,dx$; (c) $\int 3e^{5x}\,dx$;

(b) $\int e^{2x}\,dx$; (d) $\int \frac{e^x + e^{-x}}{2}\,dx$.

6. Making the substitution $q = a + bx$, show that

$$\int \frac{1}{a + bx}\,dx = \frac{1}{b} \cdot \ln (a + bx) + C$$

and use this formula to evaluate the following integrals:

(a) $\int \frac{1}{1 + x}\,dx$; (c) $\int \left(\frac{1}{x + 3} - \frac{1}{x + 2}\right) dx$;

(b) $\int \frac{1}{2 - 3x}\,dx$; (d) $\int \frac{x}{x + 1}\,dx$.

[*Hint:* in part (d) write the numerator as $x + 1 - 1$, and then divide by $x + 1$.]

7. Making the substitutions suggested on page 417, evaluate the following integrals:

(a) $\int x^4(1 + x^5)^8\, dx$;

(b) $\int e^{2x}(1 - 3e^{2x})^4\, dx$;

(c) $\int x^8 \cdot e^{x^9}\, dx$.

8. INTEGRATION BY PARTS. The product rule of Section 12.4 tells us that

$$\frac{d}{dx} f(x)\cdot g(x) = f(x)\cdot g'(x) + g(x)\cdot f'(x)$$

so that anti-differentiation yields

$$\begin{aligned} f(x)\cdot g(x) &= \int [f(x)\cdot g'(x) + g(x)\cdot f'(x)]\, dx + C \\ &= \int f(x)\cdot g'(x)\, dx + \int g(x)\cdot f'(x)\, dx + C \end{aligned}$$

or

$$\int f(x)\cdot g'(x)\, dx = f(x)\cdot g(x) - \int g(x)\cdot f'(x)\, dx + C$$

where we changed $-C$ to $+C$, which is immaterial. This last formula is the basic formula for *integration by parts;* it expresses one integral in terms of another, and *the objective is to choose $f(x)$ and $g'(x)$ in such a way that $\int g(x)\cdot f'(x)\, dx$ is easier to integrate than $\int f(x)\cdot g'(x)\, dx$.* To illustrate, let us evaluate

$$\int x\cdot e^x\, dx$$

and let us see what will happen if we let $f(x) = x$ and $g'(x) = e^x$. Since the derivative of x is 1 and the anti-derivative of e^x is e^x, we find that $f'(x) = 1$ and $g(x) = e^x$, so that substitution into the formula for integration by parts yields

$$\begin{aligned} \int x\cdot e^x\, dx &= x\cdot e^x - \int e^x\cdot 1\, dx + C \\ &= x\cdot e^x - \int e^x\, dx + C \\ &= x\cdot e^x - e^x + C \end{aligned}$$

Critical, of course, was our choice of $f(x)$ and $g'(x)$, so that their product equaled the integrand and $g(x)\cdot f'(x)$ was easy to integrate. All this is largely a matter of experience.

(a) Use integration by parts to evaluate the integral

$$\int x(1 + x)^5\, dx$$

(b) Use integration by parts with $f(x) = \ln x$ and $g'(x) = 1$ to show that

$$\int (\ln x)\, dx = x(\ln x) - x + C$$

(c) Use integration by parts and the result of our illustration to evaluate the integral

$$\int x^2 \cdot e^x\, dx$$

9. **INTEGRATION OF TRIGONOMETRIC FUNCTIONS.** Since the derivatives of $\sin x$ and $\cos x$ are, respectively, $\cos x$ and $-\sin x$, see page 365, the anti-derivatives of $\sin x$ and $\cos x$ are, respectively, $-\cos x$ and $\sin x$. Thus,

$$\int \sin x\, dx = -\cos x + C \qquad \text{and} \qquad \int \cos x\, dx = \sin x + C$$

Use these formulas to evaluate the following integrals:

(a) $\int 3 \cdot \sin (x - 2)\, dx$; (c) $\int x \cdot \sin x\, dx$;

(b) $\int \sin x(\cos x)^2\, dx$; (d) $\int \tan x\, dx$.

[*Hints:* in part (b) make the substitution $q = \cos x$, in part (c) use integration by parts (see Exercise 8), and in part (d) make use of the identity $\tan x = \dfrac{\sin x}{\cos x}$ and then let $q = \cos x$.]

10. **DIFFERENTIAL EQUATIONS.** A differential equation is an equation which involves derivatives, and the solution of a differential equation is an equation relating the same variables which does *not* involve derivatives. Thus, solving a differential equation is essentially a problem of anti-differentiation; for instance, the differential equation $\dfrac{dy}{dx} = 2x$ has the solution $y = x^2 + C$.

(a) Solve the differential equation $\dfrac{dy}{dx} + x = x^3$;

(b) Solve the differential equation $x \cdot \dfrac{dy}{dx} = x^2 + 5$;

(c) Making use of the fact that $\dfrac{d}{dx}(\ln y) = \dfrac{1}{y} \cdot \dfrac{dy}{dx}$, solve the differential equation

$$\frac{dy}{dx} = ky$$

where k is a constant. (This differential equation arises in many problems relating to economic growth, as it applies *whenever the rate at which a quantity grows is proportional to its size.*)

(d) Verify that $y = x^3 + 3x$ is a solution of the differential equation

$$3y - x \cdot \frac{dy}{dx} - 2 \cdot \frac{d^2y}{dx^2} + 6x = 0$$

by twice differentiating $y = x^3 + 3x$ and then substituting into the differential equation.

11. The *marginal cost* of an item is the *rate* at which the total production cost changes when there is a change in the quantity produced, namely, the derivative of the total cost with respect to the quantity produced.

(a) The marginal cost of producing a certain kind of baby food is given by

$$c(x) = 30 \cdot x^{-2/3}$$

where x, the number of cans produced, is in thousands, and the cost is in dollars. Find a formula for $C(x)$, the total cost of producing x thousand cans of the baby food, given that 8,000 cans can be produced at a cost of \$600. How much will it cost to produce 125,000 cans?

(b) The marginal cost of producing a certain kind of cake mix is given by

$$c(x) = 225 - 1{,}200e^{-2x}$$

where x, the number of packages produced, is in dozens, and the cost is in cents. Find a formula for $C(x)$, the total cost of producing x dozen packages of the cake mix, given that 2 dozen can be produced at a cost of \$8.00. How much will it cost to produce 4 dozen packages of the mix?

12. The *marginal revenue* of an item is the *rate* at which its total sales revenue changes when there is a change in demand, namely, the derivative of its total sales revenue with respect to demand.

(a) For a certain kind of leather belt, the marginal revenue is given by

$$6 - \frac{4}{\sqrt{D}}$$

when there is a demand for D belts; the sales revenue, itself, is in dollars. Find a formula expressing the total sales revenue in terms of the demand, given that for $D = 100$ the sales revenue is \$500. What total sales revenue corresponds to a demand for 400 of these belts?

(b) For a certain kind of watch, the marginal revenue is given by

$$6{,}000 - \frac{4{,}000}{(1 + D)^2}$$

where the demand is in thousands of watches and the total sales revenue is in dollars. Find a formula which expresses the total sales revenue in terms of D, given that for $D = 1$ (thousand watches) the total sales revenue is \$3,800. What would be the total sales revenue if the demand increased to 4,000 of these watches?

13. For the monthly operation of a large turkey farm, the *marginal productivity* (see page 412) is given by

$$n(x) = 40 - \frac{1{,}000}{x}$$

where x is the capitalization of the farm in thousands of dollars. Find a formula which expresses the number of turkeys they can produce per month in terms of x, given that they can produce 14,000 turkeys per month when their capitalization is \$500,000. What would be their monthly production if they increased the capitalization to \$1,000,000? (Use $\ln 500 = 6.2$ and $\ln 1000 = 6.9$.)

14. The rate at which a secretary's efficiency (expressed as a percentage) changes with respect to time is given by

$$40 - 10t$$

where t is the number of hours she has been at work. If her efficiency is 76 percent after she has been working for 2 hours, find a formula which expresses her efficiency in terms of t, and use it to determine her efficiency after she has been working (a) for 4 hours, and (b) for 8 hours.

15. The rate at which a newly-built skyscraper is settling into the ground is $12e^{-4t}$ inches per year, where t is its age in years. Find a formula which expresses the number of inches the building has settled into the ground in terms of t, making use of the fact that the whole process begins when $t = 0$. How many inches will the building have settled (a) after 1 year, and (b) after 2 years?

16. The *marginal profit* of a real estate development with respect to the amount of money spent on advertising is given by

$$100e^{-x/5} - 20 \cdot xe^{-x/5} - 1$$

where x, the amount of money spent on advertising, and the profit are both in thousands of dollars. Find a formula which expresses the real estate development's profit in terms of x, given that its profit is \$2,125,000 when they spend \$10,000 on advertising. What would their profit be if they spent \$40,000 on advertising? [*Hint:* use the integration formula

$$\int x \cdot e^{ax}\, dx = \frac{e^{ax}(ax - 1)}{a^2} + C$$

or make use of *integration by parts* (see Exercise 8).]

14.6 SOME FURTHER APPLICATIONS

In this section we shall return to our original problem, namely, that of evaluating *definite integrals*. To this end, let us simplify our notation by writing the fundamental theorem of Section 14.4 as

$$\int_a^b f(x)\, dx = F(x)\Big]_a^b$$

where the expression on the right-hand side of the equation is simply another way of writing $F(b) - F(a)$. In the example on page 410 we could thus have written

$$\begin{aligned}\int_1^2 (120 + 144x^2)\, dx &= 120x + 48x^3\Big]_1^2 \\ &= (120 \cdot 2 + 48 \cdot 2^3) - (120 \cdot 1 + 48 \cdot 1^3) \\ &= 456\end{aligned}$$

This is no different from what we did on page 410, but it saves us the trouble of writing down separately the values of $F(x)$, $F(2)$, and $F(1)$, and finally $F(2) - F(1)$; also, there is no need now for a constant of integration.

For our first example, let us return to the problem of Section 4.8 where the demand and the supply for certain ceramic insulators (in hundreds) were related to their price (in cents) by means of the equations

$$D = 231 - 18p \qquad \text{and} \qquad S = 2p + 4p^2$$

Solving these two equations simultaneously, we showed that the market for the insulators would be *in equilibrium* (that is, supply would equal demand) when $p = 5.5$ cents, in which case there is a demand for $D = 231 - 18(5.5) = 132$ hundred of the ceramic insulators. Now, it is clear from the equation

$$D = 231 - 18p$$

that some persons would buy the insulators even if they cost more than 5.5 cents; for $p = 8$ cents there would be a demand for $231 - 18(8) = 87$ hundred, for $p = 10$ cents there would be a demand for $231 - 18(10) = 51$ hundred, and only for $p = \frac{231}{18} = 12\frac{15}{18}$ cents would the demand be zero. Thus, some consumers benefit from the fact that the market is in equilibrium when the price is 5.5 cents, and their combined overall gain, called the *consumers' surplus*, is given by the area of the region under the demand curve shaded in Figure 14.10. This area is given by the definite integral

$$\int_{5.5}^{\frac{231}{18}} (231 - 18p)\, dp$$

which equals

$$231p - 9p^2 \Big]_{5.5}^{\frac{231}{18}} = \left[231\left(\frac{231}{18}\right) - 9\left(\frac{231}{18}\right)^2\right] - \left[231(5.5) - 9(5.5)^2\right]$$

$$= 484$$

The result is in *dollars*, since D was given in hundreds (of insulators) and p in cents. Since the shaded region of Figure 14.10 is a triangle, it would actually have been easier to get this result by making use of the fact that the area of a triangle is half the product of the base and the height; we would thus have gotten $\frac{1}{2}\left[\frac{231}{18} - 5.5\right]\left[231 - 18(5.5)\right] = \frac{1}{2}\cdot\frac{22}{3}\cdot 132 = 484$. Incidentally, this \$484 represents the consumers' combined savings that are due to the existence of a market in which everybody can buy the insulators at the price for which supply equals demand.

For our second example, let us refer to the problem on page 149, where

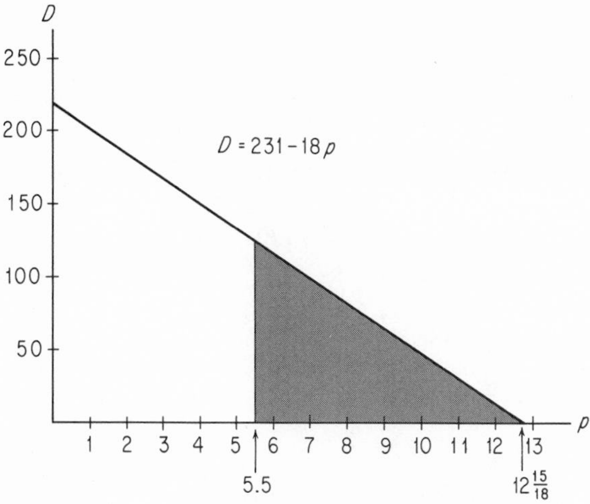

FIG. 14.10

the sales of a new meat tenderizer (in thousands of packages) was given by

$$y = 100 - 94e^{-x}$$

with x representing the number of years the product has been on the market. To determine the *total sales* of the meat tenderizer during the first

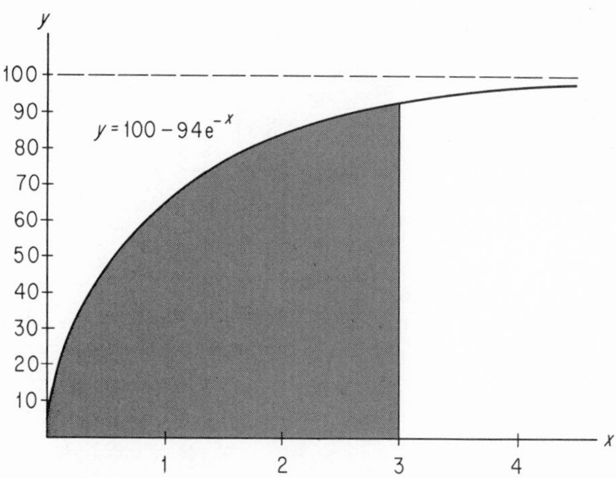

FIG. 14.11

three years, we must look for the area of the region shaded in Figure 14.11; that is, we must evaluate the definite integral

$$\int_0^3 (100 - 94e^{-x})\, dx$$

Thus, we get

$$100x - 94 \cdot \frac{e^{-x}}{-1}\Big]_0^3 = (100 \cdot 3 + 94e^{-3}) - (100 \cdot 0 + 94e^0)$$

$$= 210.7 \text{ thousand packages}$$

where the value of e^{-3} was obtained from Table III, and e^0 is, of course, equal to 1.

Finally, let us consider an inventory problem in which a regional distributor receives a shipment of 4,500 cans of processed meat every 30 days. The pattern is always the same: the inventory depletes slowly at the beginning of each month (when plenty of money is available to buy *fresh* meat), but then the demand speeds up, so that after t days his inventory is reduced to

$$I = 4{,}500 - 5t^2$$

cans of processed meat (see Figure 14.12). If the cost of holding one can of the processed meat in inventory for one day is 0.025 cents, then the total

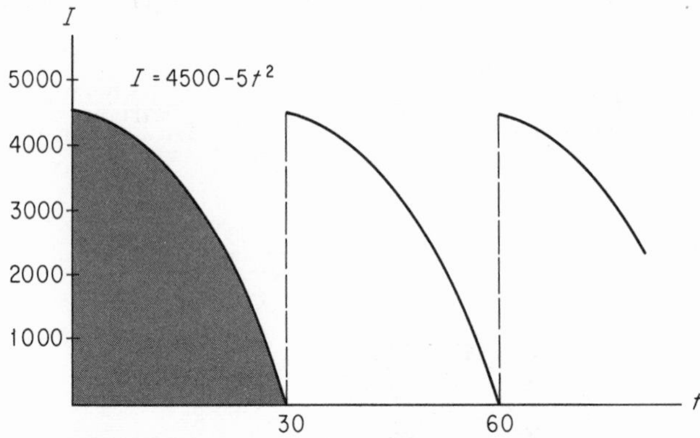

FIG. 14.12

cost of maintaining inventory for 30 days is 0.025 times the area of the shaded region of Figure 14.12, namely,

$$0.025 \cdot \int_0^{30} (4{,}500 - 5t^2)\, dt$$

Evaluating this integral, we get

$$4{,}500t - 5 \cdot \frac{1}{3} \cdot t^3\Big]_0^{30} = \left(4{,}500 \cdot 30 - \frac{5}{3} \cdot 30^3\right) - \left(4{,}500 \cdot 0 - \frac{5}{3} \cdot 0^3\right)$$

$$= 90{,}000$$

so that the total cost of maintaining inventory for 30 days is 0.025(90,000) = 2,250 cents, or \$22.50. Further problems dealing with definite integrals will be given in Section 16.6, where definite integrals will be used to define (and, hence, determine) *probabilities* relating to continuous measurements.

If we make a *substitution*, that is, *change variable*, while evaluating a definite integral, we can either express the result in terms of the original variable and then substitute the limits of integration, or we can leave the result in terms of the new variable but *change the limits of integration*. The first alternative requires no explanation, but to illustrate the second, let us evaluate the integral

$$\int_1^2 (3 + 2x)^5\, dx$$

If we let $q = 3 + 2x$, it follows that $\frac{dq}{dx} = 2$, and we can substitute q for $3 + 2x$ and $\frac{1}{2}\, dq$ for dx. Not only that, but since the values of q which correspond to the limits of integration, $x = 1$ and $x = 2$, are

$$q = 3 + 2(1) = 5 \qquad \text{and} \qquad q = 3 + 2(2) = 7$$

we can use these values as our new limits of integration and write

$$\int_1^2 (3 + 2x)^5\, dx = \int_5^7 q^5 \cdot \frac{1}{2}\, dq = \frac{1}{12} \cdot q^6 \Big]_5^7 = \frac{1}{12}(7^6 - 5^6)$$
$$= 8{,}502$$

Thus, we did not have to go back to the original variable, x, and this eliminated some of the steps.

EXERCISES

1. Evaluate the area represented by the definite integral of part (a) of Exercise 4 on page 409.
2. Evaluate the area represented by the definite integral of part (d) of Exercise 4 on page 409.
3. Evaluate the area represented by the definite integral of part (h) of Exercise 4 on page 409.
4. Evaluate the definite integral

$$\int_1^2 x\sqrt{13 + 3x^2}\, dx$$

by making the substitution $q = 13 + 3x^2$, and correspondingly changing the limits of integration.

5. Evaluate the definite integral

$$\int_{-1}^{1/2} (1 - 2x)^3\, dx$$

by making the substitution $q = 1 - 2x$, and correspondingly changing the limits of integration.

6. Evaluate the definite integral

$$\int_{-1}^{1} (x^3 - x)\, dx$$

and *explain* the result by drawing the region whose area the definite integral is supposed to represent (see also Exercise 3 on page 408).

7. In Exercise 4 on page 131, the supply and the demand for a product were given by

$$S = 56p + p^2 \qquad \text{and} \qquad D = 120 - p^2$$

where p was the price in dollars per carton, and D and S were in units of 1,000 cartons. Using the result of that exercise, namely, that the market for the product is in equilibrium when $p = 2$, find the *consumer surplus.*

8. In Exercise 5 on page 131, the supply and the demand for a product were given by

$$S = 2p + p^2 \qquad \text{and} \qquad D = 40 - p^2$$

where p was the price of the product in dollars and S and D were both in units of 1,000. Using the result of that exercise, namely, that the market for the product is in equilibrium when $p = 4$, show that the *consumer surplus* amounts to \$29,988.

9. The supply curve of the example on page 424, namely, $S = 2p + 4p^2$, shows that *some producers would have been willing to supply the product below the price at which the market is in equilibrium.* Hence, they gain by the fact that the insulators sell at $p = 5.5$ cents, and their combined overall gain, called the *producer's surplus,* is given by the area of the region under the supply curve shaded in Figure 14.13. Show that it equals \$252 (to the nearest dollar).

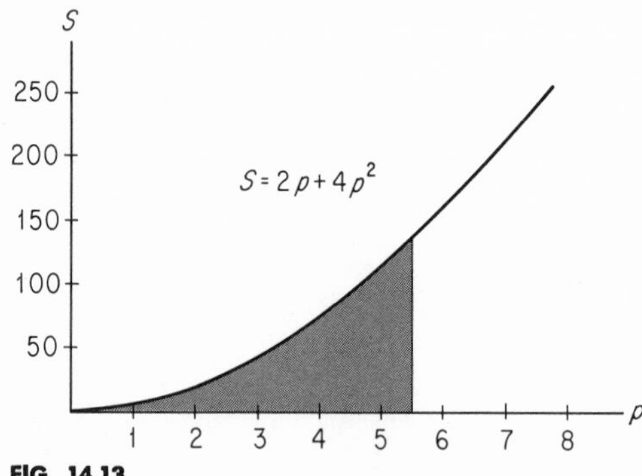

FIG. 14.13

10. Find the *producer's surplus* (see Exercise 9) for the situation described in Exercise 7.

11. With reference to Exercise 6 on page 358, find the company's total sales revenue for the first 10 years.

12. With reference to Exercise 3 on page 385, find the company's total gross earnings for the first five years it was in business.

13. A company which leases office equipment has found that the maintenance cost of an electric typewriter increases continuously with its age, and that it equals

$$22\frac{1}{2} + \frac{1}{10}e^{x} \text{ dollars}$$

when the typewriter is x years old. If 20 new typewriters are to be leased to a firm for 6 years and the *same* maintenance charge is to be included in the total fee for each year, what should this charge be?

14. The manager of a new donut shop expects his daily sales to grow continuously so that he will be able to sell $100 + 4t$ donuts after t days. On which day should he plan to sell his 10,000th donut? (*Hint:* set up the definite integral which represents his total sales during the first x days, put it equal to 10,000, and solve for x.)

15. The *marginal cost* (see Exercise 11 on page 422) of processing a certain grade of tuna is given by

$$200 - 30\sqrt{x}$$

where x, the number of cans, is in thousands, and the cost is in dollars. What would be the total increase in cost if production were increased from 4,000 cans to 25,000 cans?

16. For a certain kind of after-shave lotion, the *marginal revenue* (see Exercise 12 on page 422) is given by

$$2.50 - 0.25e^{0.2D}$$

where the demand, D, is in thousands of bottles, and the sales revenue is in thousands of dollars. How will the sales revenue be affected by an increase in demand from 1,000 bottles to 10,000 bottles.

17. IMPROPER INTEGRALS. When we defined definite integrals in Section 14.3, we assumed that the limits of integration are constants, and, hence, our definition does not really apply if we want to find the area of the region bounded by the x-axis, the y-axis, and the graph of $f(x) = e^{-x}$, namely, the area of the region shaded in the first diagram of Figure 14.14. *Of course, the difficulty*

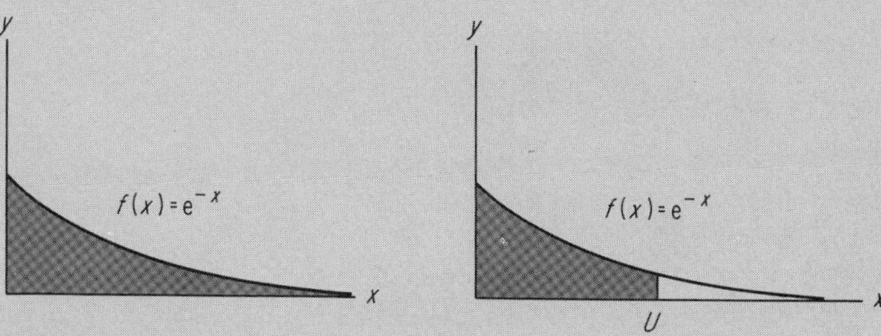

FIG. 14.14

arises from the fact that the upper limit of integration is infinite. To take care of situations like this, we introduce an arbitrary upper limit of integration U (as in the second diagram of Figure 14.14), perform the integration, and then take the limit as $U \to \infty$. Thus, we get

$$\int_0^U e^{-x}\,dx = -e^{-x}\Big]_0^U = -e^{-U} - (-e^{-0}) = 1 - e^{-U}$$

and, finally,

$$\int_0^\infty e^{-x}\,dx = \lim_{U\to\infty} \int_0^U e^{-x}\,dx = \lim_{U\to\infty} (1 - e^{-U}) = 1$$

This kind of integral is referred to as *improper*, and, being a limit, it may or it may not converge; in other words, the corresponding area may be finite (that is, equal to some fixed number) or it may be infinite or undefined. Evaluate, if possible, the following improper integrals:

$$\text{(a)}\ \int_2^\infty \frac{3}{x^2}\,dx; \qquad \text{(b)}\ \int_0^\infty x\cdot e^{-x^2}\,dx; \qquad \text{(c)}\ \int_1^\infty \frac{1}{x}\,dx.$$

Also, draw the regions whose areas these integrals are supposed to represent.

15

POSSIBILITIES AND PROBABILITIES

15.1 INTRODUCTION

With one exception (that of fitting curves by the method of least squares), the mathematical models which we have studied have all been *deterministic;* the relationships between the variables were always expressed in terms of mathematical equations *which left nothing to chance.* Thus, when we said on page 127 that a manufacturer's cost of producing x television sets is $C = 12{,}000 + 80x$ dollars, we were able to substitute $x = 300$ and thus arrive at the conclusion that the cost of producing 300 sets is \$36,000, *not a penny more nor a penny less.* Similarly, when we claimed on page 149 that the sales of a certain meat tenderizer are given by $y = 100 - 94e^{-x}$, we were able to substitute $x = 5$ and thus conclude that the product will sell at an annual rate of 99.4 million packages after it has been on the market for five years—not 99.8 million packages nor 98.7, but 99.4 million *on the nose.*

To a practical businessman, results like these (or, at least, their interpretation) must surely look very unreasonable. In the first example he might be willing to say, though, that the *expected* production cost is \$36,000 (without having to guarantee that it will not turn out to be \$35,750 or \$36,455), and in the second example he might feel "pretty sure" that after five years the product will sell at an annual rate of anywhere from 99 to 100 million packages. All this serves to illustrate that many of the models which we have discussed apply only in the sense of approximations (not necessarily bad ones), or that they must be interpreted as *averages* or *expectations.* Even more so, however, they serve to illustrate the need for mathematical models which allow for the vagaries of chance. Thus, we shall devote the remainder of this book to *probabilistic models,* also called *statistical models* or *stochastic models,* namely, to mathematical models which teach us *how to behave "rationally" in the face of uncertainties.*

The key to these models is the concept of *probability,* which we shall introduce briefly in Section 15.6, and then study in some detail in Chapter 16. First, though, we shall devote Sections 15.2 through 15.5 to methods which enable us to determine *what is possible* in a given situation—after all, how can anyone be expected to judge what is likely or unlikely, what is probable or improbable, or what is credible or incredible, unless he knows at least what is possible?

15.2 COUNTING

In contrast to the complex nature of most of the methods used in modern management science, the simple process of counting still plays an important role. One still has to count 1, 2, 3, 4, . . . , say, to determine the number of persons attending a stockholders' meeting, the size of the response to a mail-order solicitation, the number of items damaged while being shipped, the number of customer complaints, and so on. Sometimes, the process of counting can be simplified by using mechanical devices (for instance, when counting spectators passing through turnstiles), or by performing counts indirectly (for instance, when subtracting the serial numbers of invoices to determine the total number of sales). At other times, the process of counting can be simplified greatly by means of special mathematical techniques; this is what we shall demonstrate below.

In the study of "what is possible," there are essentially two kinds of problems: first there is the problem of *listing everything that can happen in a given situation,* and then there is the problem of *determining how many different things can happen* (*without actually constructing a complete list*). The second kind of problem is especially important, because there are many problems in which we really do not need a complete list, and, hence, can save ourselves a great deal of unnecessary work.

Although the first kind of problem may seem straightforward and easy, this is not always the case. Suppose, for instance, that in a small community, tests for drivers' licenses are given only once a week, and that we are interested in what can happen to three applicants in three consecutive weeks. To be specific, we are interested only in *how many of them pass the test each week.* Clearly, there are many possibilities: all three of the applicants might pass on the first try; one might pass on the first try, another on the third try, while the third applicant fails every time; one applicant might pass on the first try and the other two on the second try, and to mention one more possibility, all three of the applicants might fail every time. Continuing this way carefully, we might come up with the correct answer that there are altogether 20 possibilities.

To handle problems like this systematically, it helps to refer to a diagram like that of Figure 15.1, which is called a *tree diagram*. This

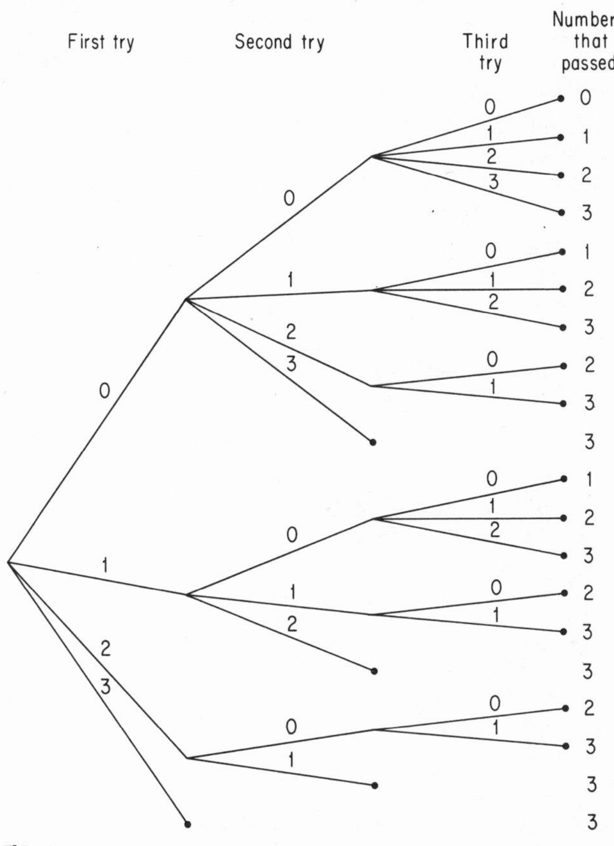

FIG. 15.1

diagram shows that for the first try there are four possibilities (four branches) corresponding to 0, 1, 2, or 3 of the applicants passing the test; for the second try there are four branches emanating from the top branch, three from the second branch, two from the third branch, and none from the bottom branch. Clearly, there are still four possibilities (0, 1, 2, or 3) when none of the applicants passes on the first try, but only three possibilities (0, 1, or 2) when one of the applicants passes on the first try, two possibilities (0 or 1) when two of the applicants pass on the first try, and there is no need to go on when all three of the applicants pass on the first try. The same sort of reasoning applies also to the third try, and we thus find that (going from left to right) there are altogether 20 different paths along the "branches" of the tree diagram of Figure 15.1. In other words, 20 different things can happen in the given situation. It can also be seen from this diagram that in *ten* of the cases all three of the applicants pass the test (sooner or later) in the first three tries, in *six* of the cases two of the applicants pass the test in the first three tries, in *three* of the cases only one of the applicants passes the test in the first three tries, and in *one* case none of the applicants passes the test in the first three tries.

To consider another example in which a tree diagram can be of some aid (at least, until we shall have studied other techniques), suppose that a brokerage house asks its stock analyst to examine six stocks with regard to their potential long-term growth, and to come up with a first and a

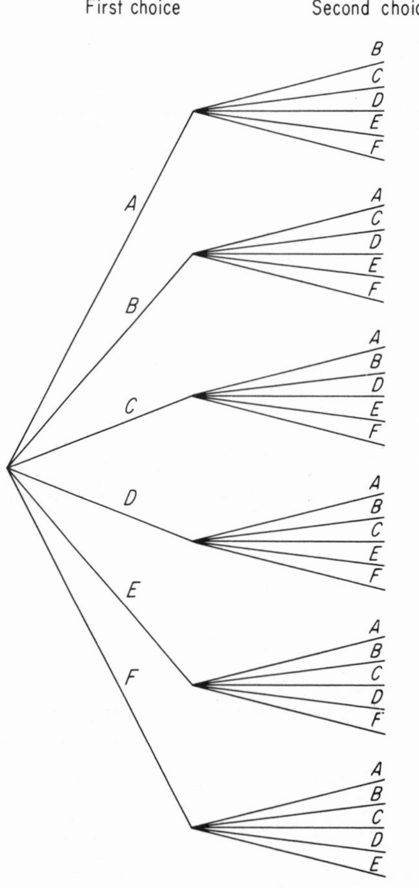

FIG. 15.2

second choice. The question is, *in how many different ways can this be done?* Drawing a tree diagram like that of Figure 15.2, where the stocks are labeled A, B, C, D, E, and F, we find practically by inspection that there are 30 possibilities, corresponding to the 30 different paths along the "branches of the tree." Starting at the top, the first path corresponds to the first choice being Stock A and the second choice being Stock B; the second path corresponds to the first choice being Stock A and the second choice being Stock C; . . . ; and the thirtieth path (namely, the one along the bottom branches of the tree) corresponds to the first choice being Stock F and the second choice being Stock E.

Note that the answer we obtained in this example is the *product* of 6 and 5, namely, the *product* of the number of ways in which the analyst can make his first choice and the number of ways in which he can subsequently make his second choice. In fact, our example illustrates the following general rule:

> *If a selection consists of two separate steps, of which the first can be made in m different ways and the second in n different ways, then the whole selection can be made in $m \cdot n$ different ways.*

Thus, if a restaurant offers 12 different kinds of dessert, which it serves with coffee, Sanka, tea, milk, or hot chocolate, there are altogether $12 \cdot 5 = 60$ different ways in which one can order a dessert and a drink. Also, if someone wants to buy one of eight different toys as a birthday gift for a child, and have it sent by parcel post, by first class mail, or by air-mail, then there are altogether $8 \cdot 3 = 24$ different ways in which the whole transaction can take place.

By using appropriate tree diagrams, it is easy to generalize the above rule so that it will apply also to selections involving more than two steps. For k steps, where k is a positive integer, we thus obtain the following rule:

> *If a selection consists of k separate steps, of which the first can be made in n_1 different ways, the second can be made in n_2 different ways, . . . , and the kth can be made in n_k different ways, then the whole selection can be made in $n_1 \cdot n_2 \cdot \ldots \cdot n_k$ different ways.*

Thus, we simply multiply the number of ways in which each step can be made, and if the stock market analyst on page 434 had been asked to include a third choice, the total number of possibilities would have been $6 \cdot 5 \cdot 4 = 120$. Also, if a new housing development advertises 2-, 3-, and 4-bedroom houses, which can be had in 4 different exterior finishes, with or without a fireplace, and with or without a garage, there are altogether $3 \cdot 4 \cdot 2 \cdot 2 = 48$ different selections a homebuyer can make. Finally, if a true-false test consists of 10 questions, there are altogether $2^{10} = 1{,}024$ different ways in which the answers can be checked; unfortunately, only one of them corresponds to the case where all answers are correct (see also Exercise 9 on page 448).

EXERCISES

1. Two used-car salesmen make a small bet each week as to who will be the first one to make two sales. (Thus, if we refer to the two salesmen as X and Y, the sequence XYX represents the case where X makes the first sale, then Y makes a sale, and then X makes another sale and wins the bet; similarly, YY represents the case where Y makes two sales and wins the bet before X even gets started.)

(a) Construct a tree diagram showing the 6 possible outcomes of this "game," and indicate in each case who wins the bet.
(b) How many possible outcomes are left if we *know* that Y makes the first sale, and in how many of them will X win the bet?

2. A bank classifies its delinquent installment-loan accounts according to whether or not they have ever been delinquent before; according to whether the amount owed is less than \$100 or \$100 or more; and according to whether payments are overdue by less than two months or by two months or more.

(a) Construct a tree diagram showing the various ways in which the bank classifies its delinquent installment-loan accounts.
(b) If there are 50 accounts in each of the categories of part (a) and a courteous reminder is sent to all those whose accounts are delinquent for the first time *or* who owe less than \$100, how many of these courteous reminders will the bank have to mail out?
(c) If a warning is sent to all those whose payments are overdue by two months or more, how many of these warnings will the bank have to mail out?
(d) How many persons with delinquent installment-loan accounts at this bank will receive a courteous reminder as well as a warning?

3. The manager of an appliance store stocks two automatic dishwashers of the same kind, reordering at the end of each day (for delivery early the next morning) if and only if both have been sold. Construct a tree diagram to show that if he starts on a Monday with two of the automatic dishwashers in stock, there are altogether 8 different ways in which he can make sales on Monday and Tuesday of that week. (*Hint:* if he sells one of the dishwashers on Monday, there are only two possibilities, 0 or 1, for Tuesday.)

4. A theatrical promoter plans to put \$10,000 into *one* Broadway production each year, so long as the number of flops in which he invests does not exceed the number of hits.

(a) Draw a tree diagram showing the 8 possible situations that can arise during the first four years the plan is in operation. (*Hint:* if the first year's play is a flop, that branch of the tree diagram ends right then and there.)
(b) In how many of the situations described in part (a) will he continue to invest in the fifth year?
(c) If the promoter loses his total investment in a flop and doubles his money in a hit, in how many of the situations described in part (a) is he exactly even after four years?

5. The Standard and Poor's Corporation regularly rates common stocks, assigning them the ratings $A+$, A, $A-$, $B+$, B, $B-$, and C.

(a) In how many ways can they rate two different common stocks?
(b) In how many ways could they have rated two different common stocks, if all we know is that their ratings are not the same?
(c) In how many ways can they rate three different common stocks, if each of the stocks rates at least $A-$?

6. If a chain of drug stores has 4 warehouses and 18 retail outlets, in how many different ways can an item be shipped from one of the warehouses to one of the stores?

7. If the five finalists in the Miss California contest are Miss Santa Barbara, Miss Orange County, Miss San Diego, Miss Los Angeles, and Miss San Francisco, in how many different ways can the judges choose the winner and the first runner-up?

8. If someone wants to vacation in one of the six New England states and travel by car, bus, train, or plane, in how many different ways can he plan his vacation?

9. Given that four airlines fly directly between Chicago and Phoenix, in how many different ways can a person fly from Chicago to Phoenix and back if

(a) he must take the same airline both ways;
(b) he can but need not take the same airline both ways;
(c) he cannot take the same airline both ways?

10. The Board of Directors of a corporation consists of Mr. Adams, Mr. Brown, Mrs. Carson, Mr. Dickson, Mrs. Elliott, Mr. Fulton, Mr. Grant, and Mrs. Holland.

(a) In how many different ways can they elect a chairman and a vice-chairman from among themselves?
(b) In how many different ways can they elect a chairman, a vice-chairman, and a treasurer from among themselves?
(c) In how many ways can they elect a chairman and a vice-chairman from among themselves, if the chairman is to be a man and the vice-chairman is to be a woman?

11. With reference to Exercise 7, in how many different ways can the judges choose the winner, a first runner-up, and a second runner-up?

12. In a certain city, a child watching television on a Saturday morning has the choice between two different cartoon shows from 7:30 to 8, three different cartoon shows from 8 to 8:30, and three different cartoon shows from 8:30 to 9. In how many ways can one of these children plan his Saturday morning entertainment of watching cartoons from 7:30 to 9?

13. A new-car buyer finds that he must not only choose between 8 different models, but that each model can be had with 3 different engines, with or without air-conditioning, and in 15 different colors. Altogether, in how many different ways can his order be placed?

14. In how many different ways can a visitor to Disneyland take in one of the 8 attractions in Tomorrowland, one of the 16 attractions in Fantasyland, one of the 9 attractions in Frontierland, and one of the 4 attractions in Adventureland?

15. A cafeteria offers 12 different soups or salads, 15 main dishes, and 8 desserts. In how many different ways can one choose a soup or salad, a main dish, and a dessert?

16. A multiple-choice test consists of 6 questions, each permitting a choice of 4 alternatives. In how many different ways can a student check off his answers to these questions?

17. THE NUMBER OF SUBSETS OF A SET. To select a subset from a given set (see page 10, we must decide for each element of the set whether it is to be included or not. Thus, for each element there is a choice between two alternatives, and if a set has n elements, there are altogether

$$\underbrace{2 \cdot 2 \cdot 2 \cdot 2 \cdot \ldots \cdot 2}_{n \text{ factors}} = 2^n$$

different ways in which the selection of a subset can be made. In other words, *a set of n elements has 2^n different subsets.* For instance, if a set consists of the two elements s and t, the $2^n = 2^2 = 4$ possibilities are

include s and include t
include s but exclude t
exclude s but include t
exclude s and exclude t

where the first subset contains s as well as t, the second subset contains s alone, the third subset contains t alone, and the fourth subset is the empty set $\varnothing$ which contains neither s nor t. Note that the order of the elements does not matter, and that *the empty set $\varnothing$ is always included when we talk about the possible subsets of a set.*

(a) In how many ways can one select a subset from a set of 6 elements, say, the set which consists of the 6 vice-presidents of a corporation?
(b) In how many ways can one choose a committee consisting of at least one of the 6 vice-presidents of a corporation?
(c) In how many ways can one select a subset from a set of 12 elements, say, the set which consists of the 12 retail outlets of the candy manufacturer referred to on page 8?

(d) In how many ways can one select a subset consisting of at least one, but not all, of the 12 retail outlets of the candy manufacturer?
(e) In how many ways can one select subsets from sets containing, respectively, 5, 10, and 20 elements?

An alternate (and rather clever) derivation of the formula for the number of subsets of a set is given in Exercise 24 on page 451.

15.3 PERMUTATIONS

The rules of the preceding section are often applied to problems in which repeated selections are made from one and the same set, and *the order in which the selections are made is of significance.* This was the case in the example on page 434 where the stock analyst had to make a first and second choice from among six stocks, and, among others, in Exercises 7 and 11 where the judges had to make several selections from among the five finalists in a beauty contest.

In general, if r objects are selected from a set of n objects, any particular arrangement of these r objects is referred to as a *permutation.* For instance, 45132 is one of many possible permutations of the first five positive integers, and so are 13524 and 25341; *Idaho, New Mexico, and Utah* is a permutation (a particular ordered arrangement) of 3 of the 8 Mountain States; *DCGE*, *CFGA*, and *BCDF* are three of many possible permutations of 4 of the first 7 letters of the alphabet; and if we were asked to list *all possible* permutations of 2 of the 5 vowels a, e, i, o, and u, our answer would be

ae ai ao au ei eo eu io iu ou
ea ia oa ua ie oe ue oi ui uo

So far as the counting of possible permutations is concerned, direct application of the rule on page 435 leads to the following result:

The number of permutation of r objects selected from a set of n objects is $n(n-1)(n-2)\cdot\ldots\cdot(n-r+1)$, *which we shall denote* ${}_nP_r$.*

To prove this formula, we have only to observe that the first selection is made from the whole set of n objects, the second selection is made from the $n-1$ objects which remain after the first selection has been made, the

* The following are some alternate symbols used to denote the number of permutations of r objects selected from a set of n objects: $P(n, r)$, P^n_r, $P_{n,r}$, and $(n)_r$.

third selection is made from the $n - 2$ objects which remain after the first two selections have been made, and the rth and final selection is made from the

$$n - (r - 1) = n - r + 1$$

objects which remain after the first $r - 1$ selections have been made. Thus, the number of ways in which 4 new territories can be assigned (one each) to 4 of a company's 7 salesmen is $7 \cdot 6 \cdot 5 \cdot 4 = 840$, and the number of ways in which a college senior can pick a first, second, and third choice among 45 potential employers is $45 \cdot 44 \cdot 43 = 85{,}140$. Incidentally, it has been assumed in our discussion that the objects with which we are dealing are *distinguishable* in some way; otherwise, there are complications, which we shall discuss very briefly in Exercise 8 on page 447. Clearly, if we have to select one after the other 4 of 20 identical slips of paper marked with the letter A, there are *not* $20 \cdot 19 \cdot 18 \cdot 17 = 116{,}280$ different permutations—all we can possibly get is the one permutation $AAAA$.

Had the stock analyst of the example on page 434 been asked to rank all six of the stocks with regard to their potential long-term growth, he could have done so in $6 \cdot 5 \cdot 4 \cdot 3 \cdot 2 \cdot 1 = 720$ different ways (barring ties), and had the judges of the Miss California contest (see Exercise 7 on page 437) been asked to pick the winner as well as a first, second, third, and fourth runner-up from among the five finalists, they could have done so in $5 \cdot 4 \cdot 3 \cdot 2 \cdot 1 = 120$ different ways. Both of these examples illustrate the fact that in the special case where $r = n$,

> *The number of permutations on n objects taken all together is* $n(n - 1)(n - 2) \cdot \ldots \cdot 3 \cdot 2 \cdot 1$.

To consider one more example, the number of ways in which 7 drivers can be assigned to 7 delivery trucks is $7 \cdot 6 \cdot 5 \cdot 4 \cdot 3 \cdot 2 \cdot 1 = 5{,}040$.

Since products of consecutive integers arise in many problems involving permutations or other kinds of special arrangements, it generally simplifies matters if we use the *factorial notation* (mentioned earlier on pages 325 and 326). In this notation, $1! = 1$, $2! = 2 \cdot 1 = 2$, $3! = 3 \cdot 2 \cdot 1 = 6$, $4! = 4 \cdot 3 \cdot 2 \cdot 1 = 24, \ldots$, and in general, $n!$, which reads "n factorial," denotes the product

$$n(n - 1)(n - 2) \cdot \ldots \cdot 3 \cdot 2 \cdot 1$$

for any positive integer n. It is customary, also, to let $0! = 1$ (by definition), because this makes it easier to express certain formulas relating to permutations and other kinds of special arrangements. Incidentally, a table of *factorials*, from $n = 0$ to $n = 15$, may be found at the end of this book.

Using the factorial notation, we can now write the formula for the number of permutations of r objects selected from a set of n objects as

$$_nP_r = \frac{n!}{(n-r)!}$$

To verify this result, observe that $_7P_3 = 7\cdot6\cdot5$, for example, can be written as

$$7\cdot6\cdot5 = \frac{7\cdot6\cdot5\cdot4!}{4!} = \frac{7\cdot6\cdot5\cdot4\cdot3\cdot2\cdot1}{4!} = \frac{7!}{4!}$$

that $_{15}P_4 = 15\cdot14\cdot13\cdot12$ can be written as

$$15\cdot14\cdot13\cdot12 = \frac{15\cdot14\cdot13\cdot12\cdot11!}{11!} = \frac{15!}{11!}$$

and that, in general, $_nP_r = n(n-1)\cdot\ldots\cdot(n-r+1)$ can be written as

$$n(n-1)\cdot\ldots\cdot(n-r+1) = \frac{n(n-1)\cdot\ldots\cdot(n-r+1)\cdot(n-r)!}{(n-r)!}$$

$$= \frac{n!}{(n-r)!}$$

Thus, the number of ways in which a chairman, a vice-chairman, a secretary, and a treasurer can be chosen from among the nine members of the executive council of a union is

$$_9P_4 = \frac{9!}{(9-4)!} = \frac{9!}{5!} = \frac{362{,}880}{120} = 3{,}024$$

where the values of 9! and 5! were obtained from Table VII. (It is easy to check this result, for all we have to do is multiply 9 times 8 times 7 times 6.)

In the special case where $r = n$, the formula for the number of permutations of n objects taken all together becomes

$$_nP_n = \frac{n!}{(n-n)!} = \frac{n!}{0!} = \frac{n!}{1} = n!$$

and, referring to Table VII, we find that the starting eleven of a professional football team can be introduced to the public before a game in

$$11! = 39{,}916{,}800$$

different ways.

15.4 COMBINATIONS

If a person gathering data for a market research organization has to interview 3 of the 48 families living in a certain apartment house, he can select these families in 17,296 different ways, but this is *not* the number of permutations of 3 objects selected from a set of 48 objects. If we cared about the order in which he visits these families, the answer would be

$$_{48}P_3 = 48\cdot47\cdot46 = 103{,}776$$

but each set of 3 families would then be counted *six times*. For instance, if the letters J, M, and S stand for Jones, Morris, and Smith (namely, three of the families who live in the given apartment house), then

$$JMS, \quad JSM, \quad MJS, \quad MSJ, \quad SMJ, \quad \text{and} \quad SJM$$

constitute six *different permutations*, but they all represent the same three families, namely, the *same subset* of 3 of the 48 families. Since this argument holds for any three families who live in the given apartment house, the total number of ways in which we can select 3 of the 48 families (without paying attention to the order in which they are chosen) is given by

$$\frac{_{48}P_3}{6} = \frac{103{,}776}{6} = 17{,}296$$

This figure is referred to as the *number of combinations of 3 objects selected from a set of 48 objects.*

Thus, "combination" has the same meaning as "subset," and when we ask for the *number of combinations of r objects selected from a set of n objects,* we are simply trying to find out *how many different subsets of r objects can be selected from a set of n objects.* To obtain a formula for this, we have only to observe that any r objects can be rearranged into $r!$ different permutations; in other words, the $r!$ permutations of the elements of any subset of r objects count only as *one combination.* Hence, the $_nP_r$ permutations of r objects selected from a set of n objects contain each combination $r!$ times, and $_nC_r$, the corresponding number of combinations, is given by $_nP_r$ divided by $r!$. Consequently,

> *The number of combinations of r objects selected from a set of n objects is**
>
> $$_nC_r = \frac{_nP_r}{r!} = \frac{n(n-1)\cdot\ldots\cdot(n-r+1)}{r!}$$

where we substituted $n(n-1)\cdot\ldots\cdot(n-r+1)$ for $_nP_r$ in accordance with the rule on page 439. The following are some alternate symbols used to denote the number of combinations of r objects selected from a set of n objects: $C(n,r)$, C^n_r, $C_{n,r}$, and above all $\binom{n}{r}$, which is referred to as a *binomial coefficient* for reasons to be explained in Section 15.5.

To consider some examples, let us see in how many ways a committee of 4 can be selected from among the 120 employees of a company, and let us determine the number of ways in which a social scientist conducting a

---

* This formula does not hold for $n = 0$, but the alternate formula on page 443 (where $_nC_r$ is expressed in terms of factorials) does—it gives $_0C_0 = 1$.

sample survey can select 5 of the 14 counties of the State of Arizona. In the first case, we find that there are

$$_{120}C_4 = \frac{120\cdot 119\cdot 118\cdot 117}{4!} = \frac{197{,}149{,}680}{24} = 821{,}457$$

ways of selecting the committee; and in the second case, we find that there are

$$_{14}C_5 = \frac{14\cdot 13\cdot 12\cdot 11\cdot 10}{5!} = \frac{240{,}240}{120} = 2{,}002$$

ways of selecting the five counties. Of course, these are *combinations*, and the internal order of the committee and the order in which the social scientist might visit the five counties are not taken into consideration.

Using factorials and the alternate formula for $_nP_r$ on page 441, we can also write the formula for the number of combinations of r objects selected from a set of n objects as

$$_nC_r = \frac{n!}{(n-r)!r!}$$

Had we used this formula to determine the number of ways in which the social scientist can select 5 of the 14 counties of the State of Arizona, we would have obtained $_{14}C_5 = \frac{14!}{9!5!}$, and we could then have continued by looking up the values of 14!, 9!, and 5! in Table VII. This would have entailed a considerable amount of work, *all of which could have been avoided by looking up the answer, 2,002, directly in Table VIII.*

As we indicated on page 442, the number of combinations of r objects selected from a set of n objects is often written as $\binom{n}{r}$ instead of $_nC_r$, and referred to as a *binomial coefficient;* this is the notation and terminology used in Table VIII, which contains the values of $\binom{n}{r}$ for $n = 0, 1, 2, \ldots,$ and 20. When n is greater than 10 and r is large, the use of Table VIII may require that we refer to the identity

$$_nC_{n-r} = {}_nC_r \quad \textit{or, in the alternate notation} \quad \binom{n}{n-r} = \binom{n}{r}$$

To prove this, we might argue that each time we select a subset of r objects we *leave* a subset of $n - r$ objects, and, hence, there are as many ways of selecting r objects as there are ways of leaving (or selecting) $n - r$ objects. To prove the identity algebraically, we have only to write

$$_nC_{n-r} = \frac{n!}{[n-(n-r)]!(n-r)!} = \frac{n!}{r!(n-r)!} = \frac{n!}{(n-r)!r!} = {}_nC_r$$

Thus, if a police captain wants to choose 15 of his 20 detectives for a special assignment, he can do so in

$$\binom{20}{15} = \binom{20}{5} = 15{,}504$$

different ways; and if a child wants to select 12 of the 16 rides in Disneyland's Fantasyland, he can do so in

$$\binom{16}{12} = \binom{16}{4} = 1{,}820$$

different ways.

15.5 THE BINOMIAL THEOREM

In algebra, we first learn how to expand expressions such as $(a + b)^2$, $(a + b)^3$, $(a + b)^4$, . . . , by actually multiplying them out term-by-term. Thus, for $(a + b)^3$ we obtained

$$\begin{aligned}(a + b)^3 &= (a + b)(a + b)(a + b)\\ &= a \cdot a \cdot a + a \cdot a \cdot b + a \cdot b \cdot a + a \cdot b \cdot b\\ &\qquad + b \cdot a \cdot a + b \cdot a \cdot b + b \cdot b \cdot a + b \cdot b \cdot b\\ &= a^3 + 3a^2b + 3ab^2 + b^3\end{aligned}$$

where each of the eight terms is the product of three letters, a or b, with one coming from each of the three factors $a + b$. For example, the three terms a^2b were obtained by multiplying the a of the first factor by the a of the second factor and the b of the third factor, by multiplying the a of the first factor by the b of the second factor and the a of the third factor, and by multiplying the b of the first factor by the a of the second factor and the a of the third factor. In other words, *there are three terms a^2b corresponding to the different ways in which two a's and one b can be selected, one from each of the factors $a + b$.* Correspondingly, the coefficient of a^3 is 1, since there is only one way in which three a's can be selected, one from each factor $a + b$; the coefficient of ab^2 is 3, since there are three ways in which two b's and one a can be selected, one from each factor $a + b$; and the coefficient of b^3 is 1, since there is only one way in which three b's can be selected, one from each factor $a + b$.

Suppose now that we want to expand $(a + b)^4$ without actually multiplying out $(a + b)(a + b)(a + b)(a + b)$ term-by-term. To this end, let us observe that if we *did* perform the multiplication, we would obtain 16 terms, each of which is the product of four letters, a or b, with one coming from each of the four factors $a + b$. Thus, each term must be of the form a^4, a^3b, a^2b^2, ab^3, or b^4, and all we have to determine is *how many there are of each kind*. So far as a^4 is concerned, there is only one such term, since there is only one way in which four a's can be selected, one from each factor $a + b$; hence, the coefficient of a^4 is 1. So far as a^3b is concerned, there are four ways in which we can select the factors from which we obtain the b (or the factors from which we obtain the three a's), and, hence, the coefficient of a^3b is $\binom{4}{1} = 4$. Similarly, the coefficient of a^2b^2 is the number of ways in which we can select the two factors from which we obtain the two b's (or the two factors from which we obtain the two a's), namely, $\binom{4}{2} = 6$. Continuing this way, we arrive at the result that

$$\begin{aligned}(a+b)^4 &= \binom{4}{0}a^4 + \binom{4}{1}a^3b + \binom{4}{2}a^2b^2 + \binom{4}{3}ab^3 + \binom{4}{4}b^4 \\ &= a^4 + 4a^3b + 6a^2b^2 + 4ab^3 + b^4\end{aligned}$$

where we substituted $\binom{4}{0} = 1$ for the coefficient of a^4; after all, the number of ways in which we can get four a's in this example is the same as the number of ways in which we can get zero b's.

If we apply the same sort of reasoning to the expansion of $(a + b)^n$, where n is a positive integer, we obtain the following result, called the *binomial theorem:*

$$\begin{aligned}(a+b)^n = \binom{n}{0}a^n + \binom{n}{1}a^{n-1}b + \binom{n}{2}a^{n-2}b^2 \\ + \ldots + \binom{n}{n-1}ab^{n-1} + \binom{n}{n}b^n\end{aligned}$$

where the first and last terms are sometimes written as $\binom{n}{0}a^nb^0$ and $\binom{n}{n}a^0b^n$, to emphasize the fact that *the sum of the exponents of a and b is always equal to n.* It is easy to verify that the above formulation of the binomial theorem is equivalent to the one on page 347, and if the reader wishes to see a more formal proof, he should be able to find one (by what is called *mathematical induction*) in most college algebra texts. Incidentally, the above formulation of the binomial theorem explains why we refer to the combinatorial quantities $\binom{n}{r}$ as *binomial coefficients.*

To illustrate the binomial theorem, let us write down the expansion of $(a + b)^8$. Although we could calculate the necessary coefficients by means of the formula

$$\binom{8}{r} = \frac{8!}{(8-r)!r!} \qquad \text{for } r = 0, 1, 2, \ldots, \text{ and } 8$$

or by following the directions on page 347, let us refer instead to Table VIII. This tells us that $\binom{8}{0} = \binom{8}{8} = 1$, $\binom{8}{1} = \binom{8}{7} = 8$, $\binom{8}{2} = \binom{8}{6} = 28$, $\binom{8}{3} = \binom{8}{5} = 56$, and $\binom{8}{4} = 70$, and, hence, that

$$(a + b)^8 = a^8 + 8a^7b + 28a^6b^2 + 56a^5b^3 + 70a^4b^4 + 56a^3b^5 + 28a^2b^6 + 8ab^7 + b^8$$

To consider a practical application of the binomial theorem, suppose we are planning to put \$1,000 into a savings account which pays 4 percent compounded annually, and we want to know how much this money will be worth 10 years hence. Ordinarily, we would look this up in an appropriate table (say, Table I), but if such a table is not available, we can obtain an approximate answer by using the first few terms of the binomial expansion of $(1 + 0.04)^{10}$. Looking up the necessary binomial coefficients in Table VIII and substituting them together with $a = 1$, $b = 0.04$, and $n = 10$ into the formula on page 445, we get

$$\begin{aligned}(1 + 0.04)^{10} &= 1^{10} + 10(1)^9(0.04) + 45(1)^8(0.04)^2 + 120(1)^7(0.04)^3 + \dots \\ &= 1 + 10(0.04) + 45(0.04)^2 + 120(0.04)^3 + \dots \\ &= 1 + 0.4 + 0.072 + 0.00768 + \dots \\ &= 1.47968 + \dots\end{aligned}$$

Thus, if we use the first four terms of this binomial expansion, we can say that after 10 years the money will be worth approximately 1,000(1.47968) = \$1,479.68 or \$1,480 *to the nearest dollar*. (This is correct, as can easily be verified by looking up the corresponding entry of Table I.) The remaining terms of the binomial expansion decrease very rapidly, and in Exercise 22 on page 450 the reader will be asked to show that if we had included the next two terms of the binomial expansion, our answer would have been correct even *to the nearest cent*.

EXERCISES

1. On each trip, a salesman visits 6 of the 9 major cities in his territory. In how many different ways can he schedule his route?
2. In how many ways can 8 new accounts be distributed among 12 advertising executives, if none of them is to receive more than one of the new accounts?
3. In how many ways can 6 executives each choose a car from a pool of 11 different kinds of cars?
4. If a television network has to choose 4 of 18 half-hour programs to put on the

air on weekday mornings from 8:30 to 10:30, in how many different ways can they arrange their schedule?

5. A company has 16 applicants for four different executive positions within its organization.

(a) In how many ways can these positions be filled?
(b) In how many ways can these positions be filled if 5 of the applicants are ruled out for various reasons?
(c) In how many ways can the position be filled if there are 6 applicants for one of the positions and 10 applicants for the other three positions? (*Hint:* in accordance with the rule on page 435, multiply the number of ways in which the first position can be filled by the number of ways the other three positions can be filled.)

6. In how many ways can a television director schedule a sponsor's six different commercials during the six time slots allocated to commercials during a 60-minute "special?" (See also Exercise 8.)

7. Three married couples have bought six seats in a row for a football game.

(a) In how many different ways can they be seated?
(b) In how many ways can they be seated if none of the men are to sit together and none of the women are to sit together? (*Hint:* add the number of possibilities where the first seat on the left is occupied by a man to the number of possibilities where the first seat on the left is occupied by a woman.)
(c) In how many ways can they be seated if all the men are to sit together and all the women are to sit together?
(d) In how many ways can they be seated if each couple is to sit together with the husband to the left of his wife?

8. PERMUTATIONS INVOLVING INDISTINGUISHABLE OBJECTS. If some of the n objects from which we select a subset are indistinguishable, the formulas for ${}_nP_r$ and ${}_nC_r$ no longer apply. Suppose, for instance, that we want to determine the number of ways in which we can arrange the letters in the word "book." If we distinguish for the moment between the two o's by referring to them as o_1 and o_2, there are indeed ${}_4P_4 = 4! = 24$ different permutations of the symbols b, o_1, o_2, and k. However, if we drop the subscripts, then bo_1ko_2 and bo_2ko_1, for example, represent the *same* permutation *boko*. Since each permutation *without* subscripts will then correspond to two permutations *with* subscripts, the answer to our original question, namely, the total number of permutations of the letters in the word "book," is $\frac{24}{2} = 12$. Similarly, if we refer to the e's in "receive" as e_1, e_2, and e_3, there are ${}_7P_7 =$ 5,040 permutations of the symbols r, e_1, c, e_2, i, v, and e_3, but since the three e's can be arranged among themselves in $3! = 6$ different ways, each permutation *without* subscripts corresponds to 6 permutations *with* subscripts, and, hence, there are only $\frac{7!}{3!} = \frac{5{,}040}{6} = 840$ different permutations of the letters in "receive." In general, this argument leads to the result that if r_1

of the n objects are alike, r_2 others are also alike, . . . , and r_k others are alike, then the total number of permutations of the n objects is given by

$$\frac{n!}{r_1! \cdot r_2! \cdot \ldots \cdot r_k!}$$

For instance, the number of permutations of the letters in "minimum" is

$$\frac{7!}{3!2!} = \frac{5{,}040}{6 \cdot 2} = 420$$

(a) How many permutations are there of the letters in "meter"?
(b) In how many ways (according only to the manufacturer) can six cars place in a stock-car race, if three of the cars are Fords, one is a Chevrolet, one is a Plymouth, and one is a Rambler?
(c) In how many ways can the television director of Exercise 6 schedule the six commercials, if the sponsor has only two commercials, each of which is to be shown three times?
(d) In how many ways can the television director of Exercise 6 schedule the six commercials, if the sponsor has three commercials, each of which is to be shown twice?
(e) In its cookbook section, a bookstore has 4 copies of the *New York Times Cookbook*, 2 copies of *The Joy of Cooking*, 5 copies of the *Better Homes and Gardens Cookbook*, and one copy of *The Secret of Cooking for Dogs.* If these books are sold one at a time, in how many different ways (that is, in how many different sequences), can they be sold?

9. On page 436 we pointed out that a true-false test consisting of 10 questions can be marked (that is, the answers can be checked off) in 1,024 different ways.

(a) In how many ways can a student take this test and get exactly 8 right answers? (Do not refer to Table VIII in either part of this exercise.)
(b) In how many ways can a student take his test and get *at least* 8 right answers? (*Hint:* add the number of ways in which he can get 8 right answers, the number of ways in which he can get 9 right answers, and the number of ways in which he can get 10 right answers.)

10. In how many different ways can a company select 3 of 11 possible sites for the construction of distribution centers? Use one of the formulas for ${}_nC_r$ and check your answer in Table VIII.

11. In how many ways can a 6-man committee be chosen from among the general managers of 20 baseball teams? Use one of the formulas for ${}_nC_r$ and check your answer in Table VIII.

12. Find the number of ways in which an accountant working for the Internal Revenue Service can select 4 of 14 tax returns for a special audit. Use one of the formulas for ${}_nC_r$ and check your answer in Table VIII.

13. Mr. Brown has 5 suits and 16 ties. In how many ways can he choose 2 suits and 5 ties to take along on a business trip? (*Hint:* multiply the respective number of possibilities in accordance with the rule on page 435.)

14. A shipment of 15 typewriters contains one that is defective. In how many ways can one choose three of these typewriters so that

(a) the defective one is not included;
(b) the defective one is included?

15. In hiring his staff, the manager of a new furniture store has to choose 6 salesmen from among 9 applicants, 2 buyers from among 4 applicants, 4 secretaries from among 12 applicants, and 3 stockroom clerks from among 8 applicants. Use Table VIII and the rule on page 435 to find the total number of ways in which he can select his staff.

16. If a linear programming problem involves k variables which must satisfy m linear inequalities (including those which say that the variables must be non-negative), and the inequalities are replaced by corresponding equations (as on page 238), then a vertex of the region of feasible solutions must be the solution of a system of k of these linear equations. Potentially, how many vertices can there be to the region of feasible solution of a linear programming problem in which

(a) there are 4 variables subject to 6 linear inequalities;
(b) there are 5 variables subject to 9 linear inequalities;
(c) there are 6 variables subject to 11 linear inequalities;
(d) there are 8 variables subject to 14 linear inequalities?

17. Prove that

$$ {}_nC_r + {}_nC_{r-1} = {}_{n+1}C_r $$

[*Hint:* use the formula on page 443 to express ${}_nC_r$ and ${}_nC_{r-1}$ in terms of factorials, get the common denominator $(n - r + 1)!\cdot r!$, and then show that the sum represents ${}_{n+1}C_r$.]

18. PASCAL'S TRIANGLE. The number of combinations of r objects selected from a set of n objects, namely, the binomial coefficients $\binom{n}{r}$ can be determined by means of the following arrangement called *Pascal's triangle:*

$$
\begin{array}{ccccccccccc}
 & & & & & 1 & & & & & \\
 & & & & 1 & & 1 & & & & \\
 & & & 1 & & 2 & & 1 & & & \\
 & & 1 & & 3 & & 3 & & 1 & & \\
 & 1 & & 4 & & 6 & & 4 & & 1 & \\
1 & & 5 & & 10 & & 10 & & 5 & & 1 \\
\cdot & \cdot & \cdot & \cdot & \cdot & \cdot & \cdot & \cdot & \cdot & \cdot & \cdot
\end{array}
$$

where each row begins with a 1, ends with a 1, and each other entry is the *sum* of the nearest two entries in the row immediately above.

(a) Referring to Table VIII, verify that the values of the first 6 rows of Pascal's triangle are, in fact, the binomial coefficients for $n = 0, 1, 2, 3, 4$, and 5.

(b) That part of the rule for the construction of Pascal's triangle which says that each row begins and ends with a 1, simply expresses the fact that $\binom{n}{0}$ and $\binom{n}{n}$ are always equal to 1. Verify for the second entry of the fourth row, the third entry of the fifth row, and the second and third entries of the sixth row, that the other part of the rule is based on the formula of Exercise 17.

(c) Following the rule for the construction of Pascal's triangle, fill in the next two (seventh and eighth) rows. Verify the results by comparing them with the corresponding entries of Table VIII.

19. Use the binomial theorem to expand each of the following, and simplify as much as possible:

(a) $(1 + 2x)^4$; (c) $(3x + 2y)^5$;
(b) $(5 - x)^3$; (d) $(2x - 1)^6$.

[*Hint:* in part (b) let $a = 5$ and $b = -x$ in the binomial formula, and in part (d) let $a = 2x$ and $b = -1$.]

20. Use the binomial theorem to evaluate each of the following complex numbers, and write the answers in the so-called "standard form" $a + bi$:

(a) $(2 + i)^3$;
(b) $(1 + 2i)^4$;
(c) $(3 - i)^5$.

21. Using the first four terms of an appropriate binomial expansion, approximate each of the following:

(a) $(1.02)^5$; (c) $(1.05)^7$;
(b) $(0.98)^4$; (d) $(0.95)^6$.

Check the answers to parts (a) and (c) in Table I. [*Hint:* in part (b) write 0.98 as $1 + (-0.02)$ and in part (d) write 0.95 as $1 + (-0.05)$.]

22. Verify that if we had calculated two more terms of the binomial expansion in the example on page 446, our answer would have been correct to the nearest cent.

23. CONTINUOUS CONVERSION OF INTEREST. In Exercise 9 on page 142 we stated that if money is invested at 6 percent compounded continuously, the effective rate is about 6.18 percent. Since this effective rate is the limit approached by

$$\left(1 + \frac{.06}{m}\right)^m - 1$$

as $m \to \infty$, verify the above claim by approximating the value of

$$\left(1 + \frac{.06}{100}\right)^{100} - 1$$

using the first three terms of the binomial expansion of $\left(1 + \frac{.06}{100}\right)^{100}$.

24. THE NUMBER OF SUBSETS OF A SET. Since $\binom{n}{0}$ is the number of ways in which we can select a subset of zero elements (namely, the set $\varnothing$) from a set of n elements, $\binom{n}{1}$ is the number of ways in which we can select a subset of one element, $\binom{n}{2}$ is the number of ways in which we can select a subset of two elements, . . . , and $\binom{n}{n}$ is the number of ways in which we can select the whole set, the total number of ways in which we can select a subset, and, hence, the *total number of subsets of a set of n elements (objects)* is

$$\binom{n}{0} + \binom{n}{1} + \binom{n}{2} + \ldots + \binom{n}{n}$$

Evaluate this sum by letting a and b equal 1 in the formula for the binomial theorem on page 445, and compare the result with that of Exercise 17 on page 438.

15.6 PROBABILITIES AND ODDS

So far, we have studied only *what is possible* in a given situation. In some instances we listed all possibilities, and in others we merely determined how many different possibilities there are. Now we shall go one step further and judge also *what is probable* and *what is improbable* (or as we put it on page 432, what is likely and what is unlikely, or what is credible and what is incredible). For instance, we shall not only list the various things that can happen when three persons try to get drivers' licenses as in the example of Section 15.2, but we shall continue by asking such questions as "what is most likely to happen to an applicant on the first try," "what are the chances that he will have to take the test at least twice," or "how much should an applicant *expect* to spend, if it costs him \$2.00 each time he takes the test." Naturally, this will complicate matters—we shall have to deal with uncertainties in a rigorous way, and it will not be good enough to use expressions such as "is likely to happen," "is apt to be profitable," "seems quite probable," "wouldn't happen in a million years," and so on.

The most common way of measuring the uncertainties connected with events (say, the success of a new product, the outcome of a baseball game, the effectiveness of an advertising campaign, the returns of an investment) is to assign them *probabilities*, or to specify the *odds* at which it would be fair to bet that the events will occur. Among the different theories of probability—and there are many—most widely held is the *frequency concept of probability,* according to which the probability of an event is interpreted as *the proportion of the time that events of the same kind will occur in the long run.* Thus, if we say that there is a probability of 0.82 that a jet from New York to Miami, Florida, arrives on time, this means that such flights will arrive on time about 82 percent of the time. More generally, we say that an event has a probability of, say, 0.90, in the same sense in which we might say that our car will start in cold weather about 90 percent of the time. *We cannot guarantee what will happen at any particular time — the car may start and then it may not — but it would be reasonable to bet* $9.00 *against* $1.00 *or* 90 *cents against a dime* (*namely, at odds of* 9 *to* 1) *that the car will start at any given try.* This would be "fair," "reasonable," or "equitable," for we would win $1.00 (or a dime) about 90 percent of the time, lose $9.00 (or ninety cents) about 10 percent of the time, and we can therefore expect to break even in the long run.

In accordance with the frequency concept of probability, we *estimate* the probability of an event by observing how often (what part of the time) similar events have occurred in the past. For instance, if data kept by a government agency show that (over a period of time) 492 of 600 jets from New York to Miami, Florida, arrived on time, we *estimate* the probability that any one flight from New York to Miami (perhaps, the next one) will arrive on time as $\frac{492}{600} = 0.82$. Similarly, if 687 of 1,854 freshmen who have attended a given college (over a number of years) dropped out before the end of their freshmen year, we *estimate* the probability that any freshman attending this college will drop out before the end of his freshman year as $\frac{687}{1{,}854} = 0.37$.

Having defined probabilities in terms of what happens to similar events in the long run, let us check for a moment whether it is at all meaningful to talk about the probability of an event which *cannot occur more than once.* Can we ask for the probability that Mrs. Barbara Smith's broken arm will heal within a month, or the probability that a certain major-party candidate will win an upcoming presidential election? If we put ourselves in the position of Mrs. Smith's doctor, we could check medical records, discover that such fractures have healed within a month in 39 percent of thousands of cases, and apply this figure to Mrs. Smith's arm. This may not be of much comfort to Mrs. Smith, but it does provide a *meaning* for a probability statement concerning her arm—the probability that it will heal within a month is 0.39. Thus, *when we make a probability statement about a specific (non-repeatable) event, the frequency concept of probability leaves us no choice but to refer to a set of similar events.* This can lead to complications, for the choice of "similar" events is often neither obvious nor easy. With reference to Mrs. Smith's arm, for example, we might consider as "similar" only those cases where the fracture was in the same (left or right) arm, we might consider only those cases in which the patients were just as old, or we might consider only those cases in which the patients were also of the same height and the same weight as Mrs. Smith. Ultimately, this is a matter of choice, and it is by no means contradictory that we can thus arrive at different probabilities concerning Mrs. Smith's arm; it should be observed, however, that the more we narrow things down, the less information we have to estimate the corresponding probability.

So far as the second example is concerned, the one concerning the presidential election, suppose we ask some persons who have conducted a poll "how sure" they are that the given candidate will actually win. If their answer is "99 percent sure," that is, if they assign the candidate's election a probability of 0.99, they are not implying that he would win 99 percent of the time if he ran for office a great many times. *No, it means that the persons who conducted the poll based their conclusion (judgment, or decision) on methods which (in the long run) will "work" 99 percent of the time.* In this sense, many of the probabilities which we use to express our faith in predictions or decisions are simply "success ratios" that apply to the methods we have employed.

An alternate point of view, which is currently gaining favor among quite a few statisticians, is to interpret probabilities as *personal* or *subjective*. To illustrate, suppose that a businessman feels that the *odds* for the success of a new venture, say, a new shoe store, are 3 to 2. This means that he would be willing to bet (or consider it fair to bet) $300 against $200, or perhaps $3,000 against $2,000, that the venture will succeed. In this way he expresses the *strength of his belief* regarding the uncertainties connected with the success of the new store. This method of dealing with uncertainties works well (and is certainly justifiable) in situations where there is very little direct evidence; in that case one may have no choice but to consider pertinent collateral information, "educated" guesses, and perhaps intuition and other subjective factors. Thus, the businessman's odds concerning the success of a new shoe store may well be based on his ideas about business conditions in general, the opinion of an expert, and his own subjective evaluation of the whole situation, including, perhaps, a small dose of optimism.

Regardless of how we interpret probabilities and odds, subjectively or in terms of frequencies or proportions, *the mathematical relationship between probabilities and odds is always the same.* If somebody considers it fair or equitable to bet a dollars against b dollars that a given event will occur, he is, in fact, assigning the event the probability $\frac{a}{a+b}$. For instance, the businessman of the preceding paragraph actually assigned the success of the new shoe store a probability of $\frac{3}{3+2} = 0.60$. Also, if the odds favoring the home team in a football game are 4 to 1 (and it would be fair to bet \$8.00 against \$2.00 that they will win), the probability that the home team will win is $\frac{4}{4+1} = 0.80$. Incidentally, the corresponding odds against them are 1 to 4, and the probability that the home team will not win is $\frac{1}{1+4} = 0.20$. Finally, if a student's odds *against* passing a certain history course are 2 to 7, then the probability that he will not pass is $\frac{2}{2+7} = \frac{2}{9}$; correspondingly, the student's odds for passing are 7 to 2, and the probability that he will pass is $\frac{7}{7+2} = \frac{7}{9}$. Observe that in both of these last two examples *the probabilities pro and con added up to 1.*

To illustrate how probabilities are converted into odds, let us refer back to the example on page 452, which dealt with the question whether or not we could start our car. As we pointed out at the time, the probability of 0.90 implies that we should win about 90 percent of the time, lose about 10 percent of the time, and, hence, that the proper odds are 9 to 1. In general, *if the probability of an event is p, then the odds for its occurrence are p to $1 - p$ and the odds against its occurrence are $1 - p$ to p.* For instance, if the probability that an item lost in a department store will never be claimed is 0.15, then the odds are 0.15 to $1 - 0.15 = 0.85$, or 3 to 17, that a lost item will never be claimed; correspondingly, the odds are 17 to 3 that such an item will be claimed. Also, if the probability that we shall not have to wait for a table at our favorite restaurant is 0.75, then the odds are 0.75 to $1 - 0.75 = 0.25$, or 3 to 1, that we shall not have to wait. Note that in both of these illustrations we followed the common practice of quoting odds as ratios of positive integers (having no common factors).

EXERCISES

1. If statistics compiled by the management of a department store show that 1,406 of 1,850 elderly ladies who entered the store (during a certain period of time) made at least one purchase, estimate the probability that an elderly lady entering this store will make at least one purchase.

2. If 378 of 600 housewives interviewed in a supermarket said that they preferred the "new and improved" detergent over the old kind, estimate the probability that any one housewife will prefer the "new and improved" detergent over the old kind.

3. A study made by a traffic engineer showed that 1,007 of 2,650 cars which approached a certain intersection from the North made a left turn. Estimate the probability that any one car approaching this intersection from the North will make a left turn.

4. Statistics show that it has rained in a certain town on Labor Day, the day a club has chosen for its annual picnic, 32 times in the last 80 years.

   (a) Estimate the probability that it will rain on the day which the club has chosen for its picnic.
   (b) What are the odds that it will rain on that day?
   (c) What are the odds that it will not rain on that day?
   (d) If somebody bets the organizer of the picnic a quarter against a dime that it will *not* rain on the day of the picnic, is this a fair bet? If not, whom does it favor?

5. Among the 375 times that Mr. G. has gone fishing, he has come back empty-handed (that is, without a single catch) 125 times.

   (a) Estimate the probability that he will come back empty-handed from his next fishing trip.
   (b) What are the odds that he will catch a fish?
   (c) If someone offered Mr. G. *even money* (that is, odds of 1 to 1) that he will *not* make a catch, who would be favored by this bet?

6. In a sample of 128 cans of mixed nuts (taken from a very large shipment), 96 were found to contain mostly peanuts.

   (a) Estimate the probability that one of these cans will contain mostly peanuts.
   (b) What are the odds that any one of these cans will contain mostly peanuts?
   (c) What are the odds that any one of these cans will not contain mostly peanuts?
   (d) If we offered the manager of the store $5.00 against his $2.00 that the next can he opens will contain mostly peanuts, would this be a smart thing to do?

7. If a stockbroker feels that 2 to 1 are fair odds that the price of a given stock will go up within a week, what is the probability (his personal probability) that this will be the case?

8. If the owner of a race horse feels that the odds are 7 to 1 against his horse coming in first, what is his personal probability that the horse will win?

9. If the odds are 11 to 9 that a newly-hired secretary will get married before she has been with the company for two years, what is the probability that this will be the case?

10. If somebody claims that the odds are 5 to 3 that a certain shipment will arrive on time, what probability does he assign to the shipment's arriving on time?

11. A friend going on an ocean cruise is anxious to bet us $22.50 against our $2.50 that he will not get seasick. What does this tell us about the probability (that is, his personal probability) that he will not get seasick? (*Hint:* the answer should read "at least . . .").

12. A businessman refuses to bet \$1.00 against \$9.00 that he will not get stuck in freeway traffic while driving home from work. What does this tell us about the probability (his personal probability) that he *will* get stuck? (*Hint:* the answer should read "greater than . . ."). What could we say about the probability (his personal probability) that he *will* get stuck if he would gladly accept odds of 49 to 1? (*Hint:* the answer should read "at most . . .").

16

PROBABILITY

16.1 INTRODUCTION

In the study of probability there are basically *three kinds of questions.* First, there is the question of what we *mean,* for example, when we say that the probability for rain is 0.80, when we say that the probability for the success of a new venture is 0.35, or when we say that the probability for a candidate's election is 0.63; then there is the question of how probabilities are *measured* (namely, how their values are determined in actual practice); and finally there is the question of *how probabilities "behave,"* namely, what mathematical rules they have to obey.

The first and second kinds of question have already been discussed to some extent in Section 15.6. As we pointed out on page 452, there is the *frequency concept* of probability in which a probability is interpreted as a proportion, or percentage, in the long run, and its value is obtained (estimated) by observing what proportion of the time similar events have occurred in the past. Such probabilities are also referred to as "objective," in contrast to *subjective,* or *personal,* probabilities, which are meant to express the strength of a person's belief. Subjective probabilities could be evaluated by simply asking a person what he considers "fair odds" that an event will occur, and then converting these odds into a probability as on page 453. More realistic, perhaps, would be to make a person "put up or shut up," namely, to see how he would react if there were really something at stake.

In this chapter we shall study the *mathematical model* which is appropriate for the study of probability, namely, the mathematical model according to which probabilities "behave." As we shall see in Section 16.3, this model consists of three relatively simple rules, and it is important to keep in mind that these rules are supposed to apply regardless of whether probabilities are interpreted objectively or subjectively.

16.2 SAMPLE SPACES AND EVENTS

Borrowing from the language of statistics, we refer to the various things that can happen in a given situation (namely, the set of all possible outcomes) as the corresponding *sample space.* For instance, in the example on page 434 the sample space consists of the 30 different recommendations which the stock analyst can make, in the example on page 440 the sample space consists of the 840 ways in which the new sales territories can be distributed among the seven salesmen, and in the example on page 442 the sample space consists of the 17,296 ways in which the person gathering the data can choose 3 of the 48 families living in the given apartment house.

In most work connected with sample spaces it is advantageous to identify the various possibilities with numbers or points—we can then talk about the things that can happen *mathematically,* without having to go through lengthy verbal details. Actually, this is what we do in sports when we refer to players by their numbers; it is what the Internal Revenue Service does when it refers to taxpayers by their social security numbers; and it is precisely what we do when we identify cities with points on a map.

The use of points rather than numbers has the added advantage that it makes it easier to visualize the various possibilities, and perhaps discover some of the features which various different outcomes have in common. To give an example, consider a study of consumer response to a television commercial, in which housewives are asked whether they dislike the commercial, like it, or don't care. The possible reactions of *one* housewife can be pictured as in Figure 16.1, where we identified the three responses

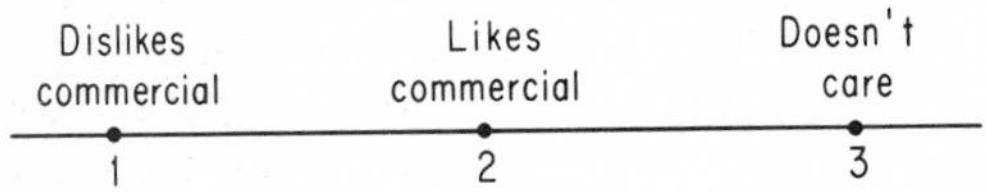

FIG. 16.1

with three points and also assigned to them the (code) numbers 1, 2, and 3. (Actually, these points could have been drawn in any pattern, and we could have assigned to them any arbitrary set of numbers.)

Had we been interested in the reactions of *two* housewives, we could have represented the various possibilities by means of the nine points of Figure 16.2, where 1, 2, and 3 again stand for "dislike the commercial," "like it," and "don't care." The advantage of the particular arrangement of Figure 16.2 is that we can use the coordinates of the points to identify the various possibilities. For instance, the point (1, 2) represents the case where the first housewife dislikes the commercial while the second housewife likes it; similarly, (3, 1) represents the case where the first housewife doesn't care while the second housewife dislikes the commercial, and (2, 2) represents the case where both housewives like the commercial. Observe that the reaction of the first housewife is always given by the first coordinate, while that of the second housewife is always given by the second coordinate.

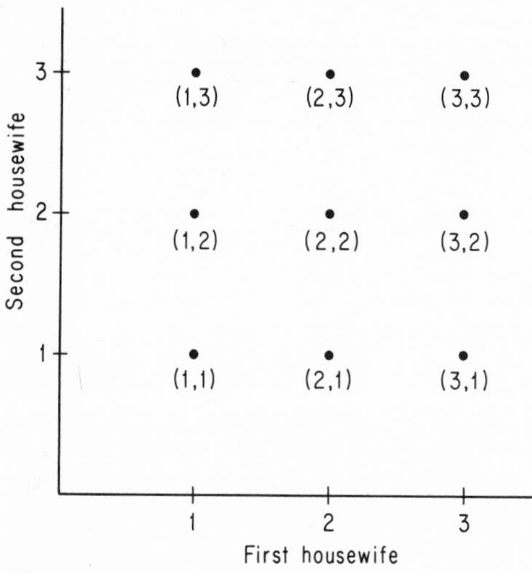

FIG. 16.2

Had we been interested in the reaction of n housewives, there would have been 3^n possibilities and as many points (in accordance with the rule on page 435). For $n = 4$, for example, there would have been $3^4 = 81$ possibilities, that is, 81 points, among which (1, 3, 1, 2) represents the case where the first housewife interviewed dislikes the commercial, the second housewife doesn't care, the third housewife also dislikes the commercial, but the fourth housewife likes it. (Since each possibility is thus represented by four numbers, we cannot picture the corresponding points as readily as in Figures 16.1 and 16.2; in fact, this would require a diagram of *four dimensions*. Of course, we could identify the 81 possibilities with any arbitrary set of 81 points, but this would probably not be of much help.)

Sample spaces are usually classified according to the number of points which they contain; especially, whether they are *finite* or *infinite*. All of the sample spaces mentioned so far in this section have been *finite;* that is, they contained a finite, or fixed, number of points. Other examples of finite, though much larger, sample spaces include the one representing the 221,760 ways in which a person can select one of 15 salads, one of 11 kinds of meat, one of 12 vegetables, one of 14 desserts, and one of 8 drinks while choosing his dinner at a cafeteria, and the sample space which represents all possible 13-card bridge hands which can be dealt with an ordinary deck of playing cards—there are more than 635 *billion* possibilities. Until we come to Section 16.6, we shall limit our discussion to sample spaces containing only a finite number of points; that is, we shall consider only situations in which the number of things that can happen is finite.

In Section 15.6 we introduced probabilities as numbers which are associated with *events*—the event that a jet will arrive on time, the event that a car will start in cold weather, the event that a presidential candidate will be elected, the event that a certain lady's arm will heal within a month, and so on. Intuitively speaking, everyone knows, of course, what is meant by the word "event," but *in probability theory we apply the term to any subset of a sample space.* (As the reader will recall from Chapter 1, a subset is any part of a set including the set as a whole and, trivially, the empty set $\varnothing$ which has no elements at all.) *Thus, "event" is the nontechnical term which corresponds to "subset of a sample space" in the language of mathematics.* Referring to Figure 16.2, for example, we find that the subset which consists of the point (2, 3) represents the *event* that the first housewife likes the commercial while the second housewife doesn't care; the subset which consists of the points (1, 1), (2, 2), and (3, 3) represents the *event* that both housewives respond the same way; and the subset which consists of the points (1, 2), (2, 1), (3, 2), and (2, 3) represents the *event* that one of the housewives likes the commercial while the other one either doesn't like it or doesn't care.

To consider another example, suppose that we are looking for a new house, and that we classify all houses advertised for sale according to whether they have 1, 2, 3, or 4 bedrooms, and also according to whether they have 1, 2, or 3 baths. *None of the houses, incidentally, have fewer bedrooms than baths.* To study the situation, we first draw a tree diagram like that of Figure 16.3, and we find that there are altogether 9 possibilities. Then, using coordinates to denote the number of bedrooms and the number of baths, we construct the sample space shown in Figure 16.4. Here (2, 1) represents the *event* that we will choose a house with 2 bedrooms and 1 bath, while (4, 3) represents the *event* that we will choose a house with 4 bedrooms and 3 baths. Also, the subset which consists of the points (3, 2) and (4, 1) represents the *event* that we will choose a house in which the number of bedrooms and baths add up to five; the set which consists of the points (2, 1), (3, 1), (3, 2), (4, 1), (4, 2), and (4, 3) represents the *event* that we will choose a house with more bedrooms than baths;

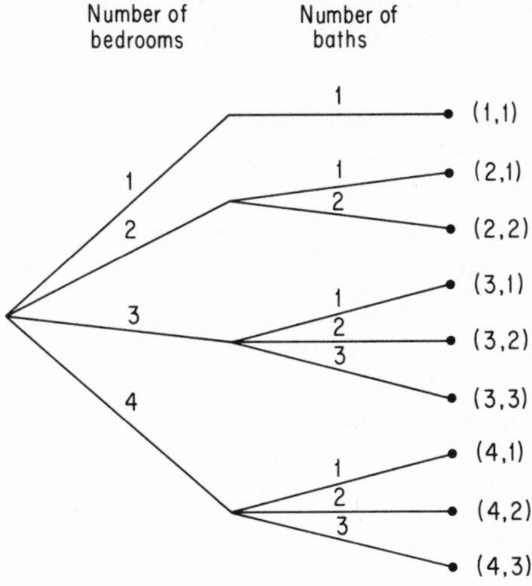

FIG. 16.3

(1, 1), (2, 1), and (2, 2) represent the *event* that we will choose a house which has at most two bedrooms; and (3, 1), (3, 2) and (3, 3) represent the *event* that we will choose a three-bedroom house. Now, if we denote these four sets D, E, F, and G (see Figure 16.4), we can form numerous other subsets (events) by applying the set operations which we discussed in Section 1.2. For instance, it can be seen from Figure 16.4 that $E \cap F$ consists of the point (2, 1) and, hence, that it represents the *event* that we will choose a two-bedroom house with 1 bath; $D \cup G$ consists of the points (3, 1), (3, 2), (3, 3), and (4, 1), and it represents the *event* that we will choose a three-bedroom house *or* a four-bedroom house with only one bath; and that E',

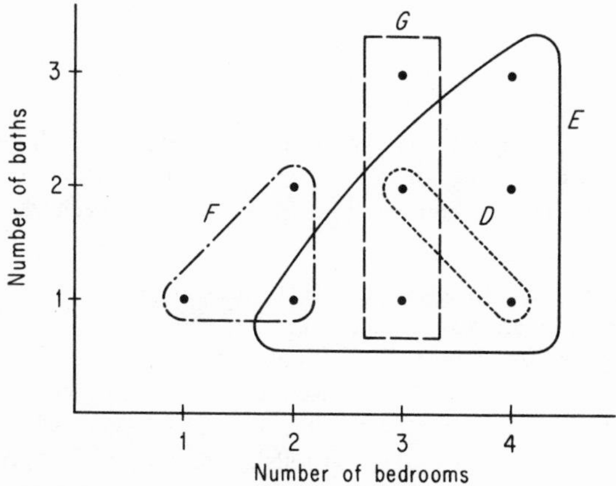

FIG. 16.4

the complement of E, consists of the points (1, 1), (2, 2), and (3, 3), and it represents the *event* that we will choose a house with as many bedrooms as baths.

Still referring to the sample space of Figure 16.4, note also that $F \cap D$ represents the *event* that we will choose a one- or two-bedroom house for which the number of bedrooms and baths add up to 5. Clearly, this is impossible in the given situation—$F \cap D$ does not contain any of the nine points of the sample space, and we write $F \cap D = \varnothing$. If two subsets such as F and D have no points in common, we refer to the events which they represent as *mutually exclusive;* as can easily be seen from Figure 16.4, D and E' are also mutually exclusive, and so are F and G. On the other hand, D and G are *not* mutually exclusive, they both contain the point (3, 2), and neither are F' and G. In fact, G is *contained* in F' and we can write $G \subset F'$ in accordance with the notation introduced on page 10; obviously, three-bedroom houses are included among those having three bedrooms or more.

EXERCISES

1. Referring to the sample space of Figure 16.2, describe *in words* the event which is represented by each of the following sets of points:

(a) (3, 3);
(b) (1, 1), (1, 2), and (1, 3);
(c) (1, 1), (1, 2), (2, 1), and (2, 2);
(d) (1, 3), (2, 3), (3, 3), (1, 2), (3, 2), (1, 1), (2, 1), (3, 1).

2. Referring to the sample space of Figure 16.4, describe *in words* the event which is represented by each of the following sets of points:

(a) (2, 2);
(b) (2, 1), and (2, 2);
(c) (1, 1), (2, 2), and (3, 3);
(d) (2, 2), (3, 2), (4, 2), (3, 3), and (4, 3).

3. A Ford dealer has 5 brand new identical Mustangs in stock, which he hopes to sell during a special week-long sale. He has two salesmen working for him, and we are interested in knowing how many of these Mustangs each salesman will sell during the special sale.

(a) Draw a tree diagram to show that there are altogether 21 possibilities. (*Hint:* either salesman may not make any sales at all.)
(b) Using two coordinates so that (3, 1), for example, represents the event that the first salesman sells three of the Mustangs while the second salesman sells one, (2, 0) represents the event that the first salesman sells two of the Mustangs while the second salesman sells none, and (1, 4) represents the event that the first salesman sells one of the Mustangs while the second

salesman sells four, draw a diagram (similar to that of Figure 16.2) showing the 21 points of the corresponding sample space.

(c) Describe *in words* the event which is represented by each of the following sets of points:

$A = \{(0, 5), (1, 4), (2, 3), (3, 2), (4, 1), (5, 0)\}$;
$B = \{(1, 0), (2, 0), (2, 1), (3, 0), (3, 1), (3, 2), (4, 0), (4, 1), (5, 0)\}$;
$C = \{(0, 2), (1, 2), (2, 2), (3, 2)\}$;
$D = \{(0, 4), (1, 4), (0, 5)\}$;
$E = \{(1, 0), (2, 1), (3, 2)\}$.

4. Referring to part (c) of Exercise 3, list the points of the sample space which belong to each of the following subsets, and describe *in words* the events which they represent:

(a) $A \cap B$; (c) $C \cap E$; (e) B';
(b) $C \cup D$; (d) $D \cap E$; (f) $D \cap A'$.

5. With reference to part (c) of Exercise 3, which of the following pairs of subsets represent *mutually exclusive events:*

(a) A and B; (c) B and D; (e) B and E;
(b) D and E; (d) C and D; (f) B' and E?

6. A company providing shuttle service between two nearby airports has two helicopters which leave the respective airports every hour on the hour.

(a) If the larger of the two helicopters can carry 4 passengers while the other one can carry only 3, draw a tree diagram to demonstrate that when the two helicopters take off at any given hour they can be occupied in 20 different ways.

(b) Using two coordinates so that (1, 3), for example, represents the event that when the helicopters take off at a given hour the larger helicopter has one passenger while the smaller helicopter has three, and (2, 0) represents the event that the larger helicopter has two passengers while the smaller helicopter is empty, draw a diagram (similar to that of Figure 16.2) showing the 20 points of the corresponding sample space.

(c) Describe *in words* the event which is represented by each of the following sets of points of the sample space:

$R = \{(2, 3), (3, 2), (3, 3), (4, 1), (4, 2), (4, 3)\}$;
$S = \{(0, 0), (1, 1), (2, 2), (3, 3)\}$;
$T = \{(0, 1), (0, 2), (0, 3), (1, 2), (1, 3), (2, 3)\}$;
$U = \{(0, 3), (1, 2), (2, 1), (3, 0)\}$;
$V = \{(4, 0), (4, 1), (4, 2), (4, 3)\}$.

7. Referring to part (c) of Exercise 6, list the points of the sample space which belong to each of the following subsets, and describe *in words* the events which they represent:

(a) $R \cup U$; (c) $S \cup T$; (e) $S \cap R$;
(b) $R \cap T$; (d) R'; (f) $U \cap V$.

8. With reference to part (c) of Exercise 6, which of the following pairs of subsets of the sample space represent *mutually exclusive events:*

(a) U and V; (c) R and U; (e) R and T;
(b) S and T; (d) V and R; (f) T and V'?

9. Suppose that in the illustration on page 459 *three* housewives had been interviewed, but that 1, 2, and 3 stand, as before, for "dislike the commercial," "like it," and "don't care."

(a) Using three coordinates so that (2, 1, 3), for example, represents the event that the first housewife likes the commercial, the second housewife dislikes it, and the third housewife doesn't care, list the coordinates of the remaining 26 points of the corresponding sample space. (*Hint:* if necessary, draw a tree diagram somewhat like that of Figure 16.3.) Also, describe *in words* what events are represented by the points (1, 2, 2), (3, 2, 3), and (3, 1, 1).
(b) Describe *in words* the event which is represented by each of the following sets of points:

$J = \{(1, 1, 1), (1, 1, 2), (1, 1, 3)\}$;
$K = \{(1, 1, 1), (2, 2, 2), (3, 3, 3)\}$;
$L = \{(1, 2, 1), (1, 2, 3), (3, 2, 1), (3, 2, 3)\}$;
$M = \{(1, 2, 3), (1, 3, 2), (2, 1, 3), (2, 3, 1), (3, 1, 2), (3, 2, 1)\}$;
$N = \{(1, 1, 1), (1, 1, 2), (1, 1, 3), (1, 2, 1), (1, 2, 2), (1, 2, 3), (1, 3, 1), (1, 3, 2), (1, 3, 3)\}$.

10. Referring to part (b) of Exercise 9, list the points of the sample space which belong to each of the following subsets, and describe *in words* the events which they represent:

(a) $L \cap N$; (c) $K \cup M$; (e) $J \cap N$;
(b) $J \cap L$; (d) N'; (f) $K \cup L$.

11. With reference to part (b) of Exercise 9, which of the following pairs of subsets of the sample space represent *mutually exclusive events:*

(a) J and K; (c) K and M; (e) L and N;
(b) J and L; (d) K and N; (f) J and N'?

12. If we let 1 and 0 represent *heads* and *tails*, the results obtained in three successive flips of a coin can be represented by means of points such as (1, 1, 0) and (0, 1, 0), where the first point represents *heads, heads, tails*, and the second point represents *tails, heads, tails*.

(a) Copy the diagram of Figure 16.5 and complete it by filling in the coordinates of the other six points of the sample space.
(b) If X represents the event that the first two tosses are *tails*, Y represents the event that at least one of the three tosses is *heads*, and Z represents the event that the tosses are either *all heads or all tails*, list the points of the sample space which belong to each of these subsets. Also describe *in words* the events which are represented by $X \cap Y$, $X \cup Z$, and $Y' \cap Z$.

13. Which of the following pairs of events are mutually exclusive? Explain your answers.

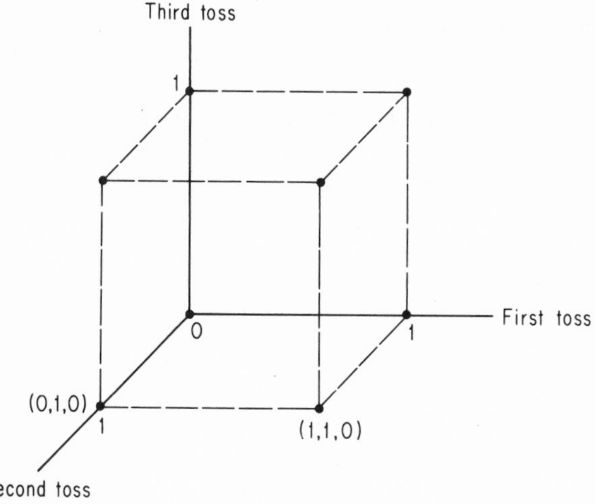

FIG. 16.5

(a) Having rain and sunshine on the 4th of July, 1975.
(b) Being under 25 years of age and being President of the U.S.
(c) One and the same person wearing black shoes and green socks.
(d) A driver getting a ticket for speeding and his getting a ticket for going through a red light.
(e) A person leaving Los Angeles by jet at 11:45 p.m. and arriving in Washington, D.C. on the same day.
(f) A baseball player getting a walk and hitting a home run in the same game.
(g) A baseball player getting a walk and hitting a home run in the same time at bat.

16.3 RULES OF PROBABILITY

To formulate the *postulates of probability* and some of their immediate consequences, we shall continue the practice of denoting events by means of capital letters, and we shall write the probability of event A as $P(A)$, the probability of event B as $P(B)$, and so forth. Furthermore, we shall follow the common practice of denoting the set of all possible outcomes, namely, the *sample space*, by the letter S. As we shall formulate them here, the three postulates of probability apply only when the sample space S is finite; some of the modifications that are required when S is *infinite* will be discussed in Sections 16.6 and 18.2.

> **Postulate 1:** *The probability of any event is a positive real number or zero; symbolically,* $P(A) \geq 0$ *for any subset* A *of any given sample space* S.

> **Postulate 2:** *The probability of any sample space is equal to 1; symbolically, $P(S) = 1$ for any sample space S.*

It is important to note that both of these postulates are satisfied by the frequency interpretation as well as the subjective concept of probability introduced in Section 15.6. So far as the first postulate is concerned, proportions are always positive or zero, and so long as a and b (the amounts bet for and against the occurrence of an event) are positive, the probability $\frac{a}{a+b}$ cannot be negative (see page 453).

The second postulate states indirectly that *certainty* is identified with a probability of 1; after all, it is always assumed that *one of the possibilities included in S must occur*, and it is to this certain event that we assign a probability of 1. So far as the frequency interpretation is concerned, a probability of 1 implies that the event will occur 100 percent of the time, or in other words, that it is certain to occur. So far as subjective probabilities are concerned, the surer we are that an event will occur, the "better" odds we should be willing to give—say, 100 to 1, 1,000 to 1, or perhaps even 1,000,000 to 1. The corresponding probabilities are $\frac{100}{100+1}$, $\frac{1{,}000}{1{,}000+1}$, and $\frac{1{,}000{,}000}{1{,}000{,}000+1}$ (or approximately 0.99, 0.999, and 0.999999), and it can be seen that *the surer we are that an event will occur, the closer its probability will be to 1.*

In actual practice, we also assign a probability of 1 to events of which we are "practically certain" that they will occur. For instance, we would assign a probability of 1 to the event that at least one person will vote in the next presidential election, and we would assign a probability of 1 to the event that among all the new cars sold during any one model year at least one will be involved in an accident before it has been driven 10,000 miles.

The third postulate of probability is especially important, and it is not quite so "obvious" as the other two:

> **Postulate 3:** *If two events are mutually exclusive, the probability that one or the other will occur equals the sum of their probabilities. Symbolically,*
>
> $$P(A \cup B) = P(A) + P(B)$$
>
> *for any two mutually exclusive events A and B.*

For instance, if the probability that the price of a stock will go up is 0.60 and the probability that its price will remain unchanged is 0.15, then the probability that the price of the stock will either go up or remain unchanged is $0.60 + 0.15 = 0.75$. Similarly, if the probability that an applicant for a certain job with the California Highway Department was born in California is 0.41 and the probability that he was born in Nevada is 0.06, then the probability that he was born in either state is $0.41 + 0.06 = 0.47$. All this agrees with the frequency interpretation of probability: if one event occurs, say, 37 percent of the time, another event occurs 58 percent of the time, *and they cannot both occur at the same time* (that is, they are mutually exclusive), then one or the other will occur $37 + 58 = 95$ percent of the time. So far as subjective probabilities are concerned, the third postulate does not follow from our discussion in Section 15.6; however, proponents of the subjective point of view generally impose the third postulate as what they call the "consistency criterion" (see also Exercise 6 on page 473).

By using the three postulates of probability, we can derive many further rules according to which probabilities must "behave"—some of them are easy to prove and some are not, but they all have important applications. Among the immediate consequences of the three postulates we find that *probabilities can never be greater than 1*, that *an event which cannot occur has the probability 0*, and that *the respective probabilities that an event will occur and that it will not occur always add up to 1*. Symbolically,

$$P(\mathrm{A}) \leq 1 \quad \textit{for any event } A$$

$$P(\varnothing) = 0$$

and

$$P(A) + P(A') = 1 \qquad \textit{or} \qquad P(A') = 1 - P(A).$$

The first of these results (which the reader will be asked to *prove* in Exercise 20 on page 476) simply expresses the fact that an event cannot occur more than 100 percent of the time, or that the probability $\frac{a}{a+b}$ cannot exceed 1 when a and b are *positive amounts* bet for and against the occurrence of an event. So far as the second result is concerned, it expresses the fact that an impossible event happens 0 percent of the time; actually, we also assign 0 probabilities to events which are *so unlikely* that we are "practically certain" that they will not occur. Thus, we would assign a probability of 0 to the event that a monkey set loose on a typewriter will by chance type Plato's *Republic* word for word without a single mistake.

The third result can be derived formally from the three postulates of probability, but it also follows immediately from the frequency interpretation as well as the subjective concept of probability. Clearly, if Miss Jones arrives at work late 18 percent of the time, then she does *not* arrive late 82 percent of the time; the respective probabilities are 0.18 and 0.82, and they add up to 1. Subjectively speaking, if a person considers it *fair*, or equitable, to bet a dollars against b dollars that a given event will occur, he is actually assigning the event the probability $\frac{a}{a+b}$ and its non-occurrence the probability $\frac{b}{b+a}$; evidently, these two probabilities also add up to 1.

The third postulate of probability applies only to *two* mutually exclusive events, but it can easily be generalized; repeatedly using this postulate, it can be shown that

> *If A_1, A_2, . . . , and A_k are k mutually exclusive events (that is, only one of them can occur), then the probability that one of them will occur is*
>
> $$P(A_1 \cup A_2 \cup \ldots \cup A_k) = P(A_1) + P(A_2) + \ldots + P(A_k)$$

where $\cup$ may again be read as "or." For instance, if the probabilities that the *Standard and Poor's Corporation* will rate a company's stock $A+$, A, or $A-$ are, respectively, 0.08, 0.14, and 0.05, then the probability that the company will get one of these ratings is $0.08 + 0.14 + 0.05 = 0.27$, and the probability that it will get a lower rating is $1 - 0.27 = 0.73$. Also, if Mr. Taylor is planning to buy a new car and the probabilities that he will buy a Chevrolet, a Plymouth, a Ford, or a Volkswagen are, respectively, 0.24, 0.17, 0.25, and 0.08, then the probability that he will buy one of these makes is

$$0.24 + 0.17 + 0.25 + 0.08 = 0.74$$

Furthermore, if the probability that he will not buy a new car at all is 0.10, then the probability that he will buy some other make car is 0.16. Why?

The job of assigning probabilities to all the events that are possible in a given situation can be a very tedious task, indeed. For a sample space with as few as 5 points representing, say, the events that a person traveling to Europe visits Paris, London, Berlin, Rome, and Amsterdam, there are already $2^5 = 32$ possibilities (see Exercise 17 on page 438); he may visit only London, or London and Rome, or Paris, Rome, and Amsterdam, . . . , he may visit all five of these cities, and then he may not visit any of them at all. Things get worse very rapidly when a sample space has more than 5 points—for 10 points, for example, there are $2^{10} = 1{,}024$ different subsets or events, and for 20 points there are $2^{20} = 1{,}048{,}576$ (see Exercise 17 on page 438).

Fortunately, it is seldom necessary to assign probabilities to all possible events, and the following rule (which is a direct application of the "generalized addition formula" on this page) makes it easy to determine the probability of any event on the basis of the probabilities which are assigned to the individual outcomes (points) of the corresponding sample space:

> *The probability of any event A is given by the sum of the probabilities of the individual outcomes comprising A.*

To illustrate this rule, let us refer again to the two-housewives-interview example on page 459, and let us suppose that the nine points of the sample space (shown originally in Figure 16.2) are assigned the probabilities given in Figure 16.6. Altogether, there are $2^9 = 512$ different subsets or events,

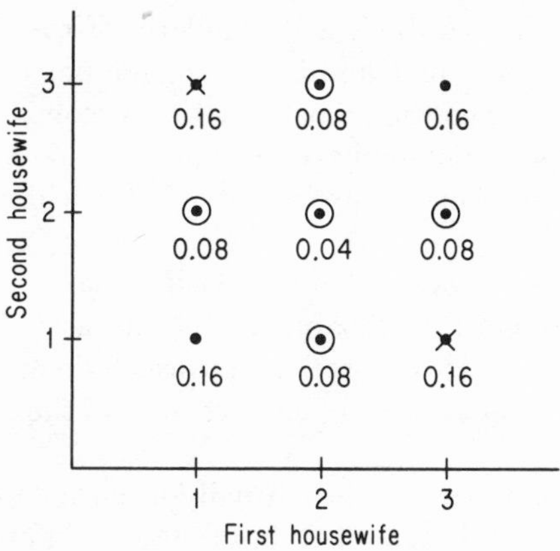

FIG. 16.6

and according to the above rule we can find the probability of any one of them by simply adding the probabilities assigned to the points which it contains. For instance, if we want to know the probability that *at least one* of the two housewives will like the commercial, we have only to add the probabilities of the points circled in Figure 16.6, and we get

$$0.08 + 0.08 + 0.04 + 0.08 + 0.08 = 0.36$$

Similarly, if we want to know the probability that one of the two housewives will dislike the commercial while the other one will say that she doesn't care, we have only to add the probabilities of the two points marked X in Figure 16.2, and we get $0.16 + 0.16 = 0.32$.

The situation is even simpler when the individual outcomes (that is, the points of the sample space) are all *equiprobable;* this is often the case in games of chance or when we "randomly" select one person to act as spokesman for a group, one of ten cities to be included in a survey, one of twelve Guinea pigs to be used in an experiment, and so on. In that case, we can use the following rule, which is an immediate consequence of the one on page 469:

> *If a sample space consists of n equiprobable outcomes of which s comprise event A, then the probability of A is*
>
> $$P(A) = \frac{s}{n}$$

Thus, the probability of drawing an ace from an ordinary (well-shuffled) deck of 52 playing cards is 4/52 (there are 4 aces among the 52 cards); the probability of getting heads with a balanced coin is 1/2, and the probability of rolling a 5 or a 6 with a balanced die is 2/6. Similarly, if the Board of Directors of a company includes 12 men and 5 women, and one of them is chosen by lot for a certain task, then the probability that a woman will get the job is 5/17; also, if a company randomly selects one of the 50 States for the construction of a new plant, then the probability that it will be one of the 8 Mountain States is 8/50. [The ratio of the *number of "successes"* (that is, outcomes comprising some event A) to the *total number of outcomes* is sometimes used as a *definition* of the probability of A, but aside from the obvious *circularity* of defining "probability" in terms of "equiprobable events," it has the shortcoming that it applies only when all of the outcomes have the same probability.]

Since the third postulate applies only to mutually exclusive events, it cannot be used, for example, to find the probability that at least one of two roommates will pass a final exam in economics, the probability that a person will break an arm or a rib in an automobile accident, or the probability that a customer will buy a shirt or a tie while shopping at Macy's department store. In the first case, both roommates can pass the exam, in the second case the person can break an arm as well as a rib, and in the third case the customer can buy a shirt as well as a tie. To obtain a formula for $P(A \cup B)$ which holds regardless of whether the events A and B are mutually exclusive, let us consider the situation illustrated by means of the Venn diagram of Figure 16.7; it concerns an insurance salesman's luck with a potential customer. The letter H stands for the event that he will sell him a homeowner's policy, M stands for the event that he will sell him a major medical policy, and it can be seen that

$$P(H) = 0.14 + 0.03 = 0.17$$
$$P(M) = 0.06 + 0.03 = 0.09$$

and

$$P(H \cup M) = 0.14 + 0.03 + 0.06 = 0.23$$

We were able to add the respective probabilities since they referred to mutually exclusive events (namely, regions of the Venn diagram which have

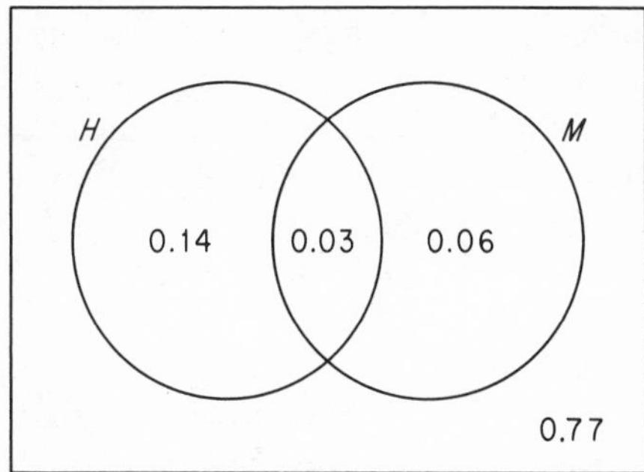

FIG. 16.7

no points in common), but had we *erroneously* used the third postulate of probability to calculate $P(H \cup M)$, we would have obtained

$$P(H) + P(M) = 0.17 + 0.09 = 0.26$$

which exceeds the *correct value* by 0.03. What happened is that $P(H \cap M) = 0.03$ was added in *twice*, once in $P(H) = 0.17$ and once in $P(M) = 0.09$, and we could correct for this by *subtracting* $P(H \cap M) = 0.03$ from the final result, namely, by writing

$$\begin{aligned} P(H \cup M) &= P(H) + P(M) - P(H \cap M) \\ &= 0.17 + 0.09 - 0.03 \\ &= 0.23 \end{aligned}$$

Since this kind of argument holds for any two events A and B, we can now state the following *general addition rule*, which applies regardless of whether A and B are mutually exclusive events:

$$P(A \cup B) = P(A) + P(B) - P(A \cap B)$$

Note that when A and B *are* mutually exclusive, then $P(A \cap B) = 0$ (since *by definition* the two events cannot both occur at the same time), and the new formula reduces to that of the third postulate of probability on page 466. To illustrate the new formula, let us refer again to the two-housewives-interview example and Figure 16.6 on page 469. If A is the event that *at least one* of the housewives will like the commercial and B is the event that both housewives will respond in the *same way*, we already know from page 469 that $P(A) = 0.36$. Since B consists of the points (1, 1), (2, 2), and (3, 3), and $A \cap B$ consists only of the point (2, 2), it follows that $P(B) = 0.16 + 0.04 + 0.16 = 0.36$, $P(A \cap B) = 0.04$, and, hence, that

$$P(A \cup B) = 0.36 + 0.36 - 0.04 = 0.68$$

As a check, we could calculate $P(A \cup B)$ directly, namely, add the probabilities assigned to the seven points comprising $A \cup B$ in Figure 16.6.

To consider another example, let us refer again to the sample space of Figure 16.4 on page 461, and let us assume that the points (1, 1), (2, 1), (3, 1), (4, 1), (2, 2), (3, 2), (4, 2), (3, 3), and (4, 3) are assigned the probabilities 0.02, 0.07, 0.14, 0.02, 0.02, 0.35, 0.08, 0.18, and 0.12. Now, subset E consists of the points (2, 1), (3, 1), (4, 1), (3, 2), (4, 2), and (4, 3), so that its probability is $0.07 + 0.14 + 0.02 + 0.35 + 0.08 + 0.12 = 0.78$; subset F consists of the points (1, 1), (2, 1), and (2, 2), so that its probability is $0.02 + 0.07 + 0.02 = 0.11$; and subset $E \cap F$ consists only of the point (2, 1), so that its probability is 0.07. Hence, the probability that we will choose a house which has *either more bedrooms than baths or at most two bedrooms* is

$$P(E \cup F) = 0.78 + 0.11 - 0.07 = 0.82$$

Had we erroneously used the third postulate in this example, the one which applies only to mutually exclusive events, we would have obtained $P(E \cup F) = 0.78 + 0.11 = 0.89$, which is obviously incorrect—it leaves a probability of 0.11 (instead of 0.18) for the selection of a 3-bedroom house with 3 baths. Another example where the incorrect use of the third postulate gives a misleading result may be found in Exercise 7 on page 473.

EXERCISES

1. Analyzing the purchasing power of the dollar, three economists made the following claims: the first economist claimed that the probabilities for the purchasing power of the dollar to go up, remain unchanged, or go down are, respectively, 0.08, 0.24, and 0.65; the second economist claimed that these probabilities are 0.12, 0.37, and 0.51; and the third economist claimed that these probabilities are 0.07, 0.39, and 0.56. Comment on these claims.

2. Explain why there must be a mistake in each of the following statements:

(a) The probabilities that a secretary will make 0, 1, 2, 3, 4, or 5 *or more* mistakes while copying a report are, respectively, 0.11, 0.24, 0.39, 0.13, 0.10, and 0.06.

(b) The probabilities that there will be 0, 1, 2, or 3 *or more* accidents during a stock-car race are, respectively, 0.03, 0.11, 0.19, and 0.65.

(c) The probability that an accountant will make *exactly one mistake* while auditing an account is 0.03, and the probability that he will make *at least one mistake* is 0.01.

(d) Mrs. Brown has two daughters; the probability that the older daughter will get married within a year is 0.25, and the probability that both daughters will get married within a year is 0.42.

3. If G is the event that the *SEC* will investigate the finances of a certain corporation and H is the event that some of the corporation's dealings are illegal, state *in words* what is meant by

(a) $P(G')$; (c) $P(G \cap H)$; (e) $P(G' \cap H')$;
(b) $P(H')$; (d) $P(G \cup H')$; (f) $P(G' \cup H)$.

4. Given two mutually exclusive events A and B for which $P(A) = 0.35$ and $P(B) = 0.42$, find

(a) $P(A')$; (c) $P(A \cup B)$; (e) $P(A' \cap B)$;
(b) $P(B')$; (d) $P(A \cap B')$; (f) $P(A' \cup B')$.

[*Hint:* draw a Venn diagram and fill in the probabilities associated with the various regions, remembering that $P(A \cap B) = 0$ when A and B are mutually exclusive.]

5. Given two events A and B for which $P(A) = 0.66$, $P(B) = 0.28$, and $P(A \cap B) = 0.12$, find

(a) $P(A')$; (c) $P(A \cup B)$; (e) $P(A' \cup B)$;
(b) $P(B')$; (d) $P(A' \cap B)$; (f) $P(A \cap B')$.

6. Asked about his chances of getting an A or a B in a course in business statistics, a student replies that the odds are 10 to 1 against his getting an A and 8 to 1 against his getting a B; furthermore, he feels that the odds are 6 to 1 against his getting either an A or a B. Discuss the "consistency" of this student's probabilities concerning the various events. (*Hint:* convert the odds into the probabilities that he will get an A, that he will get a B, and that he will get an A or a B.)

7. The manager of a supermarket has found that 40 percent of his customers spend at least \$20.00 each time they shop at his store, while 55 percent spend at least \$8.00 on meat. Thus, he concludes, the probability that a customer will spend at least \$8.00 on meat *or* at least \$20.00 altogether is $0.40 + 0.55 = 0.95$. Discuss the validity of this argument.

8. In a certain city, the probabilities that a driver will receive 0, 1, 2, 3, or 4 *or more* traffic citations within a year are, respectively, 0.31, 0.45, 0.13, 0.08, and 0.03.

(a) What is the probability that a driver will receive at least 2 traffic citations?
(b) What is the probability that a driver will receive at most 2 traffic citations?
(c) What is the probability that a driver will receive at least 1 traffic citation? (As a check, calculate this probability in two different ways; once by adding the probabilities of the various possibilities, and once by subtracting from 1 the probability of getting zero traffic citations.)

9. Using the probabilities of Figure 16.6, find the probabilities of the events which are represented by the subsets of the four parts of Exercise 1 on page 462.

10. Referring to the sample space of Figure 16.4 and the probabilities assigned to its nine points on page 472, find

(a) the probabilities that we will choose a 1-, 2-, 3-, or 4-bedroom house;
(b) the probabilities that we will choose a house with 1, 2, or 3 baths;
(c) the probabilities of the events which are represented by the subsets of parts (b), (c), and (d) of Exercise 2 on page 462.

11. Referring to Exercise 3 on page 462, suppose that each of the 21 points of the sample space has the same probability of 1/21.

(a) What are the probabilities that they will sell 0, 1, 2, 3, 4, or 5 of the cars during the special sale?
(b) Find the probabilities of the events which are represented by sets A, B, C, D, and E of part (c) of Exercise 3 on page 463.

12. Suppose that in Exercise 6 on page 463 the points (0, 0), (1, 0), (2, 0), (3, 0), (4, 0), (0, 1), (1, 1), (2, 1), (3, 1), (4, 1), (0, 2), (1, 2), (2, 2), (3, 2), (4, 2), (0, 3), (1, 3), (2, 3), (3, 3), and (4, 3) of the sample space are assigned the probabilities 0.01, 0.01, 0.01, 0,03, 0.04, 0.01, 0.01, 0.01, 0.03, 0.04, 0.03, 0.03, 0.03, 0.09, 0.12, 0.05, 0.05, 0.05, 0.15, and 0.20.

(a) What are the respective probabilities that the larger helicopter will have 0, 1, 2, 3, or 4 passengers?
(b) What are the respective probabilities that the smaller helicopter will have 0, 1, 2, or 3 passengers?
(c) Find the probabilities of the events which are represented by sets R, S, T, and U of part (c) of Exercise 6 on page 463.

(*Hint:* refer to the sample space constructed in part (b) of Exercise 6 on page 463 and fill in the probabilities attached to the various points as in Figure 16.6.)

13. Sometimes Mrs. Jones has lunch by herself at home, sometimes she has lunch out by herself while shopping, sometimes she goes to luncheon meetings sponsored by the various clubs to which she belongs, sometimes she is invited out for lunch by friends, and sometimes she skips lunch to lose weight. If the probabilities of these alternatives are, respectively, 0.32, 0.14, 0.18, 0.15, and 0.21, find

(a) the probability that she will eat lunch by herself;
(b) the probability that she will not go out for lunch;
(c) the probability that she will have lunch out, but not by herself.

14. Referring to Exercise 12 on page 464 and assuming that each point of the sample space has the same probability of 1/8, find

(a) the respective probabilities of getting 0, 1, 2, and 3 heads in three successive flips of a coin;
(b) the probabilities of events X, Y, and Z of part (b) of Exercise 12 on page 464.

(*Hint:* refer to the diagram of Figure 16.5 on page 465 and fill in the probabilities attached to the eight points of the sample space.).

15. The probabilities that a company's switchboard will receive 0, 1, 2, 3, 4, 5, 6, 7, or 8 *or more* calls during the lunch hour are, respectively, 0.02, 0.08, 0.15, 0.20, 0.20, 0.16, 0.10, 0.06, and 0.03.

(a) What is the probability that there will be fewer than 4 incoming calls?
(b) What is the probability that there will be at least 3 incoming calls?
(c) What is the probability that there will be anywhere from 2 to 6 incoming calls, inclusive?

(d) What is the probability that there will be at least one incoming call? (Check your answer by calculating this probability in two different ways; once by adding the respective probabilities, and once by subtracting from 1 the probability of 0 calls.)

16. The probability that a patient visiting his dentist will have a tooth extracted is 0.06, the probability that he will have a cavity filled is 0.23, and the probability that he will have a tooth extracted as well as a cavity filled is 0.02.

(a) What is the probability that a patient visiting his dentist will have a tooth extracted but no cavity filled?
(b) What is the probability that a patient visiting his dentist will have a tooth extracted or a cavity filled, possibly both?
(c) What is the probability that a patient visiting his dentist will have a tooth extracted or a cavity filled, but not both?
(d) What is the probability that a patient visiting his dentist will have neither a tooth extracted nor a cavity filled?

(*Hint:* draw a Venn diagram like that of Figure 16.7.)

17. For married couples living in a certain suburb, the probability that the husband will vote in a School Board election is 0.17, the probability that his wife will vote in the election is 0.28, and the probability that they will both vote is 0.11. What is the probability that at least one of them will vote?

18. Among the 80 executives of a corporation 48 are married men, 35 are college graduates, and 22 of the 48 married men are also college graduates. If one of these executives is chosen by lot to attend a convention (that is, if each of the executives has a probability of 1/80 of being selected), what is the probability that the person selected is neither married nor a college graduate?

19. MORTALITY TABLES. To calculate life insurance premiums, the size of annuity payments which are made only so long as a person is alive, retirement pensions, and the like, it is essential to know something about the probabilities that a person will stay alive for any given length of time. Actuaries base these probabilities on various kinds of *mortality tables*, which report such things as deaths per 1,000 for any given age, life expectancies for any given age, or (as in Table XI at the end of this book) the number of persons still alive at any given age from among 100,000 persons alive at age 10. Most of these tables are based on the mortality experience among lives insured by several large American life insurance companies, and they are continually revised in the light of medical advances, changes in living conditions, health standards, and so on. The numbers which we denote l_x in Table XI are based on the so-called *American Experience Mortality Tables* (1843–1858), and they represent the number of persons one can expect to be alive at age x from among 100,000 persons alive at age 10. Assuming that the probabilities of survival are the same for all persons of the same age (which is good enough for actuaries who are interested only in averages, anyhow), we could use Table XI, say, to determine the probability that a person aged

40 will still be alive at 65. The answer is given by the *ratio* of the number of persons alive at age 65 to the number of persons alive at age 40, namely,

$$\frac{l_{65}}{l_{40}} = \frac{49{,}341}{78{,}106} = 0.63$$

In general, the probability that a person aged x will still be alive at age y is given by the ratio l_y/l_x. Also, the probability that a person aged 54 will die within a year is the *ratio* of the number of persons alive at age 54 *minus* the number of persons alive at age 55 to the number of persons alive at age 54, namely,

$$\frac{l_{54} - l_{55}}{l_{54}} = \frac{65{,}706 - 64{,}563}{65{,}706} = 0.017$$

In general, the probability that a person aged x will die within a year is given by the ratio

$$\frac{l_x - l_{x+1}}{l_x}$$

(a) What is the probability that a person aged 33 will still be alive at age 50?

(b) What is the probability that a person aged 18 will die within a year?

(c) What is the probability that a person aged 20 will still be alive at age 30? What is the probability that a person aged 20 will no longer be alive at age 30? *In general, the probability that a person aged x will no longer be alive at age y is given by the ratio*

$$\frac{l_x - l_y}{l_x}$$

(d) Use the formula of part (c) to find the probabilities that a person aged 27 will die before he is 45, and that a person aged 38 will die before he is 50.

(e) What are the probabilities that a person aged 35 will be alive at age 50 and that he will be alive at age 60? What is the probability that a person aged 35 will be alive at age 50 but die before reaching 60? *In general, the probability that a person aged x will be alive at age y but die before reaching z is given by the ratio*

$$\frac{l_y - l_z}{l_x}$$

(f) Use the formula of part (e) to find the probabilities that a person aged 15 will be alive at 25 but die before he is 50, and that a person aged 62 will be alive at 70 but die before he is 75.

20. The following is a proof of the rule on page 467 which states that $P(A) \leq 1$ for any event A. Making use of the fact that *by definition* (see page 11) A and A' represent mutually exclusive events, and that $A \cup A' = S$ (since A and A' together contain all of the points of the sample space S), we can write $P(A \cup A') = P(S)$, and, hence,

$P(A) + P(A') = P(S)$	*Step 1*
$P(A) + P(A') = 1$	*Step 2*
$P(A) = 1 - P(A')$	*Step 3*
$P(A) \leq 1$	*Step 4*

State which of the three postulates of probability justify the first, second, and fourth steps of this proof; the third step is simple arithmetic. Note also that in Step 2 we have actually proved the third of the rules given on page 467.

16.4 CONDITIONAL PROBABILITY

Very often, it is meaningless (or at least very confusing) to speak of the probability of an event without specifying the sample space with which we are concerned. For instance, if we ask for the probability that a lawyer makes more than \$15,000 a year, we may well get many different answers *and they can all be correct.* One of these might apply to all lawyers in the United States, another might apply to lawyers handling only divorce cases, a third might apply only to lawyers employed by corporations, another might apply to lawyers handling only tax cases, and so on. Since the choice of the sample space (namely, the set of all possibilities under consideration) is by no means always self-evident, it is helpful to use the symbol $P(A \mid S)$ to denote the *conditional probability* of event A relative to the sample space S, or as we often call it "the probability of A given S." The symbol $P(A \mid S)$ makes it explicit that we are referring to the sample space S (that is, a *particular* sample space S), and it is generally preferable to the abbreviated notation $P(A)$ unless the tacit choice of S is clearly understood. It is also preferable when we have to refer to *different* sample spaces in one and the same problem, as in the examples which follow.

To elaborate on the idea of a *conditional probability,* let us consider the following problem: there are 200 applicants for a minor position in the personnel department of a large concern, and since there is practically no time to screen the applicants, we shall assume that each one has the same probability of 1/200 of getting the job. It is known, though, that among the 200 applicants some have had previous experience in personnel work and some have had formal training in personnel administration, with the actual breakdown being as follows:

	Formal Training	*No Formal Training*
Previous Experience	16	32
No Previous Experience	24	128

As can be seen from this table, the chances of selecting a person with previous experience *and* formal training are rather slim—the probability is $\frac{16}{200} = 0.08$, to be exact. Letting E denote the selection of an applicant with previous experience, and T the selection of an applicant with formal training, we can write this probability as

$$P(E \cap T) = 0.08$$

Furthermore, it can be seen that the probability of their selecting someone with previous experience is

$$P(E) = \frac{16 + 32}{200} = 0.24$$

and the probability of their selecting someone with formal training is

$$P(T) = \frac{16 + 24}{200} = 0.20$$

where each of these probabilities was obtained by means of the special formula for equiprobable events on page 470.

Since all of these probabilities are fairly low, suppose that the management of the concern decides to limit the selection to applicants who have had some formal training. As a result of this decision, the number of applicants is reduced to 40, and if we assume that each of them still has an equal chance, we find that

$$P(E \mid T) = \frac{16}{40} = 0.40$$

This is the conditional probability of their selecting someone with previous experience *given that he must have had some formal training.*

Note that this conditional probability can also be written as

$$P(E \mid T) = \frac{16/200}{40/200} = \frac{P(E \cap T)}{P(T)}$$

namely, as the *ratio* of the probability of their selecting a person *with previous experience and formal training* to the probability of their selecting someone *with formal training.* Generalizing from this example, let us now make the following definition which applies to any two events A and B belonging to a given sample space S:

> *If $P(B)$ is not equal to zero, then the conditional probability of A relative to B, namely, the "probability of A given B," is given by*
>
> $$P(A \mid B) = \frac{P(A \cap B)}{P(B)}$$

Had the selection been limited to applicants *with previous experience* in our example, we can now argue that the probability of their selecting someone with *formal training* is given by

$$P(T \mid E) = \frac{P(T \cap E)}{P(E)} = \frac{0.08}{0.24} = \frac{1}{3}$$

where we made use of the fact that $T \cap E = E \cap T$ (see page 19). Of course, this result could have been obtained directly by observing that among the 48 applicants with previous experience, 16 (or 1/3) have also had some formal training.

Although we justified the formula for $P(A \mid B)$ by means of an example in which all outcomes were *equiprobable*, this is *not* a requirement for its use. To consider an example in which we are *not* dealing with equiprobable events, let us refer again to the two-housewives-interview example and Figure 16.6. If we let A denote the event that the second housewife will like the commercial while B denotes the event that the first housewife will say that she doesn't care, we find that

$$P(A) = 0.08 + 0.04 + 0.08 = 0.20$$
$$P(B) = 0.16 + 0.08 + 0.16 = 0.40$$

and

$$P(A \cap B) = 0.08$$

Then, if we substitute the last two values into the formula for $P(A \mid B)$, we get

$$P(A \mid B) = \frac{P(A \cap B)}{P(B)} = \frac{0.08}{0.40} = 0.20$$

and what is *special* (and interesting) about this result is that

$$P(A \mid B) = 0.20 = P(A)$$

This means that the probability of event A is the same regardless of whether event B has occurred (occurs, or will occur), and we say that *event A is independent of event B*. Intuitively speaking, this means that *the occurrence of A is in no way affected by the occurrence or non-occurrence of B*, and this is something we should really have expected in this example—there should be no relationship (dependence) between the responses of two housewives interviewed in a scientifically conducted "impartial" survey. Note that in the first example of this section event E was *not* independent of event T; whereas $P(E)$ equalled 0.24, $P(E \mid T)$ equalled 0.40, and this is indicative of the fact that the probability of selecting someone with previous experience *became larger* when they decided to consider only applicants with some formal training.

As it can be shown in general that *event B is independent of event A whenever event A is independent of event B*, namely $P(B) = P(B \mid A)$

whenever $P(A) = P(A \mid B)$, it is customary to say simply that A *and* B *are independent* whenever one is independent of the other. As the reader will be asked to verify in Exercise 12 on page 487 for the two-housewives-interview example, the independence of A and B implies also that A is independent of B' and B is independent of A', namely, that $P(A \mid B') = P(A)$ and $P(B \mid A') = P(B)$. If two events A and B are *not independent*, we say that they are *dependent*.

So far we have used the formula $P(A \mid B) = \dfrac{P(A \cap B)}{P(B)}$ only to calculate conditional probabilities, which, of course, was the reason for which it was introduced. However, if we multiply the expressions on both sides of this equation by $P(B)$, we get

$$P(B) \cdot P(A \mid B) = P(A \cap B)$$

and this provides us with a formula, sometimes referred to as a *multiplication rule*, which enables us to calculate the probability that two events will both occur. In words, the formula states that *the probability that two events will both occur is the product of the probability that one of the events will occur and the conditional probability that the other event will occur given that the first event has occurred* (*occurs, or will occur*). As it does not matter which event is referred to as A and which event is referred to as B, the above formula can also be written as

$$P(A) \cdot P(B \mid A) = P(B \cap A)$$

and, of course, $P(A \cap B) = P(B \cap A)$, as we already pointed out on page 479.

To illustrate the use of these formulas, suppose we want to determine the probability of having the *bad luck* of randomly picking 2 defective television sets from a shipment of 15 sets among which 3 are defective. Assuming equal probabilities for each selection (which is what we mean by "randomly picking" the two sets), we find that the probability that the first one is defective is 3/15, and that the probability that the second one is defective *given that the first set was defective* is 2/14. Clearly, there are only 2 defectives among the 14 sets which remain after one defective set has been picked. Hence, the probability of choosing two sets which are *both defective* is

$$\frac{3}{15} \cdot \frac{2}{14} = \frac{1}{35}$$

A similar argument leads to the result that the probability of choosing two sets which are *not defective* is

$$\frac{12}{15} \cdot \frac{11}{14} = \frac{22}{35}$$

and it follows, by subtraction, that the probability of getting one good set and one defective set is $1 - \frac{1}{35} - \frac{22}{35} = \frac{12}{35}$. An alternate way of handling problems of this kind will be discussed in Section 18.2.

When A and B are *independent events*, we can substitute $P(A)$ for $P(A \mid B)$ into the first form of the multiplication rule on page 480, or $P(B)$ for $P(B \mid A)$ into the second, and we obtain the *special multiplication rule*

$$P(A \cap B) = P(A) \cdot P(B)$$

This formula can be used, for example, to find the probability of getting two *heads* in a row with a balanced coin or the probability of drawing two aces in a row from an ordinary deck of 52 playing cards *provided the first card is replaced before the second is drawn.* For the two flips of the coin we get $\frac{1}{2} \cdot \frac{1}{2} = \frac{1}{4}$ and for the two aces we get $\frac{4}{52} \cdot \frac{4}{52} = \frac{1}{169}$, since there are 4 aces among the 52 cards. (Had the first card not been replaced before the second card was drawn, the probability of getting two aces in a row would have been $\frac{4}{52} \cdot \frac{3}{51} = \frac{1}{221}$; this distinction will be discussed further in Section 18.2, as it is important in *statistics*, where we speak of "sampling with or without replacement.") The following are two further applications of the special multiplication rule: if the probability that a person will make a mistake in his income tax return is 0.12, then the probability that two totally unrelated persons (who do not use the same accountant) will both make a mistake is $(0.12)(0.12) = 0.0144$; if the probability that a person will choose blue as his favorite color is 0.24, then the probability that neither of two totally unrelated persons will choose blue is $(0.76)(0.76) = 0.5776$.

The special multiplication rule can easily be extended so that it applies to the occurrence of three or more independent events—*we simply multiply all of the respective probabilities.* For instance, the probability of getting 4 *heads* in a row with a balanced coin is $\frac{1}{2} \cdot \frac{1}{2} \cdot \frac{1}{2} \cdot \frac{1}{2} = \frac{1}{16}$, and the probability of first rolling two 1's and then some other number in three rolls of a balanced die is $\frac{1}{6} \cdot \frac{1}{6} \cdot \frac{5}{6} = \frac{5}{216}$. For dependent events the formulas become somewhat more complicated, as is illustrated in Exercise 16 on page 487.

16.5 BAYES' RULE

Although the two symbols $P(A \mid B)$ and $P(B \mid A)$ look very much alike, there is a great difference between the corresponding probabilities. As we saw in the first example of Section 16.4, $P(E \mid T)$ is the probability that they (the given concern) will hire someone with previous experience *given that he must have had some formal training*, $P(T \mid E)$ is the probability that they will hire someone with formal training *given that he must have had some experience*, and the values of these two probabilities were 2/5 and 1/3. Similarly, if C represents the event that a certain person committed a crime and G represents the event that he is judged guilty, then $P(G \mid C)$ is the probability that the person will be judged guilty *given that he actually committed the crime*, and $P(C \mid G)$ is the probability that the person actually did commit the crime *given that he has been judged guilty*—clearly, there is a big difference between these two conditional probabilities.

Since there are many problems which involve such pairs of conditional probabilities, let us try to find a formula which expresses $P(B \mid A)$ in terms of $P(A \mid B)$ for any two events A and B. Fortunately, we do not have to look very far; all we have to do is equate the two expressions for $P(A \cap B)$ on page 480, and we get

$$P(A) \cdot P(B \mid A) = P(B) \cdot P(A \mid B)$$

and, hence,

$$P(B \mid A) = \frac{P(B) \cdot P(A \mid B)}{P(A)}$$

after dividing the expressions on both sides of the equation by $P(A)$. To illustrate the use of this formula, suppose that a store employs two salesladies: Jane who works Mondays, Wednesdays, and Fridays, and Nancy who works on Tuesdays and Thursdays. The owner of the store knows from past experience that Jane (who has been working for him for a long time) makes a mistake in about 2 percent of her sales, that altogether the two salesladies make mistakes in 4.8 percent of their sales, and that just about as many sales are made on Monday as on Tuesday, Wednesday, Thursday, and Friday; the store is closed on Saturdays and Sundays. Now suppose that a customer complains of having been overcharged on something he bought, but he cannot remember whether it was sold to him by Nancy or by Jane. *What is the probability that the mistake was made by Jane?* If we let A denote the event that there is a mistake while B denotes the event that a sale is made by Jane, the above information can be expressed by writing $P(A \mid B) = 0.02$, $P(A) = 0.048$, and $P(B) = 3/5 = 0.60$, so that substitution into the formula for $P(B \mid A)$ yields

$$P(B \mid A) = \frac{(0.60)(0.02)}{0.048} = 0.25$$

This is the probability that the mistake was made by Jane, and it follows by subtraction that the corresponding probability for Nancy is $1 - 0.25 = 0.75$. Thus, the odds are 3 to 1 that the mistake was made by Nancy rather than Jane (even though Nancy works fewer days than Jane).

The formula which we used in this last example is a very simple version of the so-called *Rule of Bayes;* although there is no question about its *validity,* questions have been raised about its *applicability.* This is due to the fact that it involves a "backward" or "inverse" sort of reasoning—namely, *reasoning from effect to cause.* In our example we asked for the probability that the mistake was "caused" by Jane, and we could use the same formula to calculate the probability that a given airplane accident was "caused" by structural failure (see Exercise 18 on page 488), or to determine the probability that a certain company's success in getting a government contract was "caused" by its major competitor's failure to bid (see Exercise 17 on page 488).

When there are more than two possible "causes," it is best to analyze the situation by means of a tree diagram like that of Figure 16.8, where the

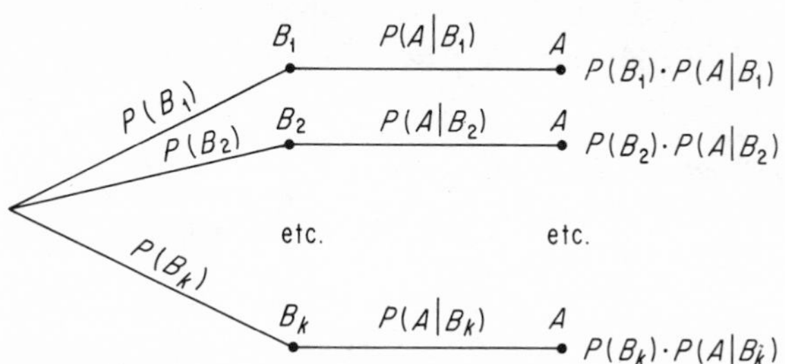

FIG. 16.8

various possible "causes" of A are labeled B_1, B_2, . . . , and B_k. With reference to this diagram we can say that $P(B_i \mid A)$ is the probability that event A is reached via the ith branch of the tree, for $i = 1, 2, \ldots,$ or k, and that its value is given by the *ratio* of the probability associated with the ith branch, namely, $P(B_i) \cdot P(A \mid B_i)$, to the *sum* of the probabilities associated with *all* of the branches of the "tree." Symbolically,

$$P(B_i \mid A) = \frac{P(B_i) \cdot P(A \mid B_i)}{P(B_1) \cdot P(A \mid B_1) + P(B_2) \cdot P(A \mid B_2) + \ldots + P(B_k) \cdot P(A \mid B_k)}$$

for $i = 1, 2, \ldots,$ or k.

To illustrate this more general form of the *Rule of Bayes,* suppose that a management consultant is asked for his opinion as to whether an executive's dissatisfied secretary quit her job mainly because she did not like the work, because she felt that she was underpaid, or because she did not like her boss. Unable to get much *direct* information about the secretary, he digs up the following "facts:" *among all dissatisfied secretaries, 20 percent are dissatisfied mainly because they dislike their work, 50 percent because they feel they are underpaid, and 30 percent because they dislike their boss. Furthermore, the corresponding probabilities that they will quit are, respectively, 0.60, 0.40, and 0.90.*

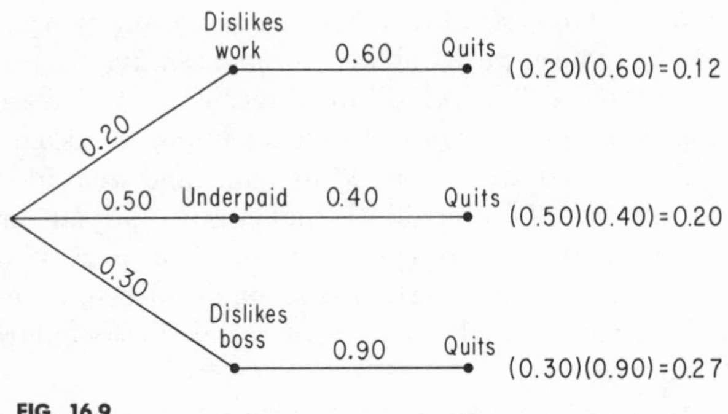

FIG. 16.9

Picturing this situation as in Figure 16.9, we find that the probabilities associated with the three branches of the tree are, respectively, $(0.20)(0.60) = 0.12$, $(0.50)(0.40) = 0.20$, and $(0.30)(0.90) = 0.27$, and that they add up to 0.59. Thus, the probability that a dissatisfied secretary has quit *mainly because she didn't like her work* is $\frac{0.12}{0.59}$ or approximately 0.20, the probability that she has quit *mainly because she felt that she was underpaid* is $\frac{0.20}{0.59}$ or approximately 0.34, and the probability that she has quit *mainly because she did not like her boss* is $\frac{0.27}{0.59}$ or approximately 0.46. It follows that *the management consultant's best bet is to say that the secretary quit mainly because she did not like her boss.*

To solve this problem by means of *Bayes' formula* (that is, without reference to a tree diagram like that of Figure 16.9), we let A represent the event that a dissatisfied secretary quits her job, while B_1, B_2, and B_3 represent the respective events that she is dissatisfied mainly because she dislikes her work, because she feels that she is underpaid, and because she does not like her boss. Thus, being given the information that $P(B_1) = 0.20$, $P(B_2) = 0.50$, $P(B_3) = 0.30$, $P(A \mid B_1) = 0.60$, $P(A \mid B_2) = 0.40$, and $P(A \mid B_3) = 0.90$, we find that the formula yields

$$P(B_1 \mid A) = \frac{(0.20)(0.60)}{(0.20)(0.60) + (0.50)(0.40) + (0.30)(0.90)} = \frac{12}{59}$$

and corresponding expressions with the *same denominator* but the numerators $(0.50)(0.40)$ and $(0.30)(0.90)$ for $P(B_2 \mid A)$ and $P(B_3 \mid A)$. The results are, of course, identical with the ones obtained before.

EXERCISES

1. If H is the event that a person is in a high income-tax bracket and M is the event that he owns municipal bonds, state *in words* what probability is expressed by each of the following:

(a) $P(M \mid H)$; (c) $P(M \mid H')$; (e) $P(M' \mid H')$;
(b) $P(H \mid M)$; (d) $P(H \mid M')$; (f) $P(H' \mid M')$.

2. If G is the event that a stock has growth potential and D is the event that it pays a high dividend, express each of the following probabilities in symbolic form:

(a) the probability that a stock which pays a high dividend will also have growth potential;
(b) the probability that a stock which has growth potential will pay a high dividend;
(c) the probability that a stock which does not pay a high dividend will have growth potential;
(d) the probability that a stock which does not have growth potential will not pay a high dividend either.

3. If K is the event that a sales executive has an M.B.A. degree, L is the event that he is at least 35 years old, M is the event that he belongs to the local country club, and N is the event that he makes at least \$25,000 a year, state *in words* what probability is expressed by each of the following:

(a) $P(N \mid K)$; (d) $P(M \mid N')$; (g) $P(M \cap N \mid L)$;
(b) $P(M \mid L)$; (e) $P(N' \mid L')$; (h) $P(L \cap M \mid K')$;
(c) $P(N \mid K')$; (f) $P(L \mid M')$; (i) $P(N \mid K \cap L)$.

4. Referring to Exercise 3, express each of the following probabilities in symbolic form:

(a) the probability that one of the sales executives has an M.B.A. degree given that he is under 35;
(b) the probability that one of the sales executives belongs to the local country club given that he makes at least \$25,000 a year;
(c) the probability that one of the sales executives who belongs to the local country club will have an M.B.A. degree and be at least 35 years old;
(d) the probability that one of the sales executives who belongs to the local country club and has an M.B.A. degree will make at least \$25,000 a year.

5. Each month, a brokerage house studies two groups of industries and rates the individual companies as being low risks or moderate-to-high risks. In a recent report it published its findings on 13 aerospace industries and 27 processors of foods with the overall results summarized as follows:

	Low risk	*Moderate-to-high risk*
Aerospace	4	9
Foods	16	11

If a person selects one of these companies at random to invest in its stock (that is, each company has a probability of 1/40 of being selected), U and R denote the events that the company he selects is a low risk or a moderate-to-high risk, while A and F denote the events that he selects an aerospace industry or a processor of foods, determine each of the following probabilities:

(a) $P(U)$; (d) $P(A \cap R)$; (g) $P(U \mid F')$;
(b) $P(R)$; (e) $P(U \mid A)$; (h) $P(A \mid R)$;
(c) $P(A \cup R)$; (f) $P(R \mid F)$; (i) $P(F \mid U)$.

6. Supposing that in Exercise 5 the investor assigns each low risk company a probability of 0.04 and each of the other companies a probability of 0.01, recalculate each of the nine probabilities of Exercise 5.

7. Referring to Exercise 16 on page 475, find

   (a) the probability that a patient who is having a tooth extracted will also have a cavity filled;
   (b) the probability that a patient who is having a cavity filled will also have a tooth extracted.

8. Referring to Exercise 17 on page 475, find

   (a) the probability that a wife will vote given that her husband is going to vote;
   (b) the probability that a husband will vote given that his wife is not going to vote.

9. Referring to Exercise 18 on page 475, find

   (a) the probability that the executive who will attend the convention will not be married given that he is a college graduate;
   (b) the probability that the executive who will attend the convention will be a college graduate given that he is married.

10. The production manager of an electronics firm has the following information: the probability that the equipment needed for a certain project will be delivered on time is 0.80, and the probability that the equipment will be delivered on time *and* the project will be completed on time is 0.60.

    (a) What is the probability that the project will be completed on time given that the equipment was delivered on time?
    (b) If the probability that the project will be completed on time is 0.64, what is the probability that the project will *not* be completed on time given that the equipment was not delivered on time?

    (*Hint:* use a Venn diagram like that of Figure 16.7.)

11. The business editor of a newspaper wants to interview 2 realtors randomly selected from among 20 realtors attending a business luncheon. If 10 of the realtors feel that business conditions will improve, 4 of them feel that things will get worse, while the other 6 feel that things will remain unchanged, find

    (a) the probability that both realtors interviewed will feel that business conditions will improve;
    (b) the probability that both realtors interviewed will feel that things will get worse;
    (c) the probability that one of the realtors interviewed will feel that business conditions will improve while the other will feel that things will remain unchanged;

(d) the probability that one of the realtors interviewed will feel that things will get worse while the other will feel that things will remain unchanged.

[*Hint:* in parts (c) and (d) add the probabilities corresponding to the two different ways in which the particular responses can be obtained.]

12. Referring to the two-housewives-interview example on page 469, verify that

(a) B is also independent of A, namely $P(B \mid A) = P(B)$;
(b) A is also independent of B', namely, $P(A \mid B') = P(A)$;
(c) B is also independent of A', namely, $P(B \mid A') = P(B)$.

13. Referring to Exercise 12 on page 474, it can be shown that the number of passengers in either helicopter is independent of the number of passengers in the other. Using the results of parts (a) and (b) of Exercise 12 on page 474, verify this at least partially by showing that

(a) the probability associated with the point (2, 1) is the product of the probabilities that the larger helicopter has 2 passengers while the smaller helicopter has only 1;
(b) the probability associated with the point (4, 2) is the product of the probabilities that the larger helicopter has 4 passengers while the smaller helicopter has 2;
(c) the probability associated with the point (0, 2) is the product of the probabilities that the smaller helicopter has 2 passengers while the larger helicopter is empty.

14. Which of the following pairs of events are independent?

(a) Getting sixes in two successive rolls of a die.
(b) Being intoxicated while driving and having an accident.
(c) Having a driver's license and owning a car.
(d) Being a college professor and having green eyes.
(e) Any two mutually exclusive events.
(f) Being born in December and having flat feet.

15. As we indicated on page 481, the probability that any number of independent events will occur is given by the product of their respective probabilities. Using this rule, find

(a) the probability of getting 6 *tails* in a row with a balanced coin;
(b) the probability of drawing (with replacement) 3 aces in a row from an ordinary deck of 52 playing cards;
(c) the probability that four totally unrelated persons aged 39 will all be alive at 65;
(d) the probability that none of 5 totally unrelated children aged 12 will live to be 80.

[*Hint:* in parts (c) and (d) refer to Table XI, which is explained in Exercise 19 on page 475.]

16. The problem of determining the probability that any number of events will occur becomes more complicated when the events are *not independent.* For three events A, B, and C, for example, the probability that they will all occur is obtained by multiplying the probability of A by the probability of B *given* A, and then multiplying the result by the probability of C *given* $A \cap B$. For instance, the probability of drawing (without replacement) 3 aces in a row from an ordinary deck of 52 playing cards is

$$\frac{4}{52}\cdot\frac{3}{51}\cdot\frac{2}{50} = \frac{1}{5{,}525}$$

Clearly, there are only 3 aces among the 51 cards which remain after the first ace has been drawn, and only 2 aces among the 50 cards which remain after the first two aces have been drawn.

(a) Referring to the illustration on page 477, what is the probability that if 3 of the applicants are randomly selected for further interviews, they will all have had some previous experience?

(b) Symbolically or in words, give a rule for the probability that four events A, B, C, and D will all occur.

(c) In a certain city, the probability of passing the test for a driver's license on the first try is 0.75; after that the probability of passing becomes 0.60, regardless of how often a person has failed. What is the probability of finally getting one's license on the fourth try?

(d) In the Fall, the probability that a rainy day will be followed by a rainy day is 0.80 and the probability that a sunny day will be followed by a rainy day is 0.40. Assuming that each day is classified as being either rainy or sunny and that the weather on any given day depends only on the weather the day before, find the probability that a rainy day is followed by three more rainy days, then two sunny days, and finally another rainy day.

17. There is a fifty-fifty chance that Firm A will bid for the construction of a new city hall. Firm B submits a bid and the probability that it will get the job is 2/3 provided Firm A does not bid; if Firm A submits a bid, the probability that Firm B will get the job is only 1/5. If Firm B gets the job, what is the probability that Firm A did not bid?

18. The probability that an airplane accident due to structural failure is diagnosed correctly is 0.72 and the probability that an airplane accident which is *not* due to structural failure is diagnosed incorrectly as being due to structural failure is 0.12. If 40 percent of all airplane accidents are due to structural failure, what is the probability that an airplane accident which is diagnosed as being due to structural failure is actually due to this cause?

19. Three gift wrappers are employed in a toy store at Christmas time. Mary, who wraps 40 percent of all parcels, fails to remove the price tag 1 time in 50; Joan, who wraps 30 percent of all parcels, fails to remove the price tag 1 time in 10, and Helen, who wraps the remaining toys, fails to remove the price tag 1 time in 20. Given that a customer complains that a price tag was not removed from a toy before it was wrapped, what is the probability that it was Mary's mistake?

20. An economics instructor knows from past experience that a student who regularly does his homework has a probability of 0.90 of getting a passing grade, while a student who does not regularly do his homework has only a probability of 0.20. If 70 percent of all his students regularly do their homework, what is the probability that a student who gets a passing grade actually did his homework regularly?

21. In a cannery, assembly lines I, II, and III account, respectively, for 40 percent, 40 percent, and 20 percent of the total output. If 0.2 percent of the cans from assembly line I are improperly sealed, while the corresponding percentages for assembly lines II and III are, respectively, 0.8 percent and 1.2 percent, what is the probability that an improperly sealed can (discovered in the final inspection of outgoing products) came from assembly line I? What is the probability that it came from assembly line II?

22. The probabilities that a brewery will decide to sponsor the televising of football games, a soap opera, or a news program are, respectively, 0.50, 0.30, and 0.20. If they decide on the football games, the probability that they will get a high rating is 0.60; if they decide on a soap opera, the probability that they will get a high rating is 0.30; and if they decide on a news program, the probability that they will get a high rating is 0.20. If it turns out that they do get a high rating, what is the probability that they chose a soap opera?

16.6 THE CONTINUOUS CASE

Continuous sample spaces arise whenever we deal with quantities that are measured on a continuous scale—when we measure the time it takes before a battery fails, when we measure the distance at which a shell hits from the center of a target, when we measure the exact amount of instant coffee in a "6-ounce" jar, and so on. In each case there is a continuum of possibilities, and instead of asking for probabilities associated with points of the sample space, we ask for probabilities associated with *intervals* or *regions*. Thus, we might ask for the probability that a battery will last anywhere from 60 to 70 hours, that a shell will hit anywhere within 100 feet from the center of a target, or that a jar of instant coffee will contain anywhere from 5.9 to 6.5 ounces of coffee. Actually, we *could* ask for probabilities associated with points, but the answer would always be zero—clearly, we should be willing to give *any odds* that a battery will not fail after having been in use for *exactly* 43.5876419564583 hours, we should be willing to give *any odds* that a shell will not hit at a point *exactly* $\sqrt{997}$ feet from the center of a target, and we should be willing to give *any odds* that a "6-ounce" jar of instant coffee will not contain *exactly* 6.000000057389546 ounces of coffee.

When probabilities are associated with intervals, it stands to reason that their values will depend not only on the lengths of the intervals, but also on their location (namely "from where to where" each interval goes). For instance, the probability that a battery will last anywhere from 40 to 80 hours should be *at least as large* as the probability that the battery will last anywhere from 60 to 70 hours, since the second interval is contained in the first; however, there is no reason why the probability that it will last anywhere from 60 to 70 hours should *equal* the probability that it will last anywhere from 5 to 15 hours, even though the two intervals have the same length. Thus, let us assume that there exists a function with the values $f(x)$, so that the probability that the battery will cease to function on the small interval from x to $x + \Delta x$ is *approximately* $f(x) \cdot \Delta x$, with the "goodness" of the approximation depending on the size of Δx. Graphically, this probability is given by the *area* of the rectangle of Figure 16.10, whose height is $f(x)$ and whose base is Δx.

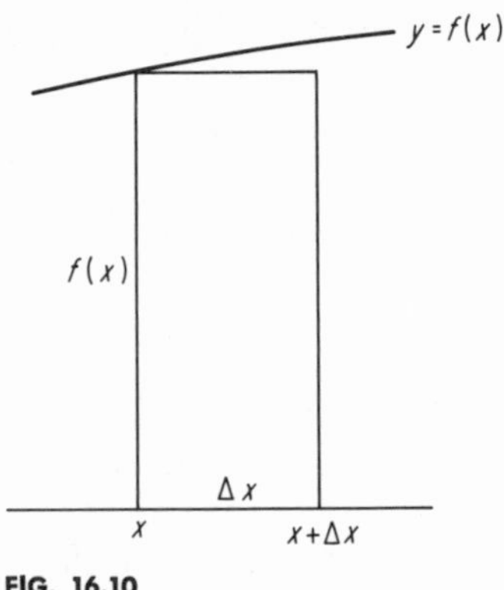

FIG. 16.10

To find the probability that the battery will fail somewhere on a larger interval, say, the interval from c to d in Figure 16.11, we have only to subdivide the interval into small intervals of length Δx. Then, if we let x_1, x_2, x_3, . . . , denote the lower endpoints of these intervals, the desired probability for the whole interval from c to d is *approximately* the sum of the areas of the rectangles of Figure 16.11, namely,

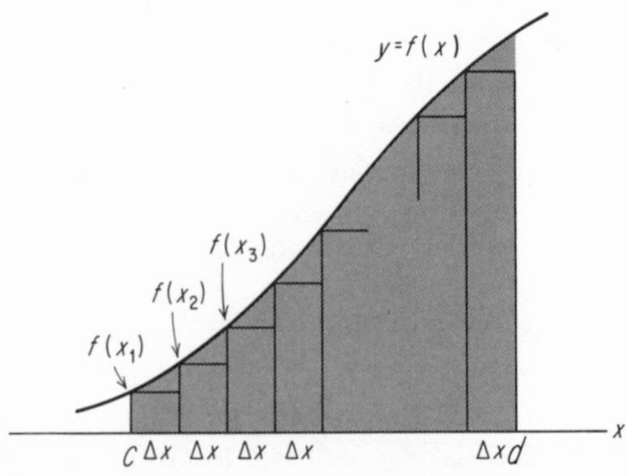

FIG. 16.11

$$f(x_1)\cdot\Delta x + f(x_2)\cdot\Delta x + f(x_3)\cdot\Delta x + \dots$$

To define the *exact* probability that the battery will fail anywhere on the interval from c to d, we simply let $\Delta x \to 0$, and we get the area under the curve shaded in Figure 16.11, namely, the definite integral

$$\int_c^d f(x)\,dx$$

The argument we have presented here is by no means limited to the study of the lifetimes of batteries; it provides the following general definition of probability for the continuous case:

> *The probability of obtaining a value (measurement or observation) on the interval from a to b is given by the definite integral*
>
> $$\int_a^b f(x)\,dx$$
>
> *where $f(x)$ denotes the values of an appropriate function, called a probability density function.*

Thus, probabilities are given by areas under curves, and in most situations the main problem is to *find the correct kind of curve.* Sometimes, the choice of the correct probability density function is dictated by the physical nature of a problem and sometimes there are theoretical reasons; generally speaking, though, the choice of the right "probability model" poses difficult questions, which we shall not be able to discuss in this book. In all of the illustrations and exercises which follow, the probability density functions will be specified.

To give a numerical example, suppose that the probability density function for the "lifetime" of the batteries we have been talking about is given by

$$f(x) = \frac{1}{50}\cdot e^{-x/50} \qquad \text{for} \qquad x \geqslant 0$$

where x is in hours, and that we want to determine the probability that such a battery will fail anywhere on the interval from 60 to 70 hours. The answer is given by the integral

$$\int_{60}^{70} \frac{1}{50}\cdot e^{-x/50}\,dx$$

and, using the integration formula of Exercise 5 on page 419, we get

$$\int_{60}^{70} \frac{1}{50}\cdot e^{-x/50}\,dx = -\,e^{-x/50}\Big]_{60}^{70} = -\,e^{-70/50} + e^{-60/50}$$

$$= -\,e^{-1.4} + e^{-1.2}$$

and this equals $-0.247 + 0.301 = 0.054$ according to Table III. Similarly, we get

$$\int_5^{15} \frac{1}{50} \cdot e^{-x/50}\,dx = -e^{-x/50}\Big]_5^{15} = -e^{-15/50} + e^{-5/50}$$
$$= -e^{-0.3} + e^{-0.1}$$
$$= 0.164$$

for the probability that such a battery will fail anywhere on the interval from 5 to 15 hours. This illustrates the point which we made earlier, namely, that two probabilities can be different even though the corresponding intervals are of the same length. An exception to this rule is the *uniform probability density function* defined, say, for the sample space which consists of the interval from α (*alpha*) to β (*beta*). It is given by the equation

$$f(x) = \frac{1}{\beta - \alpha} \qquad \text{for} \qquad \alpha \leqslant x \leqslant \beta$$

and, as the reader will be asked to verify in Exercise 2 on page 494, the probability associated with any interval is actually proportional to its length.

Since a probability density function, integrated between any two constants, yields a probability (see Figure 16.12), such a function cannot be

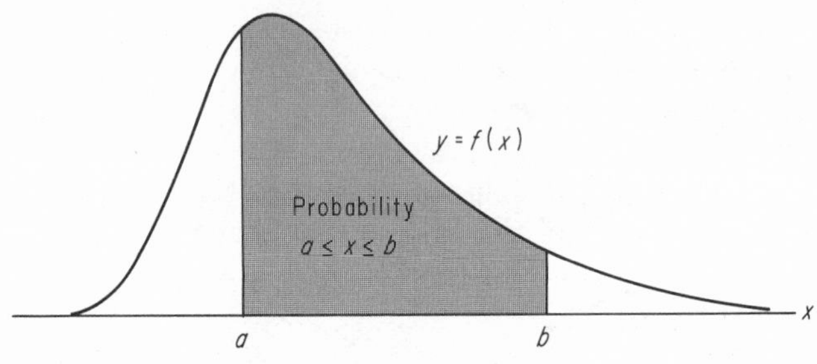

FIG. 16.12

just any (integrable) function. In accordance with Postulates 1 and 2 on page 465, we shall have to impose the conditions that $f(x) \geqslant 0$ *for all values of* x *within the domain of the function, namely, the sample space,* and that *for the entire sample space the integral of the function must equal 1*. In the first of the two examples of the preceding paragraph the domain of the function was $x \geqslant 0$, in the second example it was $\alpha \leqslant x \leqslant \beta$, and it will be left to the reader to verify in Exercises 1 and 2 on pages 493 and 494 that

$$\int_0^{\infty} \frac{1}{50} \cdot e^{-x/50}\,dx = 1 \qquad \text{and} \qquad \int_{\alpha}^{\beta} \frac{1}{\beta - \alpha}\,dx = 1$$

(So far as the third postulate is concerned, it will have to be generalized so that it applies to the union of infinitely many mutually exclusive events; also, in the continuous case an event cannot be just any subset of a sample space—only an interval or the union of two intervals or more.)

Most of the probability density functions which are of any practical significance are difficult to integrate, and have therefore been tabulated. Tables of areas under the *standard normal curve*, for instance, are given in most textbooks on probability or statistics, so that probabilities related to this important probability density function can be obtained without the use of calculus (or, for that matter, without any knowledge of calculus).

EXERCISES

1. The probability density function which we used in the battery example on page 491 is a special case of the *exponential probability density* given by

$$f(x) = \frac{1}{\theta} \cdot e^{-x/\theta} \qquad \text{for } x \geqslant 0$$

where θ (*theta*) is a positive constant, whose significance will be explained in Exercise 24 on page 540.

(a) Calculate the values of this function for $\theta = 50$ and $x = 0, 50, 100, 150, 200, \ldots,$ and 450, and sketch its graph.

(b) Verify that the integral of an exponential probability density over the entire sample space (that is, from $x = 0$ to $x = \infty$) is, indeed, equal to 1. (*Hint:* use the method of Exercise 17 on page 429 to evaluate the required *improper* integral.)

(c) With reference to the example on page 491, find the probability that the battery will fail anywhere on the interval from 40 to 80 hours.

Exponential probability density functions are often used in connection with *waiting times* between successive events, say, the times between the arrival of cars at a service station, the times that elapse between the hearings of court cases, the times between the arrival of customers at a candy store, the times between trucks arriving at unloading docks, and so on.

(d) If the waiting time between the arrival of customers at a theater ticket office has an exponential probability density with $\theta = 5$ minutes, what is the probability that there will be a time lapse from 8 to 10 minutes between the arrival of successive customers?

(e) If the waiting time of persons waiting for a table at a popular restaurant has an exponential probability density with $\theta = 10$ minutes, what is the probability that a person will have to wait anywhere from 20 to 40 minutes till he gets a table?

(f) In a certain brokerage house, the time a customer has to wait for confirmation of a transaction has an exponential probability density with $\theta = 20$ minutes. What is the probability that a person will have to wait anywhere from half an hour to an hour for a confirmation of a transaction?

2. With reference to the *uniform probability density function* on page 492,

(a) sketch its graph for the special case where $\alpha = 1$ and $\beta = 5$;
(b) verify that the integral over the entire sample space, namely, from α to β, is equal to 1;
(c) verify that the probability associated with the interval from a to b, where $\alpha \leqslant a \leqslant b \leqslant \beta$, is proportional to $b - a$;
(d) find the probability that anywhere from 40 to 60 percent of a class did worse in the final examination than a student whom we selected at random, given that this percentage has a uniform probability density with $\alpha = 0$ and $\beta = 100$.

3. For a certain mail-order house, the proportion of orders processed within 24 hours has the probability density function

$$f(x) = 20 \cdot x^3(1 - x) \qquad \text{for} \qquad 0 \leqslant x \leqslant 1$$

which is a special case of the so-called *beta probability density function.*

(a) Calculate the values of this function for $x = 0, 0.1, 0.2, \ldots,$ and 1.0, and sketch its graph.
(b) What is the probability that over a fairly long period of time at least 80 percent of all orders are processed within 24 hours?
(c) What is the probability that fewer than 30 percent of all orders are processed within 24 hours?
(d) What is the probability that anywhere from 50 to 60 percent of all orders will be processed within 24 hours?
(*Hint:* write the percentages as proportions.)

4. In a large department store, the December sales volume of nylon stockings has the probability density function

$$f(x) = \frac{1}{4} \cdot x \cdot e^{-x/2} \qquad \text{for} \quad x \geqslant 0$$

where x is in thousands of pairs; this is a special case of the so-called *gamma probability density function.*

(a) Calculate the values of this function for $x = 0, 2, 4, 6, \ldots,$ and 18, and sketch its graph.
(b) Using the integration formula of Exercise 16 on page 423, find the probability that they will sell fewer than 10,000 pairs.
(c) Using the integration formula of Exercise 16 on page 423, find the probability that they will sell anywhere from 6,000 to 12,000 pairs.
(d) Using the integration formula of Exercise 16 on page 423, find the probability that they will sell at least 15,000 pairs (by calculating the probability that they will sell fewer than 15,000 pairs and then subtracting that answer from 1). Check the answer by evaluating the *improper* integral directly by the method of Exercise 17 on page 429.

5. In a certain country, family income has the probability density function

$$f(x) = \frac{2x}{(1 + x^2)^2} \qquad \text{for} \quad x \geqslant 0$$

where x is in thousands of dollars. Making the substitution $q = 1 + x^2$, calculate

(a) what proportion of the families has incomes of less than \$6,000;
(b) what proportion of the families has incomes anywhere from \$2,000 to \$8,000;
(c) what proportion of the families has incomes over \$10,000. (*Hint:* evaluate the probability that a family will have an income of less than \$10,000 and subtract from 1, or calculate the *improper* integral directly by the method of Exercise 17 on page 429.)

17

EXPECTATIONS, DECISIONS, AND GAMES

17.1 INTRODUCTION

One of the most important developments of recent years has been the increasing role played by mathematics in decision making on the managerial level. This is very clearly reflected by the appearance of textbooks with titles such as *Mathematical Analysis for Business Decisions*, *Quantitative Analysis for Business Decisions*, *Executive Decisions and Operations Research*, *Decision Mathematics*, *Probability and Statistics for Business Decisions*, and *Statistical Analysis for Business Decisions*. Aside from this, there is a whole new branch of mathematics called *decision theory*, and great interest in the reappraisal of some of the highly-controversial philosophical concepts which underlie decision-making in general. (See, for example, the book by R. C. Jeffrey referred to at the end of this chapter.)

To paraphrase the title of Chapter 15, we cannot judge what is probable unless we know what is possible, but in order to make intelligent decisions, even that is not enough—we must also know something about the consequences (profits, losses, gains, penalties, or rewards) of everything that can possibly take place. Needless to say, this complicates matters, and we shall have to limit our discussion in this book to some of the most fundamental techniques used in basing business decisions (or, for that matter, any kind of decision) on probabilities as well as the potential consequences of our actions.

17.2 MATHEMATICAL EXPECTATION

When we say that in Florida a couple can expect to have 1.46 children, that a person living in the United States can expect to eat 161.5 pounds of meat and 20.1 apples a year, or that a resident of Geneva, Switzerland, can expect to go to the movies 25.2 times a year, it must be obvious that we are not using the word "expect" in its colloquial sense. Some of these events cannot possibly occur, and it would certainly be very surprising if a person actually did eat 161.5 pounds of meat during a calendar year. So far as the Florida couples are concerned, some of them will have no children, some will have one child, some will have two children, some will have three, . . . , and the 1.46 figure must be interpreted as an *average,* or as we shall call it here, a *mathematical expectation.*

Originally, the concept of a mathematical expectation arose in connection with games of chance, and in its simplest form it is given by the *product* of the amount a player stands to win and the probability that he will win. Thus, if we stand to win \$5.00 if a balanced coin comes up *tails,* our mathematical expectation is $5(1/2) = \$2.50$. Similarly, if we consider buying one of 1,000 raffle tickets issued for a prize (say, a television set) worth \$480.00, our mathematical expectation is $480(0.001) = 0.48$ or 48 cents; thus, it would be foolish to pay more than 48 cents for the ticket unless the proceeds of the raffle went to a worthy cause (or the difference could be credited to whatever pleasure a person might derive from placing a bet). Note that in this example 999 of the tickets will not pay anything at all, one ticket will pay \$480.00 (or the equivalent in merchandize), so that altogether the 1,000 tickets pay \$480, or *on the average* 48 cents per ticket.

The cost of a *pure endowment* is another simple example of a mathematical expectation; it is an insurance policy which will pay a person a specified sum of money after a given number of years *provided he is still alive.* To illustrate, suppose that someone age 48 wants to buy a pure endowment which will pay him \$20,000 at age 65. As we explained in Exercise 19 on page 475, the probability that he will still be alive at age 65 is given by

$$\frac{l_{65}}{l_{48}} = \frac{49{,}341}{71{,}627} = 0.689$$

where l_{48} and l_{65} denote, respectively the number of persons still alive at these two ages from among 100,000 persons alive at age 10; the values of l_{48} and l_{65} were obtained from Table XI at the end of the book. (Of course, it is assumed here that the person is of average health and that he is not engaged in any high-risk activities.)

Now, it would be a bad mistake to say that the mathematical expectation is $20{,}000(0.689) = \$13{,}780$, and that this is the net single premium the man should pay. Since the money will not have to be paid out for 17 years, if at all, the probability should not be multiplied by \$20,000, but by its *present value*, which (at 4 percent compounded annually) is

$$20{,}000(1.04)^{-17} = 20{,}000(0.513373) = \$10{,}267.46$$

Thus, the net premium should be

$$10{,}267.46(0.689) = \$7{,}074$$

to the nearest dollar. A general formula for calculating the net single premium of a pure endowment is given in Exercise 8 on page 501.

So far, we have considered only examples in which there was a single "payoff," namely, one prize or a single payment. To demonstrate how the concept of a mathematical expectation can be generalized, let us change the raffle for the television set so that there is also a second prize (say, a record player) worth \$120.00 and a third prize (say, a radio) worth \$40.00. Now we can argue that 997 of the tickets will not pay anything at all, one ticket will pay the equivalent of \$480, another will pay the equivalent of \$120, while a third will pay the equivalent of \$40; altogether, the 1,000 raffle tickets will thus pay \$480 + \$120 + \$40 = \$640, or *on the average* 64 cents per ticket—this is the *mathematical expectation* for each ticket. Looking at the problem in a different way, we could argue that if the raffle were repeated many times, we would lose 99.7 percent of the time and win each of the three prizes 0.1 percent of the time. On the average we would thus win

$$0(0.997) + 480(0.001) + 120(0.001) + 40(0.001) = \$0.64$$

which is the sum of the products obtained by multiplying each amount by the corresponding probability. Generalizing from this example, let us now make the following definition:

> *If the probabilities of obtaining the amounts $a_1, a_2, a_3, \ldots,$ or a_k, are, respectively, $p_1, p_2, p_3, \ldots,$ and p_k, then the mathematical expectation is*
>
> $$E = a_1p_1 + a_2p_2 + a_3p_3 + \ldots + a_kp_k$$

Each amount is multiplied by the corresponding probability, and the mathematical expectation, E, is given by the sum of all these products. So far as the a's are concerned, it is important to remember that they are *positive* when they represent profits, winnings, or gains (namely, amounts which we receive), and that they are *negative* when they represent losses, penalties, or deficits (namely, amounts which we have to pay). For instance, if we bet \$5.00 on the flip of a coin (that is, we either win \$5.00 or lose \$5.00 depending on the outcome), the amounts a_1 and a_2 are $+5$ and -5, the probabilities are $p_1 = 0.50$ and $p_2 = 0.50$, and the mathematical expectation is

$$E = 5(0.50) + (-5)(0.50) = 0$$

This is what it should be in an *equitable game,* namely, in a game which does not favor either player.

To consider another example, suppose that Mr. Brown is interested in investing in a piece of property for which the probabilities are 0.22, 0.36, 0.28, and 0.14 that he will sell it at a profit of \$2,500, that he will sell it at a profit of \$1,000, that he will break even, or that he will sell it at a loss of \$1,500. If we substitute all these figures into the formula for E, we get

$$\begin{aligned} E &= 2{,}500(0.22) + 1{,}000(0.36) + 0(0.28) + (-1{,}500)(0.14) \\ &= \$700 \end{aligned}$$

and this is his *expected gross profit.* (Whether a profit of \$700 makes the transaction worthwhile is another matter; this would have to depend on such things as sales commissions, money spent on advertising, the length of time the cash investment will be tied up, and so on.)

Important applications of the formula for a mathematical expectation arise in connection with *life annuities,* such as pension payments which are made for a certain period of time or so long as a person is alive. To give an example, let us return to the problem on page 312, where money was to be provided for a child's higher education by means of a lump sum invested on his 10th birthday. However, let us modify the problem by making each of the \$5,000 payments which he is to receive on his 17th, 18th, 19th, 20th, and 21st birthdays contingent upon his remaining alive. The present values of these payments are still $5{,}000(1.05)^{-7}$, $5{,}000(1.05)^{-8}$, $5{,}000(1.05)^{-9}$, $5{,}000(1.05)^{-10}$, and $5{,}000(1.05)^{-11}$, assuming that the interest is compounded annually at 5 percent, and these are the quantities a_1, a_2, a_3, a_4, and a_5 in the formula for E. The only other quantities needed are the probabilities that a child aged 10 will still be alive at 17, 18, 19, 20, and 21, and these are given by

$$p_1 = \frac{l_{17}}{l_{10}} = 0.94818, \quad p_2 = \frac{l_{18}}{l_{10}} = 0.94089,$$

$$p_3 = \frac{l_{19}}{l_{10}} = 0.93362, \quad p_4 = \frac{l_{20}}{l_{10}} = 0.92637,$$

and $$p_5 = \frac{l_{21}}{l_{10}} = 0.91914$$

according to Table XI. Now, if we substitute all these quantities into the formula for a mathematical expectation, we find that A, the amount which will have to be invested on the child's 10th birthday, is given by

$$\begin{aligned} A = {} & 5{,}000(1.05)^{-7}(0.94818) + 5{,}000(1.05)^{-8}(0.94089) \\ & + 5{,}000(1.05)^{-9}(0.93362) + 5{,}000(1.05)^{-10}(0.92637) \\ & + 5{,}000(1.05)^{-11}(0.91914) \end{aligned}$$

Factoring out 5,000 and looking up the necessary powers of 1.05 in Table II, we obtain

$$\begin{aligned} A &= 5{,}000[(0.710681)(0.94818) + (0.676839)(0.94089) \\ &\quad + (0.644609)(0.93362) + (0.613913)(0.92637) \\ &\quad + (0.584679)(0.91914)] \\ &= \$15{,}093 \end{aligned}$$

to the nearest dollar. This is the amount which has to be invested on the child's 10th birthday so that he will get \$5,000 on his 17th, 18th, 19th, 20th, and 21st birthdays, provided in each case that he is still alive. This is quite a bit less than the \$16,159 which had to be invested under the plan of Chapter 11, but of course there is the possibility (heaven forbid) that there will be no payments at all, or perhaps only 1, 2, 3, or 4.

The kind of annuity we have been discussing is a *deferred temporary life annuity*—"temporary" because there are no payments after a fixed number of years, "deferred" because there are no payments until the end of the seventh year, and "life" because each payment is contingent upon the recipient's still being alive. If a life annuity is not deferred it is referred to as *immediate* or *ordinary*, and if payments continue so long as the recipient is alive, it is referred to as a *whole life annuity*. (We shall not work any problems involving whole life annuities in this book although, in principle, they do not differ from the others. However, since whole life annuities generally require the addition of many terms, it is much more convenient to refer to tables specially constructed for this purpose.)

EXERCISES

1. As part of a promotional scheme, a soap manufacturer offers a first prize of \$50,000 and a second prize of \$10,000 to anyone willing to try a new product (distributed without charge) and send in his name on the label. The winners will be drawn at random in front of a large television audience.

(a) What would be each entrant's mathematical expectation, if 1,500,000 persons were to send in their names?
(b) Would this make it worthwhile to spend the 6 cents postage it costs to send in an entry?

2. A jeweler wants to "unload" 5 watches that cost him \$80.00 each and 45 watches that cost him \$12.00 each. If he wraps these watches in identically-shaped unmarked boxes and lets each customer take his pick, find

(a) each customer's mathematical expectation;
(b) the jeweler's expected profit per customer, if he charges \$25.00 for the privilege of taking a pick.

3. The two finalists in a bowling tournament play one 3-game series, with the winner getting \$5,000 and the runner-up getting \$2,000. What are the two players' mathematical expectations if

(a) they are evenly matched;
(b) the better player should be favored by odds of 3 to 1?

4. A contractor is bidding on a road construction job which promises a profit of \$40,000 with a probability of 0.60 or a loss of \$15,000 (due to faulty estimates, strikes, late delivery of materials, etc.) with a probability of 0.40. What is the contractor's mathematical expectation?

5. The probability that someone will sell his house at a profit of \$3,000 is 0.06, the probability that he will sell it at a profit of \$1,000 is 0.24, the probability that he will break even is 0.29, the probability that he will sell it at a loss of \$1,000 is 0.23, and the probability that he will sell it at a loss of \$2,000 is 0.18. What is his expected profit or loss?

6. If it is extremely cold in the East a guest ranch in Arizona will have 120 guests during the Christmas season; if it is cold (but not extremely cold) in the East they will have 104 guests, and if the weather is moderate in the East they will have only 75 guests. How many guests can they expect if the probabilities for extremely cold, cold, or moderate weather in the East are, respectively, 0.32, 0.54, and 0.14?

7. If the two league champions are evenly matched, the probabilities that a "best of seven" basketball play-off will take 4, 5, 6, or 7 games are, respectively, 1/8, 1/4, 5/16, and 5/16. Under these conditions, how many games can we expect such a play-off to last?

8. As we explained on page 497, a *pure endowment* is a policy which pays a person a specified amount after a fixed number of years *provided he is still alive.*

(a) Explain why the single net premium a person of age x has to pay for a pure endowment paying A dollars after n years is

$$A\left(1+\frac{i}{m}\right)^{-mn}\cdot\left(\frac{l_{x+n}}{l_x}\right)$$

where the interest rate is i, compounded m times a year.

(b) Find the net single premium for a 15-year pure endowment of \$50,000 issued to a person aged 45, if money pays 5 percent compounded annually. [*Hint:* use Table XI in this part and also in parts (c) and (d).]

(c) Find the net single premium for a 10-year pure endowment of \$12,000 issued to a person aged 32, if money pays 4 percent compounded quarterly.

(d) Find the net single premium for an 18-year pure endowment of \$8,000 issued to a person aged 47, if money pays 6 percent compounded semi-annually.

9. A person aged 60 wants to buy an annuity which will provide annual payments of \$6,000 from his 61st through 70th birthdays, inclusive, provided in each case that he is still alive. If the interest rate is 0.04 compounded annually, what single net premium will he have to pay for this *temporary ordinary life annuity?*

10. A person aged 50 wants to buy an annuity which will provide annual payments of \$10,000 from his 65th through 70th birthdays, inclusive, provided in each case that he is still alive. If the interest rate is 0.03 compounded semi-annually, what single net premium will he have to pay for this *temporary deferred life annuity?*

11. MATHEMATICAL EXPECTATIONS AND SUBJECTIVE PROBABILITIES. The following example illustrates how mathematical expectations can be used to determine subjective probabilities: suppose we let a friend choose his own birthday present by either accepting an outright gift of \$5.00 or by accepting a gamble on the outcome of a football game, where he is to receive \$20.00 if his team wins or ties and nothing if it loses. Now then, if he feels that his team's chances of winning or tying are given by the probability p, the mathematical expectation of the gamble is

$$E = 20p + 0(1 - p) = 20p$$

and if he prefers this to the outright gift of \$5.00, we can argue that $20p > 5$ and, hence, that $p > \frac{5}{20}$ (namely, that p is greater than 1/4). Similarly, if he prefers the outright gift of \$5.00, we can argue that $20p < 5$ and, hence, that $p < \frac{5}{20}$ (namely, that p is less than 1/4); finally, if he cannot make up his mind, we can argue that $20p = 5$ and, hence, that he really feels that his team's chances are given by a probability of 1/4.

(a) A recent college graduate is faced by a decision which cannot wait, namely, that of accepting or rejecting a job paying \$7,800 a year. What can we say about the probability which he assigns to his only other prospect, a job paying \$11,700 a year, if he decides to take the \$7,800 job?

(b) An insurance company agrees to pay the promoter of a rodeo \$4,000 in case the event has to be cancelled because of rain. If the company's actuary feels that a fair net premium for this insurance would be \$640.00, what probability does he assign to the prospect that the rodeo will have to be cancelled because of rain?

(c) A playwright is offered the option of either taking an immediate cash payment of \$5,000 for his script, or gambling on the success of the play—in which case he will receive \$20,000 if it is a success and only a token fee of \$1,000 if it fails. What can we say about the probability which he assigns to the success of the play if he is willing to take the risk?

12. MATHEMATICAL EXPECTATIONS AND THE MEASUREMENT OF UTILITY. Mathematical expectations can also be used to measure the utility which a person assigns to anything of value (even intangibles). Suppose, for instance, that a music lover claims that he would "give his right arm" for a ticket to a concert which has been sold out for weeks. To see how far he might go, suppose furthermore that we propose the following deal: *for* \$10.00 *we will* *let him draw one of* 10 *sealed envelopes,* 9 *of which contain a dollar bill while the other one contains a ticket to the concert.* If the utility, or "cash value," he assigns to the ticket equals U, the mathematical expectation of the gamble is

$$U \cdot (0.1) + (\$1.00) \cdot (0.9)$$

and if he considers this gamble worth *at least* \$10.00, we can argue that

$$U \cdot (0.1) + (\$1.00) \cdot (0.9) > \$10.00$$

and, hence, that $U \cdot (0.1) > \$9.10$ and $U > \$91.00$. Thus, we have found that he feels this concert ticket is worth *at least* \$91.00, and if we varied the odds and the amounts (the number of envelopes and the amounts which they contain) we could narrow it down more than that.

(a) Mr. Green has the choice of staying home and reading a good book or going to a party. If he goes to the party he might have a terrible time (to which he assigns a utility of 0), or he might have a wonderful time (to which he assigns a utility of 40 units). If he feels that the odds against his having a good time are 8 to 2 and he decides not to go, what can we say about the utility which he assigns to staying home and reading a good book?

(b) Mr. Jones would love to beat Mr. Brown in an upcoming tennis tournament, but his chances are nill unless he takes \$400.00 worth of extra lessons, which (according to the tennis pro at his club) will give him a fifty-fifty chance. If Mr. Jones assigns the utility U to his beating Mr. Brown and the utility $-\frac{1}{5}U$ to his losing to Mr. Brown, find U if Mr. Jones decides that it is just about worthwhile to spend the \$400.00 on extra lessons.

(c) It is a well-known fact that the utility which a person assigns to money is not necessarily its *monetary* value. To a college student who needs money to take his girlfriend to a dance, \$20.00 would be worth *more than twenty times* \$1.00 (which wouldn't be enough even to buy tickets); on the other hand, to someone who has been very successful in business, the second million may very well *not be worth as much* as the first. If the utility which a certain person assigns to money equals its monetary value up to \$10.00, what can we say about the utility he assigns to \$100.00, if he *turns down* the privilege of paying \$6.00 for drawing one of 20 sealed envelopes of which 10 contain \$1.00, 9 contain \$2.00, and the other one contains \$100.00?

17.3 DECISION MAKING

When we are faced by uncertainties, mathematical expectations can often be used to a great advantage in making decisions. Generally speaking, if we have to choose between several alternatives, it is considered "rational" to select the one with the "most promising" mathematical expectation: the one which *maximizes expected profits, minimizes expected costs, maximizes expected tax advantages, minimizes expected losses,* and so on.

Although this approach to decision making has great intuitive appeal and sounds very logical, it is not without complications—there are many problems in which it is hard, if not impossible, to assign values to all of the a's (amounts) and all of the p's (probabilities) in the formula for E on page 498. To illustrate some of these difficulties, let us consider the following situation: Mr. Mason, the director of research and development of a large textile manufacturer, must decide to either terminate a project for the development of a new synthetic fiber, or to authorize funds for its continuation. If the project is continued and turns out to be successful, this will be worth \$100,000 to Mr. Mason's company; if it is continued but proves to be unsuccessful, this will entail a loss of \$60,000. If the project is abandoned but another company successfully develops the fiber, this will entail a loss of \$40,000 to Mr. Mason's company (partly, for being put at a competitive disadvantage); finally, if the project is abandoned and nobody else finds it possible to develop the fiber, there is a gain of \$10,000 (accounted for by funds allocated to the project which remained unspent). Schematically, all this information can be summarized as follows:

	The fiber can be developed	*The fiber cannot be developed*
The project is continued	100,000	−60,000
The project is terminated	−40,000	10,000

Obviously, it will be better to continue the project if and only if the fiber can be developed, and Mr. Mason's decision will therefore have to depend on his own evaluation of the chances that it can be done. Suppose, for example, that (on the basis of many years of experience) he judges the odds to be 3 to 2 *against* the project's success; in other words, he assigns the project's success the probability $\frac{2}{2+3} = 0.40$, and its failure the probability $\frac{3}{2+3} = 0.60$. He can then argue that *if the project is continued,* the company's *expected gain* is

$$100{,}000(0.40) + (-60{,}000)(0.60) = \$4{,}000$$

and *if the project is terminated,* the company's *expected gain* is

$$(-40{,}000)(0.40) + 10{,}000(0.60) = -\$10{,}000$$

Since an *expected gain* of \$4,000 is obviously preferable to an *expected loss* (negative gain) of \$10,000, it stands to reason that Mr. Mason should not hesitate in deciding to continue the project. *Or should he?* What if he was a bit hasty in assessing the odds as 3 to 2 against the project's success? What if the odds should have been 4 to 1 against the project's success, or perhaps only 2 to 1? The point we are trying to make is that *one should use mathematical expectations as criteria for making decisions only if one is good at assessing odds, namely, if one's probabilities (or probability estimates) are "correct" (or at least close)*. As the reader will be asked to verify in Exercise 2 on page 508, Mr. Mason should decide to terminate the project when the odds against its success are 4 to 1, and the whole situation is a toss-up when the odds against the project's success are 2 to 1.

To go on with the analysis, let us suppose that the 3 to 2 odds against the project's success are correct, but let us add another alternative: if the project is continued for another month at a cost of \$20,000, it will then be known *for sure* whether the fiber can be made. Thus, Mr. Mason is faced with the problem of having to decide whether it is worthwhile to spend this fairly large amount of money before reaching a final decision. One way of handling this kind of situation is to determine what is called the *expected value of perfect information.* If he knew for sure whether or not the fiber can be made, Mr. Mason could act accordingly and assure his company either a gain of \$100,000 (when the fiber can be made) or a gain of \$10,000 (when the fiber cannot be made); using the same probabilities as before, namely, 0.40 and 0.60, he finds that the *expected gain* of the company would thus become

$$100{,}000(0.40) + 10{,}000(0.60) = \$46{,}000$$

and this is what we call the *expected value of perfect information.* In general, *the expected value of perfect information is the amount one can expect to gain (profit, or win) in any given situation provided one always makes the right decision.* So far as Mr. Mason is concerned, we have shown that he can increase his company's *expected gain* from \$4,000 (corresponding to his decision to continue the project) to \$46,000 (corresponding to his delaying his decision for a month at a cost of \$20,000). Since this increase *exceeds* \$20,000, the *cost of getting the perfect information,* it stands to reason that he should decide to continue the project for another month. In fact, it would have been worthwhile to continue the project for another month (and then know for sure whether the fiber can be made) so long as the extra cost is less than \$46,000 − \$4,000 = \$42,000.

The way in which we have studied this problem is referred to as a *Bayesian analysis.* In this kind of analysis, probabilities are assigned to the conditions about which uncertainties exist (the so-called "states of Nature," which in our example are the possibility or impossibility of making the fiber); *then, the alternative which is ultimately decided upon is the one which has the greatest expected profit or gain.* As we saw in our example, a Bayesian analysis can also include the possibility of delaying any final action until further information is obtained. This is of special importance in statistics, where we generally deal with sample data obtained from surveys or experiments, and may have to decide how large a sample to take, whether a given sample is adequate for reaching a decision, or whether further observations will have to be made.

Let us now examine briefly what Mr. Mason might have done in our example if he had had no idea whatsoever about the project's chances for success, and, hence, could not have based his decision on mathematical expectations. To suggest one possibility, suppose that Mr. Mason is a *confirmed optimist;* looking at the situation through rose-colored glasses, he notes that if the project is continued the company might gain as much as $100,000, whereas the decision to terminate the project could lead at best to a gain of $10,000. Always expecting the best (perhaps, in the sense of wishful thinking), Mr. Mason would thus decide to continue the project, and we might say that by doing so he is *maximizing the company's maximum gain.* (In other words, he is choosing the alternative for which the company's greatest possible gain is a maximum.)

Now suppose that Mr. Mason is a *confirmed pessimist;* looking at the situation through dark-colored glasses, he notes that if the project is continued the company might lose as much as $60,000, whereas the decision to terminate the project could lead at worst to a loss of $40,000. Always expecting the worst (perhaps, in the sense of fear or resignation), Mr. Mason would thus decide to terminate the project, and we might say that by doing so he is *minimizing the company's maximum losses.* (In other words, he is choosing the alternative for which the company's greatest losses are a minimum, and we refer to this as the *minimax criterion.*)

There are various other ways in which decisions can be made in the absence of any knowledge about the probabilities of the various "states of Nature." Suppose, for example, that Mr. Mason is the kind of person who is always afraid to *lose out on a good deal.* This might lead him to the argument that if he decided to continue the project and it turned out unsuccessful, his company would have been better off by $10{,}000 - (-60{,}000) = \$70{,}000$ if he had terminated the project in the first place; also, if he decided to terminate the project and it turned out that it could have been successful, his company would have been better off by $100{,}000 - (-40{,}000) = \$140{,}000$ if he had continued the project. These differences are generally referred to as *opportunity losses* (or *regrets*), and the whole situation can be pictured as follows:

	The fiber can be developed	*The fiber cannot be developed*
The project is continued	0	70,000
The project is terminated	140,000	0

To explain the two 0's, note that when the project is continued and it turns out that the fiber can be developed *there is no loss of opportunity;* the same is true also in the case where the project is terminated and it turns out that the fiber could not have been developed anyhow. Now, if Mr. Mason were the kind of person who always wants to hold his opportunity losses to a minimum, he would probably apply the *minimax criterion* (namely, choose the alternative for which the greatest opportunity loss is a minimum) and decide that the project should be continued.

There are also situations where the various criteria which we have discussed are outweighed by other considerations. Suppose, for instance, that Mr. Mason has discovered that he will be fired unless the project turns out to be a success. In that case he would be foolish (though, perhaps, unselfish) not to continue the project, which at least would have given him a chance. The situation would be quite different if he discovered that he will be fired if the company loses more than $50,000 on the project. In that case he could *play it safe* by terminating the project, and this may well outweigh all other considerations. Other examples of situations in which extraneous factors play important roles in making decisions are given in Exercises 6 and 7 on page 510, and it is hoped that they will make it clear that *there is no universal rule or criterion which will always lead to the best possible decision.*

Earlier in this section, we pointed out that it is sometimes difficult to base decisions on mathematical expectations, since this requires knowledge of all the a's (amounts) and p's (probabilities) in the formula for E on page 498. As we indicated on page 505, different probabilities assigned to the "states of Nature" can lead to different decisions (see also Exercise 2 on page 508), and in Exercise 4 on page 509 the reader will be asked to show that the same is true also for changes in the "pay-offs," namely, changes in the a's. We did not worry about this in the example in the text, assuming that the figures in the table on page 504 were given correctly by the company's accountants. Generally speaking, though, the problem of assigning "cash values" to the consequences of one's decisions can pose serious difficulties, and this is true, especially, when the consequences involve such intangibles as the overall effects of a bankruptcy, the pleasure a person may get from playing cards even if he does not win, the possible side-effects of a new drug, the emotional effects of a broken home, the satisfaction a salesman may get from making a sale, and so on. The whole problem of assigning numerical *utilities* (or *desirabilities*) to the consequences of one's actions is not an easy one, but it is not insolvable, as we saw in Exercise 12 on page 502.

EXERCISES

1. The Board of Regents of a university is faced with the problem of having to decide whether to authorize funds for the construction of a new football stadium. They are told that if the new stadium is built and the university has a good football team, there will be a profit of $410,000; if the new stadium is built and the university has a poor football team, there will be a deficit of $100,000; if the old stadium is used and the university has a good football team, there will be a profit of $200,000; and if the old stadium is used and the university has a poor football team, there will be a profit of $20,000 (mostly from games played away from home).

(a) Present all this information in a table like the one on page 504.
(b) Believing their athletic director when he tells them that the odds are 2 to 1 that they will *not* have a good football team, what should the regents decide so as to maximize the expected profit?
(c) Believing the sports editor of the local newspaper who tells them that the odds are 3 to 2 that they will *not* have a good football team, what should the regents decide so as to maximize the expected profit?
(d) If Regent Moore is a confirmed pessimist, which way would he be inclined to vote? Explain your answer.
(e) If Regent Wilson is a confirmed optimist, which way would he be inclined to vote? Explain your answer.
(f) Construct a table like the one on page 507 showing the opportunity losses associated with the various possibilities. What action should the regents take if they wanted to hold the greatest possible opportunity losses to a minimum? Using the odds of part (b), what should the regents do so as to minimize their *expected opportunity losses?*
(g) Using the odds of part (b), what is the expected value of perfect information? Would it be worthwhile to pay an "infallible" forecaster $10,000 to tell them for sure whether the university will have a good football team?

2. Referring to the example in the text, find the company's expected gains corresponding to the project being continued and being terminated, if

(a) the odds against its success are 4 to 1;
(b) the odds against its success are 2 to 1.

In each case state which decision would maximize the company's expected gain.

3. Mr. Nolan is planning to attend a sales meeting in Scottsdale, Arizona, and he must send in his room reservation immediately. The sales meeting is so large that the activities are held partly in Hotel A and partly in Hotel B, and Mr. Nolan does not know whether the particular session he wants to attend will be held at Hotel A or Hotel B. He is planning to stay only one day, which would cost him \$21.00 at Hotel A and \$18.00 at Hotel B, but it will cost him an extra \$5.00 for cab fare if he stays at the wrong hotel.

(a) Present all this information in a table like the one on page 504.
(b) Where should he make his reservation if he wants to minimize his expected expenses and feels that the odds are 5 to 1 that the session he wants to attend will be held at Hotel A?
(c) Where should he make his reservation if the odds quoted in part (b) should have been 2 to 1 instead of 5 to 1?
(d) Where should he make his reservation if the odds quoted in part (b) should have been 4 to 1 instead of 5 to 1?
(e) Where should he make his reservation if he were a confirmed optimist?
(f) Where should he make his reservation if he were a confirmed pessimist?
(g) Referring to the odds of part (b), what is the *expected value of perfect information?* Would it be worthwhile to spend \$1.50 on a long-distance call to find out where the session will be held?
(h) Where should he make his reservation if he wants to minimize the greatest possible loss of opportunity?

4. Referring to the example in the text, suppose that the accounting department discovers the following mistake: if the project is abandoned and nobody else finds it possible to develop the fiber, there is a gain of \$35,000 (instead of \$10,000) due to unused funds. Recalculate the company's *expected gains* corresponding to the project being continued or terminated, and check whether this will affect Mr. Mason's *original* decision. (Use the same odds as on page 504.)

5. A dinner guest wants to show his appreciation to his hostess by sending her either a pound of candy or a bottle of wine. He remembers, though, that she is either on a strict reducing diet or a teetotaler, but he can't remember which. In any case, he feels that her reaction to his gift will be as shown in the following table, where the numbers are in *units of "appreciation:"*

	Hostess is dieting	*Hostess is teetotaler*
Take candy	−3	5
Take wine	2	−10

(a) What should he take so as to maximize the *expected appreciation* of his gift, if he feels that the odds are 2 to 1 that the hostess is a teetotaler rather than dieting?
(b) What should he take so as to maximize the *expected appreciation* of his gift, if he feels that the odds are 7 to 1 that the hostess is dieting rather than a teetotaler?
(c) What should he do so as to maximize the *expected appreciation* if he feels

that the odds are 3 to 1 that the hostess is dieting rather than a teetotaler? (Careful!)

(d) Using the odds of part (b), what is the expected value of perfect information? Would it be worth a $2.00 long-distance phone call to find out whether she is dieting or a teetotaler? (Assume that each unit of appreciation is equivalent to $1.00.)

(e) What should he do if he wanted to minimize the greatest possible loss of opportunity?

6. About a month before the scheduled harvesting of his citrus crop, Mr. Lewis has to decide whether to accept a firm offer for his crop which will yield him a profit of $45,000. If he does not sell now but waits till after the crop has been harvested, he figures that he can make a profit of $60,000 provided there will be no frost; however, if there is a frost, he will suffer a loss of $30,000.

(a) What should he do if he wants to maximize his expected profit and feels that the probability for a frost is 1/2?

(b) What should he do if he wants to maximize his expected profit and feels that the probability for a frost is 1/10?

(c) What should he do if he wants to minimize the greatest possible loss of opportunity?

(d) What should he do if he owed a bank $40,000 and would have to go out of business unless the loan can be repaid?

(e) What should he do if he owed a bank $55,000 and would have to go out of business unless the loan can be repaid?

7. A contractor has to choose between two jobs. The first job promises a profit of $240,000 with a probability of 3/4 or a loss of $60,000 (due to strikes and other delays) with a probability of 1/4; the second job promises a profit of $360,000 with a probability of 1/2 or a loss of $90,000 with a probability of 1/2.

(a) Which job should the contractor choose if he wants to maximize his expected profit?

(b) Which job would the contractor probably choose if his business is in fairly bad shape and he will go broke unless he can make a profit of at least $300,000 on his next job?

17.4 GAMES OF STRATEGY

The example of the preceding section may well have given the impression that Mr. Mason was playing a game—a game between Mr. Mason and *Nature* as his opponent. In fact, on page 505 we actually referred to the two alternatives concerning the feasibility of making the fiber as "states of Nature." Each of the "players" in the game had the choice of two moves: Mr. Mason had the choice of terminating the project or authorizing its continuation, and Nature controlled whether or not the fiber could actually be made. Depending on the choice of their moves there were certain *payoffs*—the figures shown in the table on page 504.

This analogy is not at all far-fetched; the problem we have been discussing is typical of the kind of situation treated in the *Theory of Games*, a relatively new branch of mathematics which has stimulated considerable interest in recent years. This theory is not limited to parlor games, as its name might suggest, but it applies to any kind of competitive situation which might arise in business, in social interactions (between nations, individuals, political parties, etc.), and even in the conduct of a war.

To introduce some of the basic concepts of the Theory of Games, let us begin by explaining what we mean by a *zero-sum two-person game*. The "two-person" means that there are two players (or, more generally, two parties with conflicting interests), and the "zero-sum" means that whatever one player wins the other one loses. Thus, in a zero-sum game there is no "cut for the house" as in professional gambling, and no capital is created or destroyed during the course of play.

Games are also classified according to the number of *strategies* (moves, choices, or alternatives) each player has at his disposal. For instance, if each player has to choose one of two alternatives, we say that they are playing a 2 × 2 game (where 2 × 2 reads "two by two"); if one player has 3 possible moves while the other has 4, we say that they are playing a 3 × 4 game, and so on. In this book we shall consider only *finite games*, that is, games in which each player has a finite, or fixed, number of possible moves.

It is customary in Game Theory to refer to the two players as Player A and Player B, with the possible strategies (moves, choices, or alternatives) of Player A labeled I, II, III, IV, . . . , and those of Player B labeled 1, 2, 3, 4, . . . The amounts of money which change hands when the players choose their respective strategies are usually shown as in the following kind of table called a *payoff matrix:*

		Player A	
		I	II
Player B	1	5	−6
	2	6	8

Here *positive amounts* represent payments which Player A makes to Player B, and *negative amounts* (for instance, the −6 in the above table) represent payments which Player B makes to Player A. Thus, if Player A chooses Strategy I in this example and Player B chooses Strategy 1, then Player A

has to pay 5 (say, dollars) to Player B; if Player A chooses Strategy II and Player B chooses Strategy 1, then Player B has to pay 6 (dollars) to Player A.

In actual practice, games such as baseball, chess, bridge, or Monopoly are described by listing the respective rules according to which these games are played. We describe the pieces (or other kinds of equipment) being used, the way in which they are manipulated, and sometimes we say whether there are any penalties or rewards depending on what happens during the course of play. All this is important, of course, if we actually want to play one of these games, but its analysis in the Theory of Games requires only that we list the strategies available to each player and the corresponding payoff amounts. Although it does not really matter, we shall assume here that all payoffs are in dollars; in actual practice, they could be expressed in terms of any goods or services, units of utility (desirability, or satisfaction), or even in terms of life or death (as in Russian roulette). It will also be assumed that *each player has to choose his strategy without knowledge of what his opponent has done or is planning to do, and that once a player has made his choice, it cannot be changed.*

The objectives of the Theory of Games are to determine *optimum strategies* (namely, strategies which are most profitable to the respective players), and the corresponding payoff, which is called the *value* of the game. To illustrate, let us return to the game on page 511 which is characterized by the *payoff matrix*

		Player A	
		I	II
Player B	1	5	−6
	2	6	8

As can be seen by inspection, it would be foolish for Player B to choose Strategy 1, since Strategy 2 will yield more than Strategy 1 *regardless of the choice made by Player A*. (Strategy 2 yields 6 rather than 5 when Player A chooses Strategy I, and it yields 8 rather than −6 when Player A chooses Strategy II.) In a situation like this we say that Strategy 1 *is dominated by* Strategy 2 (or that Strategy 2 *dominates* Strategy 1), and it stands to reason that any strategy which is dominated by another should be eliminated (ignored or crossed out). If we do this in our example, we find that Player B's *optimum strategy* is Strategy 2, the only one left, and that Player A's *optimum strategy* is Strategy I, which makes him lose \$6.00 rather than \$8.00; the value of the game is the corresponding payoff, namely, \$6.00.

To consider another example, suppose that the payoffs of a 3×2 zero-sum two-person game are as shown in the following table

		Player A		
		I	II	III
Player B	1	−3	2	8
	2	5	4	6

Thus, Player A has three different moves, Player B has two, and all but one of the payoffs go from Player A to Player B; the -3 indicates that if Player A chooses Strategy I and Player B chooses Strategy 1, then Player B must pay \$3.00 to Player A. In this game neither strategy of Player B dominates the other (5 is greater than -3, 4 is greater than 2, yet 6 is less than 8), but it can be seen that the third strategy of Player A is dominated by each of the other two; that is, Player A's third strategy is worse than either of the other two *regardless of what Player B decides to do.* (Clearly, 8 is greater than -3 as well as 2, *and* 6 is greater than 5 as well as 4.) Thus, we can cross out the third column of the table, getting

−3	2
5	4

and we now find that Strategy 2 of Player B dominates his Strategy 1. (Evidently, 5 is greater than -3, and 4 is greater than 2.) It follows that Player B's *optimum choice* is Strategy 2, and since Player A would obviously prefer to lose \$4.00 rather than \$5.00, his *optimum choice* is Strategy II. The value of this game is the payoff corresponding to Strategies 2 and II (namely, \$4.00).

The process of discarding dominated strategies can be of great help in finding the solution of a game (namely, in finding optimum strategies and the value of a game), but *what do we do when no dominances exist?* To illustrate one possibility, consider the following 3×3 zero-sum two-person game:

		Player A		
		I	II	III
	1	−2	5	−3
Player B	2	1	3	5
	3	−3	−7	11

where, as before, each player must select one of his strategies without knowledge of the other's choice. As can easily be verified, there are no dominances among the strategies of either player, but if we look at the problem from Player A's point of view, we might argue as follows: if he chooses Strategy I, the worst that can happen is that he loses \$1.00; if he chooses Strategy II, the worst that can happen is that he loses \$5.00; and if he chooses Strategy III, the worst that can happen is that he loses \$11.00. Looking at the problem from this rather *pessimistic* point of view, it would seem advantageous to Player A if he *minimized his maximum losses* by choosing Strategy I. Using the terminology introduced on page 506, we are thus suggesting that Player A apply the *minimax criterion* to the losses he might incur.

If we apply the same kind of argument to select a strategy for Player B, we find that if he chooses Strategy 1, the most he can lose is \$3.00; if he chooses Strategy 2, the worst that can happen is that he wins \$1.00; and if he chooses Strategy 3, the most he can lose is \$7.00. Thus, Player B would *minimize his maximum losses* (or *maximize his minimum gain,* which is the same) by choosing Strategy 2.

The selection of Strategies I and 2, appropriately called *minimax strategies,* is really quite reasonable. By choosing Strategy I, Player A makes sure that his opponent can win at most \$1.00, and by choosing Strategy 2, Player B makes sure that he actually does win this amount. Thus, the value of the game is \$1.00, which means that it favors Player B, but we could easily make it "equitable" by charging Player B a dollar for the privilege of playing the game, while letting Player A play for free.

A very important aspect of minimax strategies is that they are completely "spyproof" in the sense that neither player can profit from any knowledge about the other's choice of strategies. Even if Player B announced publicly that he is going to choose Strategy 2, it would still be best for Player A to choose Strategy I, and the same is true for Player B if Player A announced that he is going to choose Strategy I.

Unfortunately, the method by which we solved this last example does not always work (that is, it does not work for every finite zero-sum two-person game), but at least there exists a criterion by which we can decide for any given game whether minimax strategies are really spyproof. What we have to look for are *saddle points,* namely, pairs of strategies for which the corresponding entry in the payoff matrix is *the smallest value of its row and the greatest value of its column* (see Exercises 2 and 3 on page 518). In the preceding example, the entry which corresponds to Strategies I and 2 *is* the smallest value of its row (1 is less than 3 or 5) and the greatest value of its column (1 is greater than -2 or -3), and, hence, it *is* a saddle point. Note that there can be more than one saddle point in a given game (see

Exercise 4 on page 519), but in that case it does not matter which one we use in selecting the optimum strategies of the two players.

If there is no saddle point, the method of the preceding example will not work, and we shall have to look for other ways of determining optimum strategies for the two players. To illustrate, let us consider the 2×2 zero-sum two-person game which is characterized by the following payoff matrix:

		Player A I	*Player A* II
Player B	1	10	−3
	2	4	8

Since the smallest values of the two rows are −3 and 4, which are *not* the greatest values of their respective columns, *there is no saddle point*, but if we applied the same sort of reasoning as in the preceding example, we might argue that so far as Player *A* is concerned, a maximum loss of $8.00 is preferable to a maximum loss of $10.00, and, hence, that Strategy II is preferable to Strategy I. Similarly, Player *B* might choose Strategy 2, arguing that a minimum gain of $4.00 is preferable to a possible loss of $3.00. If Players *A* and *B* actually used these *minimax strategies*, the payoff would be $8.00, which should come as a very pleasant surprise to Player *B*—it is more than the minimum gain of $4.00 which he tried to assure for himself by choosing Strategy 2. So far as Player *A* is concerned, things turned out as expected, but had he known that Player *B* always chooses minimax strategies (and, hence, that he would choose Strategy 2), he could have chosen Strategy I and thus held his losses down to $4.00. This would have worked nicely, unless *B* had been smart enough to reason that this is precisely what Player *A* intends to do; he could then have played Strategy 1 and won $10.00. *This argument can be continued ad infinitum.* If Player *A* thought that Player *B* would try to outsmart him by choosing Strategy 1, he could in turn try to outsmart Player *B* by choosing Strategy II and winning $3.00; if Player *B* thought that this is precisely what Player *A* would do, he would only have to switch to Strategy 2 to assure himself a payoff of $8.00; and so on, and so on.

An important aspect of this example is that the minimax strategies are *not spyproof*, and that one player can outsmart the other if he knows how his opponent will react in a given situation. To avoid this possibility, it suggests itself that each player should somehow *mix up his strategies intentionally*, and the best way of doing this is by introducing an element of chance into his final selection. Suppose, for instance, that Player *B* used a gambling device [dice, cards, numbered slips of paper, or so-called *random numbers* (see Section 18.3)] which leads to the choice of Strategy 1 with the probability x, and to the choice of Strategy 2 with the probability $1 - x$. He could then argue as follows: *if Player A chooses Strategy I*, he (Player B) can *expect* to win

$$E = 10x + 4(1 - x)$$

and *if Player A chooses Strategy II*, he (Player B) can *expect* to win

$$E = -3x + 8(1 - x)$$

Graphically, this situation is described in Figure 17.1, where we have plotted the two lines whose equations are

$$E = 10x + 4(1 - x) \qquad \text{and} \qquad E = -3x + 8(1 - x)$$

for values of x from 0 to 1. (Actually, we plotted these two lines by connecting the respective values of E which correspond to $x = 0$ and $x = 1$.)

Now suppose that we apply the *minimax criterion* to the expected winnings of Player B. (Actually, we shall *maximize minimum gains* rather than *minimize maximum losses*, but this amounts to the same thing, and it doesn't really matter whether we refer to the criterion as *minimax* or *maximin*.) By studying Figure 17.1, we find that *the least* Player B can expect to win (namely, the smaller of the two values of E for any given value of x) is *greatest* where the two lines intersect, and to find the corres-

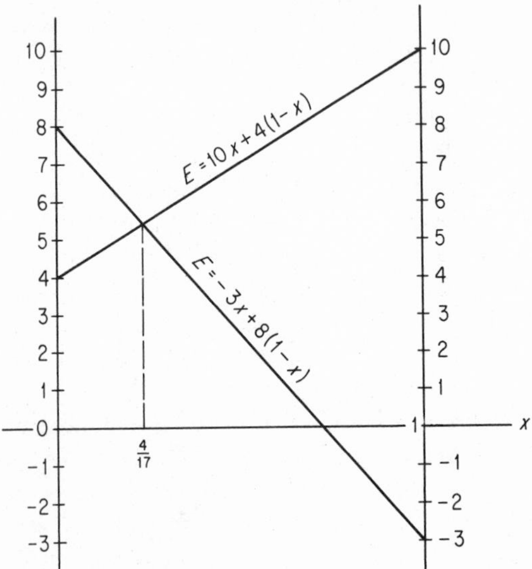

FIG. 17.1

ponding value of x we have only to put $10x + 4(1 - x)$ equal to $-3x + 8(1 - x)$, and solve for x. Thus, we get

$$\begin{aligned} 10x + 4(1 - x) &= -3x + 8(1 - x) \\ 10x + 4 - 4x &= -3x + 8 - 8x \\ 17x &= 4 \end{aligned}$$

and, finally,

$$x = \frac{4}{17}$$

This means that if Player B labels 4 slips of paper "Strategy 1," 13 slips of paper "Strategy 2," shuffles them thoroughly, and then acts according to which kind he randomly selects, he will be applying the *minimax principle* to his *expected winnings*, and he will be assuring for himself *expected winnings* of

$$10\left(\frac{4}{17}\right) + 4\left(\frac{13}{17}\right) = 5\frac{7}{17}$$

or \$5.41 to the nearest cent.

If a player's ultimate choice is thus left to chance, his overall strategy is referred to as *randomized* or *mixed.* Note that the *optimum mixed strategy* (with $x = 4/17$) assures Player B expected winnings of \$5.41, whereas the direct choice of one of his *pure strategies* (Strategy 1 or Strategy 2) guarantees him at best minimum winnings of \$4.00. So far as Player A is concerned, the analysis is very much the same; as the reader will be asked to show in Exercise 8 on page 519, Player A can minimize his maximum expected losses by choosing between Strategies I and II with respective probabilities of 11/17 and 6/17, and he will thus be holding his expected losses down to $5\frac{7}{17}$ or approximately \$5.41. Incidentally, the \$5.41 to which Player B can *raise his expected winnings* and to which Player A can *hold down his expected losses* is again called the *value* of the game.

The examples of this section were all given without any "physical" interpretation, and this was done mainly because most games that are of any practical importance involve so many possible moves (strategies) that their analysis requires a prohibitive amount of work. In any case, we were interested mainly in introducing some of the mathematical concepts that are basic to the Theory of Games. Had we studied the "real" decision problem of Section 17.3 as if it were a 2×2 zero-sum two-person game, we would have arrived at the conclusion that Mr. Mason should randomize his decision and choose between continuing or terminating the project with respective probabilities of $\frac{5}{21}$ and $\frac{16}{21}$ (see Exercise 9 on page 520). His company's *expected losses* would then be \$6,667, and this is much better than the potential losses of $60,000 and $40,000 to which he is exposed by either of his pure strategies. Of course, this assumes that Mr. Mason has no idea about the probability that the fiber can be made. It must be remembered, also, that this game-theoretical analysis of the problem assumes that Nature (which controls whether or not the fiber can be made) is a *malevolent opponent,* who is trying to make things as difficult as possible for Mr. Mason and his company. Whether or not this kind of assumption is reasonable can only be judged separately for each individual problem. In this case, let us say that Mr. Mason (being the director of research and development of the company) *should* have some idea about the feasibility of the project, and, hence, that the problem should be solved by the methods of Section 17.3.

EXERCISES

1. Each of the following is the payoff matrix (the payments Player A makes to Player B) for a zero-sum two-person game. Eliminate all dominated strategies and determine the best strategy for each player as well as the value of the game:

(a)

2	−3
4	6

(b)

8	5
10	−2

(c)

−2	3	6
−3	0	0
−9	2	4

(d)

0	3	1
1	1	4
0	−2	2

2. Find the saddle point of each of the games of Exercise 1. (*Hint:* determine the smallest value of each row and check whether it is also the largest value of its column.)

3. Each of the following is the payoff matrix (the payments Player A makes to Player B) for a zero-sum two-person game. Find the saddle point (or saddle points) as well as the value of each game.

(a)

4	−3	−2
2	0	−1
−5	4	−3

(b)

9	3	2	4
3	4	4	4
6	5	6	5
9	5	7	5

4. **SOME THEORY ABOUT SADDLE POINTS.** If a 3×3 zero-sum two-person game has a saddle point corresponding to Strategies I and 3 and another corresponding to Strategies III and 1, explain why there must also be a saddle point corresponding to Strategies I and 1 and another corresponding to Strategies III and 3, and that all four of these saddle points must have the same payoff.

5. The following is a payoff matrix of a zero-sum two-person game:

3	−4
−3	1

(a) What randomized strategy should Player A use so as to minimize his maximum expected losses?
(b) What randomized strategy should Player B use so as to maximize his minimum expected gain?
(c) What is the value of this game and whom does it favor?

6. First eliminate all dominated strategies and then determine the best randomized strategy of each player and the value of each of the following games:

(a)

−3	−5	5
5	2	−3
2	−2	8

(b)

3	2	7	12
10	9	5	10

Note that when a dominated strategy is eliminated, we are (so to speak) assigning it a probability of 0 in the overall randomized strategy.

7. The following is the payoff matrix of a zero-sum two-person game:

6	18	15
12	6	10

(a) Show that the third strategy of Player A is dominated by the strategy which consists of choosing between his first two strategies by flipping a coin.
(b) Making use of the result of part (a), that is, eliminating the third strategy of Player A, find optimum strategies for both players and the value of the game.

8. Referring to the example on page 516, show that Player A's optimum strategy is to choose between Strategies I and II with respective probabilities of 11/17 and 6/17.

9. Referring to the illustration of Section 17.3 and the table on page 504, show that Mr. Mason's optimum strategy is to randomize his decision and to choose between either continuing or terminating the project with respective probabilities of 5/21 and 16/21.

10. A country has two airfields with installations worth \$500,000 and \$2,000,000, respectively. It can defend only one of these airfields against an attack by its enemy. The enemy, on the other hand, can attack only one of these airfields, and can do so successfully only if the airfield is left undefended. Considering the payoff to the defending country to be the *total value* of the installations it holds after the attack, find the optimum strategies for that country and its enemy, and also the value of this "game." Explain why the "obvious" strategy of defending the more valuable airfield is not necessarily the best.

11. Two friends agree to play the following game: the first writes either 9 or 4 on a slip of paper, and at the same time the other writes either 5 or 6 on a slip of paper. If S, the sum of the two numbers, is *even*, the first player wins $\frac{S}{2} - 5$ dollars from the second; if S is *odd*, the second player wins $8 - \frac{S}{3}$ dollars from the first.

(a) Find the best randomized strategy for each player.
(b) How much should the second player pay the first for the "privilege" of playing the game, so as to make the game equitable?

12. Referring to Exercise 3 on page 508, how should Mr. Nolan randomize his choice between the two hotels, so as to minimize his maximum expected expenses?

13. Referring to Exercise 5 on page 509, how should the dinner guest randomize his decision, so as to maximize the minimum expected appreciation of his gift? Would he be better off not taking any gift at all?

14. The supplier of glue used in the manufacture of a laminated fiberboard guarantees delivery on schedule, but he cannot say whether it will be Glue K, Glue L, or Glue M. Because of time requirements, however, the manufacturer must set up his production process before he knows which kind of glue he is going to receive. All three glues can be used with either of two production methods between which the manufacturer has to choose, but for technical reasons the unit profit differs substantially from one method to the other depending on which glue is being used. If the manufacturer gets Glue K, the unit profits will be \$1.60 and \$0.80, respectively, for the two methods of production; if he gets Glue L, the corresponding unit profits will be \$0.90 and \$1.10; and if he gets Glue M, the corresponding unit profits will be \$0.70 and \$1.50. *How should the manufacturer decide which production method to use so as to maximize his minimum expected unit profit?* [*Hint:* letting x be the probability that he chooses the first production method and $1 - x$ the probability that he chooses the second, draw three lines like those of Figure 17.1 (one for each kind of glue) and find the value of x for which the *smallest* of the corresponding values on the three lines is *as large as possible.*]

17.5 LINEAR PROGRAMMING AND THE SOLUTION OF A GAME

The examples of the preceding section were designed to introduce the reader to some of the basic ideas of the Theory of Games—payoff matrices, dominating strategies, saddle points, minimax solutions, pure and randomized strategies, and so on. Our illustrations were intentionally very simple since the only difference between simple and complicated zero-sum two-person games is in the amount of mathematical detail. As might be expected, though, further complications arise when a game is not "two-person" or "zero-sum," namely, when there are more than two players or when capital is created or destroyed during the course of play.

There are no general methods for handling all kinds of games, but there exists a systematic way of dealing with all *finite zero-sum two-person games* (which are sometimes also referred to as *rectangular games* or as *matrix games*). It is based on the fact that the solution of any finite zero-sum two-person game—namely, the determination of optimum strategies and the value of the game—can be translated into a *linear programming* problem, and hence can be handled by the methods of Chapters 8 and 10. To simplify matters, we shall demonstrate how this is done *only* for the 2×2 game on page 515, namely, the one whose payoff matrix is

		Player A I	*Player A* II
Player B	1	10	−3
	2	4	8

As on page 516, we shall let x denote the probability that Player B will choose Strategy 1, and $1 - x$ the probability that he will choose Strategy 2. Thus, Player B's expected gain is again $10x + 4(1 - x)$ when Player A chooses Strategy I, and $-3x + 8(1 - x)$ when Player A chooses Strategy II. If we now let z denote the *smaller* of these two expected gains (for a given value of x), we can write

$$10x + 4(1 - x) \geqslant z$$
$$-3x + 8(1 - x) \geqslant z$$

and it is to Player B's advantage to make z as large as possible, *since this would maximize his minimum expected gain.* In order to find this maximum value of z, let us change the first of these two inequalities into an equation by introducing a non-negative *slack variable* u (see Section 10.2). We thus get

$$10x + 4(1 - x) = z + u$$

and the quantity we shall want to maximize can be written as

$$z = 10x + 4(1 - x) - u = 6x - u + 4$$

The restriction imposed on x and u are $x \geqslant 0$ and $x \leqslant 1$ since x is a probability, $u \geqslant 0$ by assumption, and

$$-3x + 8(1 - x) \geqslant 10x + 4(1 - x) - u$$

This last inequality, which can also be written as

$$17x - u \leqslant 4$$

was obtained by substituting $10x + 4(1 - x) - u$ for z into the second of the original pair of inequalities (on page 521).

Observe that we have thus arrived at the following linear programming problem: *we must maximize the linear expression*

$$6x - u + 4$$

where x and u are subject to the linear restrictions

$$x \geqslant 0, \quad x \leqslant 1, \quad u \geqslant 0, \quad \text{and} \quad 17x - u \leqslant 4$$

From here on in, we can employ any one of the linear programming techniques which we studied in Chapters 8 and 10. For instance, the geometrical method of Section 8.2 yields the region of feasible solutions shown in Figure 17.2, and it can be seen that within this region $6x - u + 4$ is a maximum at the point (4/17, 0). (Evidently, it is up to this point that we

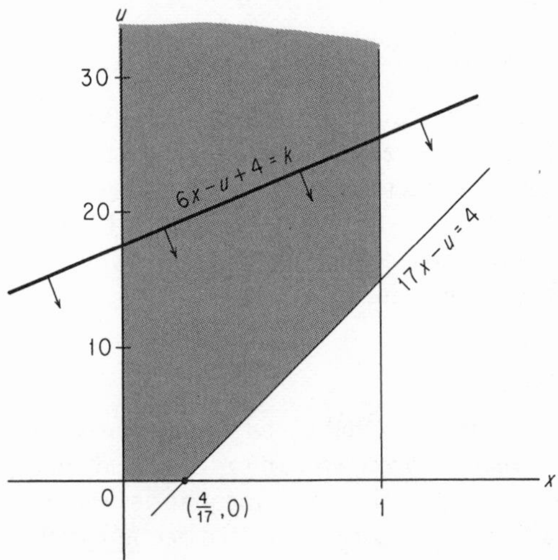

FIG. 17.2

can move the line $6x - u + 4 = k$ parallel to itself in the direction of the arrows and stay within the shaded region of feasible solutions.)

This agrees with the result obtained on page 517, where we showed by other means that Player B's optimum strategy is to assign the probabilities 4/17 and 13/17 to his choice of Strategies 1 and 2. The value of the game is the quantity we tried to maximize, namely, $6x - u + 4$, and for $x = 4/17$ and $u = 0$ it is equal to

$$6 \cdot \frac{4}{17} - 0 + 4 = 5\frac{7}{17}$$

This also agrees with the result which we obtained in Section 17.4. In Exercise 1 below, the reader will be asked to set up a linear programming problem, analogous to the one we have just solved, which will provide the corresponding optimum strategies for Player A.

The purpose of this section has been to illustrate *how* the solution of a finite zero-sum two-person game can be translated into a linear programming problem. Naturally, what we have done here is much more complicated than what we did with the same problem in Section 17.4, and ordinarily we would not use linear programming to solve a 2×2 game. It is important, however, to realize that any finite zero-sum two-person game *can* be solved with the use of linear programming, whereas the geometrical method of Section 17.4 *cannot* be used when both players have more than 2 strategies. Further illustrations may be found in the books by A. M. Glicksman and J. C. C. McKinsey referred to at the end of this chapter.

EXERCISES

1. With reference to the game on page 521, show that if Player A chooses between Strategies I and II with the probabilities y and $1 - y$, his optimum strategy can be found by solving the following linear programming problem: *minimize*

   $$z = 13y + u - 3$$

   where y *and* u *must satisfy the inequalities* $y \geqslant 0$, $y \leq 1$, $u \geqslant 0$, *and* $17y + u \geqslant 11$. Also, solve the problem by the method of Section 8.2.

2. With reference to the 2×2 game of Exercise 5 on page 519, set up a linear programming problem whose solution will yield the optimum strategy of Player B and the value of the game.

3. With reference to the 2×2 game of Exercise 5 on page 519, set up a linear programming problem whose solution will yield the optimum strategy of Player A and the value of the game.

4. With reference to Exercise 14 on page 520, show that if the manufacturer chooses between the two production methods with the probabilities x and

$1 - x$, his optimum "strategy" can be found by solving the following linear programming problem: *maximize*

$$z = 8x - u + 8$$

where x and u are subject to the restrictions $x \geqslant 0$, $x \leqslant 1$, $u \geqslant 0$, $10x - u \leqslant 3$, *and* $16x - u \leqslant 7$. Also, solve the problem by the method of Section 8.2.

5. Referring to Exercise 7 on page 519, show that if Player A chooses between Strategies I, II, and III with the probabilities x_1, x_2, and $1 - x_1 - x_2$, his optimum strategy can be found by solving the following linear programming problem: *minimize*

$$z = 15 - 9x_1 + 3x_2 + u$$

where x_1, x_2, and u are subject to the restrictions $x_1 \geqslant 0$, $x_2 \geqslant 0$, $x_1 + x_2 \leqslant 1$, $u \geqslant 0$, and $11x_1 - 7x_2 - u \leqslant 5$. Also, solve the problem by the Simplex method.

REFERENCES

Jeffrey, R. C., *The Logic of Decision.* New York: McGraw-Hill Book Co., 1965.

Glicksman, A. M., *An Introduction to Linear Programming and the Theory of Games.* New York: John Wiley & Sons, Inc., 1963.

McKinsey, J. C. C., *Introduction to the Theory of Games.* New York: McGraw-Hill Book Co., 1952.

18

SIMULATION

18.1 INTRODUCTION

The term "random process" refers to any physical process which is partly or entirely controlled by chance—it applies to repeated flips of a coin, the attendance at a drive-in theater, fluctuations in the price of a stock, a bakery's hourly sales of pies, regularly-published figures of the *Consumer Price Index,* the annual tonnage of grapes harvested in California, and even to vibrations of airplane wings, the spreading of rumors, and the static which one gets on the radio.

In this chapter we shall present some of the mathematical models that are used in the description of random processes, and we shall demonstrate how these models can be *simulated* (namely, imitated, duplicated, or reproduced) in the office or in the laboratory. The simulation techniques which we shall discuss are referred to as *Monte Carlo methods,* and they have been used with considerable success in the comparison of merchandizing or inventory practices, in finding answers to questions relating to the allocation of resources, the routing of shipments, and the scheduling of production; they have even made it possible to compare military strategies *without actually fighting any wars* and, hence, they have made it possible to study competitive situations *before they ever arise.*

18.2 PROBABILITY FUNCTIONS

The simplest kind of random process that depends *entirely on chance* is the one which concerns repeated flips of a balanced coin. Its mathematical model consists of the two rules that *successive flips must be independent* (see page 480), and that *the probabilities for heads and tails must remain the same* (*namely*, 1/2 *and* 1/2) *for each flip of the coin*. With these two rules we can answer many questions about the process—some fairly easy and some very hard. For instance, it would be easy to find the probability of getting 2 heads and 1 tail in 3 flips of a balanced coin, or the probability that a person betting on heads will lose 7 times before he finally wins; it would be more tedious to find the probability of getting at least 50 heads in 100 flips of a balanced coin, and it would be very difficult, indeed, to determine the probability that a person betting on heads (say, in a sequence of 400 flips of a balanced coin) will be ahead throughout the course of play at least 80 percent of the time.

To answer the first of these questions, namely, the one concerning 3 flips of a balanced coin, observe that if H stands for "head" and T for "tail," here are the eight possible outcomes

$$HHH \quad HHT \quad HTH \quad HTT \quad THH \quad THT \quad TTH \quad TTT$$

which we obtained by means of the tree diagram of Figure 18.1. Each of these eight possibilities has a probability of $\frac{1}{2}\cdot\frac{1}{2}\cdot\frac{1}{2} = \frac{1}{8}$, and since *one* of

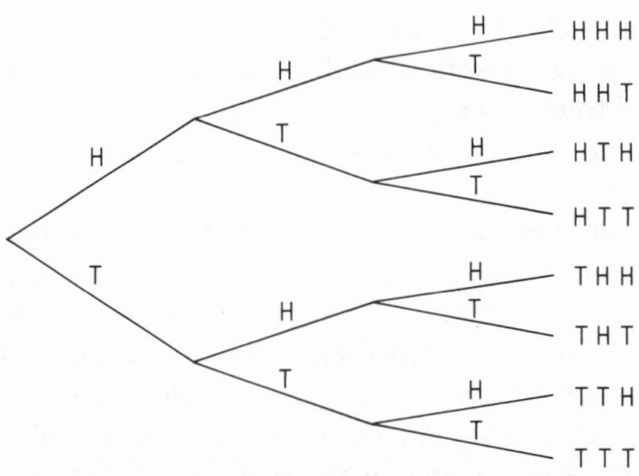

FIG. 18.1

them represents 0 heads and 3 tails, *three* represent 1 head and 2 tails, *three* represent 2 heads and 1 tail, and *one* represents 3 heads and 0 tails, the probabilities associated with getting 0, 1, 2, or 3 heads in 3 flips of a balanced coin are as shown in the following table:

Number of heads	*Probability*
0	1/8
1	3/8
2	3/8
3	1/8

The relationship expressed by means of this table is referred to as a *probability function.* Not only does it answer the original question about the probability of getting 2 heads and 1 tail in 3 flips of a balanced coin, but it provides a probability for each possible value of the *random variable* (*chance variable,* or *stochastic variable*) "the number of heads which we obtain in 3 flips of a balanced coin." It is very often helpful to picture tables like this graphically as in Figure 18.2, where the first diagram is called a *bar chart* and the other is called a *histogram.*

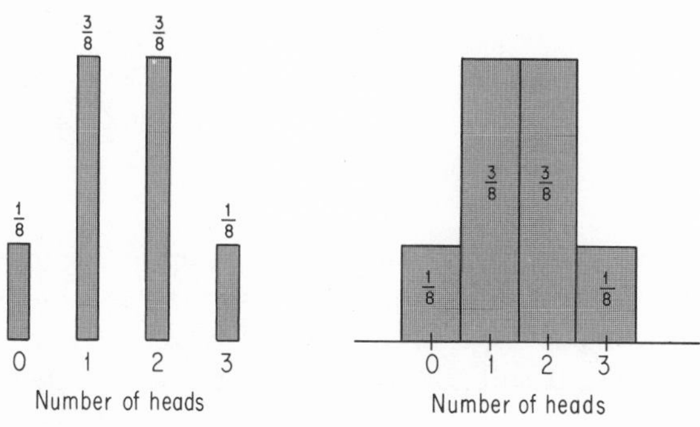

FIG. 18.2

To consider an example which is similar but slightly more complicated, suppose that a manufacturer of major appliances knows from experience that 75 percent of his automatic dishwashers require major repairs during the first year. Given this information, let us see whether we can determine the probabilities that among 4 of these automatic dishwashers 0, 1, 2, 3, or 4 will require major repairs during the first year. To find the values of this probability function, observe first of all that if R stands for "requires repairs" and N stands for "does not require repairs," there are now the 16 possibilities

$RRRR$	$RRRN$	$RRNR$	$RRNN$
$RNRR$	$RNRN$	$RNNR$	$RNNN$
$NRRR$	$NRRN$	$NRNR$	$NRNN$
$NNRR$	$NNRN$	$NNNR$	$NNNN$

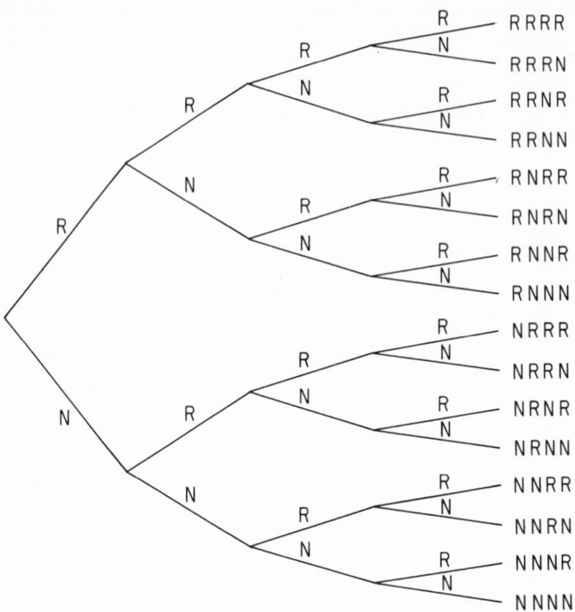

FIG. 18.3

which we obtained with the use of the tree diagram of Figure 18.3. In contrast to the first example, these 16 possibilities are *not equally likely;* the probability that any one of the dishwashers will require major repairs is 3/4, the probability that it will not require major repairs is 1/4, so that the probability associated with *RRRR*, for example, is $\frac{3}{4}\cdot\frac{3}{4}\cdot\frac{3}{4}\cdot\frac{3}{4} = \frac{81}{256}$; similarly, the probability associated with *RRRN* is $\frac{3}{4}\cdot\frac{3}{4}\cdot\frac{3}{4}\cdot\frac{1}{4} = \frac{27}{256}, \ldots,$ the probability associated with *NRNR* is $\frac{1}{4}\cdot\frac{3}{4}\cdot\frac{1}{4}\cdot\frac{3}{4} = \frac{9}{256}, \ldots,$ and the probability associated with *NNNN* is $\frac{1}{4}\cdot\frac{1}{4}\cdot\frac{1}{4}\cdot\frac{1}{4} = \frac{1}{256}$. Thus, the probability that *none* of the dishwashers will require major repairs during the first year is $\frac{1}{256}$, and the probability that *exactly one* will require major repairs during the first year is the *sum* of the probabilities associated with *RNNN*, *NRNN*, *NNRN*, and *NNNR*. Since each of these probabilities is the product of *three* factors 1/4 (corresponding to the three *N*'s) and one factor 3/4 (corresponding to the one *R*) and, hence, $\frac{3}{256}$, the probability that exactly one of the four dishwashers will require major repairs during the first year is $4\left(\frac{3}{256}\right) = \frac{12}{256}$. Applying the same kind of reasoning to the other three cases where 2, 3, and 4 of the dishwashers will require major repairs during the first year (see Exercise 1 on page 536), we obtain the results shown in the following table:

Number of dishwashers requiring repairs	*Probability*
0	1/256
1	12/256
2	54/256
3	108/256
4	81/256

As a check, observe that the sum of these probabilities is equal to one.

The main thing which the coin-tossing and dishwasher examples have in common is that in each case we are concerned with the number of "successes" in a given number of "trials." In the coin-tossing example the "trials" were the successive flips of the coin, while the "successes" were the ones in which the coin came up heads; in the dishwasher example the "trials" were the different dishwashers, while the "successes" were the ones which required major repairs during the first year. (This very strange usage of the words "trial" and "success" is a carry-over from the days when probability theory was applied only to games of chance; incidentally, when the outcome of a trial is *not* a success, it is referred to as a "failure," even though this might mean that a dishwasher does *not* require major repairs, that a person does *not* die from a disease, or that a company will *not* go bankrupt.)

There are many applied problems in which we are concerned with the probability of getting x "successes" in n "trials," namely, the probability that an event will take place x times out of n. For example, we may be interested in the probability of getting 35 replies to 120 mail questionnaires, the probability that 58 of 75 families (interviewed as part of a census survey) own at least one television set, the probability that 4 of 15 new restaurants in a resort area will show a profit during the first year, or the probability that there will be 3 rainy days during someone's 10-day vacation.

In the coin-tossing and dishwasher examples we assumed that the trials were independent and that the probability of a success remained constant (that is, fixed) from trial to trial. These assumptions may not apply to all of the examples listed in the preceding paragraph, but they are often met in actual practice, and they lead to what is called the *binomial probability* *function.** If p denotes the probability of a success on any given trial, then the value which this function assigns to the probability of getting x successes in n trials is given by

$$f(x) = \binom{n}{x} \cdot p^x(1-p)^{n-x} \qquad \text{for} \qquad x = 0, 1, 2, \ldots, \text{ and } n$$

As in Chapter 15, $\binom{n}{x}$ denotes the number of *combinations* of x objects selected from a set of n objects, and it is referred to as a *binomial coefficient.* The reason we refer to this particular probability function as the *binomial probability function* is that its values for $x = 0, 1, 2, \ldots,$ and n are given by the successive terms of the binomial expansion of $[p + (1-p)]^n$. Incidentally, since $p + (1-p) = 1$, this verifies that the sum of the probabilities for all values of x is, in fact, equal to 1.

To derive the formula for the binomial probability function, we have only to observe that the probability of getting x successes and $n - x$ failures in a *specific order* is $p^x(1-p)^{n-x}$. There is one factor p for each success, one factor $1 - p$ for each failure, and the x factors p and $n - x$ factors $1 - p$ are all multiplied together by virtue of the assumption that the trials are independent. Since this probability applies to *any* specific sequence of n trials in which there are x successes and $n - x$ failures, the desired probability for x successes in n trials *in any order* is simply the product of $p^x(1-p)^{n-x}$ and $\binom{n}{x}$, the number of ways in which x successes can occur among the n trials. Observe that the argument used in this proof is identical (in principle) to the one which we used in the coin-tossing example on page 526 and the dishwasher example on page 527.

To illustrate the use of the formula for the binomial probability function, suppose that a department store detective claims that if a woman leaves the store with a coat over her arm (a good place to hide things), the chances are 1 in 10 that she has not paid for everything she is carrying out of the store. As it can be very costly to make false accusations, the management of the store is greatly concerned about various probabilities related to this random process. Suppose, for instance, that they want to know the probabilities that among 5 women leaving the store with a coat over their arm, 0, 1, 2, 3, 4, or 5 did not pay for everything they are carrying out. Substituting $n = 5$, $p = 0.10$, and, respectively, $x = 0, 1, 2, 3, 4,$ and 5, they get

---

* It has been and still is common practice to refer to probability functions as *probability distributions*, and, hence, to the binomial probability function as the *binomial distribution;* after all, it tells us how the total probability of 1 is *distributed* among the various possible values of x.

$$f(0) = \binom{5}{0}(0.10)^0(1 - 0.10)^{5-0} = 0.59049$$

$$f(1) = \binom{5}{1}(0.10)^1(1 - 0.10)^{5-1} = 0.32805$$

$$f(2) = \binom{5}{2}(0.10)^2(1 - 0.10)^{5-2} = 0.07290$$

$$f(3) = \binom{5}{3}(0.10)^3(1 - 0.10)^{5-3} = 0.00810$$

$$f(4) = \binom{5}{4}(0.10)^4(1 - 0.10)^{5-4} = 0.00045$$

$$f(5) = \binom{5}{5}(0.10)^5(1 - 0.10)^{5-5} = 0.00001$$

where the values of the binomial coefficients could have been calculated according to the formula on page 443, or they could have been looked up in Table VIII. Actually, the final results (rounded to three decimals) could also have been obtained directly from Table IX, which contains binomial probabilities for selected values of p and n; more extensive tables are referred to at the end of this chapter. Note that our calculations have shown that the odds are just about 3 to 2 that *none* of the five women is a shoplifter.

To consider another example, let us calculate the probability that a secretary will misfile 3 of 12 letters, if she is known to misfile about 1 letter in 20. Substituting $n = 12$, $x = 3$, and $p = \frac{1}{20} = 0.05$ into the formula for the binomial probability function, we get

$$\begin{aligned} f(3) &= \binom{12}{3}(0.05)^3(1 - 0.05)^{12-3} \\ &= 220(0.05)^3(0.95)^9 \\ &= 0.017 \end{aligned}$$

This final result could have been calculated with the use of logarithms, although we simply looked it up in Table IX.

To introduce another type of probability function, let us suppose that certain electric razors are shipped in lots of 16; when they arrive at their destination, an inspector selects 3 from each lot, and *the whole lot is accepted only if all* 3 *are in good working condition.* It is easy to see that this kind of sampling inspection involves certain risks; in fact, a lot could be accepted even though 13 of the 16 razors do not work. More realistically, it may be of interest to know the probability that a lot will be accepted even though, say, 4 of the 16 razors are defective. Since we would then be interested in the probability of getting 3 successes (non-defectives) in 3 trials (among the 3 razors selected), we might be tempted to argue that the probability of getting a non-defective razor is $\frac{12}{16} = 0.75$, and, hence, that the desired probability is

$$\begin{aligned} f(3) &= \binom{3}{3}(0.75)^3(1 - 0.75)^{3-3} \\ &= 1 \cdot (0.75)^3 \\ &= 0.422 \end{aligned}$$

This result would be correct if we sampled *with replacement,* namely, if each razor were replaced before the next one is drawn; otherwise, the basic assumption that *the trials must be independent* is violated. When the first razor is chosen for inspection, the probability that it is non-defective is 12/16, but once it has been found to be in good condition, the probability that the next one is non-defective is 11/15 rather than 12/16. Similarly, after the first two razors have checked out satisfactorily, the probability that the third one is non-defective is 10/14, and the probability of choosing 3 good ones in a row is thus

$$\frac{12}{16} \cdot \frac{11}{15} \cdot \frac{10}{14} = \frac{11}{28}$$

or approximately 0.393. (The method we have used here is the one explained in Exercise 16 on page 487.)

To solve the problem correctly, we could also have argued that there are altogether $\binom{16}{3} = 560$ ways in which 3 razors can be selected from a lot of 16, that there are $\binom{12}{3} = 220$ ways in which 3 razors can be selected from among the 12 razors which are not defective, and, hence, that the probability of getting 3 razors in good working condition is

$$\frac{\binom{12}{3}}{\binom{16}{3}} = \frac{220}{560} = 0.393$$

This is a simple application of the rule for equiprobable outcomes on page 470, and a special case of the *hypergeometric probability function,* which applies when n elements are selected *without replacement* from a set containing a elements of one kind (successes) and b elements of another kind (failures). The probability that the n elements which we randomly select (without replacement) will contain x successes and $n - x$ failures is given by

$$f(x) = \frac{\binom{a}{x}\binom{b}{n-x}}{\binom{a+b}{n}}$$

for $x = 0, 1, 2, \ldots$, and n *or* a (whichever is smaller); also, $n - x$ cannot exceed b. In our numerical example we had $x = 3$, $n = 3$, $a = 12$, $b = 4$, and hence we obtained

$$f(3) = \frac{\binom{12}{3}\binom{4}{0}}{\binom{12+4}{3}} = \frac{220 \cdot 1}{560} = 0.393$$

It is of interest to note that this value does not differ by too much from 0.422, the first result which we obtained by mistakenly using the formula for the binomial probability function. In fact, we often approximate hypergeometric probabilities (pertaining to sampling *without replacement*) with binomial probabilities (pertaining to sampling *with replacement*); this is quite satisfactory so long as n is small compared to $a + b$ (see Exercise 13 on page 538).

The hypergeometric probability function has many important applications. It can be used, for example, to determine the probability that the Internal Revenue Service will catch 2 income tax returns with illegitimate deductions, if it randomly chooses 6 returns from among 20 income tax returns of which 8 contain illegitimate deductions. Substituting $x = 2$, $n = 6$, $a = 8$, and $b = 12$ into the formula for the hypergeometric probability function, we get

$$f(2) = \frac{\binom{8}{2}\binom{12}{4}}{\binom{20}{6}} = \frac{28 \cdot 495}{38{,}760} = 0.358$$

and if we had wanted to find the probability that they will catch *at most* 2 tax returns with illegitimate deductions, we would also have calculated

$$f(0) = \frac{\binom{8}{0}\binom{12}{6}}{\binom{20}{6}} = \frac{1 \cdot 924}{38{,}760} = 0.024$$

$$f(1) = \frac{\binom{8}{1}\binom{12}{5}}{\binom{20}{6}} = \frac{8 \cdot 792}{38{,}760} = 0.163$$

and the answer would have been $0.358 + 0.024 + 0.163 = 0.545$. Thus, it is almost an even-money bet that with this sampling procedure they will not catch more than 2 of the 8 income tax returns with illegitimate deductions.

On page 526 we suggested that it may be of interest to know the probability that a person betting on heads will lose 7 times in a row before he finally wins. This would certainly be of concern to someone who gambles with very limited funds, but, strangely enough, very similar questions arise in many other (seemingly unrelated) areas. In the testing of light switches, for example, it may be of interest to know the probability that a switch can be turned on and off 3,000 times before it finally fails; in criminology it may be of interest to know the probability that a burglar will finally get caught on his fourth "job;" and in driver training it may be of interest to know the probability that a student will fail the road test 5 times before he finally gets his license. In each of these examples we are interested in the probability that the *first success* occurs on the xth trial, namely, that $x - 1$ failures are finally followed by a success. Probabilities like these are easy to determine *if we assume that the trials are independent and that the probabilities for success and failure have the same values p and $1 - p$ in each trial.* We can then argue that the probability of getting $x - 1$ failures in a row is $(1 - p)^{x-1}$, the probability of finally getting a success on the xth trial is p, and, hence, that the desired probabilities are given by

$$f(x) = p(1 - p)^{x-1} \qquad \text{for} \qquad x = 0, 1, 2, 3, \ldots$$

This defines what we call the *geometric probability function;* its values are the probabilities of getting the first success on the xth trial, and it owes its name to the fact that for successive values of x the probabilities constitute a *geometric progression.* An important feature of this probability function is that its domain is *countably infinite*—there are as many possible values of x as there are whole numbers, and this requires that we modify the third postulate of probability and its generalization on page 468 so that it applies to any sequence of mutually exclusive events A_1, A_2, A_3, . . .

Returning now to the original question concerning the probability of getting the first head on the 8th flip of a balanced coin, we find that the answer is

$$\begin{aligned} f(8) &= \frac{1}{2}\left(1 - \frac{1}{2}\right)^{8-1} \\ &= \frac{1}{2}\left(\frac{1}{2}\right)^{7} \\ &= \frac{1}{256} \end{aligned}$$

where $p = \dfrac{1}{2}$ is the probability of getting heads with a balanced coin.

Similarly, if the probability that a burglar will get caught at any given job is 0.30, the probability that he will finally get caught on his fourth job is

$$\begin{aligned} f(4) &= (0.30)(1 - 0.30)^{4-1} \\ &= 0.103 \text{ (approximately)} \end{aligned}$$

and if the probability that a student driver will pass the road test on any given try is 0.60, the probability that he will not get his license until the sixth try is

$$\begin{aligned} f(6) &= (0.60)(1 - 0.60)^{6-1} \\ &= 0.006 \text{ (approximately)} \end{aligned}$$

Another important probability function whose domain is countably infinite is that of the *Poisson distribution;* its equation is

$$f(x) = \frac{e^{-\lambda} \cdot \lambda^x}{x!} \qquad \text{for } x = 0, 1, 2, 3, \ldots .$$

where λ (the Greek letter *lambda*) denotes a numerical constant whose significance will be explained below, and x is the number of "successes"; as always, e is the irrational number whose value is approximately 2.71828. In contrast to the binomial probability function where we always had a fixed number of trials, $f(x)$ now gives the number of successes per "unit of observation," say, the number of telephone calls arriving at a switchboard during a fixed period of time, the number of imperfections found in a roll of cloth, the number of smugglers caught annually by government agents, the number of morsels of chicken found in a can of chicken soup, and so on.

The constant λ which appears in the formula for the Poisson probability function represents the *expected* (or *average*) *number of successes,* and like any mathematical expectation it is the sum of the products obtained by multiplying each value of x by the corresponding probability (see also Exercise 22 on page 539). Thus, if a small car-rental agency averages 1.5 customers per day, the probabilities that it will rent out 0, 1, 2, or 3 cars on any given day are, respectively,

$$f(0) = \frac{e^{-1.5}(1.5)^0}{0!} = 0.223$$

$$f(1) = \frac{e^{-1.5}(1.5)^1}{1!} = 0.335$$

$$f(2) = \frac{e^{-1.5}(1.5)^2}{2!} = 0.251$$

and

$$f(3) = \frac{e^{-1.5}(1.5)^3}{3!} = 0.125$$

The value of $e^{-1.5}$ was obtained from Table III, and in Exercise 18 on page 538 the reader will be asked to continue this example by showing that

$f(4) = 0.047$, $f(5) = 0.014$, $f(6) = 0.004$, and $f(7) = 0.001$. For larger values of x the probabilities become negligible; in fact, those for $x = 0$ through $x = 7$ (rounded to three decimals) already add up to 1. Finally, if we add the products obtained by multiplying each value of x by the corresponding probability, we get

$$0(0.223) + 1(0.335) + 2(0.251) + 3(0.125) + 4(0.047) + 5(0.014) + 6(0.004) + 7(0.001) = 1.501$$

and this verifies the fact that $\lambda = 1.5$ *is* the average daily demand.

EXERCISES

1. With reference to the example on page 527, verify that the probabilities of 2, 3, and 4 of the dishwashers requiring major repairs during the first year are, respectively, 54/256, 108/256, and 81/256.
2. Using the formula for the binomial probability function, find
   (a) the probability of rolling exactly 2 *ones* in 4 rolls of a balanced die;
   (b) the probability of rolling at most 2 *ones* in 4 rolls of a balanced die;
   (c) the probability of getting exactly 5 heads in 7 flips of a balanced coin;
   (d) the probability of getting at least 5 heads in 7 flips of a balanced coin.

   Use Table IX to check the results of parts (c) and (d).
3. A mutual fund salesman knows from experience that if he manages to get an appointment with a potential customer, the probability of making a sale is 0.30. If he has 5 appointments scheduled for a weekend, find the probability that he will make 2 sales
   (a) by using the formula for the binomial probability function;
   (b) by referring to Table IX.
4. In a certain county, 40 percent of all losses due to fraudulent, dishonest, or criminal acts are indemnified by insurance. If 6 such cases are randomly selected from court files, find the probability that exactly 2 of them were indemnified by insurance
   (a) by using the formula for the binomial probability function;
   (b) by referring to Table IX.
5. It has been claimed that among all drivers whose cars are equipped with seat-belts only 70 percent use them on long trips. If 5 cars (equipped with seat-belts) are stopped at a road block, find the probability that *at least* 4 of the drivers will be using their seat belt
   (a) by using the formula for the binomial probability function;
   (b) by referring to Table IX.
6. When the shipping room clerk of a publishing house is in a hurry to go home, the probability that he will make a mistake in an address is 0.20. If he has to

send out 8 shipments just before closing time, find the probability that he will make a mistake in addressing *at least* 3 of these shipments

(a) by using the formula for the binomial probability function;
(b) by referring to Table IX.
(*Hint:* subtract from 1 the probabilities of his making 0, 1, or 2 mistakes.)

7. In a certain State, incompatibility is the legal reason given for 9 out of 10 divorce cases. Using Table IX, find the probabilities that among 15 randomly selected divorce cases

(a) exactly 12 are due to incompatibility;
(b) at least 12 are due to incompatibility;
(c) fewer than 11 are due to incompatibility.

8. A multiple-choice test has 20 questions and 5 answers to each question. If a student plans to answer each question by rolling a die (and omitting the 6), use Table IX to find the probabilities that

(a) he will answer exactly 5 questions correctly;
(b) he will answer at least 8 questions correctly;
(c) he will answer fewer than 2 questions correctly;
(d) he will answer 4, 5, or 6 questions correctly.

9. A manufacturer of color television tubes claims that only 5 percent of his tubes have any sort of imperfection. If 15 of these tubes are randomly selected for inspection, use Table IX to find the probabilities that 0, 1, 2, 3, 4, . . . , will have imperfections, and draw a bar chart or a histogram (see Figure 18.2) of this binomial probability function. (Assume that either sampling is with replacement, or the lot from which the tubes are selected is so large that successive selections are for all practical purposes independent.)

10. On page 532 we showed that the probability of randomly selecting 3 non-defective razors from a lot of 16 among which 4 are defective is 11/28. Use the formula for the hypergeometric probability function to show that

(a) the corresponding probability of selecting 2 non-defective and 1 defective razors is 33/70;
(b) the corresponding probability of selecting 1 non-defective and 2 defective razors is 9/70;
(c) the corresponding probability of selecting 3 defective razors is 1/140.

11. A secretary is supposed to send 4 of 10 letters by special delivery. If she gets them all mixed up and randomly puts special delivery stamps on 4 of them, what is the probability that

(a) she puts all the special delivery stamps on the wrong letters;
(b) she puts 2 of them on letters which were supposed to go by special delivery and the other two on letters which were not supposed to go by special delivery;
(c) she puts all of the special delivery stamps on the right letters?

12. When she buys a dozen eggs, Mrs. Murphy always inspects 3 of the eggs for cracks, and if at least one of them has a crack she looks for another carton. If she randomly selects the eggs which she inspects, what are the probabilities that Mrs. Murphy will

(a) buy a carton with 2 cracked eggs;
(b) buy a carton with 3 cracked eggs;
(c) buy a carton with 4 cracked eggs?

13. Among the 120 employees of a company 80 are union members while the others are not. If 4 of the employees are chosen by lot to serve on a committee which administrates the pension fund, what is the probability that 2 of them will be union members while the other 2 are not? Also show that if we had erroneously used the formula for the binomial probability function and calculated the probability of 2 successes in 4 trials with $p = \frac{80}{120} = \frac{2}{3}$, we would have been off by less than 0.004. (As we indicated on page 533, binomial probabilities are often used to approximate hypergeometric probabilities when n is small compared to $a + b$; a good rule of thumb is to use this approximation whenever n is not more than 5 percent of $a + b$.)

14. In a file of 500 invoices exactly 8 contain errors. If an auditor randomly selects 3 invoices from this file, what is the probability that none of them contains an error? By how much would we have been off in this example if we had erroneously used the binomial probability function to calculate the probability of 0 successes in 3 trials when $p = \frac{8}{500} = 0.016$? (See comment to Exercise 13.)

15. A life insurance salesman spends all of his time calling on families that have recently moved to the Los Angeles area, even though he figures that the odds are 4 to 1 against his making a sale.

(a) What is the probability that he will make his first sale of the week to the third family on which he calls?
(b) What is the probability that he will make his first sale of the week to the fifth family on which he calls?
(c) What is the probability that he will still be waiting to make his first sale of the week after having visited 10 families?

16. In a "torture test," a watch is dropped from a very tall building until it finally breaks. If the probability that it will break any time that it is dropped from the building is 0.01 (and it is reasonable to assume independence between successive "trials"), what is the probability that the watch will not break until after the 3rd time that it has been dropped.

17. Given that the switchboard of a department store has on the average 3 incoming calls per minute, find the probabilities that there will be

(a) no incoming calls within a minute;
(b) 2 incoming calls within a minute;
(c) 4 incoming calls within a minute.

18. Continue the illustration on page 535 by showing that the probabilities that the car-rental agency will rent out 4, 5, 6, or 7 cars are, respectively, 0.047, 0.014, 0.004, and 0.001.

19. A person fishing at a certain spot on the East Verde river can expect to catch 1.6 trout per hour.

(a) What is the probability that a person fishing at this spot for an hour will not catch a single trout?

(b) What is the probability that a person fishing at this spot for an hour will catch exactly one trout?

(c) What is the probability that a person fishing at this spot for an hour will catch at least two trout? [*Hint:* use the results of parts (a) and (b).]

(d) What is the probability that a person fishing at this spot for *two hours* will not catch a single trout?

20. If there are on the average 2 accidents per week at a busy downtown intersection, find the probabilities (rounded to two decimals) that during any given week there will be 0, 1, 2, 3, 4, 5, or 6 accidents. Also draw a *histogram* (with the heights of the rectangles proportional to the probabilities) of this Poisson distribution.

21. When n is large and p is small, binomial probabilities can generally be approximated very closely with corresponding Poisson probabilities having $\lambda = n \cdot p$. Use this approximation to calculate the following probabilities:

(a) If a large shipment of textbooks contains 2 percent with imperfect bindings, what is the probability that among 300 textbooks (taken at random from this shipment) exactly 5 will have imperfect bindings?

b) To meet specifications, each can of fruit cocktail is supposed to contain at least one cherry. If the fruit cocktail coming from a certain cannery is such that 1.2 percent of the cans are without cherries, what is the probability that among 200 cans delivered from this cannery to a supermarket *at least* 2 are without cherries? (*Hint:* calculate the probabilities for 0 and 1 "successes," and subtract from 1.)

22. **THE MEAN.** If $f(x)$ is the probability that a variable assumes the value x, we can calculate its *mathematical expectation* by means of the formula

$$\sum x \cdot f(x)$$

where the summation extends over all possible values of x. In statistics, we refer to this expected value, or *average value*, of x as its *mean* and denote it with the Greek letter μ(*mu*). For instance, for the number of heads in 3 flips of a balanced coin, the probabilities on page 527 yield

$$\mu = 0\left(\frac{1}{8}\right) + 1\left(\frac{3}{8}\right) + 2\left(\frac{3}{8}\right) + 3\left(\frac{1}{8}\right) = 1.5$$

In other words, *on the average* we get 1.5 heads in 3 flips of a balanced coin.

(a) The following table gives the probabilities that a woman who enters a dress shop will buy 0, 1, 2, 3, 4, or 5 dresses:

Number of dresses, x	0	1	2	3	4	5
$f(x)$	.449	.360	.144	.038	.008	.001

Find the mean of this probability distribution, namely, the average number of dresses a woman will buy at the store.

(b) In Exercise 10 the reader was asked to show that if 3 razors are randomly selected from a lot of 16 among which 4 are defective, the probabilities of getting 0, 1, 2, or 3 defectives are, respectively, 11/28, 33/70, 9/70, and 1/140. Find the mean.

(c) A new-car dealer sent invitations to 20 of his best customers to come to his showroom to look at a new model car, and he figures that for each of these customers the odds are 4 to 1 that he will not come. Use Table IX to find the probabilities that 0, 1, 2, 3, . . . , of the customers will come and calculate the mean (that is, the *average number* he can expect to come).

23. THE MEAN, CONTINUED. In the illustration of Exercise 22 and in its part (c) we could have saved ourselves quite a bit of work by making use of the fact that *the mean of a binomial distribution is given by the product* $n \cdot p$, namely, by the product of the number of trials and the probability of success on an individual trial.

(a) Verify this formula for the illustration of Exercise 22 and also for its part (c).

(b) The probabilities of getting 0, 1, 2, 3, or 4 heads in 4 flips of a balanced coin are, respectively, 1/16, 4/16, 6/16, 4/16, and 1/16. Use these probabilities to calculate the average number of heads one can expect in 4 flips of a balanced coin, and verify that the result equals $n \cdot p$, namely, the product of 4 and 1/2.

(c) The probability that any family with children vacationing in Southern California will visit Disneyland is 0.84. On the average, how many of 600 families with children vacationing in Southern California will visit Disneyland?

(d) The manager of a restaurant figures that 7 out of 10 of his customers have cocktails before dinner. Use Table IX to find the probabilities that among 12 of his customers 0, 1, 2, 3, . . . , will have cocktails before dinner and calculate the mean. Verify that the result equals the product of the number of "trials" and the probability of "success" on an individual trial.

24. THE MEAN, CONTINUED. In the continuous case, probability densities take the place of probability functions, integration takes the place of summation, and the *mean* is given by

$$\mu = \int x \cdot f(x)\, dx$$

where the integration is performed over the whole sample space, namely, over all possible values of x.

(a) The probability density that a building contractor's cost estimate is off by x percent is given by

$$f(x) = \frac{1}{5} - \frac{x}{50} \qquad \text{for} \qquad 0 \leqslant x \leqslant 10$$

On the average, by how many percent can he be expected to be off?

(b) With reference to Exercise 3 on page 494, what proportion of the mail-order house's orders are processed *on the average* within 24 hours?
(c) With reference to the example on page 491, show that the batteries have an *average* lifetime of 50 hours. (*Hint:* make use of the integration formula of Exercise 16 on page 423 and the method of Exercise 17 on page 429.)

25. **MULTINOMIAL PROBABILITIES.** An important generalization of the binomial probability function arises when each trial has more than two possible outcomes. (For instance, in market research a person interviewed may say that he favors Product A, that he favors Product B, or that he is indifferent; a potential car buyer may have to choose from among 5 or 6 makes of cars; a stock may be rated as being a high risk, a moderate risk, or a low risk; and so on.) In general, if each trial has k possible outcomes, whose respective probabilities are $p_1, p_2, \ldots,$ and p_k, then the *multinomial probability* that among n independent trials there will be x_1 outcomes of the first kind, x_2 outcomes of the second kind, . . . , and x_k outcomes of the kth kind is

$$\frac{n!}{x_1! \cdot x_2! \cdot \ldots \cdot x_k!}(p_1)^{x_1}(p_2)^{x_2} \cdot \ldots \cdot (p_k)^{x_k}$$

Note that the sum of the p's must always equal 1 and the sum of the x's must always equal n.

(a) In a city which has two television stations, the probability that a person contacted in the evening by phone is watching Station A is 0.10, the probability that he is watching Station B is 0.30, and the probability that he is not watching television at all is 0.60. What is the probability that among 10 persons contacted in the evening by phone, 2 will be watching Station A, 3 will be watching Station B, and 5 will not be watching television at all?
(b) A supermarket carries four grades of ground beef, and the probabilities that a housewife will choose the poorest, third best, second best, and best kinds are, respectively, 0.10, 0.20, 0.50, and 0.20. What is the probability that among 12 housewives buying ground beef at this market 1 will choose the poorest kind, 4 will choose the third best kind, 6 will choose the second best kind, and only 1 will choose the best kind?
(c) Suppose that 70 percent of all State income tax returns filed in Arizona are correct, 20 percent contain mistakes favoring the tax payer, and 10 percent contain mistakes favoring the State. What is the probability that among 8 of these State income tax returns randomly selected for audit 6 are correct, 1 contains a mistake favoring the tax payer, and 1 contains a mistake favoring the State?

18.3 SIMULATION: THE USE OF RANDOM NUMBERS

Whenever a random process is simulated (namely, imitated, duplicated, or reproduced), we are really substituting one random process for another.

For instance, we can simulate the roll of a die by randomly drawing suitably-numbered slips of paper out of a hat, or we can play "heads or tails" by repeatedly drawing (with replacement) one of two slips of paper marked H and T (or by repeatedly cutting a deck of cards with red cards representing heads and black cards representing tails). Similarly, we can simulate the responses one obtains in market research, the number of errors a typist makes per page, the number of defectives found in weekly shipments from a vendor, the daily number of stocks whose value goes up, . . . , by drawing numbered slips of paper out of a hat, with a suitable number of each kind to assure the right probabilities.

Numbered slips of paper provide an effective way of simulating random processes, so long as we do not have to use too many and we can make sure that each slip actually has the same chance of being drawn. This means that the slips of paper must all be of the same size and weight, they must be thoroughly shuffled or mixed, and they must be drawn in such a way that none is "favored" in any way. All this is much easier said than done, and in actual practice we leave these worries to others by using published tables of *random numbers*. Such tables consist of many pages (like those of Table X at the end of this book) in which the digits 0, 1, 2, 3, 4, 5, 6, 7, 8, and 9 are recorded as if they had been generated by a gambling device (such as the spinner of Figure 18.4), which assigns each of

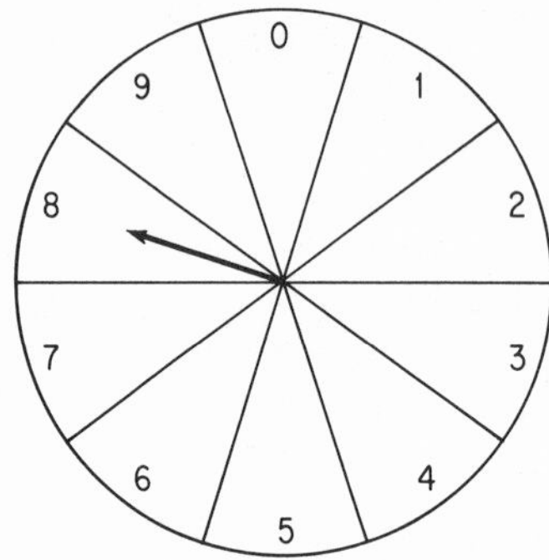

FIG. 18.4

the digits a probability of 1/10. Actually, most commercially-published random numbers are generated by means of electronic computers and are subjected to various statistical tests (standards, or criteria) to assure their "randomness." In other words, they are subjected to tests which serve to check whether the digits can really be looked upon as the results of a random process for which the individual "trials" are independent and the probability for each digit is 1/10.

Using random numbers, we can simulate repeated flips of a coin in many different ways; one possibility is to regard the even numbers 0, 2,

4, 6, and 8 as representing *heads,* and the odd numbers 1, 3, 5, 7, and 9 as representing *tails.* Thus, if we arbitrarily used the eleventh column of the table on page 584 starting at the top, we would get 8, 7, 7, 8, 0, 1, 4, 9, 9, 5, 7, 6, . . . , and we would interpret this as *head, tail, tail, head, head, tail, head, tail, tail, tail, tail, head,* . . . . .

Perhaps the most obvious way of simulating a process in which we repeatedly flip 3 balanced coins is to proceed as in the preceding paragraph and use 3 random digits, one for each coin. Thus if we arbitrarily used the third, fourth, and fifth columns of the table on page 584 starting with the sixth row, we would get 187, 228, 720, 222, 703, 369, 331, 053, 104, . . . , and we would interpret this as representing 1 head, 3 heads, 2 heads, 3 heads, 1 head, 1 head, 0 heads, 1 head, 2 heads, . . . , corresponding to the number of *even numbers* there are in each case. Although this method is perfectly alright, we still have to *count* how many even digits there are in each case. To avoid this extra work (which could be troublesome, say, if we talked about the flips of 400 coins) let us refer to the probability function on page 527, according to which 0, 1, 2, and 3 heads occur with probabilities of 1/8, 3/8, 3/8, and 1/8 in 3 flips of a balanced coin (or when we flip 3 balanced coins). Thus, we could use the following scheme.

Number of heads	*Probability*	*Random digits*
0	1/8	0
1	3/8	1, 2, 3
2	3/8	4, 5, 6
3	1/8	7

where the digits 8 and 9 are simply skipped whenever they will occur. Note that 0 heads is represented by *one* random digit, 1 head is represented by *three* random digits, 2 heads is represented by *three* random digits, and 3 heads is represented by *one* random digit, so that these different outcomes have the correct probabilities of 1/8, 3/8, 3/8, and 1/8. Thus, if we arbitrarily used the sixteenth column of the table on page 585 starting at the top (but skipping the first 8 and later the 9), we would get 7, 6, 1, 5, 3, 0, 0, 3, 1, 5, 3, . . . , and we would interpret this as 3 heads, 2 heads, 1 head, 2 heads, 1 head, 0 heads, 0 heads, 1 head, 1 head, 2 heads, 1 head, ... If we did not want to skip any of the digits, we could use the following scheme

Number of heads	*Probability*	*Random numbers*
0	1/8	000–124
1	3/8	125–499
2	3/8	500–874
3	1/8	875–999

where we chose 3-digit random numbers because 1,000 happens to be divisible by 8. This enabled us to allocate 125 (or *one-eighth*) of the random numbers from 000 through 999 to 0 heads, 375 (or *three-eighths*) to 1 head, another 375 to 2 heads, and the remaining 125 to 3 heads. Had we arbitrarily used the 31st, 32nd, and 33rd columns of the table on page 585 starting at the top, we would have gotten 473, 118, 228, 186, 682, 648, 425, 247, 293, 889, . . . , and we would have interpreted this as 1 head, 0 heads, 1 head, 1 head, 2 heads, 2 heads, 1 head, 1 head, 1 head, 3 heads, . . . , corresponding to the grouping to which each of these numbers belongs.

Proceeding as we did in this last example, we can simulate any probability function (with the probabilities rounded to a suitable number of decimals), and this is generally much more satisfactory than flipping coins, rolling dice, drawing numbered slips of paper out of hats, or gambling with other kinds of devices. If the probabilities are given (or rounded) to two decimals, we represent them by means of the two-digit random numbers from 00 through 99; if they are given (or rounded) to three decimals, we represent them by means of the three-digit random numbers from 000 through 999; if they are given (or rounded) to four decimals, we represent them by means of the four-digit random numbers from 0000 through 9999, and so on.

To give another example—one which does not directly pertain to a game of chance—let us refer to the probability function on page 535 and simulate the car-rental agency's business for a period of 30 days. Since the probabilities were rounded to three decimals, we shall use the three-digit random numbers from 000 through 999 and let the first 223 (the ones from 000 through 222) represent a day on which they rent 0 cars. The next 335 (the ones from 223 through 557) are used to represent a day on which they rent 1 car; the next 251 after that (the ones from 558 through 808) are used to represent a day on which they rent 2 cars; and so on. We thus get

Number of cars	*Probability*	*Random numbers*
0	0.223	000–222
1	0.335	223–557
2	0.251	558–808
3	0.125	809–933
4	0.047	934–980
5	0.014	981–994
6	0.004	995–998
7	0.001	999

and if we arbitrarily use the third, fourth, and fifth columns of the table on page 584 starting with the 21st row, we get 047, 776, 419, 844, 350, 960, 420,

945, 206, 847, 303, 732, 809, 700, 870, 493, 630, 234, 107, 657, 948, 746, 939, 032, 188, 236, 337, 732, 113, and 797. This corresponds to a daily demand for 0 cars, 2 cars, 1 car, 3 cars, 1 car, 4 cars, 1 car, 4 cars, 0 cars, 3 cars, 1 car, 2 cars, 3 cars, 2 cars, 3 cars, 1 car, 2 cars, 1 car, 0 cars, 2 cars, 4 cars, 2 cars, 4 cars, 0 cars, 0 cars, 1 car, 1 car, 2 cars, 0 cars, and 2 cars.

EXERCISES

1. Use random numbers to simulate 100 flips of a balanced coin. (Although it doesn't really matter which five digits represent heads and which five digits represent tails, use the same scheme as on page 543.)

2. The probabilities of getting 0, 1, or 2 heads in two flips of a balanced coin (or when flipping two balanced coins) are, respectively, 1/4, 1/2, and 1/4.
   (a) Using *two* random digits (with 0, 2, 4, 6, and 8 representing *heads* and 1, 3, 5, 7, and 9 representing *tails*) to stand for the results obtained when flipping *two* balanced coins, simulate an experiment which consists of 80 flips of two coins. Also construct a table which shows the number of times that 0, 1, and 2 heads were obtained as well as the corresponding *expected frequencies* of 20, 40, and 20.
   (b) Repeat part (a) letting 0, 1, and 2 heads be represented by the respective two-digit random numbers 00 through 24, 25 through 74, and 75 through 99.

3. Using the digits 1, 2, 3, 4, 5, and 6 to represent the corresponding faces of a die (and omitting 0, 7, 8, and 9), simulate 120 rolls of a balanced die. Also construct a table showing the number of times the die came up 1, 2, 3, 4, 5, and 6, as well as the corresponding *expected frequencies,* which are all equal to 20.

4. The probabilities that a real estate broker will sell 0, 1, 2, 3, 4, 5, or 6 houses in a week are, respectively, 0.18, 0.31, 0.26, 0.15, 0.06, 0.03, and 0.01.
   (a) Distribute the two-digit numbers from 00 through 99 among these seven possibilities so that the corresponding random numbers can be used to simulate the number of houses the broker sells in a week.
   (b) Use the results of part (a) to simulate the real estate broker's weekly sales during 25 consecutive weeks.
   (c) Use the results of part (b) to calculate his *average weekly sales* and compare this figure with the *mean* of the original probability distribution (see Exercise 22 on page 539).

5. A large corporation has the policy of having its executives take various psychological tests before they are considered for a promotion. If the probability that any one executive will "pass" these tests is 0.80 and the corporation has 6 of its executives take the tests each month, we find from Table IX that the probabilities that 1, 2, 3, 4, 5, or all 6 of the executives will "pass" are, respectively, 0.002, 0.015, 0.082, 0.246, 0.393, and 0.262.

(a) Distribute the three-digit numbers from 000 through 999 among these six possibilities, so that the corresponding random numbers can be used to simulate the executives' performance of these tests.

(b) Use the results of part (a) to simulate what might happen to 120 of the corporation's executives during 20 consecutive months.

6. The owner of a bakery knows that the daily demand for a highly-perishable cheese cake is as shown in the following table:

Daily demand (number of cheese cakes)	*Probability*
0	0.05
1	0.15
2	0.25
3	0.25
4	0.20
5	0.10

(a) Distribute the two-digit numbers from 00 through 99 among these six possibilities so that the corresponding random numbers can be used to simulate the daily demand.

(b) Use the results of part (a) to simulate the demand for the cheese cake on 30 consecutive business days.

(c) If the baker makes a profit of \$2.00 on each cake that he sells, but loses \$1.00 on each cake that goes to waste (namely, each cake that cannot be sold on the day it is baked), find the baker's profit or loss for each of the 30 days of part (b), assuming that each day he bakes 3 of these cakes. Also find his *average profit* per day.

(d) Repeat part (c) assuming that each day he bakes 4 rather than 3 of these cakes. Which of the two appears to be more profitable?

(e) Referring to the original probabilities, calculate the baker's *expected daily profit* if he bakes 3 cakes each day and also if he bakes 4. (*Hint:* if he bakes 3 and sells 0 he loses \$3.00, and this happens with a probability of 0.05; if he bakes 3 and sells 1 he breaks even, and this happens with a probability of 0.15; if he bakes 3 and sells 2 he makes a profit of \$3.00, and this happens with a probability of 0.25; and if he bakes 3 and sells them all he makes a profit of \$6.00, and this happens with a probability of $0.25 + 0.20 + 0.10 = 0.55$.)

18.4 SIMULATION: AN EXAMPLE

To illustrate how simulation techniques can provide quick and inexpensive answers to questions arising in the operation of a business, let us consider the case of a chain of candy stores, whose management is faced with customers' complaints that they have to wait too long to get served *and* employees' complaints that they are kept much too busy. Thus, the management wants to find out whether these complaints are valid, and also whether the difficulties might be alleviated by putting two salesladies into each store instead of one.

Both of these questions *could* be answered by means of direct observations and some experimentation. To answer the first question, they have only to observe what goes on in some of the stores, but *how should they decide which stores are to be observed*, and *how should they decide when all this is to be done?* After all, the results could turn out to be very misleading if they studied a store which is in a shopping center where there happens to be a carnival and a special sale; they could also be very misleading if a competing chain had just opened a nearby store, or if it just happened to be the day before Mother's Day. All these complications would also have to be considered if they wanted to experiment by using two salesladies, in which case their results might even be biased by the salesladies' knowledge that something special is going on.

All these difficulties can be avoided if the operation of the candy stores is *simulated* as it would be with one saleslady and also as it would be with two. To illustrate, let us suppose that the management of the stores knows from past experience that under average conditions the probability function for the number of minutes it takes to serve a customer is given by

Time required to serve a customer (minutes)	*Probability*
1	0.22
2	0.17
3	0.14
4	0.10
5	0.08
6	0.07
7	0.05
8	0.04
9	0.03
10	0.03
11	0.02
12	0.02
13	0.01
14	0.01
15	0.01

Note that this is the time it actually takes a customer to get served, and it does *not* include the time he spends waiting to be served. As can be seen from this table, more than half of the customers can be served in 3 minutes or less, but there are also customers requiring as much as 13, 14, and even 15 minutes. (Of course, this may include the time it takes the saleslady to answer the phone or attend to other duties.)

So far as the arrival of customers is concerned, the management of the stores also knows that under normal conditions the probability function for the number of minutes between the arrival of successive customers is given by

Time between arrival of successive customers (minutes)	*Probability*
1	0.18
2	0.15
3	0.12
4	0.10
5	0.09
6	0.07
7	0.05
8	0.05
9	0.04
10	0.03
11	0.03
12	0.02
13	0.02
14	0.01
15	0.01
16	0.01
17	0.01
18	0.01

Observe that there is a fairly constant stream of customers since the odds are almost 2 to 1 that the "waiting time" between successive arrivals will not be more than 5 minutes. On the other hand, sometimes there are intervals up to 18 minutes during which not a single customer will enter the store.

To simulate the operation of these candy stores, we shall have to simulate *both* the arrival of the customers as well as the time it takes each one to get served. In view of the fact that all of the probabilities are rounded to two decimals, we shall use the following schemes, where in the left-hand table the first 22 random numbers (from 00 through 21) give a probability of 0.22 to 1 minute, the next 17 random numbers (from 23 through 38) give a probability of 0.17 to 2 minutes, and so on. Similarly, in the right-hand table the first 18 random numbers (from 00 through 17) give a probability of 0.18 to 1 minute, the next 15 random numbers (from 18 through 32) give a probability of 0.15 to 2 minutes, and so on.

Time required to serve a customer	*Random numbers*
1	00–21
2	22–38
3	39–52
4	53–62
5	63–70
6	71–77
7	78–82
8	83–86
9	87–89
10	90–92
11	93–94
12	95–96
13	97
14	98
15	99

Time between arrival of successive customers	*Random numbers*
1	00–17
2	18–32
3	33–44
4	45–54
5	55–63
6	64–70
7	71–75
8	76–80
9	81–84
10	85–87
11	88–90
12	91–92
13	93–94
14	95
15	96
16	97
17	98
18	99

For each customer we thus need *four* random digits—two to determine his arrival and two to determine the actual time it takes him to get served.

Arbitrarily choosing the last four columns of the table on page 584 to simulate the operation of one of these candy stores with one saleslady, we obtain the results shown on pages 550 and 551. The first column contains four random digits for each customer, with the first two determining how many minutes he arrives after the arrival of the preceding customer, and the other two digits determine how many minutes it takes him to get served. Observe that we ignored the first two random digits of the first customer and arbitrarily set his arrival at 9:12 a.m. His last two random digits, 93, indicate that it takes him 11 minutes to get served, so that he is served from 9:12 to 9:23; being the first customer he obviously did not have to wait. The second customer arrives 1 minute after the first (since his first two random digits are 03) and it takes him 1 minute to get served (since his last two random digits are 17); however, he has to wait 10 minutes till the saleslady is finished with the first customer at 9:23, and he gets served from 9:23 to 9:24. Corresponding to the random digits 44 46, the third customer arrives 3 minutes after the second and it takes him 3 minutes to get served; however, he has to wait 8 minutes until the saleslady is finished with the second customer at 9:24, and he gets served from 9:24 to 9:27. Corresponding to the random digits 26 66, the fourth customer arrives 2 minutes after the third and it takes him 5 minutes to get served; however, he has to wait 9 minutes from 9:18 to 9:27, and he gets served from 9:27 to 9:32. Continuing in this way, we obtain the results shown on

OPERATION OF STORE WITH ONE SALESLADY

	Random number	*Time between arrivals*	*Service time*	*Time of arrival*	*Serviced from*	*Serviced until*	*Time spent waiting*
Customer 1	45 93		11	9:12	9:12	9:23	0
Customer 2	03 17	1	1	9:13	9:23	9:24	10
Customer 3	44 46	3	3	9:16	9:24	9:27	8
Customer 4	26 66	2	5	9:18	9:27	9:32	9
Customer 5	98 62	17	4	9:35	9:35	9:39	0
Customer 6	15 56	1	4	9:36	9:39	9:43	3
Customer 7	97 74	16	6	9:52	9:52	9:58	0
Customer 8	44 14	3	1	9:55	9:58	9:59	3
Customer 9	06 20	1	1	9:56	9:59	10:00	3
Customer 10	31 21	2	1	9:58	10:00	10:01	2
Customer 11	27 96	2	12	10:00	10:01	10:13	1
Customer 12	49 44	4	3	10:04	10:13	10:16	9
Customer 13	07 03	1	1	10:05	10:16	10:17	11
Customer 14	30 46	2	3	10:07	10:17	10:20	10
Customer 15	18 10	2	1	10:09	10:20	10:21	11
Customer 16	03 04	1	1	10:10	10:21	10:22	11
Customer 17	73 81	7	7	10:17	10:22	10:29	5
Customer 18	40 90	3	10	10:20	10:29	10:39	9
Customer 19	19 97	2	13	10:22	10:39	10:52	17
Customer 20	89 17	11	1	10:33	10:52	10:53	19
Customer 21	91 65	12	5	10:45	10:53	10:58	8
Customer 22	64 34	6	2	10:51	10:59	11:00	7
Customer 23	64 69	6	5	10:57	11:00	11:05	3
Customer 24	03 00	1	1	10:58	11:05	11:06	7
Customer 25	78 95	8	12	11:06	11:06	11:18	0

OPERATION OF STORE WITH ONE SALESLADY (CONTINUED)

	Random number	*Time between arrivals*	*Service time*	*Time of arrival*	*Serviced from*	*Serviced until*	*Time spent waiting*
Customer 26	42 91	3	10	11:09	11:18	11:28	9
Customer 27	14 36	1	2	11:10	11:28	11:30	18
Customer 28	51 61	4	4	11:14	11:30	11:34	16
Customer 29	81 81	9	7	11:23	11:34	11:41	11
Customer 30	49 86	4	8	11:27	11:41	11:49	14
Customer 31	30 44	2	3	11:29	11:49	11:52	20
Customer 32	59 57	5	4	11:34	11:52	11:56	18
Customer 33	53 03	4	1	11:38	11:56	11:57	18
Customer 34	24 73	2	6	11:40	11:57	12:03	17
Customer 35	61 80	5	7	11:45	12:03	12:10	18
Customer 36	86 81	10	7	11:55	12:10	12:17	15
Customer 37	75 49	7	3	12:02	12:17	12:20	15
Customer 38	96 20	15	1	12:17	12:20	12:21	3
Customer 39	06 20	1	1	12:18	12:21	12:22	3
Customer 40	79 11	8	1	12:26	12:26	12:27	0
Customer 41	09 72	1	6	12:27	12:27	12:33	0
Customer 42	00 63	1	5	12:28	12:33	12:38	5
Customer 43	38 47	3	3	12:31	12:38	12:41	7
Customer 44	84 31	9	2	12:40	12:41	12:43	1
Customer 45	90 19	11	1	12:51	12:51	12:52	0
Customer 46	70 49	6	3	12:57	12:57	1:00	0
Customer 47	27 32	2	2	12:59	1:00	1:02	1
Customer 48	09 82	1	7	1:00	1:02	1:09	2
Customer 49	04 41	1	3	1:01	1:09	1:12	8
Customer 50	70 18	6	1	1:07	1:12	1:13	5

OPERATION OF STORE WITH TWO SALESLADIES

	Random number	*Time between arrivals*	*Service time*	*Time of arrival*	*Serviced by Saleslady A from*	*until*	*Serviced by Saleslady B from*	*until*	*Time spent waiting*
Customer 1	45 93		11	9:12	9:12	9:23			0
Customer 2	03 17	1	1	9:13			9:13	9:14	0
Customer 3	44 46	3	3	9:16			9:16	9:19	0
Customer 4	26 66	2	5	9:18			9:19	9:24	1
Customer 5	98 62	17	4	9:35	9:35	9:39			0
Customer 6	15 56	1	4	9:36			9:36	9:40	0
Customer 7	97 74	16	6	9:52	9:52	9:58			0
Customer 8	44 14	3	1	9:55			9:55	9:56	0
Customer 9	06 20	1	1	9:56			9:56	9:57	0
Customer 10	31 21	2	1	9:58	9:58	9:59			0
Customer 11	27 96	2	12	10:00			10:00	10:12	0
Customer 12	49 44	4	3	10:04	10:04	10:07			0
Customer 13	07 03	1	1	10:05	10:07	10:08			2
Customer 14	30 46	2	3	10:07	10:08	10:11			1
Customer 15	18 10	2	1	10:09	10:11	10:12			2
Customer 16	03 04	1	1	10:10			10:12	10:13	2
Customer 17	73 81	7	7	10:17	10:17	10:24			0
Customer 18	40 90	3	10	10:20			10:20	10:30	0
Customer 19	19 97	2	13	10:22	10:24	10:37			2
Customer 20	89 17	11	1	10:33			10:33	10:34	0
Customer 21	91 65	12	5	10:45			10:45	10:50	0
Customer 22	64 34	6	2	10:51	10:51	10:53			0
Customer 23	64 69	6	5	10:57			10:57	11:02	0
Customer 24	03 00	1	1	10:58	10:58	10:59			0
Customer 25	78 95	8	12	11:06	11:06	11:18			0

OPERATION OF STORE WITH TWO SALESLADIES (CONTINUED)

	Random number	Time between arrivals	Service time	Time of arrival	Serviced by Saleslady A from	until	Serviced by Saleslady B from	until	Time spent waiting
Customer 26	42 91	3	10	11:09			11:09	11:19	0
Customer 27	14 36	1	2	11:10	11:18	11:20			8
Customer 28	51 61	4	4	11:14			11:19	11:23	5
Customer 29	81 81	9	7	11:23	11:23	11:30			0
Customer 30	49 86	4	8	11:27			11:27	11:35	0
Customer 31	30 44	2	3	11:29	11:30	11:33			1
Customer 32	59 57	5	4	11:34	11:34	11:38			0
Customer 33	53 03	4	1	11:38			11:38	11:39	0
Customer 34	24 73	2	6	11:40	11:40	11:46			0
Customer 35	61 80	5	7	11:45			11:45	11:52	0
Customer 36	86 81	10	7	11:55	11:55	12:02			0
Customer 37	75 49	7	3	12:02			12:02	12:05	0
Customer 38	96 20	15	1	12:17	12:17	12:18			0
Customer 39	06 20	1	1	12:18			12:18	12:19	0
Customer 40	79 11	8	1	12:26	12:26	12:27			0
Customer 41	09 72	1	6	12:27			12:27	12:33	0
Customer 42	00 63	1	5	12:28	12:28	12:33			0
Customer 43	38 47	3	3	12:31	12:33	12:36			2
Customer 44	84 31	9	2	12:40			12:40	12:42	0
Customer 45	90 19	11	1	12:51	12:51	12:52			0
Customer 46	70 49	6	3	12:57			12:57	1:00	0
Customer 47	27 32	2	2	12:59	12:59	1:01			0
Customer 48	09 82	1	7	1:00			1:00	1:07	0
Customer 49	04 41	1	3	1:01	1:01	1:04			0
Customer 50	70 18	6	1	1:07	1:07	1:08			0

pages 550 and 551, and it should be observed that quite a few of the customers had to wait 10 minutes or more—one had to wait as long as 20 minutes and only seven of the customers (not counting the first) did not have to wait at all. So far as the saleslady is concerned, the reader will be asked to verify in Exercise 1 on page 555 that she was "free" for a total of 29 minutes, *on the average* about 35 seconds between customers, though actually she had only five breathing spells, one each of 3, 4, 5, 8, and 9 minutes.

Now let us see what would have happened to the same 50 customers (arriving at the identical times and taking as long as before to get served) if there had been two salesladies working at the store. This leads us to pages 552 and 553, where the first four columns are the same as before. Note, however, that now the second customer does not have to wait as he is being served by Saleslady B from 9:13 to 9:14; the third customer also does not have to wait, and the fourth customer has to wait only one minute until Saleslady B takes care of him at 9:19. In each case we assigned the newly-arrived customer to whichever saleslady was free, and when they were both free we assigned him to the saleslady which had been free for the longest time.

Continuing in this way, we find that with two salesladies there is only one "pile up" of customers shortly after 11 o'clock. Actually, only two of the customers had to wait for more than 2 minutes and (not counting the first two) 38 of the other 48 customers did not have to wait at all. As the reader will be asked to verify in Exercise 1 on page 555, both salesladies averaged better than five minutes between customers, which should give them ample time to take inventory, clean up, and perform other duties. Whether or not the management of the chain of candy stores should actually adopt the policy of using two salesladies in each store is another matter; this would have to depend on how they weigh customer goodwill and the indirect benefits derived from improved working conditions against the increase in the cost of operating the stores.

In our example we simulated the operation of a store for roughly four hours, but in actual practice it would most likely be preferable to continue the simulation over a longer period of time (with the hope of getting more reliable results). If the work is done with a computer, which nowadays is common practice, the additional cost would be negligible, since most of the expense is in preparing the *program* (instructions to the computer) and in storing all of the required information (including random numbers).

The illustration of this section is essentially a problem in *queuing theory,* or the theory of *waiting lines,* which has been finding more and more applications in management science. It is used with the loading of ships or trucks; the handling of customers at service stations, airline ticket offices, bank windows, or supermarket checkout stands; the repair of machinery; the processing of tax returns and relief applications; and so on. In contrast to our candy-store example, the time between successive arrivals is usually treated as a *continuous variable,* and as we pointed out in Exercise 1 on page 493, such times between arrivals are often assumed to have *exponential probability densities.* If this assumption is made also for the time it takes the service to be performed, many questions relating to waiting times can be answered by means of special theory (see Exercise 7 which follows).

EXERCISES

1. Verify that in the one-saleslady simulation on pages 550 and 551, the saleslady averaged about 35 seconds of "rest" between customers, and that in the two-saleslady simulation on pages 552 and 553 both salesladies averaged better than 5 minutes between customers.
2. With reference to the candy-store simulations, *on the average* how many minutes did a customer spend in the store
   (a) when there was only one saleslady;
   (b) when there were two salesladies?
3. With reference to the one-saleslady simulation on pages 550 and 551, check how many customers were *waiting to be served* at 9:15, 9:20, 9:25, 9:30, . . . , 1:00, 1:05, and 1:10. *On the average,* how many customers were there in the store at these times waiting to be served?
4. The arrival of customers at a post office and the time it takes them to get served have the following probability functions:

Time between arrivals (minutes)	*Probability*	*Service time (minutes)*	*Probability*
1	0.35	1	0.51
2	0.24	2	0.26
3	0.16	3	0.13
4	0.10	4	0.07
5	0.07	5	0.03
6	0.05		
7	0.02		
8	0.01		

   (a) Simulate the arrival and service of 100 customers at this post office with one clerk on duty. Starting (arbitrarily) with the first customer arriving at 8:00 a.m. record the time at which each customer arrives and the time (from when to when) he is being served.
   (b) Determine how long each customer had to wait until he got served.

(c) Taking a spot check every 5 minutes starting at 8:10, determine how many persons there were *on the average* waiting to get served.

5. The number of days between successive suits being filed at a court and the number of days in court it takes to get them settled have the following probability functions:

Time between filing of suits (days)	*Probability*	*Time to get suit settled (days)*	*Probability*
1	0.24	2	0.40
2	0.19	3	0.25
3	0.15	4	0.15
4	0.12	5	0.09
5	0.09	6	0.06
6	0.07	7	0.03
7	0.05	8	0.02
8	0.04		
9	0.03		
10	0.02		

(a) Numbering the days 1, 2, 3, 4, . . . , beginning with the day on which the first suit is filed and brought to trial, simulate the hearing of 60 consecutive suits by one judge. Record the day on which each suit was filed, the day on which it was brought to trial, and the day on which it was settled.

(b) How many days did each case have to wait before it was brought to trial? Not counting the first case, how long *on the average* did each suit have to wait before it was brought to trial?

(c) Taking a spot check every 5th day starting with the 3rd, determine how many cases there were *on the average* waiting to be brought to trial.

6. Repeat Exercise 5 with two judges hearing different cases at the same time.

7. QUEUING THEORY. If the time between the arrival of successive customers and the time it takes a customer to get served *both* have exponential probability functions (see Exercise 1 on page 493), λ (*lambda*) is the average number of arrivals per unit time and μ (*mu*) is the average number of customers served per unit time (by a single attendant), it can be shown that

The average time a customer must wait to be served is $\dfrac{\lambda}{\mu(\mu - \lambda)}$

The average time a customer spends waiting and being served is $\dfrac{1}{\mu - \lambda}$

The average number of customers waiting to be served (namely, the average length of the queue) is $\dfrac{\lambda^2}{\mu(\mu - \lambda)}$

Assuming that the necessary assumptions are met in the operation of an oil company's service station with one attendant having on the average 10 customers per hour taking on the average 5 minutes to be served, find

(a) the average number of customers served per hour;
(b) the average time a customer must wait for service;
(c) the average time a customer spends in the gas station;
(d) the average number of cars waiting to be served at any time.

8. QUEUING THEORY, CONTINUED. Assuming that the necessary assumptions can be met (at least approximately) in Exercise 4, find

(a) the *means* (see Exercise 22 on page 539) of the two probability functions;
(b) the number of customers arriving at the post office per minute and the number of customers being served per minute;
(c) the average time a customer has to wait, and compare this figure with the result obtained in part (b) of Exercise 4;
(d) the average length of the queue, and compare with the result obtained in part (c) of Exercise 4.

9. QUEUING THEORY, CONTINUED. Assuming that the necessary assumptions can be met (at least approximately) in Exercise 5, find

(a) the *means* (see Exercise 22 on page 539) of the two probability functions;
(b) the number of cases filed per day and the number of cases settled per day;
(c) the average number of days it takes before a suit comes to trial, and compare with the result of part (b) of Exercise 5;
(d) the average length of the queue, and compare with the result of part (c) of Exercise 5.

REFERENCES

Tables of the Binomial Probability Distribution, National Bureau of Standards Applied Mathematics Series No. 6. Washington, D.C.: U.S. Government Printing Office, 1950.

Romig, H. G., *50–100 Binomial Tables*. New York: John Wiley & Sons, Inc., 1953.

APPENDIX: TABLES

TABLE I. Values of $(1 + i)^n$

n	$i = 0.005$	$i = 0.0075$	$i = 0.01$	$i = 0.0125$	$i = 0.015$
1	1.005000	1.007500	1.010000	1.012500	1.015000
2	1.010025	1.015056	1.020100	1.025156	1.030225
3	1.015075	1.022669	1.030301	1.037971	1.045678
4	1.020150	1.030339	1.040604	1.050945	1.061364
5	1.025251	1.038067	1.050110	1.064082	1.077284
6	1.030378	1.045852	1.061520	1.077383	1.093443
7	1.035529	1.053696	1.072135	1.090850	1.109845
8	1.040707	1.061599	1.082857	1.104486	1.126493
9	1.045911	1.069561	1.093685	1.118292	1.143390
10	1.051140	1.077583	1.104622	1.132271	1.160541
11	1.056396	1.085664	1.115668	1.146424	1.177949
12	1.061678	1.093807	1.126825	1.160755	1.195618
13	1.066986	1.102010	1.138093	1.175264	1.213552
14	1.072321	1.110276	1.149474	1.189955	1.231756
15	1.077683	1.118603	1.160969	1.204829	1.250232
16	1.083071	1.126992	1.172579	1.219890	1.268986
17	1.088487	1.135445	1.184304	1.235138	1.288020
18	1.093929	1.143960	1.196147	1.250577	1.307341
19	1.099399	1.152540	1.208109	1.266210	1.326951
20	1.104896	1.161184	1.220190	1.282037	1.346855
21	1.110420	1.169893	1.232392	1.298063	1.367058
22	1.115972	1.178667	1.244716	1.314288	1.387564
23	1.121552	1.187507	1.257163	1.330717	1.408377
24	1.127160	1.196414	1.269735	1.347351	1.429503
25	1.132796	1.205387	1.282432	1.364193	1.450945
26	1.138460	1.214427	1.295256	1.381245	1.472710
27	1.144152	1.223535	1.308209	1.398511	1.494800
28	1.149873	1.232712	1.321291	1.415992	1.517222
29	1.155622	1.241957	1.334504	1.433692	1.539981
30	1.161400	1.251272	1.347849	1.451613	1.563080

TABLE I. Values of $(1 + i)^n$ (Continued)

n	$i = 0.005$	$i = 0.0075$	$i = 0.01$	$i = 0.0125$	$i = 0.015$
31	1.167207	1.260656	1.361327	1.469759	1.586526
32	1.173043	1.270111	1.374941	1.488131	1.610324
33	1.178908	1.279637	1.388690	1.506732	1.634479
34	1.184803	1.289234	1.402577	1.525566	1.658996
35	1.190727	1.298904	1.416603	1.544636	1.683881
36	1.196681	1.308645	1.430769	1.563944	1.709140
37	1.202664	1.318460	1.445076	1.583493	1.734777
38	1.208677	1.328349	1.459527	1.603287	1.760798
39	1.214721	1.338311	1.474123	1.623328	1.787210
40	1.220794	1.348349	1.488864	1.643619	1.814018
41	1.226898	1.358461	1.503752	1.664165	1.841229
42	1.233033	1.368650	1.518790	1.684967	1.868847
43	1.239198	1.378915	1.533978	1.706029	1.896880
44	1.245394	1.389256	1.549318	1.727354	1.925333
45	1.251621	1.399676	1.564811	1.748946	1.954213
46	1.257879	1.410173	1.580459	1.770808	1.983526
47	1.264168	1.420750	1.596263	1.792943	2.013279
48	1.270489	1.431405	1.612226	1.815355	2.043478
49	1.276842	1.442141	1.628348	1.838047	2.074130
50	1.283226	1.452957	1.644632	1.861022	2.105242
51	1.289642	1.463854	1.661078	1.884285	2.136821
52	1.296090	1.474833	1.677689	1.907839	2.168873
53	1.302571	1.485894	1.694466	1.931687	2.201406
54	1.309083	1.497038	1.711410	1.955833	2.234428
55	1.315629	1.508266	1.728525	1.980281	2.267944
56	1.322207	1.519578	1.745810	2.005034	2.301963
57	1.328818	1.530975	1.763268	2.030097	2.336493
58	1.335462	1.542457	1.780901	2.055473	2.371540
59	1.342139	1.554026	1.798710	2.081167	2.407113
60	1.348850	1.565681	1.816697	2.107181	2.443220

TABLE I. Values of $(1+i)^n$ *(Continued)*

n	$i = 0.02$	$i = 0.03$	$i = 0.04$	$i = 0.05$	$i = 0.06$
1	1.020000	1.030000	1.040000	1.050000	1.060000
2	1.040400	1.060900	1.081600	1.102500	1.123600
3	1.061208	1.092727	1.124864	1.157625	1.191016
4	1.082432	1.125509	1.169859	1.215506	1.262477
5	1.104081	1.159274	1.216653	1.276282	1.338226
6	1.126162	1.194052	1.265319	1.340096	1.418519
7	1.148686	1.229874	1.315932	1.407100	1.503630
8	1.171659	1.266770	1.368569	1.477455	1.593848
9	1.195093	1.304773	1.423312	1.551328	1.689479
10	1.218994	1.343916	1.480244	1.628895	1.790848
11	1.243374	1.384234	1.539454	1.710339	1.898299
12	1.268242	1.425761	1.601032	1.795856	2.012196
13	1.293607	1.468534	1.665074	1.885649	2.132928
14	1.319479	1.512590	1.731676	1.979932	2.260904
15	1.345868	1.557967	1.800944	2.078928	2.396558
16	1.372786	1.604706	1.872981	2.182875	2.540352
17	1.400241	1.652848	1.947900	2.292018	2.692773
18	1.428246	1.702433	2.025817	2.406619	2.854339
19	1.456811	1.753506	2.106849	2.526950	3.025600
20	1.485947	1.806111	2.191123	2.653298	3.207135
21	1.515666	1.860295	2.278768	2.785963	3.399564
22	1.545980	1.916103	2.369919	2.925261	3.603537
23	1.576899	1.973587	2.464716	3.071524	3.819750
24	1.608437	2.032794	2.563304	3.225100	4.048935
25	1.640606	2.093778	2.665836	3.386355	4.291871

TABLE I. Values of $(1 + i)^n$ *(Continued)*

n	$i = 0.02$	$i = 0.03$	$i = 0.04$	$i = 0.05$	$i = 0.06$
26	1.673418	2.156591	2.772470	3.555673	4.549383
27	1.706886	2.221289	2.883369	3.733456	4.822346
28	1.741024	2.287928	2.998703	3.920129	5.111687
29	1.775845	2.356566	3.118651	4.116136	5.418388
30	1.811362	2.427263	3.243398	4.321942	5.743491
31	1.847589	2.500080	3.373133	4.538039	6.088101
32	1.884541	2.575083	3.508059	4.764941	6.453387
33	1.922231	2.652335	3.648381	5.003186	6.840590
34	1.960676	2.731905	3.794316	5.253348	7.251025
35	1.999890	2.813862	3.946089	5.516015	7.686087
36	2.039887	2.898278	4.103933	5.791816	8.147252
37	2.080685	2.985227	4.268090	6.081407	8.636087
38	2.122299	3.074783	4.438813	6.385477	9.154252
39	2.164745	3.167027	4.616366	6.704751	9.703507
40	2.208040	3.262038	4.801021	7.039989	10.285718
41	2.252200	3.359899	4.993061	7.391988	10.902861
42	2.297244	3.460696	5.192784	7.761588	11.557033
43	2.343189	3.564517	5.400495	8.149667	12.250455
44	2.390053	3.671452	5.616515	8.557150	12.985482
45	2.437854	3.781596	5.841176	8.985008	13.764611
46	2.486611	3.895044	6.074823	9.434258	14.590487
47	2.536344	4.011895	6.317816	9.905971	15.465917
48	2.587070	4.132252	6.570528	10.401270	16.393872
49	2.638812	4.256219	6.833349	10.921333	17.377504
50	2.691588	4.383906	7.106683	11.467400	18.420154

TABLE II. Values of $(1 + i)^{-n}$

n	$i = 0.005$	$i = 0.0075$	$i = 0.01$	$i = 0.0125$	$i = 0.015$
1	0.995025	0.992556	0.990099	0.987654	0.985222
2	0.990074	0.985167	0.980296	0.975461	0.970662
3	0.985149	0.977833	0.970590	0.963418	0.956317
4	0.980248	0.970554	0.960980	0.951524	0.942184
5	0.975371	0.963329	0.951466	0.939777	0.928260
6	0.970518	0.956158	0.942045	0.928175	0.914542
7	0.965690	0.949040	0.932718	0.916716	0.901027
8	0.960885	0.941975	0.923483	0.905398	0.887711
9	0.956105	0.934963	0.914340	0.894221	0.874592
10	0.951348	0.928003	0.905287	0.883181	0.861667
11	0.946615	0.921095	0.896324	0.872277	0.848933
12	0.941905	0.914238	0.887449	0.861509	0.836387
13	0.937219	0.907432	0.878663	0.850873	0.824027
14	0.932556	0.900677	0.869963	0.840368	0.811849
15	0.927917	0.893973	0.861349	0.829993	0.799852
16	0.923300	0.887318	0.852821	0.819746	0.788031
17	0.918707	0.880712	0.844377	0.809626	0.776385
18	0.914136	0.874156	0.836017	0.799631	0.764912
19	0.909588	0.867649	0.827740	0.789759	0.753607
20	0.905063	0.861190	0.819544	0.780009	0.742470
21	0.900560	0.854779	0.811430	0.770379	0.731498
22	0.896080	0.848416	0.803396	0.760868	0.720688
23	0.891622	0.842100	0.795442	0.751475	0.710037
24	0.887186	0.835831	0.787566	0.742197	0.699544
25	0.882772	0.829609	0.779768	0.733034	0.689206
26	0.878380	0.823434	0.772048	0.723984	0.679021
27	0.874010	0.817304	0.764404	0.715046	0.668986
28	0.869662	0.811220	0.756836	0.706219	0.659099
29	0.865335	0.805181	0.749342	0.697500	0.649359
30	0.861030	0.799187	0.741923	0.688889	0.639762

TABLE II. Values of $(1 + i)^{-n}$ (*Continued*)

n	$i = 0.005$	$i = 0.0075$	$i = 0.01$	$i = 0.0125$	$i = 0.015$
31	0.856746	0.793238	0.734577	0.680384	0.630308
32	0.852484	0.787333	0.727304	0.671984	0.620993
33	0.848242	0.781472	0.720103	0.663688	0.611816
34	0.844022	0.775654	0.712973	0.655494	0.602774
35	0.839823	0.769880	0.705914	0.647402	0.593866
36	0.835645	0.764149	0.698925	0.639409	0.585090
37	0.831487	0.758461	0.692005	0.631515	0.576443
38	0.827351	0.752814	0.685153	0.623719	0.567924
39	0.823235	0.747210	0.678370	0.616018	0.559531
40	0.819139	0.741648	0.671653	0.608413	0.551262
41	0.815064	0.736127	0.665003	0.600902	0.543116
42	0.811008	0.730647	0.658419	0.593484	0.535089
43	0.806974	0.725208	0.651900	0.586157	0.527182
44	0.802959	0.719810	0.645445	0.578920	0.519391
45	0.798964	0.714451	0.639055	0.571773	0.511715
46	0.794989	0.709133	0.632728	0.564714	0.504153
47	0.791034	0.703854	0.626463	0.557742	0.496702
48	0.787098	0.698614	0.620260	0.550856	0.489362
49	0.783182	0.693414	0.614119	0.544056	0.482130
50	0.779286	0.688252	0.608039	0.537339	0.475005
51	0.775409	0.683128	0.602019	0.530705	0.467985
52	0.771551	0.678043	0.596058	0.524153	0.461069
53	0.767713	0.672995	0.590156	0.517682	0.454255
54	0.763893	0.667986	0.584313	0.511291	0.447542
55	0.760093	0.663013	0.578528	0.504979	0.440928
56	0.756311	0.658077	0.572800	0.498745	0.434412
57	0.752548	0.653178	0.567129	0.492587	0.427992
58	0.748804	0.648316	0.561514	0.486506	0.421667
59	0.745079	0.643490	0.555954	0.480500	0.415435
60	0.741372	0.638700	0.550450	0.474568	0.409296

TABLE II. Values of $(1 + i)^{-n}$ (*Continued*)

n	$i = 0.02$	$i = 0.03$	$i = 0.04$	$i = 0.05$	$i = 0.06$
1	0.980392	0.970874	0.961538	0.952381	0.943396
2	0.961169	0.942596	0.924556	0.907029	0.889996
3	0.942322	0.915142	0.888996	0.863838	0.839619
4	0.923845	0.888487	0.854804	0.822702	0.792094
5	0.905731	0.862609	0.821927	0.783526	0.747258
6	0.887971	0.837484	0.790315	0.746215	0.704961
7	0.870560	0.813092	0.759918	0.710681	0.665057
8	0.853490	0.789409	0.730690	0.676839	0.627412
9	0.836755	0.766417	0.702587	0.644609	0.591898
10	0.820348	0.744094	0.675564	0.613913	0.558395
11	0.804263	0.722421	0.649581	0.584679	0.526788
12	0.788493	0.701380	0.624597	0.556837	0.496969
13	0.773033	0.680951	0.600574	0.530321	0.468839
14	0.757875	0.661118	0.577475	0.505068	0.442301
15	0.743015	0.641862	0.555264	0.481017	0.417265
16	0.728446	0.623167	0.533908	0.458112	0.393646
17	0.714163	0.605016	0.513373	0.436297	0.371364
18	0.700159	0.587395	0.493628	0.415521	0.350344
19	0.686431	0.570286	0.474642	0.395734	0.330513
20	0.672971	0.553676	0.456387	0.376889	0.311805
21	0.659776	0.537549	0.438834	0.358942	0.294155
22	0.646839	0.521892	0.421955	0.341850	0.277505
23	0.634156	0.506692	0.405726	0.325571	0.261797
24	0.621721	0.491934	0.390121	0.310068	0.246979
25	0.609531	0.477606	0.375117	0.295303	0.232999

TABLE II. Values of $(1 + i)^{-n}$ (*Continued*)

n	$i = 0.02$	$i = 0.03$	$i = 0.04$	$i = 0.05$	$i = 0.06$
26	0.597579	0.463695	0.360689	0.281241	0.219810
27	0.585862	0.450189	0.346817	0.267848	0.207368
28	0.574375	0.437077	0.333477	0.255094	0.195630
29	0.563112	0.424346	0.320651	0.242946	0.184557
30	0.552071	0.411987	0.308319	0.231377	0.174110
31	0.541246	0.399987	0.296460	0.220359	0.164255
32	0.530633	0.388337	0.285058	0.209866	0.154957
33	0.520229	0.377026	0.274094	0.199873	0.146186
34	0.510028	0.366045	0.263552	0.190355	0.137912
35	0.500028	0.355383	0.253415	0.181290	0.130105
36	0.490223	0.345032	0.243669	0.172657	0.122741
37	0.480611	0.334983	0.234297	0.164436	0.115793
38	0.471187	0.325226	0.225285	0.156605	0.109239
39	0.461948	0.315754	0.216621	0.149148	0.103056
40	0.452890	0.306557	0.208289	0.142046	0.097222
41	0.444010	0.297628	0.200278	0.135282	0.091719
42	0.435304	0.288959	0.192575	0.128840	0.086527
43	0.426769	0.280543	0.185168	0.122704	0.081630
44	0.418401	0.272372	0.178046	0.116861	0.077009
45	0.410197	0.264439	0.171198	0.111297	0.072650
46	0.402154	0.256737	0.164614	0.105997	0.068538
47	0.394268	0.249259	0.158283	0.100949	0.064658
48	0.386538	0.241999	0.152195	0.096142	0.060998
49	0.378958	0.234950	0.146341	0.091564	0.057546
50	0.371528	0.228107	0.140713	0.087204	0.054288

TABLE III. Values of e^x and e^{-x}

x	e^x	e^{-x}	x	e^x	e^{-x}
0.0	1.000	1.000	**2.5**	12.18	0.082
0.1	1.105	0.905	**2.6**	13.46	0.074
0.2	1.221	0.819	**2.7**	14.88	0.067
0.3	1.350	0.741	**2.8**	16.44	0.061
0.4	1.492	0.670	**2.9**	18.17	0.055
0.5	1.649	0.607	**3.0**	20.09	0.050
0.6	1.822	0.549	**3.1**	22.20	0.045
0.7	2.014	0.497	**3.2**	24.53	0.041
0.8	2.226	0.449	**3.3**	27.11	0.037
0.9	2.460	0.407	**3.4**	29.96	0.033
1.0	2.718	0.368	**3.5**	33.12	0.030
1.1	3.004	0.333	**3.6**	36.60	0.027
1.2	3.320	0.301	**3.7**	40.45	0.025
1.3	3.669	0.273	**3.8**	44.70	0.022
1.4	4.055	0.247	**3.9**	49.40	0.020
1.5	4.482	0.223	**4.0**	54.60	0.018
1.6	4.953	0.202	**4.1**	60.34	0.017
1.7	5.474	0.183	**4.2**	66.69	0.015
1.8	6.050	0.165	**4.3**	73.70	0.014
1.9	6.686	0.150	**4.4**	81.45	0.012
2.0	7.389	0.135	**4.5**	90.02	0.011
2.1	8.166	0.122	**4.6**	99.48	0.010
2.2	9.025	0.111	**4.7**	109.95	0.009
2.3	9.974	0.100	**4.8**	121.51	0.008
2.4	11.023	0.091	**4.9**	134.29	0.007

TABLE III. Values of e^x and e^{-x} *(Continued)*

x	e^x	e^{-x}	x	e^x	e^{-x}
5.0	148.4	0.0067	**7.5**	1,808.0	0.00055
5.1	164.0	0.0061	**7.6**	1,998.2	0.00050
5.2	181.3	0.0055	**7.7**	2,208.3	0.00045
5.3	200.3	0.0050	**7.8**	2,440.6	0.00041
5.4	221.4	0.0045	**7.9**	2,697.3	0.00037
5.5	244.7	0.0041	**8.0**	2,981.0	0.00034
5.6	270.4	0.0037	**8.1**	3,294.5	0.00030
5.7	298.9	0.0033	**8.2**	3,641.0	0.00027
5.8	330.3	0.0030	**8.3**	4,023.9	0.00025
5.9	365.0	0.0027	**8.4**	4,447.1	0.00022
6.0	403.4	0.0025	**8.5**	4,914.8	0.00020
6.1	445.9	0.0022	**8.6**	5,431.7	0.00018
6.2	492.8	0.0020	**8.7**	6,002.9	0.00017
6.3	544.6	0.0018	**8.8**	6,634.2	0.00015
6.4	601.8	0.0017	**8.9**	7,332.0	0.00014
6.5	665.1	0.0015	**9.0**	8,103.1	0.00012
6.6	735.1	0.0014	**9.1**	8,955.3	0.00011
6.7	812.4	0.0012	**9.2**	9,897.1	0.00010
6.8	897.8	0.0011	**9.3**	10,938	0.00009
6.9	992.3	0.0010	**9.4**	12,088	0.00008
7.0	1,096.6	0.0009	**9.5**	13,360	0.00007
7.1	1,212.0	0.0008	**9.6**	14,765	0.00007
7.2	1,339.4	0.0007	**9.7**	16,318	0.00006
7.3	1,480.3	0.0007	**9.8**	18,034	0.00006
7.4	1,636.0	0.0006	**9.9**	19,930	0.00005

TABLE IV. Logarithms

N	0	1	2	3	4	5	6	7	8	9
10	0000	0043	0086	0128	0170	0212	0253	0294	0334	0374
11	0414	0453	0492	0531	0569	0607	0645	0682	0719	0755
12	0792	0828	0864	0899	0934	0969	1004	1038	1072	1106
13	1139	1173	1206	1239	1271	1303	1335	1367	1399	1430
14	1461	1492	1523	1553	1584	1614	1644	1673	1703	1732
15	1761	1790	1818	1847	1875	1903	1931	1959	1987	2014
16	2041	2068	2095	2122	2148	2175	2201	2227	2253	2279
17	2304	2330	2355	2380	2405	2430	2455	2480	2504	2529
18	2553	2577	2601	2625	2648	2672	2695	2718	2742	2765
19	2788	2810	2833	2856	2878	2900	2923	2945	2967	2989
20	3010	3032	3054	3075	3096	3118	3139	3160	3181	3201
21	3222	3243	3263	3284	3304	3324	3345	3365	3385	3404
22	3424	3444	3464	3483	3502	3522	3541	3560	3579	3598
23	3617	3636	3655	3674	3692	3711	3729	3747	3766	3784
24	3802	3820	3838	3856	3874	3892	3909	3927	3945	3962
25	3979	3997	4014	4031	4048	4065	4082	4099	4116	4133
26	4150	4166	4183	4200	4216	4232	4249	4265	4281	4298
27	4314	4330	4346	4362	4378	4393	4409	4425	4440	4456
28	4472	4487	4502	4518	4533	4548	4564	4579	4594	4609
29	4624	4639	4654	4669	4683	4698	4713	4728	4742	4757
30	4771	4786	4800	4814	4829	4843	4857	4871	4886	4900
31	4914	4928	4942	4955	4969	4983	4997	5011	5024	5038
32	5051	5065	5079	5092	5105	5119	5132	5145	5159	5172
33	5185	5198	5211	5224	5237	5250	5263	5276	5289	5302
34	5315	5328	5340	5353	5366	5378	5391	5403	5416	5428
35	5441	5453	5465	5478	5490	5502	5514	5527	5539	5551
36	5563	5575	5587	5599	5611	5623	5635	5647	5658	5670
37	5682	5694	5705	5717	5729	5740	5752	5763	5775	5786
38	5798	5809	5821	5832	5843	5855	5866	5877	5888	5899
39	5911	5922	5933	5944	5955	5966	5977	5988	5999	6010
40	6021	6031	6042	6053	6064	6075	6085	6096	6107	6117
41	6128	6138	6149	6160	6170	6180	6191	6201	6212	6222
42	6232	6243	6253	6263	6274	6284	6294	6304	6314	6325
43	6335	6345	6355	6365	6375	6385	6395	6405	6415	6425
44	6435	6444	6454	6464	6474	6484	6493	6503	6513	6522
45	6532	6542	6551	6561	6571	6580	6590	6599	6609	6618
46	6628	6637	6646	6656	6665	6675	6684	6693	6702	6712
47	6721	6730	6739	6749	6758	6767	6776	6785	6794	6803
48	6812	6821	6830	6839	6848	6857	6866	6875	6884	6893
49	6902	6911	6920	6928	6937	6946	6955	6964	6972	6981
50	6990	6998	7007	7016	7024	7033	7042	7050	7059	7067
51	7076	7084	7093	7101	7110	7118	7126	7135	7143	7152
52	7160	7168	7177	7185	7193	7202	7210	7218	7226	7235
53	7243	7251	7259	7267	7275	7284	7292	7300	7308	7316
54	7324	7332	7340	7348	7356	7364	7372	7380	7388	7396

TABLE IV. Logarithms (*Continued*)

N	0	1	2	3	4	5	6	7	8	9
55	7404	7412	7419	7427	7435	7443	7451	7459	7466	7474
56	7482	7490	7497	7505	7513	7520	7528	7536	7543	7551
57	7559	7566	7574	7582	7589	7597	7604	7612	7619	7627
58	7634	7642	7649	7657	7664	7672	7679	7686	7694	7701
59	7709	7716	7723	7731	7738	7745	7752	7760	7767	7774
60	7782	7789	7796	7803	7810	7818	7825	7832	7839	7846
61	7853	7860	7868	7875	7882	7889	7896	7903	7910	7917
62	7924	7931	7938	7945	7952	7959	7966	7973	7980	7987
63	7993	8000	8007	8014	8021	8028	8035	8041	8048	8055
64	8062	8069	8075	8082	8089	8096	8102	8109	8116	8122
65	8129	8136	8142	8149	8156	8162	8169	8176	8182	8189
66	8195	8202	8209	8215	8222	8228	8235	8241	8248	8254
67	8261	8267	8274	8280	8287	8293	8299	8306	8312	8319
68	8325	8331	8338	8344	8351	8357	8363	8370	8376	8382
69	8388	8395	8401	8407	8414	8420	8426	8432	8439	8445
70	8451	8457	8463	8470	8476	8482	8488	8494	8500	8506
71	8513	8519	8525	8531	8537	8543	8549	8555	8561	8567
72	8573	8579	8585	8591	8597	8603	8609	8615	8621	8627
73	8633	8639	8645	8651	8657	8663	8669	8675	8681	8686
74	8692	8698	8704	8710	8716	8722	8727	8733	8739	8745
75	8751	8756	8762	8768	8774	8779	8785	8791	8797	8802
76	8808	8814	8820	8825	8831	8837	8842	8848	8854	8859
77	8865	8871	8876	8882	8887	8893	8899	8904	8910	8915
78	8921	8927	8932	8938	8943	8949	8954	8960	8965	8971
79	8976	8982	8987	8993	8998	9004	9009	9015	9020	9025
80	9031	9036	9042	9047	9053	9058	9063	9069	9074	9079
81	9085	9090	9096	9101	9106	9112	9117	9122	9128	9133
82	9138	9143	9149	9154	9159	9165	9170	9175	9180	9186
83	9191	9196	9201	9206	9212	9217	9222	9227	9232	9238
84	9243	9248	9253	9258	9263	9269	9274	9279	9284	9289
85	9294	9299	9304	9309	9315	9320	9325	9330	9335	9340
86	9345	9350	9355	9360	9365	9370	9375	9380	9385	9390
87	9395	9400	9405	9410	9415	9420	9425	9430	9435	9440
88	9445	9450	9455	9460	9465	9469	9474	9479	9484	9489
89	9494	9499	9504	9509	9513	9518	9523	9528	9533	9538
90	9542	9547	9552	9557	9562	9566	9571	9576	9581	9586
91	9590	9595	9600	9605	9609	9614	9619	9624	9628	9633
92	9638	9643	9647	9652	9657	9661	9666	9671	9675	9680
93	9685	9689	9694	9699	9703	9708	9713	9717	9722	9727
94	9731	9736	9741	9745	9750	9754	9759	9763	9768	9773
95	9777	9782	9786	9791	9795	9800	9805	9809	9814	9818
96	9823	9827	9832	9836	9841	9845	9850	9854	9859	9863
97	9868	9872	9877	9881	9886	9890	9894	9899	9903	9908
98	9912	9917	9921	9926	9930	9934	9939	9943	9948	9952
99	9956	9961	9965	9969	9974	9978	9983	9987	9991	9996

To find the square root of any positive number rounded to two digits, use the following rule to decide whether to take the entry of the $\sqrt{n}$ or the $\sqrt{10n}$ column:

> *Move the decimal point an even number of places to the right or to the left until a number greater than or equal to 1 but less than 100 is reached. If the resulting number is less than 10 go to the $\sqrt{n}$ column; if it is 10 or more go to the $\sqrt{10n}$ column.*

Thus, to find the square root of 14,000 or 0.032 we go to the $\sqrt{n}$ column since the decimal point has to be moved, respectively, 4 places to the left to give 1.4 or 2 places to the right to give 3.2. Similarly, to find the square root of 2,200 or 0.000016 we go to the $\sqrt{10n}$ column since the decimal point has to be moved, respectively, 2 places to the left to give 22 or 6 places to the right to give 16.

Having found the entry in the appropriate column of Table V, the only thing that remains to be done is to put the decimal point in the right place in the result. To this end we use the following rule:

> *Having previously moved the decimal point an even number of places to the left or to the right to get a number greater than or equal to 1 but less than 100, the decimal point of the appropriate entry of Table V is moved half as many places in the opposite direction.*

For example, to find the square root of 14,000 we first note that the decimal point has to be moved *four places to the left* to give 1.4. We thus take the entry of the $\sqrt{n}$ column corresponding to 1.4, move its decimal point *two places to the right*, and get $\sqrt{14{,}000} = 118.322$. Similarly, to find the square root of 0.000016 we note that the decimal point has to be moved *six places to the right* to give 16. We thus take the entry of the $\sqrt{10n}$ column corresponding to 16, move the decimal point *three places to the left*, and get $\sqrt{0.000016} = 0.004$.

TABLE V. Square roots

n	$\sqrt{n}$	$\sqrt{10n}$	n	$\sqrt{n}$	$\sqrt{10n}$
1.0	1.00000	3.16228	**3.5**	1.87083	5.91608
1.1	1.04881	3.31662	**3.6**	1.89737	6.00000
1.2	1.09545	3.46410	**3.7**	1.92354	6.08276
1.3	1.14018	3.60555	**3.8**	1.94936	6.16441
1.4	1.18322	3.74166	**3.9**	1.97484	6.24500
1.5	1.22474	3.87298	**4.0**	2.00000	6.32456
1.6	1.26491	4.00000	**4.1**	2.02485	6.40312
1.7	1.30384	4.12311	**4.2**	2.04939	6.48074
1.8	1.34164	4.24264	**4.3**	2.07364	6.55744
1.9	1.37840	4.35890	**4.4**	2.09762	6.63325
2.0	1.41421	4.47214	**4.5**	2.12132	6.70820
2.1	1.44914	4.58258	**4.6**	2.14476	6.78233
2.2	1.48324	4.69042	**4.7**	2.16795	6.85565
2.3	1.51658	4.79583	**4.8**	2.19089	6.92820
2.4	1.54919	4.89898	**4.9**	2.21359	7.00000
2.5	1.58114	5.00000	**5.0**	2.23607	7.07107
2.6	1.61245	5.09902	**5.1**	2.25832	7.14143
2.7	1.64317	5.19615	**5.2**	2.28035	7.21110
2.8	1.67332	5.29150	**5.3**	2.30217	7.28011
2.9	1.70294	5.38516	**5.4**	2.32379	7.34847
3.0	1.73205	5.47723	**5.5**	2.34521	7.41620
3.1	1.76068	5.56776	**5.6**	2.36643	7.48331
3.2	1.78885	5.65685	**5.7**	2.38747	7.54983
3.3	1.81659	5.74456	**5.8**	2.40832	7.61577
3.4	1.84391	5.83095	**5.9**	2.42899	7.68115

TABLE V. Square roots *(Continued)*

n	$\sqrt{n}$	$\sqrt{10n}$	n	$\sqrt{n}$	$\sqrt{10n}$
6.0	2.44949	7.74597	**8.0**	2.82843	8.94427
6.1	2.46982	7.81025	**8.1**	2.84605	9.00000
6.2	2.48998	7.87401	**8.2**	2.86356	9.05539
6.3	2.50998	7.93725	**8.3**	2.88097	9.11043
6.4	2.52982	8.00000	**8.4**	2.89828	9.16515
6.5	2.54951	8.06226	**8.5**	2.91548	9.21954
6.6	2.56905	8.12404	**8.6**	2.93258	9.27362
6.7	2.58844	8.18535	**8.7**	2.94958	9.32738
6.8	2.60768	8.24621	**8.8**	2.96648	9.38083
6.9	2.62679	8.30662	**8.9**	2.98329	9.43398
7.0	2.64575	8.36660	**9.0**	3.00000	9.48683
7.1	2.66458	8.42615	**9.1**	3.01662	9.53939
7.2	2.68328	8.48528	**9.2**	3.03315	9.59166
7.3	2.70185	8.54400	**9.3**	3.04959	9.64365
7.4	2.72029	8.60233	**9.4**	3.06594	9.69536
7.5	2.73861	8.66025	**9.5**	3.08221	9.74679
7.6	2.75681	8.71780	**9.6**	3.09839	9.79796
7.7	2.77489	8.77496	**9.7**	3.11448	9.84886
7.8	2.79285	8.83176	**9.8**	3.13050	9.89949
7.9	2.81069	8.88819	**9.9**	3.14643	9.94987

TABLE VI. Trigonometric functions

DEGREES	SINE	COSINE	TANGENT	COTAN.	DEGREES
0	.0000	1.0000	.0000		**90**
1	.0175	.9998	.0175	57.290	**89**
2	.0349	.9994	.0349	28.636	**88**
3	.0523	.9986	.0524	19.081	**87**
4	.0698	.9976	.0699	14.301	**86**
5	.0872	.9962	.0875	11.430	**85**
6	.1045	.9945	.1051	9.5144	**84**
7	.1219	.9925	.1228	8.1443	**83**
8	.1392	.9903	.1405	7.1154	**82**
9	.1564	.9877	.1584	6.3138	**81**
10	.1736	.9848	.1763	5.6713	**80**
11	.1908	.9816	.1944	5.1446	**79**
12	.2079	.9781	.2126	4.7046	**78**
13	.2250	.9744	.2309	4.3315	**77**
14	.2419	.9703	.2493	4.0108	**76**
15	.2588	.9659	.2679	3.7321	**75**
16	.2756	.9613	.2867	3.4874	**74**
17	.2924	.9563	.3057	3.2709	**73**
18	.3090	.9511	.3249	3.0777	**72**
19	.3256	.9455	.3443	2.9042	**71**
20	.3420	.9397	.3640	2.7475	**70**
21	.3584	.9336	.3839	2.6051	**69**
22	.3746	.9272	.4040	2.4751	**68**
23	.3907	.9205	.4245	2.3559	**67**
24	.4067	.9135	.4452	2.2460	**66**
25	.4226	.9063	.4663	2.1445	**65**
26	.4384	.8988	.4877	2.0503	**64**
27	.4540	.8910	.5095	1.9626	**63**
28	.4695	.8829	.5317	1.8807	**62**
29	.4848	.8746	.5543	1.8040	**61**
30	.5000	.8660	.5774	1.7321	**60**
31	.5150	.8572	.6009	1.6643	**59**
32	.5299	.8480	.6249	1.6003	**58**
33	.5446	.8387	.6494	1.5399	**57**
34	.5592	.8290	.6745	1.4826	**56**
35	.5736	.8192	.7002	1.4281	**55**
36	.5878	.8090	.7265	1.3764	**54**
37	.6018	.7986	.7536	1.3270	**53**
38	.6157	.7880	.7813	1.2799	**52**
39	.6293	.7771	.8098	1.2349	**51**
40	.6428	.7660	.8391	1.1918	**50**
41	.6561	.7547	.8693	1.1504	**49**
42	.6691	.7431	.9004	1.1106	**48**
43	.6820	.7314	.9325	1.0724	**47**
44	.6947	.7193	.9657	1.0355	**46**
45	.7071	.7071	1.0000	1.0000	**45**
DEGREES	COSINE	SINE	COTAN.	TANGENT	DEGREES

TABLE VII. Factorials

n	$n!$	$\log n!$
0	1	0.0000
1	1	0.0000
2	2	0.3010
3	6	0.7782
4	24	1.3802
5	120	2.0792
6	720	2.8573
7	5,040	3.7024
8	40,320	4.6055
9	362,880	5.5598
10	3,628,800	6.5598
11	39,916,800	7.6012
12	479,001,600	8.6803
13	6,227,020,800	9.7943
14	87,178,291,200	10.9404
15	1,307,674,368,000	12.1165

TABLE VIII. Binomial coefficients

n	$\binom{n}{0}$	$\binom{n}{1}$	$\binom{n}{2}$	$\binom{n}{3}$	$\binom{n}{4}$	$\binom{n}{5}$	$\binom{n}{6}$	$\binom{n}{7}$	$\binom{n}{8}$	$\binom{n}{9}$	$\binom{n}{10}$
0	1										
1	1	1									
2	1	2	1								
3	1	3	3	1							
4	1	4	6	4	1						
5	1	5	10	10	5	1					
6	1	6	15	20	15	6	1				
7	1	7	21	35	35	21	7	1			
8	1	8	28	56	70	56	28	8	1		
9	1	9	36	84	126	126	84	36	9	1	
10	1	10	45	120	210	252	210	120	45	10	1
11	1	11	55	165	330	462	462	330	165	55	11
12	1	12	66	220	495	792	924	792	495	220	66
13	1	13	78	286	715	1287	1716	1716	1287	715	286
14	1	14	91	364	1001	2002	3003	3432	3003	2002	1001
15	1	15	105	455	1365	3003	5005	6435	6435	5005	3003
16	1	16	120	560	1820	4368	8008	11440	12870	11440	8008
17	1	17	136	680	2380	6188	12376	19448	24310	24310	19448
18	1	18	153	816	3060	8568	18564	31824	43758	48620	43758
19	1	19	171	969	3876	11628	27132	50388	75582	92378	92378
20	1	20	190	1140	4845	15504	38760	77520	125970	167960	184756

If necessary, use the identity $\binom{n}{k} = \binom{n}{n-k}$.

TABLE IX. Binomial probabilities

		p										
n	*x*	0.05	0.1	0.2	0.3	0.4	0.5	0.6	0.7	0.8	0.9	0.95
2	0	0.902	0.810	0.640	0.490	0.360	0.250	0.160	0.090	0.040	0.010	0.002
	1	0.095	0.180	0.320	0.420	0.480	0.500	0.480	0.420	0.320	0.180	0.095
	2	0.002	0.010	0.040	0.090	0.160	0.250	0.360	0.490	0.640	0.810	0.902
3	0	0.857	0.729	0.512	0.343	0.216	0.125	0.064	0.027	0.008	0.001	
	1	0.135	0.243	0.384	0.441	0.432	0.375	0.288	0.189	0.096	0.027	0.007
	2	0.007	0.027	0.096	0.189	0.288	0.375	0.432	0.441	0.384	0.243	0.135
	3		0.001	0.008	0.027	0.064	0.125	0.216	0.343	0.512	0.729	0.857
4	0	0.815	0.656	0.410	0.240	0.130	0.062	0.026	0.008	0.002		
	1	0.171	0.292	0.410	0.412	0.346	0.250	0.154	0.076	0.026	0.004	
	2	0.014	0.049	0.154	0.265	0.346	0.375	0.346	0.265	0.154	0.049	0.014
	3		0.004	0.026	0.076	0.154	0.250	0.346	0.412	0.410	0.292	0.171
	4			0.002	0.008	0.026	0.062	0.130	0.240	0.410	0.656	0.815
5	0	0.774	0.590	0.328	0.168	0.078	0.031	0.010	0.002			
	1	0.204	0.328	0.410	0.360	0.259	0.156	0.077	0.028	0.006		
	2	0.021	0.073	0.205	0.309	0.346	0.312	0.230	0.132	0.051	0.008	0.001
	3	0.001	0.008	0.051	0.132	0.230	0.312	0.346	0.309	0.205	0.073	0.021
	4			0.006	0.028	0.077	0.156	0.259	0.360	0.410	0.328	0.204
	5				0.002	0.010	0.031	0.078	0.168	0.328	0.590	0.774
6	0	0.735	0.531	0.262	0.118	0.047	0.016	0.004	0.001			
	1	0.232	0.354	0.393	0.303	0.187	0.094	0.037	0.010	0.002		
	2	0.031	0.098	0.246	0.324	0.311	0.234	0.138	0.060	0.015	0.001	
	3	0.002	0.015	0.082	0.185	0.276	0.312	0.276	0.185	0.082	0.015	0.002
	4		0.001	0.015	0.060	0.138	0.234	0.311	0.324	0.246	0.098	0.031
	5			0.002	0.010	0.037	0.094	0.187	0.303	0.393	0.354	0.232
	6				0.001	0.004	0.016	0.047	0.118	0.262	0.531	0.735
7	0	0.698	0.478	0.210	0.082	0.028	0.008	0.002				
	1	0.257	0.372	0.367	0.247	0.131	0.055	0.017	0.004			
	2	0.041	0.124	0.275	0.318	0.261	0.164	0.077	0.025	0.004		
	3	0.004	0.023	0.115	0.227	0.290	0.273	0.194	0.097	0.029	0.003	
	4		0.003	0.029	0.097	0.194	0.273	0.290	0.227	0.115	0.023	0.004

TABLE IX. Binomial probabilities *(Continued)*

		p										
n	x	0.05	0.1	0.2	0.3	0.4	0.5	0.6	0.7	0.8	0.9	0.95
7	5			0.004	0.025	0.077	0.164	0.261	0.318	0.275	0.124	0.041
	6				0.004	0.017	0.055	0.131	0.247	0.367	0.372	0.257
	7					0.002	0.008	0.028	0.082	0.210	0.478	0.698
8	0	0.663	0.430	0.168	0.058	0.017	0.004	0.001				
	1	0.279	0.383	0.336	0.198	0.090	0.031	0.008	0.001			
	2	0.051	0.149	0.294	0.296	0.209	0.109	0.041	0.010	0.001		
	3	0.005	0.033	0.147	0.254	0.279	0.219	0.124	0.047	0.009		
	4		0.005	0.046	0.136	0.232	0.273	0.232	0.136	0.046	0.005	
	5			0.009	0.047	0.124	0.219	0.279	0.254	0.147	0.033	0.005
	6			0.001	0.010	0.041	0.109	0.209	0.296	0.294	0.149	0.051
	7				0.001	0.008	0.031	0.090	0.198	0.336	0.383	0.279
	8					0.001	0.004	0.017	0.058	0.168	0.430	0.663
9	0	0.630	0.387	0.134	0.040	0.010	0.002					
	1	0.299	0.387	0.302	0.156	0.060	0.018	0.004				
	2	0.063	0.172	0.302	0.267	0.161	0.070	0.021	0.004			
	3	0.008	0.045	0.176	0.267	0.251	0.164	0.074	0.021	0.003		
	4	0.001	0.007	0.066	0.172	0.251	0.246	0.167	0.074	0.017	0.001	
	5		0.001	0.017	0.074	0.167	0.246	0.251	0.172	0.066	0.007	0.001
	6			0.003	0.021	0.074	0.164	0.251	0.267	0.176	0.045	0.008
	7				0.004	0.021	0.070	0.161	0.267	0.302	0.172	0.063
	8					0.004	0.018	0.060	0.156	0.302	0.387	0.299
	9						0.002	0.010	0.040	0.134	0.387	0.630
10	0	0.599	0.349	0.107	0.028	0.006	0.001					
	1	0.315	0.387	0.268	0.121	0.040	0.010	0.002				
	2	0.075	0.194	0.302	0.233	0.121	0.044	0.011	0.001			
	3	0.010	0.057	0.201	0.267	0.215	0.117	0.042	0.009	0.001		
	4	0.001	0.011	0.088	0.200	0.251	0.205	0.111	0.037	0.006		
	5		0.001	0.026	0.103	0.201	0.246	0.201	0.103	0.026	0.001	
	6			0.006	0.037	0.111	0.205	0.251	0.200	0.088	0.011	0.001
	7			0.001	0.009	0.042	0.117	0.215	0.267	0.201	0.057	0.010
	8				0.001	0.011	0.044	0.121	0.233	0.302	0.194	0.075
	9					0.002	0.010	0.040	0.121	0.268	0.387	0.315
	10						0.001	0.006	0.028	0.107	0.349	0.599

TABLE IX. Binomial probabilities *(Continued)*

		p										
n	x	0.05	0.1	0.2	0.3	0.4	0.5	0.6	0.7	0.8	0.9	0.95
11	0	0.569	0.314	0.086	0.020	0.004						
	1	0.329	0.384	0.236	0.093	0.027	0.005	0.001				
	2	0.087	0.213	0.295	0.200	0.089	0.027	0.005	0.001			
	3	0.014	0.071	0.221	0.257	0.177	0.081	0.023	0.004			
	4	0.001	0.016	0.111	0.220	0.236	0.161	0.070	0.017	0.002		
	5		0.002	0.039	0.132	0.221	0.226	0.147	0.057	0.010		
	6			0.010	0.057	0.147	0.226	0.221	0.132	0.039	0.002	
	7			0.002	0.017	0.070	0.161	0.236	0.220	0.111	0.016	0.001
	8				0.004	0.023	0.081	0.177	0.257	0.221	0.071	0.014
	9				0.001	0.005	0.027	0.089	0.200	0.295	0.213	0.087
	10					0.001	0.005	0.027	0.093	0.236	0.384	0.329
	11							0.004	0.020	0.086	0.314	0.569
12	0	0.540	0.282	0.069	0.014	0.002						
	1	0.341	0.377	0.206	0.071	0.017	0.003					
	2	0.099	0.230	0.283	0.168	0.064	0.016	0.002				
	3	0.017	0.085	0.236	0.240	0.142	0.054	0.012	0.001			
	4	0.002	0.021	0.133	0.231	0.213	0.121	0.042	0.008	0.001		
	5		0.004	0.053	0.158	0.227	0.193	0.101	0.029	0.003		
	6			0.016	0.079	0.177	0.226	0.177	0.079	0.016		
	7			0.003	0.029	0.101	0.193	0.227	0.158	0.053	0.004	
	8			0.001	0.008	0.042	0.121	0.213	0.231	0.133	0.021	0.002
	9				0.001	0.012	0.054	0.142	0.240	0.236	0.085	0.017
	10					0.002	0.016	0.064	0.168	0.283	0.230	0.099
	11						0.003	0.017	0.071	0.206	0.377	0.341
	12							0.002	0.014	0.069	0.282	0.540
13	0	0.513	0.254	0.055	0.010	0.001						
	1	0.351	0.367	0.179	0.054	0.011	0.002					
	2	0.111	0.245	0.268	0.139	0.045	0.010	0.001				
	3	0.021	0.100	0.246	0.218	0.111	0.035	0.006	0.001			
	4	0.003	0.028	0.154	0.234	0.184	0.087	0.024	0.003			
	5		0.006	0.069	0.180	0.221	0.157	0.066	0.014	0.001		
	6		0.001	0.023	0.103	0.197	0.209	0.131	0.044	0.006		
	7			0.006	0.044	0.131	0.209	0.197	0.103	0.023	0.001	

TABLE IX. Binomial probabilities (*Continued*)

n	x	0.05	0.1	0.2	0.3	0.4	0.5	0.6	0.7	0.8	0.9	0.95
						p						
13	8			0.001	0.014	0.066	0.157	0.221	0.180	0.069	0.006	
	9				0.003	0.024	0.087	0.184	0.234	0.154	0.028	0.003
	10				0.001	0.006	0.035	0.111	0.218	0.246	0.100	0.021
	11					0.001	0.010	0.045	0.139	0.268	0.245	0.111
	12						0.002	0.011	0.054	0.179	0.367	0.351
	13							0.001	0.010	0.055	0.254	0.513
14	0	0.488	0.229	0.044	0.007	0.001						
	1	0.359	0.356	0.154	0.041	0.007	0.001					
	2	0.123	0.257	0.250	0.113	0.032	0.006	0.001				
	3	0.026	0.114	0.250	0.194	0.085	0.022	0.003				
	4	0.004	0.035	0.172	0.229	0.155	0.061	0.014	0.001			
	5		0.008	0.086	0.196	0.207	0.122	0.041	0.007			
	6		0.001	0.032	0.126	0.207	0.183	0.092	0.023	0.002		
	7			0.009	0.062	0.157	0.209	0.157	0.062	0.009		
	8			0.002	0.023	0.092	0.183	0.207	0.126	0.032	0.001	
	9				0.007	0.041	0.122	0.207	0.196	0.086	0.008	
	10				0.001	0.014	0.061	0.155	0.229	0.172	0.035	0.004
	11					0.003	0.022	0.085	0.194	0.250	0.114	0.026
	12					0.001	0.006	0.032	0.113	0.250	0.257	0.123
	13						0.001	0.007	0.041	0.154	0.356	0.359
	14							0.001	0.007	0.044	0.229	0.488
15	0	0.463	0.206	0.035	0.005							
	1	0.366	0.343	0.132	0.031	0.005						
	2	0.135	0.267	0.231	0.092	0.022	0.003					
	3	0.031	0.129	0.250	0.170	0.063	0.014	0.002				
	4	0.005	0.043	0.188	0.219	0.127	0.042	0.007	0.001			
	5	0.001	0.010	0.103	0.206	0.186	0.092	0.024	0.003			
	6		0.002	0.043	0.147	0.207	0.153	0.061	0.012	0.001		
	7			0.014	0.081	0.177	0.196	0.118	0.035	0.003		
	8			0.003	0.035	0.118	0.196	0.177	0.081	0.014		
	9			0.001	0.012	0.061	0.153	0.207	0.147	0.043	0.002	
	10				0.003	0.024	0.092	0.186	0.206	0.103	0.010	0.001
	11				0.001	0.007	0.042	0.127	0.219	0.188	0.043	0.005

TABLE IX. Binomial probabilities *(Continued)*

n	x	0.05	0.1	0.2	0.3	0.4	0.5	0.6	0.7	0.8	0.9	0.95
15	12					0.002	0.014	0.063	0.170	0.250	0.129	0.031
	13						0.003	0.022	0.092	0.231	0.267	0.135
	14							0.005	0.031	0.132	0.343	0.366
	15								0.005	0.035	0.206	0.463
16	0	0.440	0.185	0.028	0.003							
	1	0.371	0.329	0.113	0.023	0.003						
	2	0.146	0.275	0.211	0.073	0.015	0.002					
	3	0.036	0.142	0.246	0.146	0.047	0.009	0.001				
	4	0.006	0.051	0.200	0.204	0.101	0.028	0.004				
	5	0.001	0.014	0.120	0.210	0.162	0.067	0.014	0.001			
	6		0.003	0.055	0.165	0.198	0.122	0.039	0.006			
	7			0.020	0.101	0.189	0.175	0.084	0.019	0.001		
	8			0.006	0.049	0.142	0.196	0.142	0.049	0.006		
	9			0.001	0.019	0.084	0.175	0.189	0.101	0.020		
	10				0.006	0.039	0.122	0.198	0.165	0.055	0.003	
	11				0.001	0.014	0.067	0.162	0.210	0.120	0.014	0.001
	12					0.004	0.028	0.101	0.204	0.200	0.051	0.006
	13					0.001	0.009	0.047	0.146	0.246	0.142	0.036
	14						0.002	0.015	0.073	0.211	0.275	0.146
	15							0.003	0.023	0.113	0.329	0.371
	16								0.003	0.028	0.185	0.440
17	0	0.418	0.167	0.023	0.002							
	1	0.374	0.315	0.096	0.017	0.002						
	2	0.158	0.280	0.191	0.058	0.010	0.001					
	3	0.041	0.156	0.239	0.125	0.034	0.005					
	4	0.008	0.060	0.209	0.187	0.080	0.018	0.002				
	5	0.001	0.017	0.136	0.208	0.138	0.047	0.008	0.001			
	6		0.004	0.068	0.178	0.184	0.094	0.024	0.003			
	7		0.001	0.027	0.120	0.193	0.148	0.057	0.009			
	8			0.008	0.064	0.161	0.185	0.107	0.028	0.002		
	9			0.002	0.028	0.107	0.185	0.161	0.064	0.008		
	10				0.009	0.057	0.148	0.193	0.120	0.027	0.001	
	11				0.003	0.024	0.094	0.184	0.178	0.068	0.004	
	12				0.001	0.008	0.047	0.138	0.208	0.136	0.017	0.001

TABLE IX. Binomial probabilities *(Continued)*

		p										
n	x	0.05	0.1	0.2	0.3	0.4	0.5	0.6	0.7	0.8	0.9	0.95
17	13					0.002	0.018	0.080	0.187	0.209	0.060	0.008
	14						0.005	0.034	0.125	0.239	0.156	0.041
	15						0.001	0.010	0.058	0.191	0.280	0.158
	16							0.002	0.017	0.096	0.315	0.374
	17								0.002	0.023	0.167	0.418
18	0	0.397	0.150	0.018	0.002							
	1	0.376	0.300	0.081	0.013	0.001						
	2	0.168	0.284	0.172	0.046	0.007	0.001					
	3	0.047	0.168	0.230	0.105	0.025	0.003					
	4	0.009	0.070	0.215	0.168	0.061	0.012	0.001				
	5	0.001	0.022	0.151	0.202	0.115	0.033	0.004				
	6		0.005	0.082	0.187	0.166	0.071	0.015	0.001			
	7		0.001	0.035	0.138	0.189	0.121	0.037	0.005			
	8			0.012	0.081	0.173	0.167	0.077	0.015	0.001		
	9			0.003	0.039	0.128	0.185	0.128	0.039	0.003		
	10			0.001	0.015	0.077	0.167	0.173	0.081	0.012		
	11				0.005	0.037	0.121	0.189	0.138	0.035	0.001	
	12				0.001	0.015	0.071	0.166	0.187	0.082	0.005	
	13					0.004	0.033	0.115	0.202	0.151	0.022	0.001
	14					0.001	0.012	0.061	0.168	0.215	0.070	0.009
	15						0.003	0.025	0.105	0.230	0.168	0.047
	16						0.001	0.007	0.046	0.172	0.284	0.168
	17							0.001	0.013	0.081	0.300	0.376
	18								0.002	0.018	0.150	0.397
19	0	0.377	0.135	0.014	0.001							
	1	0.377	0.285	0.068	0.009	0.001						
	2	0.179	0.285	0.154	0.036	0.005						
	3	0.053	0.180	0.218	0.087	0.017	0.002					
	4	0.011	0.080	0.218	0.149	0.047	0.007	0.001				
	5	0.002	0.027	0.164	0.192	0.093	0.022	0.002				
	6		0.007	0.095	0.192	0.145	0.052	0.008	0.001			
	7		0.001	0.044	0.153	0.180	0.096	0.024	0.002			
	8			0.017	0.098	0.180	0.144	0.053	0.008			
	9			0.005	0.051	0.146	0.176	0.098	0.022	0.001		

TABLE IX. Binomial probabilities *(Continued)*

		p										
n	x	0.05	0.1	0.2	0.3	0.4	0.5	0.6	0.7	0.8	0.9	0.95
19	10			0.001	0.022	0.098	0.176	0.146	0.051	0.005		
	11				0.008	0.053	0.144	0.180	0.098	0.017		
	12				0.002	0.024	0.096	0.180	0.153	0.044	0.001	
	13				0.001	0.008	0.052	0.145	0.192	0.095	0.007	
	14					0.002	0.022	0.093	0.192	0.164	0.027	0.002
	15					0.001	0.007	0.047	0.149	0.218	0.080	0.011
	16						0.002	0.017	0.087	0.218	0.180	0.053
	17							0.005	0.036	0.154	0.285	0.179
	18							0.001	0.009	0.068	0.285	0.377
	19								0.001	0.014	0.135	0.377
20	0	0.358	0.122	0.012	0.001							
	1	0.377	0.270	0.058	0.007							
	2	0.189	0.285	0.137	0.028	0.003						
	3	0.060	0.190	0.205	0.072	0.012	0.001					
	4	0.013	0.090	0.218	0.130	0.035	0.005					
	5	0.002	0.032	0.175	0.179	0.075	0.015	0.001				
	6		0.009	0.109	0.192	0.124	0.037	0.005				
	7		0.002	0.055	0.164	0.166	0.074	0.015	0.001			
	8			0.022	0.114	0.180	0.120	0.035	0.004			
	9			0.007	0.065	0.160	0.160	0.071	0.012			
	10			0.002	0.031	0.117	0.176	0.117	0.031	0.002		
	11				0.012	0.071	0.160	0.160	0.065	0.007		
	12				0.004	0.035	0.120	0.180	0.114	0.022		
	13				0.001	0.015	0.074	0.166	0.164	0.055	0.002	
	14					0.005	0.037	0.124	0.192	0.109	0.009	
	15					0.001	0.015	0.075	0.179	0.175	0.032	0.002
	16						0.005	0.035	0.130	0.218	0.090	0.013
	17						0.001	0.012	0.072	0.205	0.190	0.060
	18							0.003	0.028	0.137	0.285	0.189
	19								0.007	0.058	0.270	0.377
	20								0.001	0.012	0.122	0.358

TABLE X. Random numbers

60359	07603	81594	66235	48154	61257	27978	64695	63165	44593
34992	97880	79115	47587	76167	47086	57064	16730	74172	60317
04887	64208	71842	97885	32616	23280	11783	19852	64266	24446
09332	86232	88199	66094	72594	30100	23673	68705	66989	42666
42326	62962	06485	04978	96639	96214	91478	12408	21457	19862
49187	42836	17042	35179	31880	48444	89877	50915	37426	21556
09228	57404	42180	07949	98750	31506	78442	45809	12725	49774
69720	73477	91252	48009	81393	76401	48168	25967	33372	84414
82222	13787	98611	95257	34753	36674	44326	66070	61131	70620
30703	00513	54586	05623	43999	55387	67189	95058	91174	13121
86369	62151	70713	41166	79321	52215	94358	28962	35868	22796
83331	99035	68506	96734	91074	24356	03035	66926	32197	54944
43053	60600	98921	43720	77342	26186	64554	46226	64244	10703
57104	49148	18487	01775	71782	04679	64369	06208	71669	63046
33177	11409	13925	18130	54242	13460	39174	63528	22670	31810
05424	76714	05732	29415	01183	45054	13493	44006	61641	80304
92950	58665	41191	69259	50244	55322	75137	90193	31989	17381
54925	20502	71767	82737	64847	04496	35921	42670	08584	54090
41980	43710	55304	57526	29616	92314	85883	21584	55045	81997
83825	70977	67987	61545	92066	71215	93967	63071	69928	98917
84047	83627	37763	07081	33048	57895	42182	73279	08032	19165
12776	69127	67921	57611	85876	30744	40886	68396	79787	76434
81419	55440	69506	09115	45032	48343	78352	39075	31689	76469
59844	03603	96297	58028	93069	35674	38479	54639	54455	10300
18350	74940	07044	11210	53622	00779	36027	51496	01694	57895
79960	18784	13376	03415	84450	78874	22050	19730	92598	54291
45420	24157	16374	22384	56892	84941	97157	99656	33978	81436
13945	09559	68152	56960	39453	51654	10617	55628	47933	85161
91206	33871	60730	96821	95808	29763	39678	73104	43398	38181
24847	08724	81499	72905	95102	63004	22223	19808	90777	54986
94303	08209	27804	49372	66392	50578	02966	90907	33164	83044
22732	95331	60954	93333	71142	38827	48222	21779	35598	95957
82809	24004	65983	01091	70431	91145	88207	52216	94846	75303
62700	79965	09610	97213	48579	43574	37652	12447	80233	42473
89870	73755	48525	32765	50818	71468	37876	28334	07762	16180
81493	24124	67928	12735	41249	24180	54740	44290	58903	38681
43630	32189	08532	43055	08080	84208	06295	07813	24068	67549
60234	18992	13283	96334	39746	07272	25295	07871	34201	49620
00107	21861	60367	48999	71634	34053	28265	02064	06290	10620
09657	36088	05976	88267	62683	57675	85265	10856	06525	37911
93948	38350	63464	08008	96607	73505	75513	91238	11042	40972
42746	29761	72298	48186	88584	90141	72879	54531	99127	60063
12939	04181	27698	48297	20574	30169	45545	04462	91067	43847
71032	55283	94804	00202	12254	22920	73225	51484	73943	08431
09188	78876	95736	70659	32725	23024	04656	48102	15904	19019
79236	54729	47052	49717	22312	06735	58347	04402	03838	97049
41337	52635	48056	43317	11599	26382	41305	04589	92877	52732
73732	99966	30485	45994	30195	40239	52751	64124	67778	60982
92113	55625	03726	76886	64237	33300	48004	37440	76329	80441
63797	22667	74860	99731	06975	63055	72287	81976	43983	97018

TABLE X. Random numbers (*Continued*)

79681	63467	02907	86515	71330	04490	47372	68791	27576	02044
30305	20743	10302	71391	18138	23412	11858	47818	22324	52031
32763	33847	58250	64362	87550	94978	22888	78355	34651	41604
59166	21978	40556	13084	31782	00518	18621	60508	93095	74017
55843	94845	30006	51045	17428	50657	68237	02969	30500	43569
33537	82468	52422	32155	54419	61661	64835	06496	16377	92607
13533	29605	31430	07663	95274	11484	42579	15718	54485	08857
24626	54219	12284	06890	05239	42846	24773	15025	15161	51340
48002	32024	17230	37523	47488	31080	29352	61444	04011	56275
03742	00004	98249	12256	94253	95378	88918	98167	46646	19727
17749	89193	37944	53702	49918	65397	72597	63520	77429	68355
34837	36219	22048	97047	68804	09633	28689	80484	59331	77577
99451	37922	90191	39229	07564	41077	91554	46657	74652	84677
74045	00036	53137	15250	19646	20451	46677	53620	74712	17246
98998	98774	98159	00032	97323	81490	21552	35001	10913	48910
61513	02266	36871	85993	23028	67082	93486	45110	86288	34493
67056	19960	53863	63917	68283	31123	17443	32019	19695	85622
83036	04625	93284	14368	10979	95800	72182	77004	07320	79516
71901	25497	76987	74388	41605	39295	75622	41203	87987	09672
46484	77860	02062	92917	70275	40593	93265	92722	39193	47099
18312	05137	64361	86541	17794	32313	52847	08862	36752	32624
63093	94089	17729	19607	19340	19022	50080	21998	49864	07107
38109	69439	62094	49578	37728	17809	11563	10073	17299	69238
41421	22003	36770	32741	10325	30892	14112	34880	92387	45169
92320	12828	57972	83551	63054	95028	50857	40315	04962	36431
42226	72413	67949	96906	17848	21446	35722	10376	84226	16403
01094	08525	21349	41981	55232	76652	00857	77173	63362	64936
75760	51119	37218	16828	89127	42801	01084	78402	28359	41533
62568	56665	42394	67135	03069	93275	11662	23607	00878	53800
77151	67677	85258	46925	92504	87860	85299	45952	76388	72989
71920	39074	15464	36753	86550	24330	17873	20798	15221	80763
99411	04216	66076	90718	67214	03688	71088	92479	27623	97466
05654	88507	03119	93043	06951	35126	26154	26820	68861	37807
65937	81013	09884	97787	85851	00011	66801	02686	73801	19522
87649	70531	88258	21822	97418	67341	54342	80836	46142	04718
57827	19642	95661	23788	19164	78112	07304	32337	12845	12588
78911	81376	22392	42570	33512	17996	29406	47329	66928	89312
91302	54963	94112	60597	31843	40120	00386	35486	27379	02873
82950	87509	65708	14385	86299	23769	87183	66267	13819	58266
21888	66504	85577	67163	46317	92073	68325	46664	03841	58572
73799	60026	87226	26744	12037	98558	66640	32882	11415	64686
48237	10339	99550	86134	30229	39131	76976	56296	89453	79556
24293	69496	20243	17738	55798	96178	86022	42073	16407	53031
18748	01580	73315	84924	81621	67021	99065	43590	82522	71919
94470	36824	89203	23689	37016	18462	59404	27230	78689	88837
87639	11791	63380	25952	20838	13638	32782	23841	16936	91384
65676	78482	33343	65797	56005	15782	27311	64066	28230	36207
94357	62236	54083	37960	43467	79372	26370	08273	18180	84100
06595	83512	74524	10051	97759	64738	10370	07874	28301	08201
34033	69035	18588	88893	83679	27789	22340	12208	00381	06023

TABLE XI. Mortalities. (l_x is the number of persons living at age x from among 100,000 persons alive at age 10.)

x	l_x	x	l_x	x	l_x
10	100,000	**40**	78,106	**70**	38,569
11	99,251	**41**	77,341	**71**	36,178
12	98,505	**42**	76,567	**72**	33,730
13	97,762	**43**	75,782	**73**	31,243
14	97,022	**44**	74,985	**74**	28,738
15	96,285	**45**	74,173	**75**	26,237
16	95,550	**46**	73,345	**76**	23,761
17	94,818	**47**	72,497	**77**	21,330
18	94,089	**48**	71,627	**78**	18,961
19	93,362	**49**	70,731	**79**	16,670
20	92,637	**50**	69,804	**80**	14,474
21	91,914	**51**	68,842	**81**	12,383
22	91,192	**52**	67,841	**82**	10,419
23	90,471	**53**	66,797	**83**	8,603
24	89,751	**54**	65,706	**84**	6,955
25	89,032	**55**	64,563	**85**	5,485
26	88,314	**56**	63,364	**86**	4,193
27	87,596	**57**	62,104	**87**	3,079
28	86,878	**58**	60,779	**88**	2,146
29	86,160	**59**	59,385	**89**	1,402
30	85,441	**60**	57,917	**90**	847
31	84,721	**61**	56,371	**91**	462
32	84,000	**62**	54,743	**92**	216
33	83,277	**63**	53,030	**93**	79
34	82,551	**64**	51,230	**94**	21
35	81,882	**65**	49,341	**95**	3
36	81,090	**66**	47,361		
37	80,353	**67**	45,291		
38	79,611	**68**	43,133		
39	78,862	**69**	40,890		

ANSWERS TO ODD-NUMBERED EXERCISES

Page 6

7. (b) Even numbers are represented by P;
(d) $P \cdot P$ means that the employee gets a raise and then another raise, $P \cdot Q$ means that the employee gets a raise but then does not get another raise, $Q \cdot P$ means that the employee does not get a raise the first time but then gets a raise, and $Q \cdot Q$ means that the employee does not get a raise and then again does not get a raise.

Page 15

1. (a) True; (b) false; (c) true; (d) false; (e) false; (f) false; (g) true; (h) false; (i) true; (j) false; (k) true; (l) false; (m) false; (n) false; (o) false; (p) false.

3. (a) TV Guide, Life, Look, Time, and Newsweek; (b) Reader's Digest, McCall's, and Ladies' Home Journal; (c) Reader's Digest, Life, Look, and Ladies' Home Journal; (d) McCall's; (e) none; (f) TV Guide, Time, and Newsweek; (g) TV Guide, Life, Look, McCall's, Time, and Newsweek; (h) all of the magazines.

5. (a) All non-color television sets in Phoenix; (b) all television sets in Phoenix which are not turned on; (c) all television sets in Phoenix which are not tuned to Channel 12; (d) all television sets in Phoenix which are not out of order; (e) all color television sets in Phoenix which are turned on; (f) all non-color television sets in Phoenix which are tuned to Channel 12; (g) all television sets in Phoenix that are turned on to Channel 12; (h) all television sets in Phoenix which are not out of order and tuned to Channel 12; (i) all television sets in Phoenix which are either color sets, turned on, or both; (j) all television sets in

Phoenix which are either color sets, tuned to Channel 12, or both; (k) all color television sets in Phoenix that are out of order; (l) all television sets in Phoenix which are either not turned on, out of order, or both; (m) all television sets in Phoenix which are either not color sets, not tuned to Channel 12, or both; (n) all non-color television sets in Phoenix that are out of order.

7. 45.

9. 125.

11. (a) 16; (b) 24; (c) 10; (d) 31.

Page 22

3. Postulate 8, Postulate 9, Postulate 6, Postulate 9, and Postulate 7.

Page 26

3. He is successful or happy.

5. (a) $T \cap A' = \varnothing$; (b) $T \cap A \neq \varnothing$; (c) $T \cap A' \neq \varnothing$; (d) $T \cap A = \varnothing$.

7. (a) No customer is dissatisfied; (b) there are no satisfied customers; (c) some customers are dissatisfied; (d) some customers are not dissatisfied.

9. Valid.

11. Not valid.

13. Some carefully planned things are ineffective.

Page 31

1. $(A \cap B) \cup (A \cap B')$.

3. $(B \cup A') \cap (B' \cup A)$.

Page 41

1. (a) Closed under addition and multiplication; (b) not closed under addition ($1 + 3 = 4$, for example) but closed under multiplication; (c) closed under addition but not closed under multiplication (-2 times -2 equals 4, for example); (d) not closed under addition ($\sqrt{3}$ plus $-\sqrt{3}$ equals 0, for example) and not closed under multiplication ($\sqrt{3}$ times $\sqrt{3}$ equals 3, for example).

3. For example, $12 \div 3$ does not equal $3 \div 12$, and $12 \div (2 \div 2)$ equals 12 while $(12 \div 2) \div 2$ equals 3.

7. The number 2 does not have a multiplicative inverse.

9. Assume that $\sqrt{3}$ is a rational number and that $\sqrt{3} = a/b$, where a and b have no common factors. Then $b\sqrt{3} = a$, $3b^2 = a^2$, a^2 is a multiple of 3, and hence a must be a multiple of 3. Thus, we can write $a = 3c$, and we get $3b^2 = (3c)^2 = 9c^2$, and $b^2 = 3c^2$. Since b^2 is a multiple of 3 it follows that b must be a multiple of 3, and we have arrived at the *contradiction* that a and b are both multiples of 3. Consequently, the original assumption that $\sqrt{3}$ is a rational number must have been incorrect.

Page 48

1. (a) 0.056; (b) $0.\overline{36}$; (c) $0.\overline{461538}$; (d) $0.6\overline{428571}$; (e) 0.325; (f) 0.046875; (g) $0.61\overline{6}$; (h) 0.2192; (i) $19.\overline{571428}$.

3. (a) 21,466; (b) 0.0181; (c) 147,630; (d) 0.0000035552; (e) 7,269,000; (f) 0.000099934.

5. (a) 0.00258; (b) 26,463; (c) −0.0000075589; (d) 5,353,600; (e) −5.316; (f) 0.0000646.

7. (a) 3,487,500; (b) 0.235; (c) −0.00000055; (d) 0.000034105; (e) −1.335; (f) 9,856.

9. (a) 2.38; (b) 0.0000500005; (c) 23,504,670; (d) 0.0000000105073; (e) 0.135; (f) 0.064537.

Page 54

1. (a) 11011; (b) 10001011; (c) 100000101; (d) 1001000111; (e) 10000100010; (f) 100101000111.

3. (a) 0.75; (b) 1.25; (c) 9.5; (d) 51.25; (e) 46.125; (f) 27.875.

5. (a) 11011.11; (b) 1110001.111; (c) 10101000101.1; (d) $111.\overline{1100}$.

7. (a) 1001; (b) 1100; (c) 1000110; (d) 110110.

9. (a) 100011; (b) 10001111; (c) 1010010111; (d) 111001110.

11. 11.

13. 101.

15. $0.0\overline{110}$.

Page 60

1. (a) D; (b) 872; (c) 266; (d) $0.AB$; (e) $0.E8$; (f) 1.8; (g) $C.03$; (h) $46.9A$.
3. (a) $7D5$; (b) $80B7$; (c) $12C51$; (d) $4AB0D$.
5. $FD.7$.
7. (a) 23; (b) 144; (c) 1002; (d) 11114; (e) 44044; (f) 134430.
9. (a) 47; (b) 107; (c) 465; (d) 1470; (e) 2013; (f) 7130.
11. (a) $1E$; (b) 54; (c) 205; (d) 1574.

Page 67

1. (a) One-to-one; (b) one-to-many; (c) many-to-one; (d) many-to-many; (e) many-to-one, generally; (f) many-to-many; (g) one-to-one; (h) many-to-one.
3. (a) Many-to-one; (b) one-to-one; (c) many-to-many; (d) many-to-many.
5. *One-to-one* if the airline stocks were all traded at different prices, and each stock only at one price; *one-to-many* if at least one of the airline stocks is traded at more than one price, but no two stocks at the same price; *many-to-one* if at least two stocks are traded at the same price, but each stock is traded at only one price; *many-to-many* if at least two of the airline stocks are traded at the same price, and at least one of the stocks is traded at more than one price. In the first and third cases the relationship would be a function.
7. (a) The domain is the set $\{45, 47, 52, 53\}$ and the range is the set $\{68, 69, 71, 72\}$; (b) one-to-many; (c) many-to-many.

Page 80

1. The range of the function is the set $\{40, 47, 52, 55, 56\}$.
3. If C is the cost of repairs and N is the number of months the machine has gone without being checked, then $C = 15 + 10N^2$. (a) $C = 15 + 10(2)^2 = \$55$; (b) $C = \$175$; (c) \$375; (d) \$655; (e) \$1,455.
5. (a) 69; (b) 30; (c) 14; (d) 5.
7. (a) 5; (b) 3; (c) 2; (d) 9/5; (e) 3/2; (f) 29/25.
9. (a) 1; (b) 1; (c) 0; (d) 2; (e) 3; (f) 5; (g) 15; (h) 20. The range is the set of all non-negative real numbers.
11. (a) $(-4, -4)$; (b) $(-2, 5)$; (c) $(5, 3)$; (d) $(3, -5)$; (e) $(-5, 2)$; (f) $(4, -3)$.

17. (b) A straight line.

19. (a) 7/5; (b) $2\left(\frac{x+2}{x}\right) + 3 = \frac{5x+4}{x}$; 19/3 and 49/9.

Page 86

3. (a) $390,000; (b) $1,580,000; (c) $5,000.

5. (a) 13; (b) -9; (c) 11; (d) 9.

7. (3, 2, 4) lies to the right of the yz-plane, in front of the xz-plane, and above the xy-plane; $(-2, 4, 6)$ lies to the left of the yz-plane, in front of the xz-plane, and above the xy-plane; $(0, 3, -1)$ lies on the yz-plane, in front of the xz-plane, and below the xy-plane; (5, 0, 0) lies to the right of the yz-plane, on the xz-plane, and on the xy-plane; (0, 4, 0) lies on the yz-plane, in front of the xz-plane, and on the xy-plane; $(-1, -2, -1)$ lies to the left of the yz-plane, behind the xz-plane, and below the xy-plane; $(0, 0, -1)$ lies on the yz-plane, on the xz-plane, and below the xy-plane; $(-4, -3, 5)$ lies to the left of the yz-plane, behind the xz-plane, and above the xy-plane.

9. The plane does not contain the point (0, 0, 1), but it does contain the points $(1\frac{1}{2}, 0, 2\frac{1}{2})$ and $(3, 4, -5)$.

Page 94

1. (a) 2; (b) 2; (c) $-1/2$; (d) 4; (e) $-8/5$; (f) 2.

3. The slope of the line segment joining the first two points is 1, that of the line segment joining the second and third points is 3/2, and since these two slopes are not equal the three points do not lie on a straight line.

5. Mr. Smith; $12,500, $13,800, and $10,750.

7. $y = 2 + 5x$; the line contains the point (2, 12) but it does not contain the point $(-1, -4)$.

9. Corresponding to each increase of 1 cent in the price per pint, the demand *decreases* by 125 pints.

Page 101

1. $98.34 (rounded up).

3. $3,454.

5. (a) $2,880; (b) 7 percent; (c) $2,955.

7. \$80,000.

9. $y = 2.45 + 0.24x$ dollars per share; \$5.09; in 1959 the company earned \$2.21 per share.

11. $y = 93.5 - 4.5x$; 12.5 thousand.

13. (a) yes, the slopes are both 2/3; (b) yes, the slopes are both 7/3; (c) no, the slopes are $-3/5$ and $3/5$; (d) the lines are parallel if the x- and y-coefficients are proportional; they are parallel but do not coincide if the x- and y-coefficients are proportional but the constant terms are *not* in the same ratio.

Page 107

1. (a) 10; (b) 13; (c) $\sqrt{37}$; (d) 17.

3. 54 miles.

5. The line segment of part (c) is perpendicular to those of parts (a), (b), and (f).

7. (a) $x^2 + y^2 = 25$; the points (4, 3), (3, -4), and (-5, 0) lie on the circle, but the point (-1, 4) does not; (b) $(x - 3)^2 + (y - 2)^2 = 100$; check whether the distance between (8, -10) and (3, 2) is less than 10 or greater than 10; (c) they overlap; (d) no, for some values of x there are two values of y and for some values of y there are two values of x.

Page 114

3. 19, 9, 3, 1, 3, 9, and 19; there seems to be a minimum at (1, 1).

5. His profit per car is $x - 2$ dollars, and his total profit is $(x - 2)(300 - 100x) = -600 + 500x - 100x^2$ dollars; \$21, \$24, \$25, \$24, and \$21; his total profit seems to be a maximum when he charges \$2.50.

Page 123

3. (a) 2 and 3; (b) 3 and -2; (c) -3 and -5; (d) 6 and -4; (e) 2 and -4; (f) 5 and -7.

5. (a) -1 and -3; (b) 3 and -5; (c) -2 and 4; (d) $1 \pm \sqrt{2}$.

7. (a) 1/2; (b) $-1/2$ and -2; (c) 1 and 1/3; (d) 1 and 1/5.

9. $2 \pm \frac{1}{2}\sqrt{5}$.

11. 22.

13. (a) $\pm 3\sqrt{3}$; (b) $-2 \pm 2\sqrt{43}$.

15. (b) There should be a demand for 10,000 boxes; yes, the curve does not turn back up.

17. (a) $2 + 11i$; (b) $2 - 12i$; (c) $4 - 3i$; (d) $-2 + 9i$.

19. (a) $-\frac{6}{25} - \frac{17}{25}i$; (b) $-\frac{45}{169} + \frac{61}{169}i$; (c) $-\frac{1}{2} + \frac{3}{2}i$.

23. (a) $3 \pm \sqrt{2}\cdot i$; (b) $1 \pm i$; (c) $2 \pm 3i$; (d) $5 \pm 2i$; (e) $1 \pm \sqrt{2}\cdot i$; (f) $2 \pm \sqrt{5}\cdot i$.

Page 130

1. $x = 3{,}000$ does not belong to the domain of the receipts function.

3. (a) 5 or 30; (b) maximum is about 17.5 thousand ornaments.

5. (a) 4 and -5, but -5 is "impossible"; (b) 4 and -5, the supply corresponding to $p = 4$ is 24,000.

Page 138

3. (a) x^2; (b) $\frac{x^6}{8y^3}$; (c) x^3y^2; (d) xy.

5. 5 and 7; by definition, a cube root of 5 is a number whose third power equals 5 and, hence, $5^{1/3}$ is a cube root of 5; by definition, a fifth root of 7 is a number whose 5th power equals 7 and, hence, $7^{1/5}$ is a fifth root of 7.

7. (a) -2; (b) -4; (c) $-3x^2$; (d) $-3/5$.

Page 141

1. \$8,240, \$9,274.19, and \$16,750.22.

3. \$2,812.16, \$3,041.63, and \$5,477.81.

7. (a) \$615.09; (b) \$646.43; (c) \$769.22.

9. (a) 0.0509; (b) 0.0404; (c) 0.0609; (d) 0.0614; (e) 0.0617.

11. \$1,671.29.

13. (a) \$2,400, \$1,920, and \$1,536; (b) \$51,233.

Page 150

1. 5/9, 5/3, 5, 15, and 45.

3. 6.25, 1.25, 0.25, 0.05, and 0.01.

5. $y = \frac{1}{4} \cdot 5^{-x}$.

7. (b) \$82,450, \$135,900, \$224,100, \$369,450, \$609,000; (c) \$1,656,000.

9. (a) 27.4, 46.2, 60.1, 78.1, 95.1, and 99.76 percent.

Page 155

1. (a) $x = \log_5 7$; (b) $2/3 = \log_7 y$; (c) $4 = \log_b 20$; (d) $x = \log_9 155$; (e) $1/3 = \log_{13} y$; (f) $5 = \log_b 100$.

3. (a) 5; (b) 1; (c) 2; (d) -4; (e) -2; (f) 0.

5. (a) 1.6232; (b) 0.3890; (c) 0.3680; (d) 0.2817; (e) 0.6990; (f) 3.2464.

7. The suggestions lead to $N^k = b^{kn}$, and hence to $\log_b N^k = kn = k(\log_b N)$.

9. -2, -1, 0, 1, 2, and 3.

Page 162

1. (a) 1.4116; (b) $0.4116 - 3$; (c) 4.4116; (d) $0.8722 - 1$; (e) 2.8722; (f) 6.8722; (g) 0.0253; (h) $0.0253 - 2$; (i) $0.9795 - 3$; (j) 2.58; (k) -2; (l) $0.9395 - 9$.

3. (a) 2.11; (b) 7.29; (c) 2.55; (d) 0.692; (e) 0.855; (f) 157.

5. (a) 1,560,000; (b) 1,170,000; (c) 500,000.

7. 300.

9. 2.69.

11. $y = 12e^{-0.223x}$.

15. (a) 3.322; (b) 3.579; (c) 0.515.

Page 176

1. (a) $\pi/3$; (b) $2\pi/3$; (c) 4π; (d) $-\pi/4$; (e) $-3\pi/2$; (f) $9\pi/4$; (g) -6π; (h) $13\pi/6$.

5. (a) 33°; (b) 80°; (c) 49°; (d) 35°; (e) 15°; (f) 60°.

9. (a) 45°; (b) 135°; (c) 76°; (d) 104°; (e) 6°; (f) 56°.

15. (a) $\cos 90° + i \cdot \sin 90°$; (b) $\sqrt{2}(\cos 315° + i \cdot \sin 315°)$; (c) $\sqrt{2}(\cos 45° + i \cdot \sin 45°)$; (d) $2(\cos 60° + i \cdot \sin 60°)$; (e) $5\sqrt{2}(\cos 135° + i \cdot \sin 135°)$; (f) $8(\cos 330° + i \cdot \sin 330°)$. (g) $\frac{3}{2} + \frac{3\sqrt{3}}{2}i$; (h) $-\frac{5\sqrt{3}}{2} + \frac{5}{2}i$; (i) $-i/2$; (j) $\sqrt{2} + i\sqrt{2}$.

Page 190

1. (a) lower the cosine curve 2 units; (b) multiply the amplitude of the cosine curve by 5; (c) raise the sine curve 7 units; (d) shorten the period of the sine curve to 60°; (e) divide the amplitude of the sine curve by 3; (f) shift the sine curve 180° to the right; (g) lengthen the period of the cosine curve to 1,440°; (h) shift the cosine curve $\pi/2$ to the left.

3. Move the cosine curve 90° to the right, move it up one unit, and multiply its amplitude by 3.

Page 201

1. (a) $x = 4$ and $y = 3$; (b) $x = 11/5$ and $y = 7/5$; (c) $u = 5$ and $v = -3$; (d) $x_1 = 13/10$ and $x_2 = -7/20$; (e) $x = 2$, $y = 1$, and $z = -1$; (f) $x_1 = 2$, $x_2 = 1$, and $x_3 = -1$.

3. (a)
$$\begin{aligned} a_{11}x_1 + a_{12}x_2 + a_{13}x_3 &= b_1 \\ a_{21}x_1 + a_{22}x_2 + a_{23}x_3 &= b_2 \\ a_{31}x_1 + a_{32}x_2 + a_{33}x_3 &= b_3; \end{aligned}$$
(b)
$$\begin{aligned} a_{11}x_1 + a_{12}x_2 + a_{13}x_3 + a_{14}x_4 &= b_1 \\ a_{21}x_1 + a_{22}x_2 + a_{23}x_3 + a_{24}x_4 &= b_2 \\ a_{31}x_1 + a_{32}x_2 + a_{33}x_3 + a_{34}x_4 &= b_3 \\ a_{41}x_1 + a_{42}x_2 + a_{43}x_3 + a_{44}x_4 &= b_4. \end{aligned}$$

7. (a) $y = \frac{1}{2} + \frac{1}{2}x$; (b) $y = \frac{7}{2} + \frac{3}{2}x$.

9. \$3.20 and \$2.40.

11. $a = 39$ and $b = 0.08$.

13. (b) $x = 8$, $y = 3$, and $z = 5$; (c) 10 and 7.

Page 210

1. (a) True; (b) false; (c) false; (d) true; (e) true; (f) false; (g) true; (h) true; (i) false.

5. (a) $x > 4$; (b) $x \leqslant 4$; (c) $x > 7$; (d) $x < 1$; (e) $x \geqslant -6$; (f) $x < 8/3$.

7. $130x \leqslant 24{,}000$; 184.

9. (a) $|x - 58.25| \leqslant 2.50$; $55.75 \leqslant x \leqslant 60.75$.

Page 221

5. (a) $5x + 10y \geqslant 50$ and $2x + y \geqslant 8$.

7. (a) $5x + 2y \leqslant 3{,}000$, $0.2x + 0.4y \leqslant 160$, $x \geqslant 0$, and $y \geqslant 0$.

9. (a) $5x + 3y + 4z \leqslant 3{,}800$ and $20x + 50y + 20z \leqslant 19{,}000$; (c) only the first and fourth.

Page 232

1. 550 and 125; \$1,400.

3. (a) 6, 0, and 2; (b) 4, 4, and 0; (c) 4, 4, and 0; 5, 2, and 1; or 6, 0, and 2; (d) 8, 0, and 0.

5. 12 and 24; \$75.60.

7. 4 and 5; 12 and 0.

11. 60, 0, and 180; \$720.

13. Any point on the line segment joining (30, 10, 20) and (30, 40, 5); if x_1, x_2, and x_3 must be integers, there are 16 solutions.

Page 241

1.

Vertex	Profit
(0, 0)	\$ 0
(600, 0)	\$1,200
(0, 400)	\$ 960
(550, 125)	\$1,400

maximum profit at (550, 125).

3. (a)

Vertex	Cost
(6, 0)	0.92
(4, 4)	1.04
(8, 0)	0.96

minimum cost at (6, 0);

(b)

Vertex	Cost
(6, 0)	0.98
(4, 4)	0.96
(8, 0)	1.04

minimum cost at (4, 4);

(c)

Vertex	Cost
(6, 0)	0.92
(4, 4)	0.92
(8, 0)	0.96

minimum cost at (6, 0), (5, 2), or (4, 4);

(d)

Vertex	Cost
(6, 0)	0.68
(4, 4)	0.76
(8, 0)	0.64

minimum cost at (8, 0).

5.

Vertex	Profit
(40, 0)	$120
(0, 0)	$ 0
(25, 7.5)	$150
(15, 11)	$155
(0, 14)	$140

maximum profit at (15, 11).

7.

Vertex	Profit
(100, 0, 0)	$600
(0, 150, 0)	$300
(0, 0, 240)	$480
(0, 105, 135)	$480
(60, 0, 180)	$720

maximum profit at (60, 0, 180).

11.

Vertex	$28x_1 + 21x_2 + 10x_3$
(0, 0, 0)	0
(0, 0, 2)	20
(0, 2, 0)	42
(0, 1, 3/2)	36
(4, 0, 0)	112
(2, 0, 3/2)	71
(24/7, 6/7, 0)	114
(2, 1/2, 5/4)	79

maximum at (24/7, 6/7, 0).

Page 248

1. (a) 2×3 matrix; (b) 3×3 square matrix; (c) 1×5 row vector; (d) 4×2 matrix; (e) 2×1 column vector; (f) 4×4 square matrix; (g) 4×1 column vector; (h) 2×5 matrix.

3. $a = -2$, $b = 0$, $c = 4$, and $d = -1$.

5. $x = 2$, $y = -2$, and $z = 0$.

7. (a) (18, 23, 9, 2); (b) (5, -9, 1, 0).

9. (a) $\begin{pmatrix} -6 & 4 \\ 12 & -2 \end{pmatrix}$, $\begin{pmatrix} 10 & -10 \\ -20 & 15 \end{pmatrix}$, $\begin{pmatrix} 4 & -6 \\ -8 & 13 \end{pmatrix}$;
(b) $\begin{pmatrix} 12 & 0 & -6 \\ -3 & 9 & 15 \end{pmatrix}$, $\begin{pmatrix} 6 & -2 & 2 \\ -2 & 4 & -8 \end{pmatrix}$, $\begin{pmatrix} 6 & 2 & -8 \\ -1 & 5 & 23 \end{pmatrix}$;
(c) $x = 5$, $y = 2$, and $z = 4$;
(d) $\begin{pmatrix} -3 & -2 & 4 \\ -2 & 1 & -5 \end{pmatrix}$; $\begin{pmatrix} 3 & -5 & 0 \\ 0 & -1 & 1 \\ -2 & 4 & -3 \end{pmatrix}$; $(-1, 3, -5, 0, -2)$; $\begin{pmatrix} -1 & 1 \\ 0 & -3 \\ -2 & 1 \\ -4 & -3 \end{pmatrix}$.

11. (a) $2 + 2i$, $-i$, 1, $-3 - 2i$, $3 + 4i$; (b) (0, 1), (1, 1), (0, 0), (−1, 0), (2, 3), (2, −1), (7, −5); (c) yes.

Page 258

1. (a) both; (b) only **B·A**; (c) neither; (d) both; (e) only **A·B**; (f) neither.

3. $\begin{pmatrix} 18{,}740 \\ 16{,}153 \end{pmatrix}$; the total sales revenue on the sets of brands X and Y which the merchant has in inventory.

5. (a) 6,406.2, the total value of the 1957 quantities at 1957 prices in millions of dollars; (b) 6,045.02, the total value of the 1957 quantities at 1964 prices in millions of dollars; (c) 94.4 percent.

7. $\begin{pmatrix} 0 & 0 \\ 0 & 0 \end{pmatrix}$.

9. The 4×1 column vector whose elements are the total attendance figures for the four games.

11.

	A	B	C	D
A	B	C	D	A
B	C	D	A	B
C	D	A	B	C
D	A	B	C	D

the tables are identical and, hence, the mathematical model for the rotation of the sales managers is the same as that for the multiplication of these matrices.

Page 269

3. (a) $x_1 = 3$ and $x_2 = -2$; (b) $x_1 = -4$ and $x_2 = 5$; (c) $x_1 = 8$ and $x_2 = 5$.

5. $\begin{pmatrix} 7 & -3 \\ -2 & 1 \end{pmatrix}$; $x_1 = 7$ and $x_2 = -2$.

7. $x_1 = 2$ and $x_2 = -1$.

9. (a) $ra_{11} + sa_{21} = 1$, $ra_{12} + sa_{22} = 0$, $ta_{11} + ua_{21} = 0$, $ta_{12} + ua_{22} = 1$; (c) the first matrix has an inverse, the second does not, the third does not, the fourth does not, the fifth does.

Page 277

1. (a) 2; (b) -56; (c) 47; (d) -22.

3. (a) the elements of the two rows (or columns) are proportional; (b) if we add the elements of the third row to the corresponding elements of the first row, we get the corresponding elements of the second row; (c) the elements of the rows (or columns) are proportional; (d) factor 14 out of the first row, 9 out of the first column, and then add 5 times each element of the second column to the corresponding element of the third column, so that it will equal the first column.

5. (a) $x_1 = 3$, $x_2 = -2$, and $x_3 = 1$; (b) $x_1 = 1$, $x_2 = 2$, and $x_3 = 1$; (c) $x_1 = 3$, $x_2 = -3/2$, and $x_3 = 3/2$.

Page 289

1. (a) *Maximize* $2x_1 + 7x_2$, where x_1, x_2, x_3, and x_4 must be non-negative and satisfy the system of equations $x_1 + 2x_2 + x_3 = 2$, $x_1 - x_2 + x_4 = 1$; the basic feasible solution is $x_1 = 0$, $x_2 = 0$, $x_3 = 2$, and $x_4 = 1$; (b) *maximize* $3x_1 + 2x_2$, where x_1, x_2, x_3, x_4, and x_5 must be non-negative and satisfy the system of equations $4x_1 + x_2 + x_3 = 200$, $x_1 + x_2 + x_4 = 80$, $\frac{1}{3}x_1 + x_2 + x_5 = 60$; the basic feasible solution is $x_1 = 0$, $x_2 = 0$, $x_3 = 200$, $x_4 = 80$, and $x_5 = 60$; (c) *minimize* $-2x_1 + x_2$, where x_1, x_2, x_3, x_4, and x_5 must be non-negative and satisfy the system of equations $3x_1 + 10x_2 + x_3 = 30$, $5x_1 + 2x_2 + x_4 = 10$, $-x_1 + x_2 + x_5 = 3$; the basic feasible solution is $x_1 = 0$, $x_2 = 0$, $x_3 = 30$, $x_4 = 10$, and $x_5 = 3$; (d) *maximize* $3x_1 - 2x_2 + 5x_3$, where x_1, x_2, x_3, x_4, x_5, and x_6 must be non-negative and satisfy the system of equations $6x_1 + 2x_2 + 3x_3 + x_4 = 6$, $-2x_2 + x_3 + x_5 = 3$, $-5x_1 + x_3 + x_6 = 2$; the basic feasible solution is $x_1 = 0$, $x_2 = 0$, $x_3 = 0$, $x_4 = 6$, $x_5 = 3$, and $x_6 = 2$; (e) *minimize* $3x_1 - 2x_2$, where x_1, x_2, x_3, x_4, x_5, and x_6 must be non-negative and satisfy the system of equations $x_1 + 4x_2 + x_3 = 40$, $2x_1 - x_2 + x_4 = 20$, $-x_1 + 2x_2 - x_5 + x_6 = 10$; the basic feasible solution is $x_1 = 0$, $x_2 = 0$, $x_3 = 40$, $x_4 = 20$, $x_5 = 0$, and $x_6 = 10$; (f) *maximize* $2x_1 + 3x_2 - x_3$, where x_1, x_2, x_3, x_4, x_5, x_6, and x_7 must be non-negative and satisfy the system of equations $20x_1 + 12x_2 + 15x_3 + x_4 = 60$, $20x_1 + 12x_2 + 15x_3 - x_5 + x_6 = 30$, $x_1 + x_2 - 2x_3 + x_7 = 0$; the basic feasible solution is $x_1 = 0$, $x_2 = 0$, $x_3 = 0$, $x_4 = 60$, $x_5 = 0$, $x_6 = 30$, and $x_7 = 0$; (g) *minimize* $2x_1 + 1.5x_2$, where x_1, x_2, x_3, x_4, x_5, and x_6 must be non-negative and satisfy the system of equations $x_1 + x_2 - x_3 + x_4 = 1$, $x_1 + 3x_2 - x_5 + x_6 = 3$; the basic feasible solution is $x_1 = 0$, $x_2 = 0$, $x_3 = 0$, $x_4 = 1$, $x_5 = 0$, $x_6 = 3$.

3. *Minimize* $2x_1 + 4x_2 + 80$, where x_1, x_2, x_3, x_4, and x_5 must be non-negative and satisfy the system of equations $x_1 + x_2 + x_3 = 8$, $2x_1 + x_2 - x_4 + x_5 = 12$; the basic feasible solution is $x_1 = 0$, $x_2 = 0$, $x_3 = 8$, $x_4 = 0$, and $x_5 = 12$.

5. *Maximize* $6x_1 + 2x_2 + 2x_3$, where x_1, x_2, x_3, x_4, and x_5 must be non-negative and satisfy the system of equations $x_1 + x_2 + x_3 + x_4 = 240$, $9x_1 + 6x_2 + 2x_3 + x_5 = 900$; the basic feasible solution is $x_1 = 0$, $x_2 = 0$, $x_3 = 0$, $x_4 = 240$, and $x_5 = 900$.

7. Subtracting 1/2 of each element of the second row from the corresponding element of the first row and then dividing each element of the second row by 8, we get

$$\left(\begin{array}{ccccc|c} 0 & 1 & 5 & 1 & -\frac{1}{2} & 20 \\ 1 & \frac{1}{4} & -\frac{1}{2} & 0 & \frac{1}{8} & -2 \end{array}\right)$$

and the solutions are $x_1 = -2$, $x_2 = 0$, $x_3 = 0$, $x_4 = 20$, and $x_5 = 0$. Then, subtracting 1/4 of each element of the first row from the corresponding element of the second row, we get

$$\left(\begin{array}{ccccc|c} 0 & 1 & 5 & 1 & -\frac{1}{2} & 20 \\ 1 & 0 & -\frac{7}{4} & -\frac{1}{4} & \frac{1}{4} & -7 \end{array}\right)$$

and the solutions are $x_1 = -7$, $x_2 = 20$, $x_3 = 0$, $x_4 = 0$, and $x_5 = 0$.

9. Adding each element of the first row to the corresponding element of the second row, adding each element of the first row to the corresponding element of the third row, and then multiplying each element of the first row by -1, we get

$$\left(\begin{array}{ccccc|c} -2 & 1 & -1 & 0 & 0 & -2 \\ 3 & 0 & 1 & 1 & 0 & 5 \\ 1 & 0 & 1 & 0 & 1 & 0 \end{array}\right)$$

and the solutions are $x_1 = 0$, $x_2 = -2$, $x_3 = 0$, $x_4 = 5$, and $x_5 = 0$.

11. Adding each element of the first row to the corresponding element of the second row, and dividing each element of the first row by 2, we get

$$\left(\begin{array}{cccccc|c} 3 & 1 & \frac{3}{2} & \frac{1}{2} & 0 & 0 & 3 \\ 6 & 0 & 4 & 1 & 1 & 0 & 9 \\ -5 & 0 & 1 & 0 & 0 & 1 & 2 \end{array}\right)$$

and the solutions are $x_1 = 0$, $x_2 = 3$, $x_3 = 0$, $x_4 = 0$, $x_5 = 9$, and $x_6 = 2$.

Page 303

1.

$$
\begin{array}{ccccccccc}
c\text{'s} & & x_1 & x_2 & x_3 & x_4 & & & \textit{Quotients} \\
0 & x_3 & 1 & 2 & 1 & 0 & \big| & 2 & 1 \\
0 & x_4 & 1 & -1 & 0 & 1 & \big| & 1 & -1 \\
\textit{Solutions:} & & 0 & 0 & 2 & 1 & & & \\
c\text{'s:} & & 2 & 7 & 0 & 0 & & & \\
\textit{Indicators:} & & 2 & 7 & 0 & 0 & & & \\
 & & & \uparrow & \downarrow & & & & \\
 & & & \text{Entering Variable} & \text{Departing Variable} & & & &
\end{array}
$$

3.

$$
\begin{array}{cccccccccc}
c\text{'s} & & x_1 & x_2 & x_3 & x_4 & x_5 & & & \textit{Quotients} \\
3 & x_1 & 1 & \frac{1}{4} & \frac{1}{4} & 0 & 0 & \big| & 50 & 200 \\
0 & x_4 & 0 & \frac{3}{4} & -\frac{1}{4} & 1 & 0 & \big| & 30 & 40 \\
0 & x_5 & 0 & \frac{11}{12} & -\frac{1}{12} & 0 & 1 & \big| & 43\frac{1}{3} & 47\frac{3}{11} \\
\textit{Solutions:} & & 50 & 0 & 0 & 30 & 43\frac{1}{3} & & & \\
c\text{'s:} & & 3 & 2 & 0 & 0 & 0 & & & \\
\textit{Indicators:} & & 0 & \frac{5}{4} & -\frac{3}{4} & 0 & 0 & & & \\
 & & & \uparrow & & \downarrow & & & & \\
 & & & \text{Entering Variable} & & \text{Departing Variable} & & & &
\end{array}
$$

5.

$$
\begin{array}{cccccccccc}
c\text{'s} & & x_1 & x_2 & x_3 & x_4 & x_5 & & & \textit{Quotients} \\
0 & x_3 & 3 & 10 & 1 & 0 & 0 & \big| & 30 & 10 \\
0 & x_4 & 5 & 2 & 0 & 1 & 0 & \big| & 10 & 2 \\
0 & x_5 & -1 & 1 & 0 & 0 & 1 & \big| & 3 & -3 \\
\textit{Solutions:} & & 0 & 0 & 30 & 10 & 3 & & & \\
c\text{'s:} & & 2 & -1 & 0 & 0 & 0 & & & \\
\textit{Indicators:} & & 2 & -1 & 0 & 0 & 0 & & & \\
 & & \uparrow & & & \downarrow & & & & \\
 & & \text{Entering Variable} & & & \text{Departing Variable} & & & &
\end{array}
$$

15. (a) The indicators are, respectively, 9, 7, 0, 0, 0, -10, and 0, so that the entering variable is x_1; the departing variable can be x_3 or x_7, since they both correspond to the smallest positive quotient of 3.

Page 313

1. (a) Alternately adding 1 and 2, the next three terms are 10, 12, and 13; (b) repeatedly dividing by -2, the next three terms are -12, 6, and -3; (c) alternately multiplying by 2 and -2, the next three terms are -256, 512, and 1,024;
(d) repeatedly adding 2 to the denominator, the next three terms are 1/11, 1/13, and 1/15;
(e) repeatedly adding $2\frac{1}{2}$, the next three terms are 20, 45/2, and 25;
(f) repeatedly increasing the amount added by 1, the next three terms are 36, 45, and 55.

3. (a) 1, 1/2, 1/3, and 1/4; (b) 1/2, 2/3, 3/4, and 4/5; (c) -1, 1/4, $-1/9$, and 1/16; (d) 6, 24, 60, and 120.

5. \$7,700.

7. (b) \$72,600; (c) \$2,600; (d) 1,925; (e) \$57,000 and \$9,835,000.

11. (b) \$1,271.60; (c) \$9,777.28; (d) \$875.98.

13. The common ratio is $1 - \frac{2}{N}$ and the first term is $\frac{2C}{N}$.

15. (a) \$470.53; (b) \$467.02.

Page 327

1. (a) converges to 1; (b) diverges, since the terms alternate between numerically larger and larger positive and negative numbers; (c) converges to 0; (d) converges to 0; (e) diverges, since the terms increase beyond any bound; (f) converges to 1; (g) converges to 7/5, which can be seen by dividing numerator and denominator by k^3; (h) converges to 0, which can be seen by dividing numerator and denominator by k^2.

3. (a) 5/9; (b) 134/99; (c) 37/9900; (d) 137/45; (e) 17/111; (f) 2/7.

5. (a) 2/3; (b) 6/7; (c) 1; (d) 4/5.

7. (a) \$61,645.44; (b) \$35,805.08; (c) \$14,153.01.

11. (a) 0.457; (b) 0.644; (c) 1.73.

13. In the geometric series each term is obtained from the preceding term by dividing by 2; in the other series each term is obtained from the preceding term by dividing by a number greater than or equal to 2; after the second term each term of the other series is thus less than the corresponding term of the geometric series, and hence it is also convergent.

Page 334

1. (a) 4; (b) 1; (c) 16; (d) -5.

3. The function is undefined for $x = 0$, but $\lim_{x \to 0} g(x) = 1$.

5. The limit exists and it is equal to 1.

7. (a) second reason; (b) first reason; (c) third reason; (d) first reason; (e) second reason; (f) third reason.

9. (a) In words, the theorems state that (1) *the limit of a constant is equal to the constant,* (2) *the limit of a constant times a function is equal to the constant times the limit of the function,* (3) *the limit of the sum of two functions is equal to the sum of the limits of the two functions,* (4) *the limit of the product of two functions is equal to the product of the limits of the two functions,* and (5) *the limit of the quotient of two functions is equal to the quotient of the limits of the two functions;* (b) 3, 2, and 1; (c) 3, 2, and 1; (d) 5, 3, and 1; (e) 1/5; (f) -20

Page 345

3. (a) 0; (b) 2; (c) 1; (d) $2x$; (e) $14x$; (f) $3x^2$; (g) $\frac{-2}{5x^3}$; (h) $\frac{1}{2\sqrt{x}}$.

5. $y = 0$.

7. $\frac{dD}{dp} = -3$.

9. $-1, 1, -1, 1, -1, 1, -1, 1, \ldots$; they alternately equal -1 and 1, and the function does not have a derivative at $x = 1$.

Page 357

1. (a) $f'(x) = 0$, $f'(0) = 0$, and $f'(2) = 0$; (b) $f'(x) = 10x^9$, $f'(0) = 0$, and $f'(2) = 5{,}120$; (c) $f'(x) = 3$, $f'(0) = 3$, and $f'(2) = 3$; (d) $f'(x) = -8x$, $f'(0) = 0$, and $f'(2) = -16$; (e) $f'(x) = 2x$, $f'(0) = 0$, and $f'(2) = 4$; (f) $f'(x) = 1 + 10x - 28x^3$, $f'(0) = 1$, and $f'(2) = -203$; (g) $f'(x) = 5x^4 - 3x^2$, $f'(0) = 0$, and $f'(2) = 68$; (h) $f'(x) = 4x^3 + 5x^4 + 9x^8$, $f'(0) = 0$, and $f'(2) = 2{,}416$; (i) $f'(x) = -5/(x-2)^2$, $f'(0) = -5/4$, $f'(2)$ is undefined; (j) $f'(x) = \frac{15 - 6x^2 - 20x^3 - 4x^5}{(2x^2 + 5)^2}$, $f'(0) = 3/5$, and $f'(2) = -297/169$; (k) $f'(x) = -30x^{-31}$, $f'(0)$ does not exist, and $f'(2) = -30/2^{31}$; (l) $f'(x) = -4/x^5$, $f'(0)$ does not exist, and $f'(2) = -1/8$.

5. 115.2.

7. (a) $\frac{dP}{dx} = 800$, profitable; (b) $\frac{dP}{dx} = -800$, not profitable.

9. 1/7.

11. $\frac{dy}{dx} = \frac{3x^2 + 6}{\pm 2\sqrt{x^3 + 6x + 5}}$, and at $x = 2$ this derivative equals ± 1.8, where the sign is the same as that of y.

13. (a) $y = \frac{1}{2}x$; (b) $\sqrt{180} = 13.4$ miles.

19. $\frac{dD}{dp} = -2$.

Page 367

1. (a) $4e^{4x}$; (b) $-12e^{-12x}$; (c) $3(\ln 4)4^{3x}$; (d) $2x \cdot e^{x^2}$; (e) $(x + 1)e^x$; (f) $6e^x(1 + 3e^x)$; (g) $\frac{-7e^x}{(1 + 2e^x)^2}$; (h) $(6x^2 - 1 - 2x^3)e^{-x}$; (i) $3^{4x}[2x + 4x^2(\ln 3)]$; (j) $\frac{2(\ln 5)5^x}{(1 - 5^x)^2}$.

3. -0.000066 and -0.000006; the percentage that is still usable diminishes at a slower and slower rate.

5. $13\frac{1}{3}$ percent and $-3\frac{1}{3}$ percent; these are the marginal *percentage* rates of change of the sales revenues.

7. 1/120 and 1/150; these are the marginal rates at which the demand for the radios is changing with respect to a change in price.

11. (a) $f'(x) = 3x^2 - 6x$ and $f''(x) = 6x - 6$; (b) $\frac{dy}{dx} = 12x^3 - 12x^2$ and $\frac{d^2y}{dx^2} = 36x^2 - 24x$; (c) $\frac{dy}{dx} = 4x^3 - 16x$ and $\frac{d^2y}{dx^2} = 12x^2 - 16$.

13. (a) $39/32 = 1.21875$; (b) $191/225 = 0.8489$; (c) $143/64 = 2.2344$; (d) $599/288 = 2.0799$.

Page 379

1. $x = 1$.

3. There is a relative maximum at (0, 5) and a relative minimum at (2, 1).

5. There is a relative minimum at $x = 0$, a relative maximum at $x = 1/4$, and a relative minimum at $x = 2$; the corresponding points on the curve are (0, 5), $(\frac{1}{4}, 5\frac{5}{256})$, and (2, 1).

9. \$2.50.

11. 31 cars.

13. \$135 per ton; 105 tons.

15. 84 by 140 feet.

17. 8 years.

19. 18 years.

Page 385

1. (a) After 2 years the manufacturer's profit is *decreasing* at an annual rate of \$5,388 or 25.1 percent; (b) after 10 years the manufacturer's profit is *decreasing* at an annual rate of \$216 or 2.53 percent.

3. (a) \$23,774.40 per year; (b) 20 percent.

5. (a) −2,500 boxes per week; (b) −1,600 boxes per week.

7. (a) \$20,000 per year; (b) \$10,000 per year; (c) 0; (d) −\$10,000 per year.

9. The total sales revenue is *decreasing* by \$10,980 per month, and the percentage rate of change is *decreasing* by $1\frac{1}{3}$ percent per month.

Page 394

1. $\dfrac{\partial z}{\partial x} = -27$, which represents the marginal rate of change in the demand for beef with respect to its price when the price of pork remains fixed; $\dfrac{\partial z}{\partial y} = 33$, which represents the marginal rate of change in the demand for beef with respect to the price of pork when the price of beef remains fixed.

3. (a) $\dfrac{\partial z}{\partial x} = 2x + 3y$, $\dfrac{\partial z}{\partial y} = 3x - 2y$, $\dfrac{\partial^2 z}{\partial x^2} = 2$, and $\dfrac{\partial^2 z}{\partial y^2} = -2$; (b) $\dfrac{\partial z}{\partial x} = 3x^2 + 2xy^2$, $\dfrac{\partial z}{\partial y} = 2x^2y - 9y^2$, $\dfrac{\partial^2 z}{\partial x^2} = 6x + 2y^2$, and $\dfrac{\partial^2 z}{\partial y^2} = 2x^2 - 18y$; (c) $\dfrac{\partial z}{\partial x} = 3 - \dfrac{1}{y}$, $\dfrac{\partial z}{\partial y} = 2 + \dfrac{x}{y^2}$, $\dfrac{\partial^2 z}{\partial x^2} = 0$, and $\dfrac{\partial^2 z}{\partial y^2} = -\dfrac{2x}{y^3}$; (d) $\dfrac{\partial z}{\partial x} = 6x - e^y$, $\dfrac{\partial z}{\partial y} = 2 - xe^y$, $\dfrac{\partial^2 z}{\partial x^2} = 6$, and $\dfrac{\partial^2 z}{\partial y^2} = -xe^y$; (e) $\dfrac{\partial z}{\partial x} = \dfrac{1}{x} + 6xy$, $\dfrac{\partial z}{\partial y} = 3x^2$, $\dfrac{\partial^2 z}{\partial x^2} = -\dfrac{1}{x^2} + 6y$, and $\dfrac{\partial^2 z}{\partial y^2} = 0$; (f) $\dfrac{\partial z}{\partial x} = \ln y + \dfrac{y}{x}$, $\dfrac{\partial z}{\partial y} = \dfrac{x}{y} + \ln x$, $\dfrac{\partial^2 z}{\partial x^2} = -\dfrac{y}{x^2}$, and $\dfrac{\partial^2 z}{\partial y^2} = -\dfrac{x}{y^2}$.

5. $x = -7$, $y = 4$, and $z = 165$.

7. $x = 4$ and $y = 18$.

9. \$6.00 and \$400.

13. $\dfrac{\partial^2 Q}{\partial a^2} = 6$, $\dfrac{\partial^2 Q}{\partial b^2} = 28$, $\dfrac{\partial^2 Q}{\partial a \partial b} = 12$, and $6 \cdot 28 - 12^2 = 24 > 0$.

Page 407

1. (c) 336.

3. $-1/4$.

Page 418

1. (a) $\dfrac{1}{4}x^4 + C$; (b) $-\dfrac{1}{3x^3} + C$; (c) $12x + C$; (d) $2\sqrt{x} + C$; (e) $\dfrac{4}{7}x^{7/4} + C$; (f) $-\dfrac{4}{\sqrt{x}} + C$; (g) $-\dfrac{1}{x} + C$; (h) $\dfrac{5}{7}x^{7/5} + C$.

3. (a) $\dfrac{3}{2}x^2 - 5e^x + C$; (b) $\dfrac{1}{2}x^2 + x + \ln x + C$; (c) $\dfrac{5^x}{\ln 5} + C$; (d) $x - e^x + C$; (e) $\dfrac{3 \cdot 2^x}{\ln 2} + C$; (f) $15(\ln x) + C$.

5. (a) $-e^{-x} + C$; (b) $\dfrac{1}{2}e^{2x} + C$; (c) $\dfrac{3}{5}e^{5x} + C$; (d) $\dfrac{e^x - e^{-x}}{2} + C$.

7. (a) $\dfrac{1}{45}(1 + x^5)^9 + C$; (b) $-\dfrac{1}{30}(1 - 3e^{2x})^5 + C$; (c) $\dfrac{1}{9}e^{x^9} + C$.

9. (a) $-3 \cdot \cos(x - 2) + C$; (b) $-\dfrac{1}{3}(\cos x)^3 + C$; (c) $\sin x - x(\cos x) + C$; (d) $-\ln(\cos x) + C$.

11. (a) $C(x) = 90x^{1/3} + 420$ and $C(125) = \$870$; (b) $C(x) = 225x + 600e^{-2x} + 339.20$ and $C(4) = \$12.39$.

13. $N(x) = 40x - 1000(\ln x) + 200$; $N(1000) = 33{,}300$ turkeys.

15. $3 - 3e^{-4t}$; (a) 2.946 inches; (b) 2.999 inches.

Page 427

1. 14.

3. 0.915.

5. 81/8.

7. \$639,000 (to the nearest \$1,000).

11. \$433$\frac{1}{3}$ million.

13. \$584.13.

15. \$1,860.

17. (a) 3/2; (b) 1/2; (c) the integral does not exist.

Page 436

1. (b) in 3 of the outcomes Y makes the first sale, and in one of these X wins the bet.

5. (a) 49; (b) 42; (c) 27.

7. 20.

9. (a) 4; (b) 16; (c) 12.

11. 60.

13. 720.

15. 1,440.

17. (a) 64; (b) 63; (c) 4,096; (d) 4,094; (e) 32, 1,024, and 1,048,576.

Page 446

1. 60,480.

3. 332,640.

5. (a) 43,680; (b) 7,920; (c) 4,320.

7. (a) 720; (b) 72; (c) 72; (d) 6.

9. (a) 45; (b) 56.

11. 38,760.

13. 43,680.

15. 13,970,880.

19. (a) $1 + 8x + 24x^2 + 32x^3 + 16x^4$; (b) $125 - 75x + 15x^2 - x^3$;
(c) $243x^5 + 810x^4y + 1{,}080x^3y^2 + 720^2y^3 + 240xy^4 + 32y^5$;
(d) $64x^6 - 192x^5 + 240x^4 - 160x^3 + 60x^2 - 12x + 1$.

21. (a) 1.10408; (b) 0.922368; (c) 1.406875; (d) 0.7350.

Page 454

1. 0.76.

3. 0.38.

5. (a) 1/3; (b) 2 to 1; (c) favorable to Mr. G, since odds are 2 to 1 that he will make a catch.

7. 2/3.

9. 0.55.

11. At least 0.90.

Page 462

1. (a) Neither housewife cares; (b) The first housewife dislikes the commercial; (c) Both housewives care one way or the other; (d) They do not both like the commercial.

3. (c) A represents the event that they sell all 5 cars; B represents the event that the first salesman sells more cars than the second; C represents the event that the second salesman sells 2 cars; D represents the event that the second salesman sells at least 4 cars; E represents the event that the first salesman sells exactly one more car than the second.

5. (a) not mutually exclusive; (b) mutually exclusive; (c) mutually exclusive; (d) mutually exclusive; (e) not mutually exclusive; (f) mutually exclusive.

7. (a) (2, 3), (3, 2), (3, 3), (4, 1), (4, 2), (4, 3), (0, 3), (1, 2), (2, 1), (3, 0); altogether there are either 3 passengers or 5 or more; (b) (2, 3); the larger helicopter has 2 passengers and the smaller helicopter has 3; (c) (0, 0), (1, 1), (2, 2), (3, 3), (0, 1), (0, 2), (0, 3), (1, 2), (1, 3), (2, 3); the smaller helicopter has at least as many passengers as the larger one; (d) (0, 0), (0, 1), (0, 2), (0, 3), (1, 0), (1, 1), (1, 2), (1, 3), (2, 0), (2, 1), (2, 2), (3, 0), (3, 1), (4, 0); altogether the two helicopters have fewer than 5 passengers; (e) (3, 3); each helicopter has 3 passengers; (f) $\varnothing$.

9. (a) (1, 2, 2) represents the event that the first housewife dislikes the commercial while the second and third housewives like it, (3, 2, 3) represents the event that the second housewife likes the commercial and the other two do not care, (3, 1, 1) represents the event that the second and third housewives dislike the commercial while the first housewife does not care; (b) J represents the event that the first two housewives dislike the commercial, K represents the event that all three feel the same way about the commercial, L represents the event that the second housewife likes the commercial while the other two either dislike it or do not care, M represents the event that all three housewives feel

differently about the commercial, and N represents the event that the first housewife dislikes the commercial.

11. (a) not mutually exclusive; (b) mutually exclusive; (c) mutually exclusive; (d) not mutually exclusive; (e) not mutually exclusive; (f) mutually exclusive.

13. (a) not mutually exclusive; (b) mutually exclusive (by law); (c) not mutually exclusive; (d) not mutually exclusive; (e) mutually exclusive (when it is 11:45 p.m. in Los Angeles, it is already the next day in Washington, D.C.); (f) not mutually exclusive; (g) mutually exclusive.

Page 472

1. Only the claim of the second economist is possible; the probabilities of the first economist add up to less than 1 and those of the third add up to more than 1.

3. (a) The probability that the SEC will not investigate the finances of the corporation; (b) The probability that none of the corporation's dealings are illegal; (c) The probability that the SEC will investigate the finances of the corporation and that some of its dealings are illegal; (d) The probability that the SEC will investigate the finances of the corporation or none of its dealings are illegal; (e) The probability that the SEC will not investigate the finances of the corporation and that none of its dealings are illegal; (f) The probability that the SEC will not investigate the finances of the corporation or that some of its dealings are illegal.

5. (a) 0.34; (b) 0.72; (c) 0.82; (d) 0.16; (e) 0.46; (f) 0.54.

7. The argument is not valid because the events (spending at least $20 and spending at least $8 on meat) are not mutually exclusive.

9. 0.16, 0.40, 0.36, and 0.96.

11. (a) 1/21, 2/21, 3/21, 4/21, 5/21, and 6/21; (b) 6/21, 9/21, 4/21, 3/21, and 3/21.

13. (a) 0.46; (b) 0.53; (c) 0.33.

15. (a) 0.45; (b) 0.75; (c) 0.81; (d) 0.98.

17. 0.34.

19. (a) 0.84; (b) 0.008; (c) 0.92 and 0.08; (d) 0.15 and 0.12; (e) 0.85 and 0.71, 0.14; (f) 0.20 and 0.23.

Page 484

1. (a) The probability that a person in a high-income bracket owns municipal bonds; (b) The probability that a person who owns municipal bonds is in a high-income bracket; (c) The probability that a person who is not in a high-income bracket owns municipal bonds; (d) The probability that a person who does not own municipal bonds is in a high-income bracket; (e) The probability that a person who is not in a high-income bracket does not own municipal bonds; (f) The probability that a person who does not own municipal bonds is not in a high-income bracket.

3. (a) The probability that a sales executive with an MBA degree makes at least \$25,000 a year; (b) The probability that a sales executive who is at least 35 years old belongs to the local country club; (c) The probability that a sales executive without an MBA degree makes at least \$25,000 a year; (d) The probability that a sales executive who makes less than \$25,000 a year belongs to the local country club; (e) The probability that a sales executive under 35 makes less than \$25,000 a year; (f) The probability that a sales executive who does not belong to the local country club is at least 35 years old; (g) The probability that a sales executive who is at least 35 years old belongs to the local country club and makes at least \$25,000 a year; (h) The probability that a sales executive without an MBA degree is at least 35 years old and belongs to the local country club; (i) The probability that a sales executive with an MBA degree who is at least 35 years old makes at least \$25,000 a year.

5. (a) 1/2; (b) 1/2; (c) 3/5; (d) 9/40; (e) 4/13; (f) 11/27; (g) 4/13; (h) 9/20; (i) 4/5.

7. (a) 1/3; (b) 2/23.

9. (a) 13/35; (b) 22/48.

11. (a) 9/38; (b) 3/95; (c) 6/19; (d) 12/95.

15. (a) 1/64; (b) 1/2,197; (c) 0.15; (d) 0.45.

17. 10/13.

19. 8/53.

21. 1/8 and 1/2.

Page 493

1. (c) 0.247.

3. (b) 0.263; (c) 0.031; (d) 0.149.

5. (a) 36/37; (b) 12/65; (c) 1/101.

Page 500

1. (a) \$0.04; (b) No.

3. (a) \$3,500 and \$3,500; (b) \$4,250 and \$2,750.

5. Expected loss of \$170.

7. $5\frac{13}{16}$ games.

9. \$40,864.

11. (a) The probability is less than 2/3; (b) 0.16.

Page 508

1. (a)

	Good football team	*Poor football team*
New stadium	410,000	−100,000
Old stadium	200,000	20,000

(b) Use old stadium; (c) build new stadium; (d) use the old stadium, since otherwise there might be a loss of \$100,000; (e) build the new stadium, since the profit may be as high as \$410,000;

(f)

	Good football team	*Poor football team*
New stadium	0	120,000
Old stadium	210,000	0

To hold the greatest possible opportunity losses to a minimum they should build the new stadium, but to minimize their expected opportunity losses they should use the old stadium; (g) \$150,000; yes, for otherwise their expected profit is only \$80,000 with the old stadium and \$70,000 with the new stadium.

3. (a)

	Meeting at Hotel A	*Meeting at Hotel B*
Stays at Hotel A	21	26
Stays at Hotel B	23	18

(b) Hotel A; (c) Hotel B; (d) doesn't matter; (e) Hotel B, it might cost him as little as \$18; (f) Hotel B, the most it can cost him is \$23; (g) \$20.50; it would not be worth \$1.50, only \$1.33; (h) Hotel B.

5. (a) Take candy; (b) take wine; (c) neither, since both expectations are negative; (d) $2\frac{3}{8}$, and it is not worthwhile to spend the \$2.00, only \$1.875; (e) take candy.

7. (a) The first job; (b) the second job.

Page 518

1. (a) I and 2, the value is 4; (b) II and 1, the value is 5; (c) I and 1, the value is -2; (d) I and 2, the value is 1.

3. (a) III and 2, the value is -1; (b) II and 3, II and 4, IV and 3, IV and 4, the value is 5.

5. (a) 5/11 and 6/11; (b) 4/11 and 7/11; (c) the value of the game is $-9/11$, and it favors Player A.

7. (b) Player A should use probabilities of 2/3 and 1/3; Player B should use probabilities of 1/3 and 2/3; the value of the game is 10.

11. (a) 1/2 and 1/2 for the first player, and 3/10 and 7/10 for the second player; (b) \$1.50.

13. 3/5 and 2/5; yes, the value of the "game" would be -1.

Page 523

3. *Minimize* $7y + u - 4$, where y and u must be non-negative, $y \leqslant 1$, and $11y + u \geqslant 5$.

Page 536

3. (a) 0.3087; (b) 0.309.

5. (a) 0.52822; (b) 0.528.

7. (a) 0.129; (b) 0.945; (c) 0.012.

11. (a) 15/210; (b) 90/210; (c) 1/210.

13. 6320/21,063 or approximately 0.30005; the binomial approximation yields 8/27 or approximately 0.29630.

15. (a) 0.128; (b) 0.8192; (c) $(0.8)^{10}$ or approximately 0.1074.

17. (a) 0.050; (b) 0.225; (c) 0.169.

19. (a) 0.202; (b) 0.323; (c) 0.475; (d) $(0.202)^2 = 0.041$, assuming that what happens in the second hour is independent of what happens in the first hour.

21. (a) 0.162; (b) 0.691.

23. (a) $3 \cdot \frac{1}{2} = 1.5$ and $20 \cdot \frac{1}{5} = 4$; (c) 504.

25. (a) 0.053; (b) 0.014; (c) 0.132.

Page 545

5. (b) 000–001, 002–016, 017–098, 099–344, 345–737, 738–999.

Page 553

7. (a) $\mu = 12$; (b) 25 minutes; (c) 30 minutes; (d) $4\frac{1}{6}$.

9. (a) 3.56 days and 3.33 days; (b) 0.281 and 0.300; (c) 49.3 days; (d) 13.85 suits.

INDEX